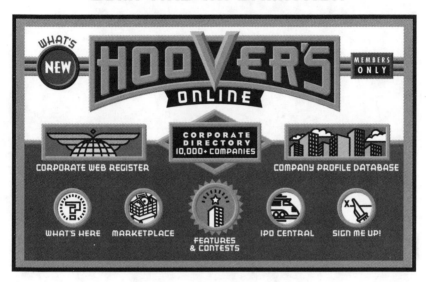

HOOVER'S GUIDE TO MEDIA COMPANIES

Hoover's
BUSINESS PRESS
Austin, Texas

Hoover's
BUSINESS PRESS

10 9 8 7 6 5 4 3 2 1

Publisher Cataloging-In-Publication Data

Hoover's Guide to Media Companies

Includes indexes.

1. Business enterprises — Directories. 2. Corporations — Directories.

HF3010   338.7

Company information and profiles from the *Hoover's* series of handbooks, guides, and directories are also available on America Online, Baseline, Bloomberg Financial Network, CompuServe, LEXIS-NEXIS, Microsoft Network, Reuters NewMedia, and on the Internet at Hoover's Online (www.hoovers.com), CNNfn (www.cnnfn.com), Farcast (www.farcast.com), IBM InfoMarket (www.infomkt.ibm.com), InfoSeek (www.infoseek.com), IBM Infosage (www.infosage.ibm.com), Pathfinder (www.pathfinder.com), PAWWS (www.pawws.com), Wall Street Journal Interactive edition (www.wsj.com), The Washington Post (www.washingtonpost.com), and others.

A catalog of Hoover's products is available on the World Wide Web (www.hoovers.com).

ISBN 1-878753-96-7

This book was produced by Hoover's Business Press using Claris Corporation's FileMaker Pro 3.0, Quark, Inc.'s Quark XPress 3.32, EM Software, Inc.'s Xdata 2.5, and fonts from Adobe's Clearface and Futura families. Cover design is by Daniel Pelavin. Electronic prepress and printing were done by Custom Printing Company at its Frederick, Maryland plant. Text paper is 60# Postmark White.

US AND WORLD DIRECT SALES
Hoover's, Inc.
1033 La Posada Drive, Suite 250
Austin, TX 78752
Phone: 512-374-4500
Fax: 512-374-4501
e-mail: info@hoovers.com

US BOOKSELLERS AND JOBBERS
Little, Brown and Co.
200 West Street
Waltham, MA 02154
Phone: 800-759-0190
Fax: 617-890-0875

US WHOLESALER ORDERS
Warner Publisher Services
Book Division
9210 King Palm Drive
Tampa, FL 33619
Phone: 800-873-BOOK
Fax: 813-664-8193

EUROPE
William Snyder Publishing Associates
5, Five Mile Drive
Oxford OX2 8HT
England
Phone & fax: +44-186-551-3186

HOOVER'S, INC.

Founder: Gary Hoover
Chairman, President, CEO, and Publisher: Patrick J. Spain

Senior Managing Editor — Production: George Sutton
Senior Managing Editor — Editorial: James R. Talbot
Senior Contributing Editor: Alan Chai
Senior Editor: Thomas Trotter
Editors: Chris Barton, Paul Mitchell, Anthony Shuga
Associate Editor: William Cargill
Editorial Coordinator: Ken Little
Assistant Editorial Coordinator: Melanie Lea Hall
Research Manager: Sherri M. Hale
Desktop Publishing Manager: Christina Thiele
Senior Researchers: Sarah Hallman, Jim Harris, Brian Pedder, David Ramirez
Researchers: Lynn Monnat, Patricia Pepin
Research Assistants: Leslie Navarro, Erica Taylor
Senior Writers: Joy Aiken, Stuart Hampton, Diane Lee, Barbara M. Spain, Jeffrey A. Twining
Financial Editor: Dennis L. Sutton
Copyeditors: Patrice Sarath, John Willis
Fact Checkers/Proofreaders: Michael G. Laster, Elizabeth Gagne Morgan, Marianne Tatom
Database Editors: Tweed Chouinard, Yvonne A. Cullinan, Karen Hill, Britton E. Jackson
Desktop Publishers: Trey Colvin, Michelle de Ybarrondo, Kevin Dodds, JoAnn Estrada, Gregory Gosdin, Elena Hernandez, Holly Hans Jackson, Louanne Jones
Database Entry: Eldridge N. Goins, Ismael Hernandez Jr., Danny Macaluso, Scott A. Smith

Director, Hoover's Online: Matt Manning
Senior Brand Manager: Leslie A. Wolke
Online Production Manager: Richard Finley
Online Content Editor: Martha DeGrasse
Online Editors: Kay Nichols, Perrin Patterson
Electronic Media Producers: Chuck Green, Rick Navarro

Senior Vice President, Sales and Marketing: Dana L. Smith
VP Finance and Administration and CFO (HR): Lynn Atchison
Vice President, Electronic Publishing: Tom Linehan
Director of Corporate Communications: Jani F. Spede
Controller: Deborah L. Dunlap
Systems Manager: Bill Crider
Fulfillment Manager: Beth DeVore
Office Manager: Tammy Fisher
Direct Marketing Manager: Marcia Harelik
Sales Manager: Shannon McGuire
Advertising Sales Manager: Joe McWilliams
Customer Service Manager: Rhonda T. Mitchell
Shipping Coordinator: Michael Febonio
Advertising Coordinator: Michelle Swann
Communications Coordinator: Angela Young
Customer Service Representatives: John T. Logan, Darla Wenzel
Publicity Assistant: Becky Hepinstall
Administrative Assistant: Margaux Bejarano

HOOVER'S, INC. MISSION STATEMENT

1. To produce business information products and services of the highest quality, accuracy, and readability.

2. To make that information available whenever, wherever, and however our customers want it through mass distribution at affordable prices.

3. To continually expand our range of products and services and our markets for those products and services.

4. To reward our employees, suppliers, and shareholders based on their contributions to the success of our enterprise.

5. To hold to the highest ethical busines standards, erring on the side of generosity when in doubt.

CONTENTS

Selected Media Companies

ABOUT *HOOVER'S GUIDE TO MEDIA COMPANIES*

The numbers tell the story, and it's only fitting that the tape probably has a digital readout.

For instance: in 1990, according to investment bankers Veronis, Suhler & Associates, the average adult American consumer spent 55 hours per year with such newerfangled media as home videos and video games, educational software, and consumer-online services. By 1999, propelled by that swash-buckling cavalry of the Digital Revolution, the World Wide Web, the number will increase to 113 hours per year, a 105 percent increase. Compare that to a 3 percent increase for usage of more traditional media such as books, magazines, newspapers, and radio-TV.

In addition, Veronis, Suhler reported, communications was the 7th fastest growing of the top 12 industries in the US between 1990 and 1994. From 1995 through 1999, it will move up to the 4th position as a result (among other reasons) of spending increases by users of emerging media.

With these numbers in mind, the editors of Hoover's Business Press decided it was time to take a closer look at the players in the media and communications industry. *Hoover's Guide to Media Companies* joins our line of affordable business reference products, which, we believe, collectively represent the most complete source of basic corporate information readily available to the general public.

As industry guides, *Hoover's Guide to Media Companies* and *Hoover's Guide to Computer Companies* (first published in 1995 with a new edition forthcoming) complement our other publications. These include *Hoover's Handbook of American Business*, *Hoover's Handbook of World Business*, *Hoover's Handbook of Emerging Companies*, *Hoover's Guide to Private Companies*, and the forthcoming *Hoover's Top 2,500 Employers*. Our company profiles and other information are also available electronically on diskette and CD-ROM and on online services (e.g., America Online and CompuServe) and the Internet on Hoover's Online at www.hoovers.com.

Hoover's Guide to Media Companies is the product of extensive research. One of the first questions we had to ask was what constitutes a media company. That's easy enough to answer with the stalwarts — newspapers, radio, and television, etc. — but when is a media company a media company, as opposed to being a high-tech company? With the

rush on to be the first on your desktop, the line is sometimes a fine one. Take Desktop Data, for example, which delivers customized, real-time news and information over an organization's local area networks (we included it).

Generally, in addition to the traditional media — books, magazines, newspapers, radio, television, advertising — we decided to concentrate on content providers as distinguished from companies that simply serve as a conduit for information. There are exceptions, such as Ingram Industries Inc., the world's largest independent book, software, and video distributor. No one who puts out a newspaper or a magazine has escaped the influence of the work done at Adobe and Quark, so we opted to include them, too. Given the ephemeral nature of national boundaries, particularly in the face of the Digital Revolution, we have also included a number of global media companies headquartered outside the US.

People are important ingredients of Hoover's profiles. We are always on the lookout for interesting characters — the faces behind the stories — from the controversial (Rupert Murdoch and News Corp.) to the simply historical (Union Army general Harrison Gray Otis and Times Mirror). Another element that sets Hoover's apart is our effort at following private companies as well as the more accessible public companies. That's why you will find in-depth profiles on 53 private companies, from Advance Publications (1995 sales of $4.8 billion) to Upside (1995 sales of $3 million).

After defining our world of media companies, we consulted Hoover's extensive database of company information to identify public and private businesses that fit our definition. We followed up with sources such as *Advertising Age, Editor & Publisher*, and other trade publication lists. We contacted all of the companies that were candidates to obtain or update our information. Most companies were helpful and cooperative; some were not. For the latter, we obtained the most reliable information we could find and in some cases made estimates regarding revenue. (In all such cases, the revenue figures are marked as estimates.)

In addition to all public media companies, *Hoover's Guide to Media Companies* covers all private companies with revenues greater than $200 million and those private companies with revenues of less than $200 million for which we could compile accurate information. We have also included partnerships (e.g., PRIMESTAR Partners L.P.) and nonprofit organizations (e.g., National Geographic Society). We believe these enterprises are as important players in the media industry as the for-profit sector.

After determining our media universe — which totaled 684 companies — we selected 205 for in-depth profiles. The 205 companies range from electronics giant Sony Corporation (1995 revenues of $42.9 billion) to the tiny Internet pioneer Yahoo! Inc. (1995 revenues of $1.4 million). We profiled 81 of the largest companies in our 2-page format, each with up to 10 years of financial data and a separate section on its history. The remainder of the profiles (mostly of highly visible or fast-growing companies under $1 billion in sales) are in our one-page format, with up to 6 years of financial data and a shorter history integrated into the overview of the company. The majority of the profiled companies are considered industry leaders, but also we have included a limited selection of interesting, smaller companies.

Hoover's Guide to Media Companies consists of 6 components:

1. The first, "Using the Profiles," describes the contents of the profiles and explains the ways in which we gathered and compiled our data.

2. The 2nd section is an overview of the media industry prepared by investment bankers Veronis, Suhler & Associates, which concentrates its activities in the media and communications industry.

3. Next we have included "A List-Lover's Compendium," which contains lists of the largest and fastest-growing companies in the book as well as selected lists from other sources to provide different viewpoints.

4. The 4th section contains the 205 in-depth profiles of media companies. The profiles are grouped according to size, first the 2-page and then the one-page, and are arranged alphabetically within groups.

5. The next section provides capsule profiles of the 720 companies. If an in-depth profile also exists for a company, the page number of that profile is included in the entry for easy reference.

6. The book concludes with 2 indexes: (1) the companies organized by headquarters location and (2) the main index of the book, containing all the names of brands, companies, and people mentioned in the in-depth profiles.

As always, we hope you find our books useful and informative. We invite your comments via phone (512-374-4500), fax (512-374-4501), mail (1033 La Posada Drive, Suite 250, Austin, TX 78752), or e-mail (comments@hoovers.com).

The Editors
Austin, Texas
July 1996

Using the Profiles

ORGANIZATION OF THE PROFILES

The company profiles are presented in either a one-page or 2-page format. The 2-page profiles contain extensive historical information, in addition to up to 10 years of financial data. The one-page profiles offer a shorter history and up to 6 years of financial data. In both, the profiles are presented in alphabetical order. (Alphabetization is word by word.) We have shown the full legal name of the enterprise at the top of the page, unless it is too long, in which case you will find it above the address in the Where section of the profile. If a company name is also a person's name, like John Wiley & Sons, it will be alphabetized under the first name; if a company name starts with initials, like A.H. Belo, look for it under the initials (here, AH). All company names (past and present) used in the profiles are indexed in the last index in the book.

Each profile lists the exchange where the company's stock is traded if it is public, the ticker symbol used by the stock exchange, and the company's fiscal year-end. This data can be found at the top left of the 2nd page for 2-page profiles and in the upper left corner of the How Much chart for one-page profiles.

The annual financial information contained in most profiles is current through fiscal year-ends occurring as late as March 1996. For certain non-public entities, such up-to-date information was not available. In those cases, we have used the most current data we could find. We have included non-financial developments, such as officer changes, through June 1996.

OVERVIEW

In this section we have tried to give a thumbnail description of the company and what it does. The description will usually include information on the company's strategy, reputation, and ownership. In the one-page profiles we also provide a brief history of the company, including the year of founding and the names of the founders where possible. We recommend that you read this section first.

WHEN

This section, which appears only in the 2-page profiles, reflects our belief that every enterprise is the sum of its history and that you have to know where you came from in order to know where you are going. While some companies have very little historical awareness and were unable to help us much, and other companies are just plain boring, we think the vast majority of the enterprises in the book have colorful backgrounds. When we could find information, we tried to focus on the people who made the enterprise what it is today. We have found these histories to be full of twists and ironies; they can make for some fascinating, quick reading.

WHO

Here we list the names of the people who run the company, insofar as space allows. In the case of public companies, we have shown the ages and pay levels of key officers. In some cases the published data are for last year, although the company has announced promotions or retirements since year-end. We have tried to show current officers, with their pay for the latest year available. The pay represents cash compensation, including bonuses, but excludes stock option programs. Our best advice is that officers' pay levels are clear indicators of who the board of directors thinks are the most important on the management team.

While companies are free to structure their management titles any way they please, most modern corporations follow standard practices. The ultimate power in any corporation lies with the shareholders, who elect a board of directors, usually including officers or "insiders" as well as individuals from outside the company. The chief officer, the person on whose desk the buck stops, is usually called the chief executive officer (CEO). Normally, he or she is also the chairman of the board. As corporate management has become more complex, it is common for the CEO to have a "right-hand person" who oversees the day-to-day operations of the company, allowing the CEO plenty of time to focus on strategy and long-term issues. This right-hand person is usually designated the chief operating officer (COO) and is often the president as well. In other cases one person is both chairman and president of the company.

A multitude of other titles exists, including chief financial officer (CFO), chief administrative officer, and vice chairman (VC). We have always tried to include the CFO, the chief legal officer, and the chief personnel or human resources officer. The people named in the profiles are indexed at the back of the book.

WHERE

Here we include the company's headquarters street address and phone and fax numbers as available. Recognizing the growing importance of the Internet, we also include the address of the company's World Wide Web site, if one exists. The back of the book includes an index of companies by headquarters locations.

We have also included as much information as we could gather and fit on the geographical distribution of the company's business, including sales and profit data. Note that these profit numbers, like those in the What section (described below), are usually operating or pretax profits rather than net profits. Operating profits are generally those before financing costs (interest income and payments) and before taxes, which are considered costs attributable to the whole company rather than to one division or part of the world. For this reason the net income figures (in the How Much section) are usually much lower, since they are after interest and taxes. Pretax profits are after interest but before taxes. When sales and operating profits by region were not available or were not appropriate, we have published other measures of geographic diversity. For example, for regional retailers we have listed the number of stores by state.

WHAT

This section lists as many of the company's products, services, brand names, divisions, subsidiaries, and joint ventures as we could fit. We have tried to include all its major lines and all familiar brand names.

The nature of this section varies by industry, company, and the amount of information available. If the company publishes sales and profit information by type of business, we have included it. The brand, division, and subsidiary names are listed in the last index in the book.

KEY COMPETITORS

In this section we list competitors. This feature is included as a quick way to locate similar companies and compare them. The universe of key competitors includes all public companies and all private companies with sales in excess of $500 million. In a number of instances we have identified smaller private companies as key competitors. All the com-

panies are listed by broad industry groups in the first index at the back of the book.

HOW MUCH

Here we present as much data about each enterprise's financial performance as we could compile in the allocated space. While the information varies somewhat from industry to industry and is less complete for private companies that do not release this information (though we always try to provide annual sales and employment), we generally present the following data:

A 10-year table (6 years for the one-page profiles), with relevant annualized compound growth rates, covering:

• Fiscal year sales (year-end assets for most financial companies)

• Fiscal year net income (before accounting changes)

• Fiscal year net income as a percent of sales (as a percent of assets for most financial firms)

• Fiscal year earnings per share (EPS, fully diluted)

• Stock price high, low, and close (for the calendar year unless otherwise noted)

• High and low price/earnings ratio (P/E, for the calendar year unless otherwise noted)

• Fiscal year dividends per share

• Fiscal year-end book value (shareholders' equity per share)

• Fiscal year-end or average number of employees

All revenue numbers are as reported by the company in its annual report.

The 10-year information on the number of employees (6 years on the one-page profiles) is intended to aid the reader interested in knowing whether a company has a long-term trend of increasing or decreasing employment. As far as we know, we are the only company that publishes this information in print.

The year at the top of each column in the How Much section is the year in which the company's fiscal year actually ends. Thus, data for a company with a January 31, 1996, year-end are shown in the 1996 column. Stock prices for companies with fiscal year-ends between January and April are for the prior calendar year and are so footnoted on the chart. Key year-end statistics in this section generally show the financial strength of the enterprise, including:

- Debt ratio (total debt as a percent of combined total debt and shareholders' equity)

- Return on equity (net income divided by the average of beginning and ending common shareholders' equity)

- Cash and marketable securities

- Current ratio (ratio of current assets to current liabilities)

- Total long-term debt, including capital lease obligations

- Number of shares of common stock outstanding (less treasury shares)

- Dividend yield (fiscal year dividends per share divided by the calendar year-end closing stock price)

- Dividend payout (fiscal year dividends divided by fiscal year EPS)

- Market value at calendar year-end (calendar year-end closing stock price multiplied by fiscal year-end number of shares outstanding)

- Research and development as a percent of sales, when available (one-page profiles only)

- Advertising as a percent of sales, when available (one-page profiles only)

For financial institutions and insurance companies, we have also included annual sales, equity as a percent of assets, and return on assets in this section.

Per share data have been adjusted for stock splits.

The data for some public companies (and private companies with public debt) have been provided to us by Media General Financial Services, Inc. Other public company information was compiled by Hoover's, Inc., which takes full responsibility for the content of this section.

In the case of private companies that do not publicly disclose financial information, we usually did not have access to such standardized data. We have gathered estimates of sales and other statistics from numerous sources; among the most helpful were trade publications such as *Advertising Age*, and *Forbes*'s list of the largest private companies.

MEDIA
Industry Overview

THE VERONIS, SUHLER & ASSOCIATES COMMUNICATIONS INDUSTRY FORECAST, 1995–1999

Excerpted and reprinted by permission from the Veronis, Suhler & Associates Communications Industry Forecast, 9th ed. Copyright 1995 by Veronis, Suhler & Associates Inc.

OVERVIEW

Spending by advertisers and end users on products and services provided by the Communications Industry totaled $233.5 billion in 1994, 7.8 percent more than in 1993. In contrast with the previous five years, advertisers paced spending growth in 1994 with an increase of 8.9 percent compared with 7.0 percent growth in end-user spending. End users accounted for 59.0 percent of 1994 Communications Industry spending with a total of $137.8 billion, and advertising reached $95.7 billion.

The strong 1994 economy spurred retail sales in general and automobile sales in particular. With consumers returning to the market, advertisers looked to enhance their market share by putting more emphasis on brand advertising. Led by automobile companies, advertising across all media enjoyed substantial increases.

We look for advertising to grow at a faster rate over the forecast period than over the last five years. We expect advertising to rise at a 5.7 percent compound annual rate over the 1994-1999 period, a rate somewhat understated since the base year includes an infusion of advertising related to the 1994 Winter Olympics and the senatorial and congressional campaigns while 1999 does not include these expenditures. Nevertheless, growth over the next five years will exceed the 5.3 percent increase for the economy as a whole. Over the last five years,

Growth of U.S. Communications Industry Spending

	Advertiser Spending	End-User Spending	Total
1994 Expenditures ($ Millions)	$95,690	$137,809	$233,499
1989-94 Compound Annual Growth (%)	3.1%	6.8%	5.2%
1994-99 Projected Compound Annual Growth (%)	5.7%	7.4%	6.8%
1999 Projected Expenditures ($ Millions)	$126,340	$197,380	$323,720

Sources: Veronis, Suhler & Associates, Wilkofsky Gruen Associates

even including 1994, advertising rose at only a 3.1 percent compound annual rate compared with 5.1 percent economic growth.

Although also reacting to the economy, end-user spending is less cyclical than advertiser spending. During the 1991 recession, end-user spending did not decline as it did for advertising, although growth slowed, and during the ensuing recovery, end-user spending did not bounce back as strongly. As for long-term trends, end-user spending has been affected by new technologies that have penetrated the market. Penetration growth of home video and cable in the 1980s fueled end-user spending, but as these industries have matured, growth has slowed. Similarly, penetration growth of the interactive digital media will stimulate spending in the 1990s. Although consumers have adopted a number of new technologies, they have not abandoned their staples. Spending on books, movies, newspapers, and magazines, for example, has continued to expand.

In 1994, end-user spending growth was curtailed by the rollback in cable rates, which allowed subscribers to pay less for their cable service while cable usage expanded. Nevertheless, end-user spending rose 7.0 percent in 1994, a faster increase than the 6.7 percent and 6.8 percent growth rates of the prior two years. Spending was boosted by the 20.1 percent growth in recorded-music sales and the 30.0 percent increase in the small but rapidly growing interactive digital media segment. Mid-single-digit growth characterized the remaining end-user categories.

The ability of the recorded-music industry to widen its appeal to a broad demographic spectrum has helped maintain double-digit growth in recorded-music sales in recent years. Penetration gains for the emerging interactive digital media have propelled spending and should ensure double-digit growth over the forecast period. New competitors to cable operators and a relaxation of regulation will enhance end-user spending on subscription video services, but penetration growth will be limited over the forecast period. Slower penetration growth will also limit increases in home video spending, but increased competition and a healthy advertising market should lift expenditures on entertainment programs by the broadcast networks and television stations.

We expect overall end-user spending to grow at a 7.4 percent compound annual rate over the forecast period, an improvement over the 6.8 percent increase of the last five years. By 1999, we forecast end-user spending to total $197.4 billion.

LONG-TERM ADVERTISING TRENDS

In addition to short-run cyclical fluctuations, advertising in the post-World War II period has exhibited several long-term trends. The U.S. economy in the immediate postwar period had endured nearly two decades of economic deprivation because of the Great Depression and World War II, leading to a pent-up demand for consumer goods. With the economy returning to normal and with a new advertising medium, television, becoming a fixture in U.S. households, advertising enjoyed a major surge. Over the 1946-1960 period, advertising rose at a 6.0 percent compound annual rate in real terms, well in excess of the 3.2 percent real growth of the economy as a whole.

Over the 1960-1975 period, by contrast, real advertising growth dropped sharply, rising at only a 1.7 percent compound annual rate, barely half as fast as the 3.3 percent expansion of the economy. During that period, large conglomerates dominated economic activity, competition from smaller U.S. companies and from foreign sources was minimal, and media markets were relatively stable. In a stable market with limited competition, advertising stagnated.

The advertising market turned around in 1976. The oil embargo of 1973-1974 effectively brought the United States into the world market and opened up trade. Japanese automobiles and numerous foreign products entered the U.S. market in large volumes and competed with domestically produced goods. Then in the early 1980s, a number of industries were deregulated, further enhancing competition. The result was a turbulent economy, increased competition, and rapid growth in advertising. Between 1975 and 1986, advertising rose at a 5.3 percent compound annual rate in real terms compared with 2.9 percent real GDP growth.

By the mid-1980s, stiffer competition began to shrink U.S. corporate profits. At the same time, the increase in acquisition activity led to a buildup in corporate debt, further eroding margins. Responding to margin pressures, companies focused their attention on cost control. Workers were laid off, corporate staffs were slashed, economic growth slowed, and advertising was curtailed. The weak sales environment led to a shift in funds from advertising to promotion. Promotion is particularly well suited to induce reluctant buyers to make purchases. Over the 1986-1993 period, advertising in inflation-adjusted terms fell at a 0.4 percent compound annual rate while real GDP rose at a 2.2 percent rate.

There is strong evidence that advertising in 1994 has entered a new phase in which it will grow faster than GDP for a number of years. The restructuring of the last decade is now virtually complete. As a result of extensive downsizing, U.S. producers have become lean and highly competitive. Corporate profits have rebounded strongly and margins have soared. Competition continues to increase, coming from emerging domestic companies as well as from foreign companies. In such an environment, brand advertising is increasingly important in maintaining market share, and companies, no longer burdened by restructuring, are devoting more resources to advertising. Consequently, regardless of the impact of short-term economic conditions, we expect that advertising spending growth will generally outpace GDP growth over the remainder of the decade.

Growth of Advertiser and End-User Spending

Year	Advertiser Spending	End-User Spending	Total
1990	2.7%	9.3%	6.3%
1991	(4.3)	4.4	0.6
1992	4.0	6.7	5.6
1993	4.7	6.8	5.9
1994	8.9	7.0	7.8
1995	5.8	8.0	7.1
1996	6.2	7.1	6.8
1997	4.5	7.6	6.3
1998	6.1	7.4	6.9
1999	5.9	7.1	6.7
Compound Annual Growth			
1989-94	3.1	6.8	5.2
1994-99	5.7	7.4	6.8

Sources: Veronis, Suhler & Associates, Wilkofsky Gruen Associates

MEDIA USAGE BY CONSUMERS

In 1994, the average adult spent 3,402 hours using consumer media, an increase of 3.0 percent compared with 1993. Newspapers, consumer magazines, and network-affiliated stations were the only categories to record declines. Increased viewing of independent stations and basic and premium networks led to a 1.6 percent rise in overall television viewing. Radio listening was up 1.8 percent, rebounding from the 5.9 percent decline of 1993. Huge growth in recorded-music sales was a reflection of a large increase in time spent listening to recorded music, while home video-game usage also rose substantially. The time spent reading consumer books grew by 3.0 percent, and the time spent with home video rose 6.1 percent.

Over the last five years, video games, basic networks, recorded music, and home video were the fastest growing in terms of time spent. Video-game usage escalated at a 29.7 percent compound annual rate, while time spent by the average consumer watching basic networks increased by 13.1 percent compounded annually over the 1989-1994 period. The time spent watching prerecorded videocassettes rose by 5.9 percent compounded annually, and recorded-music usage grew 6.0 percent. Further penetration gains should continue to spur video-game and home video usage, as well as basic network viewing, but growth in each of these categories will be much slower than over the last five years. The broadening demographic base and the inherent popularity of music should lead to continued expansion in the time spent listening to recorded music at rates comparable to those posted over the 1989-1994 period.

The time spent watching television rose at a 1.0 percent rate over the last five years, and we expect a similar increase over the forecast period. Radio listening, however, fell at a 0.9 percent compound annual rate, and we expect that trend to continue as well. Price increases due to rising paper costs will adversely affect the print media in the near term, while consolidation will continue to reduce newspaper usage. The long-term drop in the number of daily newspapers has depleted overall readership since the surviving papers in a market generally do not capture all of the readers of a discontinued paper.

The time spent reading consumer books rose 3.0 percent in 1994 and at a 1.2 percent compound annual rate over the last five years, paced by the large increases in adult trade book sales. We look for dips over the next two years, with modest growth thereafter. Older people tend to read books

Shares, by Industry Segment, of 1994 Communications Industry Spending

Industry Segment	Advertising	End-User
Television Broadcasting	100%	0%
Radio Broadcasting	100	0
Subscription Video Services	12	88
Filmed Entertainment	6	94
Recorded Music	0	100
Newspaper Publishing	79	21
Book Publishing	0	100
Magazine Publishing	61	39
Business Information Services	0	100
Interactive Digital Media*	0	100
Total	41	59

Sources: Veronis, Suhler & Associates, Wilkofsky Gruen Associates
*Excludes about $30 million in advertising

more than younger people, and as the size of the older demographic swells, reading time per capita should expand. The time spent reading consumer magazines declined at a 1.4 percent compound annual rate over the last five years. We expect a continued decrease over the next few years as price increases hamper circulation. By 1998 and 1999, however, circulation will begin to rise again, and per capita time spent will stabilize.

The per capita time spent with movies in theaters averaged 12 hours over the last two years, helped by an unusually large number of popular films. That average will drop to 11 hours per year in the absence of an above-average slate of titles.

The time spent in 1994 using consumer online/Internet-access services and educational software averaged only three hours and two hours per person, respectively. As these media become established, we look for the time spent to rise significantly over the forecast period along with expansion of computer penetration. By 1999, the time spent using online and Internet-access services will average an estimated 14 hours per person, and usage of educational software will average five hours.

Consumers spent $456.26 per person on media in 1994, up 6.6 percent from 1993. Per capita spending for consumer online and Internet-access services rose 39.1 percent, and spending on educational software increased 112.5 percent, in both cases fueled by penetration gains. Recorded music and home video games were the only other categories to post double-digit increases in 1994.

Subscription video services was the largest segment in 1994 with $110 in per capita spending, up a scant 1.3 percent owing to rollbacks in basic cable rates. Consumer books was the next-largest category at $79.22, up 5.8 percent, followed by home video at $72.97 per person, up 6.7 percent. After subscription video services, daily newspapers, consumer magazines, and movies in theaters were the slowest-growing categories, with spending per person rising 2.1 percent, 3.1 percent, and 3.6 percent, respectively.

The least expensive media, on an hourly basis, tend to be the most widely used. Broadcast television and radio, of course, are free to consumers and account for the largest amount of time spent. Subscription video services, next in terms of time spent, cost only 23 cents per hour in 1994. Recorded music ranked fourth in time spent, and its hourly cost was 19 cents.

The most expensive media on an hourly basis were consumer online and Internet-access services ($2.48), movies in theaters ($2.10), home video ($1.40), and educational software ($1.22), each costing more than $1. Books and home video games were the next-most-expensive at 78 cents and 77 cents per hour, respectively. The hourly cost of reading newspapers was 29 cents and of reading consumer magazines, 43 cents. These two media receive much of their funding from advertisers, helping to keep down the cost to end users.

COMMUNICATIONS IN THE U.S. ECONOMY

Communications ranked ninth among the 12 largest U.S. industries in 1994, the same position the industry held in 1989. Communications was the seventh-fastest-growing of the top-12 industries over the last five years, with a compound annual growth rate of 5.2 percent. Over the next five years communications will move up to the fourth position in growth on the strength of spending increases by end users on emerging media, coupled with continued support of existing media, and an improved advertising market. Electronic equipment and components, travel services, and telecommunications services will be the fastest growing of the top-12 industries over the next five years.

Top 12 U.S. Industries Ranked by Five-Year Growth

U.S. Industry	1989-94		1994-99	
	Growth*	Rank	Growth*	Rank
Health and Medical Services	9.4%	1	3.5%	11
Telecommunications Services	9.8	2	7.9	3
Electronic Equipment and Components	7.1	3	9.4	1
Motor Vehicles and Parts	6.4	4	5.5	7
Insurance	6.1	5	6.0	6
Educational Services	5.7	6	6.5	5
COMMUNICATIONS	5.2	7	6.8	4
Travel Services	4.9	8	8.1	2
Food and Related Products	4.1	9	4.1	9
Aerospace	3.8	10	3.8	10
Construction	2.9	11	5.1	8
Apparel and Related Goods	1.7	12	2.4	12
Top 12 Total	5.9		5.5	
Nominal GDP	5.1		5.3	

Sources: Veronis, Suhler & Associates, Wilkofsky Gruen Associates, U.S. Department of Commerce
*Compound annual growth

Hours Per Person Per Year Using Media

Year	Television Network-Affiliated Stations*	Independent Stations*	Basic Networks†	Premium Channels	Total TV	Radio	Recorded Music
1989	835	345	210	95	1,485	1,155	220
1990	780	340	260	90	1,470	1,135	235
1991	838	227	340	90	1,495	1,115	219
1992	914	159	359	78	1,510	1,150	233
1993	920	162	375	78	1,535	1,082	248
1994	919	172	388	81	1,560	1,102	294
1995	913	185	398	84	1,580	1,092	317
1996	909	205	408	78	1,600	1,087	323
1997	896	221	420	78	1,615	1,077	343
1998	899	224	435	77	1,635	1,067	365
1999	884	231	449	81	1,645	1,060	387

Sources: Veronis, Suhler & Associates, Wilkofsky Gruen Associates
*Affiliates of the Fox network are counted as network affiliates for part of
  1991 and all of 1992, but as independent stations in earlier years.
†Includes TBS beginning in 1992
‡Playback of prerecorded tapes only
§Less than 1 hour

THE OUTLOOK FOR COMMUNICATIONS INDUSTRY SPENDING

The expected slowdown of the economy over the next two years will cause advertising growth to moderate. Since we do not expect a repeat of the strong 1994 economic performance, we do not look for advertising growth to return to high single-digit rates. Nevertheless, in contrast with the last five years, advertising will expand at steady mid-single-digit rates over the forecast period and will outpace economic growth.

The relaxation of cable regulation and sharp increases in print media end-user prices will raise end-user spending in 1995. Thereafter, spending will grow steadily at rates ranging from 7 to 8 percent. For the Communications Industry as a whole, we expect faster overall growth over the forecast period than in the 1989-1994 period. We project spending to rise at a 6.8 percent compound annual rate over the next five years, 1.6 percentage points faster than the 5.2 percent annual increase of the last five years. Total Communications Industry spending will climb from $223.5 billion in 1994 to an estimated $323.7 billion in 1999.

TELEVISION BROADCASTING

Network advertising grew at a 3.4 percent compound annual rate over the last five years, helped by 1994's 8.5 percent increase. The broadcast networks provide advertisers with the ability to reach millions of people at once. With restructuring at an end and advertising on the upswing, the broadcast networks will do better over the next five years. Moreover, with penetration growth of subscription video services moderating, the broadcast networks have substantially reduced the rate of audience erosion. We project network advertising to rise at a 4.8 percent compound annual rate over the next five years, a rate that would be measurably higher except for the fact that advertising in 1994 included the Winter Olympics (in 1999 there will be no Olympics). Advertising in 1999 will total an estimated $14.0 billion, up from $11.1 billion in 1994.

The trend for television stations was virtually the same as for the networks. Television station advertising grew by 3.7 percent compounded annu-

Daily Newspapers	Consumer Books	Consumer Magazines	Home Video‡	Movies in Theaters	Home Video Games	Consumer On-Line/ Internet-Access Services	Educational Software	Total
175	96	90	39	12	6	§	§	3,278
175	95	90	42	12	12	1	§	3,267
169	98	88	43	11	18	1	§	3,257
172	100	85	46	11	19	2	1	3,329
170	99	85	49	12	19	2	1	3,302
169	102	84	52	12	22	3	2	3,402
164	101	82	53	12	25	5	3	3,434
163	100	81	54	11	27	8	3	3,457
161	101	80	56	11	30	11	4	3,489
160	103	80	57	11	33	13	4	3,528
159	105	80	58	11	36	14	5	3,560

NOTE: Estimates of time spent were derived using rating data for television and radio, survey research and consumer purchase data for recorded music, newspapers, magazines, books, home video, and admissions for movies. Adults 18 and older were the basis for estimates except for recorded music, movies in theaters, and video games, where estimates included persons 12 and older.

ally over the last five years, hurt not only by weakness among national advertisers but by the effects of local restructuring, which limited spending by department stores and other major advertisers. In 1994, however, station advertising rose by 10.7 percent, boosted by both Olympics-related advertising and widespread political advertising. Stations, along with the broadcast networks, will benefit from the improved advertising climate, and the introduction of new broadcast networks will help stations affiliated with them. We project television station advertising to grow at a 5.6 percent compound annual rate over the forecast period. Television station advertising will expand from $18.0 billion in 1994 to an estimated $23.6 billion by 1999.

Total advertiser spending on broadcast television will increase to $37.6 billion in 1999 from $29.0 billion in 1994, rising at a 5.3 percent compound annual rate, a 1.7-percentage-point improvement over the 3.6 percent growth of the last five years.

RADIO BROADCASTING

Advertising on radio stations, which grew at a 4.5 percent compound annual rate over the last five

years, rose at an average rate of better than 9 percent in 1993-1994. Local restructuring and the weak economy impacted radio as it did other local advertising media in 1991 and 1992, but over the last two years local advertising expanded significantly. With local advertising returning to health, radio stations should experience much faster growth over the forecast period. We project radio station advertising to rise at a 7.2 percent compound annual rate, growing from $9.8 billion in 1994 to $13.9 billion in 1999.

Network radio advertising growth was only 0.8 percent compounded annually over the last five years. After a steep decline in 1992, network radio advertising recovered strongly over the last two years, rising at an 8.0 percent rate. We look for an additional year of high single-digit growth, a downturn in 1996, and moderate growth thereafter. We project that network radio advertising will rise from $495 million in 1994 to an estimated $600 million by 1999, improving at a 3.9 percent compound annual rate. Radio advertising as a whole will total an estimated $14.5 billion by 1999, growing at a 7.1 percent compound annual rate from $10.3 billion in 1994.

SUBSCRIPTION VIDEO SERVICES

Spending on subscription video services rose at an 8.8 percent compound annual rate over the last five years — 11.3 percent for basic services, 0.8 percent for premium channels, 31.0 percent for pay-per-view movies, and 13.9 percent for advertising. Spending on basic services increased at double-digit rates until 1994 when it abruptly fell by 0.1 percent owing to the rollback of basic cable fees. With the regulatory environment easing, cable rates should move up. The market is becoming more competitive, however. Direct broadcast satellite (DBS) is now available, wireless cable is becoming a force, and video dial tone services may be offered during the forecast period. The emergence of these competing delivery channels should keep rate increases by cable operators in check. Since one or another of the various subscription video services is already available in nearly all television households, there will be fewer new subscribers to generate subscription spending growth over the next five years, even with the increased competition. For the five-year forecast period, we project spending on basic services to rise at a 7.3 percent compound annual rate. By 1999, spending on basic services should total $22.1 billion, up from $15.6 billion in 1994.

Premium channels should benefit from increased competition at the basic services level. With lower growth in basic fees, subscribers will have more money to spend for premium channels. Digital compression will allow for an increase in channel capacity, and the availability to more households of multiplexed premium services should spur subscribership. Spending on premium channels rose 8.8 percent in 1994, and we project spending to continue to grow at about that rate — 8.7 percent compounded annually — over the forecast period, increasing from $5.3 billion in 1994 to an estimated $8.0 billion in 1999.

Pay-per-view movies represent a small component of the subscription video services segment but one that is growing rapidly. Over the last five years, spending rose at a 31.0 percent compound annual rate. DBS should help PPV continue to expand by offering greater selection, more convenient viewing options, and attractive pricing. We expect spending to rise at a 28.7 percent rate compounded annually over the next five years, climbing to $1.0 billion in 1999 from $297 million in 1994.

We expect that advertising will continue to grow at double-digit rates over most of the forecast period.

End-User Spending Per Person Per Year

| | Television | | | | | | |
Year	Broadcast Television	Subscription Video Services	Total TV	Radio	Recorded Music	Daily Newspapers	Consumer Books
1989	$0.00	$77.86	$77.86	$0.00	$32.25	$45.71	$61.24
1990	0.00	87.90	87.90	0.00	36.64	47.55	63.90
1991	0.00	94.44	94.44	0.00	37.73	46.56	68.18
1992	0.00	101.28	101.28	0.00	43.05	48.54	71.37
1993	0.00	108.54	108.54	0.00	47.42	48.25	74.90
1994	0.00	110.00	110.00	0.00	56.35	49.28	79.22
1995	0.00	117.84	117.84	0.00	62.36	52.67	84.20
1996	0.00	128.65	128.65	0.00	65.07	55.78	88.89
1997	0.00	137.16	137.16	0.00	70.76	58.08	93.91
1998	0.00	145.75	145.75	0.00	77.29	60.61	100.03
1999	0.00	154.30	154.30	0.00	83.92	62.76	107.19

Sources: Veronis, Suhler & Associates, Wilkofsky Gruen Associates, Paul Kagan Associates, Motion Picture Association of America, Recording Industry Association of America, Newspaper Association of America, Book Industry Study Group, Magazine Publishers of America, Electronic Industries Association, Software Publishers Association, Jupiter Communications, Interactive Media Associates

Larger audiences and a strong advertising climate should fuel spending. We forecast advertising on subscription video services to grow at an 11.1 percent compound annual rate over the forecast period, rising to $5.0 billion from $2.9 billion in 1994.

Total spending on subscription video services will grow at an 8.4 percent compound annual rate, from $24.1 billion in 1994 to $36.1 billion in 1999.

FILMED ENTERTAINMENT

Box-office spending notched up at a 1.4 percent compound annual rate over the last five years. The success of individual releases affects overall box-office performance and helped lift spending by 5.8 percent in 1993 and 4.7 percent in 1994, offsetting declines in 1990 and 1991 and sluggish growth in 1992. Since we do not attempt to predict the likelihood of high-grossing movies, our forecast is predicated on the assumption of relatively stable admissions levels, with modest fluctuations mirroring the economy, and steady but moderate price increases. These factors lead to a projection of spending increases averaging 2.7 percent annually. By 1999, box-office spending will total an estimated $6.2 billion, up from $5.4 billion in 1994.

Home video spending grew at an 8.6 percent compound annual rate over the last five years. The principal driver was the increase in VCR penetration of television households from 64.3 percent in 1989 to 81.6 percent in 1994. As penetration growth slows in coming years, home video spending growth will also moderate, although expanding sell-through sales will fuel growth over the forecast period. We project spending to grow at a 6.1 percent rate over the next five years. In 1999, consumers will spend an estimated $18.9 billion renting or purchasing prerecorded videocassettes, up from $14.0 billion in 1994.

Spending on television programs rose at a 4.7 percent compound annual rate between 1989 and 1994. Double-digit growth in barter syndication and 9.7 percent growth in spending by subscription video networks offset sluggish increases on the broadcast side during this five-year period. Television networks have increasingly inserted less-expensive magazine and reality programming in their prime-time schedules in an effort to reduce costs, while the weak advertising environment combined with the glut of off-network programs led to soft prices in the program syndication market in the early 1990s. Going forward, new networks and

Consumer Magazines	Home Video	Movies in Theaters	Home Video Games	Consumer On-Line/ Internet-Access Services	Educational Software	Total
$31.49	$50.71	$24.67	$5.39	$2.22	$0.10	$331.65
33.14	56.35	24.40	12.39	2.93	0.22	365.43
33.45	58.69	23.13	12.47	3.61	0.48	378.77
34.26	63.23	23.24	13.08	4.39	0.70	403.15
35.27	68.42	24.33	14.56	5.35	1.15	428.19
36.36	72.97	25.20	17.00	7.44	2.44	456.26
38.79	78.19	25.13	18.95	11.23	2.99	492.35
40.53	81.47	24.83	20.70	16.34	3.48	525.74
42.12	86.47	25.82	22.89	21.82	4.28	563.32
43.75	89.85	26.61	25.38	27.03	5.24	601.55
45.53	93.56	27.39	28.13	29.95	6.43	639.17

Veronis, Suhler & Associates Inc. Communications Industry Forecast

Industry Segment	1989 Gross Expenditures ($ Millions)	1989-94 Compound Annual Growth (%)	1994 Gross Expenditures ($ Millions)	1994-99 Compound Annual Growth (%)	1999 Gross Expenditures ($ Millions)
Television Broadcasting	$24,356	3.6%	$29,045	5.3%	$37,550
Radio Broadcasting	8,323	4.3	10,295	7.1	14,505
Subscription Video Services	15,785	8.8	24,078	8.4	36,119
Filmed Entertainment	22,352	5.7	29,512	5.8	39,054
Recorded Music	6,580	12.9	12,068	9.4	18,916
Newspaper Publishing	44,148	1.7	48,055	5.1	61,706
Book Publishing	18,036	5.7	23,794	6.9	33,150
Magazine Publishing	18,693	3.5	22,240	6.0	29,742
Business Information Services	21,314	6.1	28,663	6.2	38,740
Interactive Digital Media	1,527	30.4	5,749	19.9	14,238
Total Spending	**$181,114**	**5.2%**	**$233,499**	**6.8%**	**$323,720**

increased competition will induce the broadcast networks to increase their use of higher-priced entertainment programming. Meanwhile, the expiration of the financial interest/syndication rules will lead to higher license fees, which include syndication rights. Over the forecast period, we look for faster growth in program spending by the broadcast networks.

As the new networks expand their programming, there will be fewer hours available for syndication, but the expected relaxation or elimination of the Prime-Time Access Rule will enhance license fees for off-network programs in the access hour. On balance, and factoring in the livelier advertising market, we look for syndication spending by television stations to grow faster over the forecast period.

In the case of basic and premium channels, increased penetration by DBS, wireless, and other delivery channels, in addition to expanded channel capacity allowing for new services to develop, will help offset slower overall penetration growth. We look for spending on entertainment programs by subscription video services to continue to rise at high single-digit rates.

Barter syndication expanded at an 11.5 percent compound annual rate over the 1989-1994 period, primarily because of an increase in the number of commercial units within syndicated programs that were available for barter. With Fox expected to expand its program hours and with new networks providing additional programming, inventory growth for barter will moderate over the forecast period. We therefore expect reduced growth in barter syndication advertising — 6.5 percent over the forecast period on a compound annual basis. By 1999, barter syndication will total an estimated $2.4 billion, up from $1.7 billion in 1994.

Total spending on filmed entertainment will rise from $29.5 billion in 1994 to an estimated $39.1 billion in 1999, growing 5.8 percent compounded annually over the next five years, about the same rate of increase as the 5.7 percent achieved over the 1989-1994 period.

RECORDED MUSIC

Spending on recorded music grew at a 12.9 percent compound annual rate between 1989 and 1994, with double-digit increases over the last three years and 20.1 percent growth in 1994. The rebounding economy and the appeal of recorded music to many demographic groups contributed to the recent surge in spending. With the underlying demand for music remaining strong, we look for spending increases over the forecast period to continue to be healthy, averaging 9.4 percent annually. We project spending to rise to $18.9 billion by 1999, up from $12.1 billion in 1994.

NEWSPAPER PUBLISHING

Advertising in daily newspapers rose at only a 1.1 percent compound annual rate over the last five years. Local restructuring dampened retail advertising, while the lackluster economy hurt the highly cyclical classified advertising sector in the early 1990s. Classified advertising bounced back strongly in 1994, rising by 11.9 percent. Nevertheless, the attrition in the number of papers affects aggregate advertising by reducing the number of outlets. With the economy expected to weaken over the next two years, classified growth will moderate. The completion of restructuring will help support the retail market, but with fewer department stores remaining, the advertising base for newspapers has narrowed. Further declines in the newspaper population could continue to bring down aggregate spending but to a lesser extent than over the last five years since we expect the pace of consolidation to slow. We project daily newspaper advertising to rise at a 4.8 percent compound annual rate over the forecast period, 3.7 points higher than growth over the last five years. Daily newspaper advertising will grow to $43.2 billion by 1999 from $34.2 billion in 1994.

The runup in newsprint costs will lead to large circulation price increases in 1995, offset somewhat by circulation declines and the continued reduction in the number of newspapers. With fewer two-paper markets remaining, however, there should be less consolidation over the forecast period. Over the forecast period, we project daily newspaper circulation spending to grow faster — 6.0 percent compounded annually — than the 2.5 percent rate of the last five years. Circulation spending will expand from $9.5 billion in 1994 to $12.7 billion in 1999.

Total spending on daily newspapers will increase to $55.9 billion by 1999, growing at a 5.1 percent compound annual rate compared with 1.4 percent over the last five years. Spending in 1994 totaled $43.7 billion.

Advertising in weekly newspapers rose at a 5.3 percent compound annual rate over the last five years. We look for a comparable rate of expansion over the next five years — 5.8 percent compounded annually — as a weaker economy in the near term is countered by healthier growth over the latter part of the forecast period. Weekly newspaper advertising will reach an estimated $5.3 billion in 1999, up from $4.0 billion in 1994.

Circulation of paid weeklies was up in 1994, after remaining essentially flat over the previous four years. Higher circulation prices, dictated by rising newsprint costs, will drive paid circulation back down to previous levels. Over the forecast period, we look for circulation spending on paid weeklies to rise at a 3.8 percent rate, down from the 4.3 percent annual growth of the last five years. Circulation spending is expected to increase from $400 million in 1994 to $483 million in 1999.

Total spending on weekly newspapers will increase at a 5.6 percent compound annual rate, from $4.4 billion in 1994 to $5.8 billion in 1999. Over the last five years, spending on weeklies grew at a 5.2 percent annual rate.

Spending on all papers — dailies and weeklies — will total $61.7 billion in 1999, up from $48.1 billion in 1994. Growth over the forecast period will average 5.1 percent compounded annually, a substantial gain over the 1.7 percent increase of the last five years.

BOOK PUBLISHING

Spending on consumer books rose at a 6.3 percent compound annual rate over the last five years, totaling $15.2 billion in 1994, the largest consumer spending category except for subscription video services. Adult trade books were the principal driver of growth, with spending increasing at double-digit rates in each of the last three years. Recent weakness in the juvenile trade category and declines in mail order kept overall growth below 7 percent. Expansion in the 35-and-over population, the principal book-reading demographic, strength in adult trade, and a continuation of the modest pickup in juvenile trade that began in 1994 should lead to faster spending growth over the forecast period. We look for spending on consumer books to rise at a 7.3 percent compound annual rate. Consumers will spend an estimated $21.7 billion purchasing books in 1999.

Spending on professional books slacked off during the 1990-1991 economic downturn but has recovered strongly, rising at high single-digit rates since then. We expect slower employment growth in the legal and health-care professions, but faster growth in managerial and scientific and technical employment. On balance, professional employment will grow at a somewhat higher rate over the next five years than over the 1989-1994 period, and spending on professional books should grow faster as well. We project professional book sales to expand at an 8.0 percent compound annual rate, up from 7.4 percent over the last five years. Spending will rise from $4.0 billion in 1994 to $5.8 billion in 1999.

Elhi textbook spending depends on school budgets, which are affected, in turn, by tax receipts and adoption cycles. The real estate slump and the recession impacted spending during the 1990-1992 period. In 1993, tax receipts were up because the real estate market rallied, a number of states that had postponed spending returned to the market, and the state of Texas made a large adoption. These factors helped produce an 11.0 percent jump in spending on elementary and high school textbooks. With the Texas money leaving the market, however, elhi spending fell 7.0 percent in 1994. Over the next three years, adoptions by a number of large states should boost spending. We estimate that spending over the forecast period will rise from $2.1 billion to $2.7 billion, growing at a 5.2 percent compound annual rate. Over the 1989-1994 period, spending growth was only 1.6 percent compounded annually.

College textbook sales are driven by enrollment since students buy textbooks directly. Over the last five years, spending on college textbooks rose at a 3.4 percent annual rate. College enrollment exhibits a countercyclical pattern with respect to the economy. As job opportunities improve, enrollment, particularly of part-time students, suffers. The slipping economy over the next two years should help enrollment, and by the latter part of the forecast period, growth in the number of college-age students will begin to pick up. On the other hand, the used-textbook market will continue to compete with the sale of new textbooks. We expect that spending on college textbooks will grow at about the same rate over the next five years — 3.5 percent compounded annually — as it did over the 1989-1994 period. Spending should increase from $2.5 billion in 1994 to an estimated $3.0 billion by 1999.

Total spending on professional and educational books will rise at a 6.1 percent compound annual rate, reaching $11.5 billion in 1999 from $8.6 billion in 1994. Over the last five years, spending grew at a 4.7 percent annual rate.

For books as a whole — consumer and professional and educational — we project spending to expand at a 6.9 percent compound annual rate, rising from $23.8 billion in 1994 to $33.1 billion in 1999. Over the last five years, spending grew at a 5.7 percent annual rate.

MAGAZINE PUBLISHING

Consumer magazine advertising displays a highly cyclical pattern that relates to the economy. Advertising fell 4.1 percent in 1991, expanded at mid-single-digit rates over the ensuing two years,

and increased by 8.5 percent in 1994. With economic growth expected to slow, we anticipate more moderate advertising gains compared with the 1994 performance. We look for growth to average 6.9 percent compounded annually, nearly twice the 3.5 percent rate of the last five years. Advertisers will spend an estimated $11.1 billion in consumer magazines in 1999, up from $8.0 billion in 1994.

Unlike newspapers and books, magazines tend to be read by a relatively younger demographic, a segment of the population that will show little growth over the forecast period. Over the last five years, unit circulation has been relatively flat, and we expect it will remain flat over the forecast period. Steeper circulation price increases, however, particularly in the near term in response to the runup in paper costs, will generate faster growth in circulation spending. Growth will average an estimated 5.6 percent over the next five years compared with 3.9 percent between 1989 and 1994. Consumer spending will rise from $7.0 billion in 1994 to $9.2 billion by 1999.

Total spending on consumer magazines grew at a 3.7 percent compound annual rate over the last five years. We look for spending to increase at a 6.3 percent annual rate over the next five years, reaching $20.3 billion by 1999 from $15.0 billion in 1994.

Advertising in business magazines depends on the industries served by those magazines. The strong economy stimulated spending in most categories in 1994, and business magazine advertising as a whole rose 9.0 percent. During the previous five years, the best performance was the 4.4 percent increase of 1992. We do not expect the economy during the forecast period to have as strong a year as 1994. On the other hand, with corporate restructuring virtually complete, the general advertising climate for business magazines will improve. We look for business magazine advertising to increase at a 5.7 percent compound annual rate over the next five years, compared with the 3.2 percent increase of the last five years. We project business magazine advertising to rise from $5.5 billion in 1994 to $7.3 billion in 1999.

Most business magazines are distributed on a controlled circulation basis to qualified readers. Circulation spending, therefore, represents a smaller percentage of total revenues for business publications than circulation spending does for consumer magazines. Expanding employment should increase the potential circulation of business magazines, and we look for paid circulation to grow at a faster rate. Circulation spending should rise at a 4.1 percent compound annual rate over the forecast period, surpassing the 3.3 percent increase of the last five years. End users will spend $2.1 billion on business magazines in 1999, up from $1.7 billion in 1994.

Total spending on business magazines will rise at a 5.3 percent compound annual rate between 1994 and 1999 compared with 3.2 percent annual growth over the last five years. Spending will total $9.4 billion in 1999, up from $7.3 billion in 1994.

Total magazine spending — consumer and business — will rise from $22.2 billion in 1994 to $29.7 billion in 1999, increasing at a 6.0 percent compound annual rate, an improvement over the 3.5 percent growth of the last five years.

BUSINESS INFORMATION SERVICES

Spending on business information services totaled $28.7 billion in 1994, growing at a 6.1 percent compound annual rate over the last five years. The industry is in equilibrium. The factors affecting growth are largely in place, and no major changes are anticipated over the forecast period. Exceptions may be the development of LAN/WAN networking, improved graphical user interface technology, and expert system software, which could result in an increase in the end-user customer base. These developments, however, will likely occur too late in the forecast period to have a meaningful impact. For the 1994-1999 period, we project spending on business information services to grow at a 6.2 percent compound annual rate, about the same pace as over the last five years, reaching $38.7 billion by 1999.

INTERACTIVE DIGITAL MEDIA

Interactive digital media have made dramatic strides over the last five years, with spending growth averaging 30.4 percent annually. The penetration of U.S. households by the personal computer has been a principal force for growth. Over the last five years, computer household penetration rose from 19.9 percent to 32.0 percent, and by 1999 we expect it to reach 44.3 percent. More and more households will also have modems and CD-ROM drives, which will enable consumers to partake of services requiring these devices.

Growing interest in the Internet will spur spending on online and Internet-access services. We expect subscription spending for these services to increase at a 33.4 percent compound annual rate over the forecast period, reaching $6.1 billion by 1999 from $1.4 billion in 1994. Spending on packaged PC/multimedia software, which includes consumer reference and general-interest titles, educational software, and computer game and entertainment software, will grow at a 23.2 percent compound annual rate, driven principally by growth in the CD-ROM universe. Spending will increase from $1.4 billion in 1994 to an estimated $4.0 billion by 1999.

Video-game console software has been available to consumers for a number of years, and is the largest and most mature component of the interactive digital media segment. We expect that most of the growth in video-game software will come from computer games. Nevertheless, spending on video-game console software will continue to expand, fueled by the introduction of new platforms, and will grow at an estimated 7.6 percent compound annual rate over the forecast period. Over the last five years, spending on video-game console software rose at a 23.9 percent annual rate. By 1999, video-game console software spending will total $4.2 billion, up from $2.9 billion in 1994.

For interactive digital media as a group, spending will rise from $5.7 billion in 1994 to an estimated $14.2 billion by 1999, growing 19.9 percent compounded annually. Although its forecasted growth is down from the 30.4 percent annual increase of the last five years, this segment will be the fastest growing in the Communications Industry.

Veronis, Suhler & Associates in an investment bank serving the media & communications industry. For information regarding VS&A's publications or merger, acquisition, and advisory services contact:

Veronis, Suhler & Associates Inc.
350 Park Avenue
New York, NY 10022

Phone: (212) 935-4990
Fax: (212) 935-0877
Web site: www.vsacomm.com

MEDIA

A List-Lovers Compendium

The 200 Largest Companies by Sales in
Hoover's Guide to Media Companies

Rank	Company	Sales ($ mil.)	Rank	Company	Sales ($ mil.)
1	Sony Corporation	44,758	51	Carlton Communications PLC	2,533
2	Time Warner Inc.	17,696	52	Nippon Television Network Corp.	2,413
3	Bertelsmann AG	14,761	53	The New York Times Company	2,409
4	Dai Nippon Printing	14,387	54	WPP Group plc	2,406
5	The Walt Disney Company	12,112	55	Tokyo Broadcasting System	2,386
6	Viacom Inc.	11,689	56	U S WEST Media Group	2,374
7	Ingram Industries Inc.	11,000	57	The Hearst Corporation	2,331
8	Lagardére Groupe	10,743	58	Dow Jones & Company, Inc.	2,284
9	Havas S.A.	9,118	59	Omnicom Group Inc.	2,258
10	The News Corporation Limited	8,641	60	CEP Communication SA	2,253
11	THORN EMI plc	7,306	61	Tribune Company	2,245
12	The Thomson Corporation	7,225	62	The Interpublic Group of Companies, Inc.	2,180
13	Best Buy Co., Inc.	7,217	63	CANAL+	2,075
14	Capital Cities/ABC, Inc.	6,879	64	Dentsu Inc.	2,026
15	R. R. Donnelley & Sons Company	6,512	65	Barnes & Noble, Inc.	1,977
16	Microsoft Corporation	5,937	66	nv Verenigd Bezit VNU	1,903
17	MCA Inc.	5,772	67	Télévision Française 1	1,863
18	Reed Elsevier PLC	5,646	68	Deluxe Corporation	1,858
19	PolyGram N.V.	5,499	69	Wolters Kluwer nv	1,837
20	The Dun & Bradstreet Corporation	5,415	70	Borders Group, Inc.	1,749
21	Aegis Group Plc	5,262	71	Musicland Stores Corporation	1,723
22	TCI Communications, Inc.	5,118	72	The Washington Post Company	1,719
23	Advance Publications, Inc.	4,855	73	United News & Media plc	1,662
24	FMR Corporation	4,270	74	Groupe de la Cité SA	1,516
25	W H Smith Group plc	4,271	75	Maruzen	1,506
26	Reuters Holdings PLC	4,188	76	Tidnings AB Marieberg	1,469
27	Publicis SA	4,178	77	Bonnierforetagen AB	1,443
28	The Rank Organisation PLC	4,139	78	Continental Cablevision, Inc.	1,442
29	Quebecor Inc.	4,067	79	CUC International Inc.	1,415
30	Gannett Co., Inc.	4,007	80	International Data Group	1,400
31	Kirchgruppe	4,000	81	Daily Mail and General Trust PLC	1,393
32	National Broadcasting Company Inc.	3,919	82	Arnoldo Mondadori Editore S.p.A.	1,359
33	Cox Enterprises, Inc.	3,806	83	Gakken	1,356
34	Granada Group PLC	3,769	84	News International PLC	1,341
35	The Times Mirror Company	3,448	85	World Color Press, Inc.	1,296
36	Turner Broadcasting System, Inc.	3,437	86	Cox Communications, Inc.	1,286
37	Comcast Corporation	3,363	87	A.C. Nielsen Co.	1,286
38	Westinghouse/CBS Group	3,333	88	British Sky Broadcasting Group plc	1,226
39	Blockbuster Entertainment Group	3,333	89	De La Rue PLC	1,211
40	The Jim Pattison Group	3,300	90	Creative Technology Ltd.	1,202
41	Compagnie Luxembourgeoise pour l'Audio-Visuel et la Finance	3,100	91	GoodTimes Entertainment Worldwide	1,200
42	The Reader's Digest Association, Inc.	3,069	92	Burda GmbH	1,188
43	Harcourt General, Inc.	3,035	93	Cordiant plc	1,178
44	British Broadcasting Corporation	3,000	94	Hersant Group	1,170
45	The McGraw-Hill Companies, Inc.	2,935	95	Grupo Televisa, S.A.	1,148
46	Pearson plc	2,931	96	Handleman Company	1,133
47	Axel Springer Verlag AG	2,888	97	Young & Rubicam Inc.	1,122
48	Virgin Group PLC	2,845	98	Hollinger Inc.	1,109
49	Knight-Ridder, Inc.	2,752	99	Maritz Inc.	1,078
50	A/S Det Ostasiatiske Kompagni	2,602	100	Cablevision Systems Corporation	1,078

The 200 Largest Companies by Sales in
Hoover's Guide to Media Companies (continued)

Rank	Company	Sales ($ mil.)	Rank	Company	Sales ($ mil.)
101	Toei	1,070	151	Primark Corporation	617
102	K-III Communications Corporation	1,046	152	Valassis Communications, Inc.	614
103	The E.W. Scripps Company	1,030	153	New World Communications Group Incorporated	605
104	Banta Corporation	1,023	154	Linotype-Hell AG	601
105	Home Shopping Network, Inc.	1,019	155	Irvin Feld & Kenneth Feld Prod.	600
106	Liberty Media Corporation	1,019	156	Journal Communication Inc.	592
107	ADVO, Inc.	1,012	157	Singapore Press Holdings Ltd.	587
108	Quad/Graphics, Inc.	1,002	158	Central Newspapers, Inc.	580
109	Rich Products Corporation	1,000	159	King World Productions, Inc.	574
110	Hollinger International, Inc.	965	160	Acclaim Entertainment, Inc.	567
111	MTS Inc.	950	161	Independent Newspapers PLC	560
112	Ziff-Davis Publishing Company	950	162	Europe 1 Communication SA	542
113	Pittway Corporation	946	163	McClatchy Newspapers, Inc.	541
114	CIA Group	938	164	Harte-Hanks Communications, Inc.	533
115	Treasure Chest Advertising Company, Inc.	897	165	Electronic Arts Inc.	532
116	Big Flower Press Holdings, Inc.	897	166	Schibsted A/S	530
117	EMAP PLC	887	167	Freedom Communications, Inc.	530
118	Meredith Corporation	885	168	Houghton Mifflin Company	529
119	COMSAT Corporation	852	169	DIRECTV, Inc.	525
120	Marvel Entertainment Group, Inc.	829	170	East Texas Distributing Inc.	525
121	West Publishing Co.	827	171	Trans World Entertainment Corp.	517
122	Bell & Howell Company	820	172	Cineplex Odeon Corporation	513
123	Follett Corporation	811	173	Shochiku	507
124	CompuServe Corporation	793	174	Landmark Communications, Inc.	501
125	Havas Advertising SA	791	175	Wherehouse Entertainment Inc.	500
126	Toho	790	176	Taylor Corporation	485
127	Baker & Taylor, Inc.	785	177	Wace Group PLC	474
128	Leo Burnett Company, Inc.	781	178	Pulitzer Publishing Company	472
129	Adobe Systems Incorporated	762	179	Chris-Craft Industries, Inc.	472
130	Scholastic Corporation	750	180	Rand McNally & Company	469
131	Southam Inc.	750	181	Justin Industries, Inc.	461
132	A. H. Belo Corporation	735	182	National Geographic Society	456
133	Mirror Group PLC	731	183	BHC Communications, Inc.	455
134	Scitex Corporation Ltd.	729	184	GC Companies Inc.	451
135	Alliance Entertainment Corp.	720	185	Camelot Music Inc.	450
136	Holdingmaatschappij De Telegraaf NV	717	186	Cowles Media Company	450
137	Media General Inc.	708	187	Abbott Mead Vickers PLC	444
138	Gaylord Entertainment Company	708	188	Lee Enterprises, Incorporated	443
139	Editoriale l'Espresso SpA	707	189	True North Communications Inc.	439
140	Grey Advertising Inc.	688	190	ASCAP	437
141	John Fairfax Holdings Ltd.	670	191	Heritage Media Corporation	436
142	Jostens, Inc.	665	192	Weider Health & Fitness	430
143	Spelling Entertainment Group Inc.	664	193	Associated Press	426
144	Publishing & Broadcasting Limited	658	194	Morris Communications Corporation	425
145	AMC Entertainment Inc.	658	195	St. Ives PLC	422
146	Bloomberg L.P.	650	196	Rodale Press, Inc.	420
147	United Artists Theatre Circuit, Inc.	646	197	The Chronicle Publishing Company	418
148	International Management Group	640	198	Graphic Industries, Inc.	417
149	D'Arcy Masius Benton & Bowles, Inc.	626	199	Century Communications Corp.	417
150	Lane Industries, Inc.	625	200	Bozell, Jacobs, Kenyon & Eckhardt	408

The 200 Largest Companies by Employees in
Hoover's Guide to Media Companies

Rank	Company	Employees	Rank	Company	Employees
1	Sony Corporation	138,000	51	Ingram Industries Inc.	13,000
2	Viacom Inc.	81,700	52	A/S Det Ostasiatiske Kompagni	12,891
3	The Walt Disney Company	71,000	53	The New York Times Company	12,300
4	Time Warner Inc.	65,500	54	Comcast Corporation	12,200
5	Bertelsmann AG	57,397	55	PolyGram N.V.	12,002
6	The Dun & Bradstreet Corporation	49,500	56	Dow Jones & Company, Inc.	11,200
7	The Thomson Corporation	48,600	57	United Artists Theatre Circuit, Inc.	11,100
8	Blockbuster Entertainment Group	45,000	58	Cordiant plc	10,570
9	Lagardere Groupe	43,622	59	Tribune Company	10,500
10	R. R. Donnelley & Sons Company	41,000	60	Young & Rubicam Inc.	10,404
11	The Rank Organisation PLC	40,094	61	nv Verenigd Bezit VNU	10,306
12	Gannett Co., Inc.	39,100	62	Carmike Cinemas, Inc.	10,082
13	Granada Group PLC	39,085	63	Gaylord Entertainment Company	10,000
14	Cox Enterprises, Inc.	38,000	64	Carlton Communications PLC	9,953
15	W H Smith Group plc	33,625	65	Daily Mail and General Trust PLC	9,520
16	THORN EMI plc	33,547	66	Groupe de la Cité SA	9,217
17	Best Buy Co., Inc.	33,500	67	Continental Cablevision, Inc.	9,200
18	Dai Nippon Printing	33,000	68	Virgin Group PLC	9,000
19	TCI Communications, Inc.	32,500	69	Westinghouse/CBS Group	9,000
20	Reed Elsevier PLC	30,400	70	Wolters Kluwer nv	8,993
21	Quebecor Inc.	28,900	71	Hollinger Inc.	8,700
22	The News Corporation Limited	26,600	72	International Data Group	8,500
23	Heritage Media Corporation	26,200	73	Quad/Graphics, Inc.	8,444
24	British Broadcasting Corporation	23,063	74	Lane Industries, Inc.	8,300
25	Knight-Ridder, Inc.	22,800	75	Tidnings AB Marieberg	8,254
26	The Times Mirror Company	21,877	76	World Color Press, Inc.	8,200
27	Barnes & Noble, Inc.	21,400	77	De La Rue PLC	8,012
28	Grupo Televisa, S.A.	20,700	78	AMC Entertainment Inc.	8,000
29	Borders Group, Inc.	20,000	79	CUC International Inc.	8,000
30	Capital Cities/ABC, Inc.	20,000	80	Taylor Corporation	8,000
31	The Interpublic Group of Companies, Inc.	19,700	81	Southam Inc.	7,864
32	Pearson plc	19,422	82	The E.W. Scripps Company	7,700
33	Omnicom Group Inc.	19,400	83	Cineplex Odeon Corporation	7,661
34	WPP Group plc	19,138	84	MTS Inc.	7,600
35	Advance Publications, Inc.	19,000	85	Follett Corporation	7,500
36	Havas S.A.	18,324	86	Media General Inc.	7,500
37	Deluxe Corporation	18,000	87	McClatchy Newspapers, Inc.	7,464
38	Microsoft Corporation	17,801	88	GC Companies Inc.	7,400
39	A.C. Nielsen Co.	17,000	89	Hollinger International, Inc.	7,220
40	Musicland Stores Corporation	17,000	90	The Washington Post Company	7,010
41	The Jim Pattison Group	16,000	91	Cinemark USA Inc.	7,000
42	U S WEST Media Group	16,000	92	Havas Advertising SA	7,000
43	Harcourt General, Inc.	15,219	93	Turner Broadcasting System, Inc.	7,000
44	The McGraw-Hill Companies, Inc.	15,004	94	West Publishing Co.	7,000
45	FMR Corporation	14,600	95	EMAP PLC	6,789
46	Reuters Holdings PLC	14,348	96	CEP Communication SA	6,770
47	United News & Media plc	13,573	97	Hollywood Entertainment Corporation	6,723
48	MCA Inc.	13,564	98	Journal Communication Inc.	6,500
49	The Hearst Corporation	13,500	99	Rich Products Corporation	6,500
50	Axel Springer Verlag AG	13,331	100	Maritz Inc.	6,410

The 200 Largest Companies by Employees in
Hoover's Guide to Media Companies (continued)

Rank	Company	Employees	Rank	Company	Employees
101	Information Resources, Inc.	6,360	151	The Copley Press, Inc.	3,500
102	D'Arcy Masius Benton & Bowles	6,333	152	Hastings Books, Music & Video, Inc.	3,500
103	K-III Communications Corporation	6,300	153	Scitex Corporation Ltd.	3,500
104	The Reader's Digest Association	6,200	154	A. H. Belo Corporation	3,489
105	Publicis SA	6,000	155	Jones Communications, Inc.	3,480
106	Bell & Howell Company	5,966	156	WMS Industries Inc.	3,381
107	Dentsu Inc.	5,910	157	Cowles Media Company	3,300
108	Banta Corporation	5,700	158	Associated Press	3,150
109	Scholastic Corporation	5,636	159	St. Ives PLC	3,141
110	Jostens, Inc.	5,600	160	Agence France-Presse	3,100
111	Freedom Communications, Inc.	5,500	161	Compagnie Luxembourgeoise pour	
112	Trans World Entertainment Corp.	5,500		l'Audio-Visuel et la Finance	3,089
113	Independent Newspapers PLC	5,495	162	British Sky Broadcasting Group plc	3,054
114	Arnoldo Mondadori Editore S.p.A.	5,430	163	Camelot Music Inc.	3,000
115	Pittway Corporation	5,400	164	COMSAT Corporation	2,991
116	Bonnierforetagen AB	5,286	165	NYNEX CableComms	2,964
117	ADVO, Inc.	5,200	166	Graphic Industries, Inc.	2,961
118	Central Newspapers, Inc.	5,188	167	Mirror Group PLC	2,907
119	Morris Communications Corp.	5,140	168	Opinion Research Corporation	2,902
120	Primark Corporation	5,131	169	Books-A-Million, Inc.	2,883
121	Justin Industries, Inc.	5,007	170	Cablevision Systems Corporation	2,801
122	Burda GmbH	5,000	171	Bowne & Co., Inc.	2,800
123	National Broadcasting Company	5,000	172	Crown Books Corporation	2,800
124	R. L. Polk & Co.	5,000	173	TeleWest Communications PLC	2,776
125	Harte-Hanks Communications, Inc.	4,957	174	Franklin Quest Co.	2,771
126	John Fairfax Holdings Ltd.	4,752	175	New World Communications	2,700
127	Lee Enterprises, Incorporated	4,700	176	Wherehouse Entertainment Inc.	2,700
128	Rand McNally & Company	4,650	177	Ziff-Davis Publishing Company	2,700
129	Holdingmaatschappij De Telegraaf	4,551	178	Johnson Publishing Company, Inc.	2,680
130	Landmark Communications, Inc.	4,500	179	ATC Communications Group, Inc.	2,617
131	MediaNews Group, Inc.	4,500	180	Editoriale l'Espresso SpA	2,577
132	Cox Communications, Inc.	4,375	181	Adelphia Communications Corp.	2,564
133	True North Communications Inc.	4,369	182	The Chronicle Publishing Company	2,500
134	Wace Group PLC	4,328	183	Irvin Feld & Kenneth Feld	2,500
135	Home Shopping Network, Inc.	4,295	184	Pulitzer Publishing Company	2,500
136	Tandycrafts, Inc.	4,200	185	America Online, Inc.	2,481
137	Treasure Chest Advertising		186	Providence Journal Company	2,480
	Company, Inc.	4,200	187	Meredith Corporation	2,400
138	News International PLC	4,163	188	Seattle Times Company	2,400
139	Handleman Company	4,147	189	American Banknote Corporation	2,380
140	Big Flower Press Holdings, Inc.	4,100	190	Cadmus Communications Corp.	2,380
141	Creative Technology Ltd.	4,100	191	Houghton Mifflin Company	2,350
142	Bozell, Jacobs, Kenyon & Eckhardt	3,931	192	Adobe Systems Incorporated	2,319
143	Trinity International Holdings PLC	3,903	193	Century Communications Corp.	2,300
144	Regal Cinemas, Inc.	3,816	194	Encyclopaedia Britannica, Inc.	2,300
145	Golden Books Family Entertainment	3,800	195	Merrill Corporation	2,253
146	Times Publishing Company	3,762	196	Johnston Press PLC	2,238
147	Linotype-Hell AG	3,761	197	Chas. Levy Companies	2,234
148	The New York Public Library	3,608	198	Schibsted A/S	2,228
149	Grolier Incorporated	3,600	199	Baker & Taylor, Inc.	2,200
150	CompuServe Corporation	3,500	200	Maruzen	2,187

The 200 Fastest-Growing Companies by Sales in
Hoover's Guide to Media Companies

Rank	Company	One-Year Sales Growth % Change	Rank	Company	One-Year Sales Growth % Change
1	Netscape Communications Corp.	11,429	51	IVI Publishing Inc.	71
2	UUNET Technologies, Inc.	662	52	Davidson & Associates, Inc.	67
3	Heartland Wireless Communications	595	53	Sinclair Broadcast Group	67
4	Moovies, Inc.	461	54	Lexi International, Inc.	67
5	PRIMESTAR Partners L.P.	400	55	National Media Corporation	66
6	Tele-Communications International	333	56	Paxson Communications Corp.	66
7	Big Entertainment, Inc.	320	57	EMAP PLC	65
8	Discreet Logic Inc.	319	58	ValueVision International, Inc.	65
9	America Online, Inc.	278	59	ATC Communications Group, Inc.	64
10	Movie Gallery, Inc.	219	60	The Harvey Entertainment Co.	63
11	Marcus Cable Company L.P.	206	61	Desktop Data, Inc.	61
12	Wired Ventures, Inc.	175	62	Marvel Entertainment Group, Inc.	61
13	Lauriat's, Inc.	175	63	Educational Development Corp.	61
14	Multi-Market Radio, Inc.	158	64	Gray Communications Systems	61
15	T-HQ, Inc.	150	65	Granite Broadcasting Corporation	59
16	Comcast Corporation	145	66	Viacom Inc.	59
17	Chancellor Broadcasting Company	144	67	LodgeNet Entertainment Corp.	57
18	Heftel Broadcasting Corporation	143	68	Young Broadcasting Inc.	55
19	GT Interactive Software Corp.	140	69	Arnoldo Mondadori Editore S.p.A.	55
20	Hollinger International, Inc.	128	70	M.A.I.D plc	55
21	Modem Media	127	71	Videotron Holdings Plc	54
22	American Telecasting, Inc.	120	72	International Management Group	54
23	Pixar Inc.	116	73	Broderbund Software, Inc.	53
24	E*TRADE Group, Inc.	114	74	YES! Entertainment Corporation	53
25	People's Choice TV Corp.	106	75	Sunset & Vine PLC	53
26	Hollywood Entertainment Corp.	104	76	New World Communications Group Incorporated	52
27	Byron Preiss Multimedia Company	103	77	The Todd-AO Corporation	52
28	Individual, Inc.	100	78	Grupo Televisa, S.A.	51
29	Multi-Media Tutorial Service	100	79	Track Data Corporation	51
30	Pro CD, Inc.	100	80	Emmis Broadcasting Corporation	49
31	Wizards of the Coast	100	81	Consolidated Graphics, Inc.	49
32	Avid Technology, Inc.	100	82	Harmony Holdings, Inc.	47
33	All American Communications, Inc.	99	83	Burda GmbH	46
34	TeleWest Communications PLC	99	84	Electronics for Imaging, Inc.	46
35	Lancit Media Productions, Ltd.	97	85	Maxis, Inc.	45
36	Edmark Corporation	94	86	Flextech plc	45
37	Fronteer Directory Company, Inc.	91	87	EZ Communications, Inc.	45
38	Sierra On-Line, Inc.	90	88	Markkinointi Viherjuuri OY	45
39	CEP Communication SA	89	89	British Sky Broadcasting Group	44
40	CST Entertainment, Inc.	85	90	LIN Television Corporation	44
41	INSO Corporation	85	91	American Radio Systems Corp.	44
42	Central European Media Enterprises, Ltd.	85	92	Big Flower Press Holdings, Inc.	44
43	Video Update, Inc.	82	93	Futuremedia Public Limited Co.	42
44	Creative Technology Ltd.	83	94	Best Buy Co., Inc.	42
45	Individual Investor Group, Inc.	82	95	Four Media Company	42
46	Reading Company	82	96	Cinar Films, Inc.	42
47	Mecklermedia Corporation	75	97	Clear Channel Communications	41
48	Cox Communications, Inc.	75	98	Regal Cinemas, Inc.	40
49	Sanctuary Woods Multimedia Corp.	75	99	Quebecor Inc.	40
50	Excalibur Technologies Corporation	73	100	DataTimes Corporation	40

Note: To be included on this list, companies must have sales greater than $5 million. These rates may have resulted from acquisitions or internal growth.

The 200 Fastest-Growing Companies by Sales in
Hoover's Guide to Media Companies (continued)

Rank	Company	One-Year Sales Growth % Change	Rank	Company	One-Year Sales Growth % Change
101	West Publishing Co.	39	151	Inside Communications Inc.	28
102	CinemaStar Luxury Theaters, Inc.	39	152	CIA Group	28
103	Unapix Entertainment, Inc.	39	153	T/SF Communications Corporation	28
104	SFX Broadcasting, Inc.	38	154	Microsoft Corporation	28
105	Metro Global Media, Inc.	38	155	Adobe Systems Incorporated	28
106	International Post Limited	38	156	Advanced Promotion Technologies	27
107	SoftKey International Inc.	38	157	International Data Group	27
108	De La Rue PLC	38	158	Printware, Inc.	27
109	Ingram Industries Inc.	37	159	Bertelsmann AG	27
110	NRJ SA	37	160	A/S Det Ostasiatiske Kompagni	27
111	Heritage Media Corporation	37	161	Showscan Entertainment Inc.	27
112	DMX Inc.	36	162	Lonely Planet Publications, Inc.	27
113	CompuServe Corporation	36	163	Video Jukebox Network, Inc.	27
114	Metatec Corporation	36	164	Graff Pay-Per-View Inc.	26
115	Argyle Television, Inc.	36	165	Banta Corporation	26
116	CUC International Inc.	35	166	Franklin Electronic Publisher	26
117	Data Transmission Network		167	Adams Media Corporation	25
	Corporation	35	168	Discovery Communications, Inc.	25
118	Zomax Optical Media, Inc.	35	169	LCS Industries, Inc.	26
119	Dorling Kindersley Holdings plc	35	170	Creative Alliance Inc.	26
120	Alliance Entertainment Corp.	35	171	Day Runner, Inc.	26
121	United Video Satellite Group, Inc.	34	172	Cowles Media Company	26
122	Independent Newspapers PLC	33	173	Quad/Graphics, Inc.	25
123	Acxiom Corporation	33	174	Dentsu Inc.	25
124	Telescan, Inc.	33	175	FactSet Research Systems Inc.	25
125	Books-A-Million, Inc.	33	176	Univision Communications Inc.	25
126	World Color Press, Inc.	33	177	U S WEST Media Group	24
127	R. R. Donnelley & Sons Company	33	178	IBC Group plc	24
128	News Communications, Inc.	32	179	Shop At Home, Inc.	24
129	NYNEX CableComms	32	180	Sony Corporation	23
130	Bonnierforetagen AB	32	181	Tidnings AB Marieberg	23
131	TRO Learning, Inc.	31	182	A&E Television Networks	23
132	Katz Digital Technologies, Inc.	31	183	Turner Broadcasting System, Inc.	22
133	Nationwide Advertising Service	31	184	Vance Publishing Corporation	22
134	Capital Radio plc	30	185	American List Corporation	22
135	BCT International, Inc.	30	186	Barnes & Noble, Inc.	22
136	Premiere Radio Networks, Inc.	30	187	International Family	
137	Evergreen Media Corporation	30		Entertainment, Inc.	22
138	IntelliQuest Information Group	30	188	ECRM Incorporated	22
139	Cox Enterprises, Inc.	29	189	Price Communications Corp.	22
140	Primark Corporation	29	190	Pittway Corporation	22
141	Euromoney Publications PLC	29	191	K-tel International, Inc.	21
142	NTN Communications, Inc.	29	192	Fallon McElligott, Inc.	21
143	Taylor Nelson AGB PLC	29	193	Virgin Group PLC	21
144	Havas S.A.	29	194	Lamar Advertising Company	21
145	Cablevision Systems Corporation	29	195	Bozell, Jacobs, Kenyon & Eckhardt	21
146	Dai Nippon Printing	29	196	FMR Corporation	21
147	Lifetime Television	29	197	Pearson plc	21
148	Omnicom Group Inc.	29	198	Edelman Public Relations Worldwide	21
149	Ultrak, Inc.	28	199	BPP Holdings PLC	21
150	Franklin Quest Co.	28	200	Metro Networks, Inc.	21

Note: To be included on this list, companies must have sales greater than $5 million. These rates may have resulted from acquisitions or internal growth.

The 200 Fastest-Growing Companies by Employees in
Hoover's Guide to Media Companies

Rank	Company	One-Year Employee Growth % Change	Rank	Company	One-Year Employee Growth % Change
1	Infoseek Corporation	545	51	K-III Communications Corp.	38
2	America Online, Inc.	371	52	Maxis, Inc.	38
3	Fronteer Directory Company	238	53	American Business Information	38
4	Lauriat's, Inc.	191	54	Trans World Entertainment Corp.	38
5	Wired Ventures, Inc.	184	55	Franklin Quest Co.	37
6	Heartland Wireless Communications, Inc.	181	56	Video Jukebox Network, Inc.	37
7	Hollywood Entertainment Corp.	179	57	TeleWest Communications PLC	36
8	Acclaim Entertainment, Inc.	171	58	Harmony Holdings, Inc.	35
9	Video Update, Inc.	124	59	Jacor Communications, Inc.	36
10	Lexi International, Inc.	114	60	Primark Corporation	35
11	Modem Media	112	61	Day Runner, Inc.	34
12	International Tourist Entertainment Corporation	110	62	Fallon McElligott, Inc.	33
13	Marcus Cable Company L.P.	93	63	Wasser, Inc.	33
14	N2K Inc.	93	64	IBC Group plc	33
15	Avid Technology, Inc.	90	65	Discreet Logic Inc.	33
16	FCL Graphics, Inc.	86	66	Best Buy Co., Inc.	32
17	Big Entertainment, Inc.	85	67	Acxiom Corporation	32
18	Central European Media	84	68	Franklin Electronic Publishers, Incorporated	32
19	PRIMESTAR Partners L.P.	83	69	NTN Communications, Inc.	31
20	Comcast Corporation	82	70	Ingram Industries Inc.	30
21	CKS Group, Inc.	80	71	Software Publishers Association	30
22	Data Broadcasting Corporation	75	72	Merrill Corporation	30
23	SoftKey International Inc.	72	73	SpectraVision, Inc.	29
24	Books-A-Million, Inc.	69	74	Edmark Corporation	29
25	Pro CD, Inc.	67	75	Spelling Entertainment Group	29
26	Providence Journal Company	65	76	Brøderbund Software, Inc.	29
27	LucasArts Entertainment	64	77	Cinemark USA Inc.	27
28	Mecklermedia Corporation	63	78	DataTimes Corporation	27
29	WMS Industries Inc.	63	79	Harry W. Schwartz Bookshops	27
30	The Todd-AO Corporation	63	80	Bozell, Jacobs, Kenyon & Eckhardt, Inc.	27
31	ATC Communications Group	57	81	StarPress, Inc.	27
32	United Video Satellite Group	57	82	Adams Media Corporation	25
33	Flextech plc	57	83	Discovery Communications, Inc.	25
34	U S WEST Media Group	56	84	W.W. Norton & Company, Inc.	25
35	Graff Pay-Per-View Inc.	54	85	YAR Communications, Inc.	25
36	Funco, Inc.	55	86	Carmike Cinemas, Inc.	25
37	NYNEX CableComms	54	87	Nightingale-Conant Corp.	24
38	International Management Group	54	88	Videotron Holdings Plc	25
39	INSO Corporation	49	89	Educational Development Corp.	24
40	LCS Industries, Inc.	47	90	CUC International Inc.	23
41	Adobe Systems Incorporated	46	91	Taylor Corporation	23
42	DMX Inc.	45	92	Time Warner Inc.	23
43	Cinar Films, Inc.	46	93	Catalina Marketing Corp.	22
44	NRJ SA	44	94	Scholastic Corporation	22
45	Consolidated Graphics, Inc.	42	95	Jones Communications, Inc.	22
46	International Post Limited	42	96	Westwood One, Inc.	22
47	Westinghouse/CBS Group	41	97	Advanced Marketing Services	22
48	Regal Cinemas, Inc.	41	98	William H. Sadlier, Inc.	21
49	CompuServe Corporation	40	99	Omnicom Group Inc.	20
50	Quebecor Inc.	39	100	Trimark Holdings, Inc.	20

Note: To be included on this list, companies must have 50 or more employees. These rates may have resulted from acquisitions or internal growth.

The 200 Fastest-Growing Companies by Employees in
Hoover's Guide to Media Companies (continued)

Rank	Company	One-Year Employee Growth % Change
101	William Morris Agency, Inc.	20
102	Borders Group, Inc.	20
103	Waverly, Inc.	20
104	McClatchy Newspapers, Inc.	19
105	Pixar Inc.	19
106	Lane Industries, Inc.	19
107	All American Communications	18
108	BBN Corporation	18
109	International Data Group	18
110	Carlton Communications PLC	18
111	Harpo Entertainment Group	18
112	Houghton Mifflin Company	18
113	New World Communications Group Incorporated	17
114	Viacom Inc.	17
115	Microsoft Corporation	17
116	Turner Broadcasting System, Inc.	17
117	West Publishing Co.	17
118	Sierra On-Line, Inc.	16
119	Capital Radio plc	16
120	Banta Corporation	16
121	Knowledge Adventure, Inc.	15
122	Electronics for Imaging, Inc.	16
123	Bonnierforetagen AB	15
124	Quark, Inc.	15
125	Powell's Books, Inc.	15
126	TCA Cable TV, Inc.	15
127	IntelliQuest Information Group	14
128	International Family Entertainment	14
129	Wolters Kluwer nv	14
130	Tandycrafts, Inc.	14
131	MTS Inc.	13
132	A. H. Belo Corporation	13
133	Pearson plc	13
134	Heftel Broadcasting Corporation	13
135	Quad/Graphics, Inc.	13
136	Berlin Industries, Inc.	13
137	Edelman Public Relations Worldwide	13
138	R. R. Donnelley & Sons Company	12
139	World Color Press, Inc.	12
140	Daily Mail and General Trust PLC	12
141	Schibsted A/S	12
142	Image Entertainment, Inc.	12
143	Chas. Levy Companies	12
144	Steck-Vaughn Publishing Corp.	12
145	Blockbuster Entertainment Group	11
146	True North Communications Inc.	11
147	Bertelsmann AG	11
148	Handleman Company	11
149	Rand McNally & Company	11
150	American Banknote Corporation	10

Rank	Company	One-Year Employee Growth % Change
151	Desktop Data, Inc.	10
152	Champion Industries, Inc.	10
153	Dai Nippon Printing	10
154	KOCH International L.P.	10
155	Veronis, Suhler & Associates Inc.	10
156	Havas Advertising SA	10
157	Metatec Corporation	10
158	Meredith Corporation	9
159	Vance Publishing Corporation	9
160	The Walt Disney Company	9
161	BPP Holdings PLC	9
162	Dow Jones & Company, Inc.	9
163	Midland Independent Newspapers	9
164	New Image Industries Inc.	9
165	Electronic Arts Inc.	9
166	Gannett Co., Inc.	9
167	Knight-Ridder, Inc.	9
168	Rodale Press, Inc.	8
169	Publicis SA	8
170	The Interpublic Group of Companies, Inc.	8
171	Lagardere Groupe	8
172	Telescan, Inc.	8
173	Rentrak Corporation	8
174	Carqueville Graphics	7
175	Gaumont SA	7
176	HTV Group PLC	7
177	American Bar Association	7
178	CMP Publications, Inc.	7
179	Heritage Media Corporation	7
180	American Medical Association	7
181	Linotype-Hell AG	7
182	Blade Communications Inc.	7
183	The Jim Pattison Group	7
184	Tattered Cover, Inc.	7
185	Musicland Stores Corporation	6
186	Sony Corporation	6
187	Chris-Craft Industries, Inc.	6
188	American Labelmark Company	5
189	Treasure Chest Advertising Company, Inc.	5
190	Reuters Holdings PLC	6
191	Continental Web Press, Inc.	6
192	Gaylord Entertainment Company	6
193	United Artists Theatre Circuit	6
194	Devon Group, Inc.	6
195	Shop At Home, Inc.	6
196	Maritz Inc.	5
197	John Wiley & Sons, Inc.	5
198	The Dun & Bradstreet Corp.	5
199	Young & Rubicam Inc.	5
200	MediaNews Group, Inc.	5

Note: To be included on this list, companies must have 50 or more employees. These rates may have resulted from acquisitions or internal growth.

Hoover's Media 50: World's Largest Media Companies

1995 Rank	Company	Headquarters	Revenue ($ mil.)
1	Time Warner Inc.	New York, NY	17,696
2	Bertelsmann AG	Gutersloh, Germany	14,761
3	The Walt Disney Company	Burbank, CA	12,112
4	Viacom Inc.	New York, NY	11,689
5	Havas S.A.	Neuilly-sur-Seine, France	9,118
6	Sony Corporation	Tokyo, Japan	*8,726
7	The News Corporation Limited	Sydney, Australia	8,641
8	THORN EMI plc	London, UK	7,306
9	The Thomson Corporation	Toronto, Canada	7,225
10	R. R. Donnelley & Sons Company	Chicago, IL	6,512
11	Lagardère Groupe	Paris, France	*5,800
12	MCA Inc.	Universal City, CA	5,772
13	Reed Elsevier plc	London, UK	5,646
14	PolyGram N.V.	Baarn, The Netherlands	5,499
15	Aegis Group plc	London, UK	5,262
16	TCI Communications, Inc.	Englewood, CO	5,118
17	The Dun & Bradstreet Corporation	Wilton, CT	*4,958
18	Advance Publications, Inc.	Staten Island, NY	4,855
19	W H Smith Group plc	London, UK	4,271
20	Reuters Holdings PLC	London, UK	4,188
21	Publicis SA	Paris, France	4,178
22	The Rank Organisation PLC	London, UK	4,139
23	Quebecor Inc.	Montreal, Canada	4,067
24	Gannett Co., Inc.	Arlington, VA	4,007
25	Kirchgruppe	Ismaning, Germany	4,000
26	National Broadcasting Company Inc.	New York, NY	3,919
27	Cox Enterprises, Inc.	Atlanta, GA	3,806
28	Granada Group PLC	London, UK	3,769
29	The Times Mirror Company	Los Angeles, CA	3,448
30	Turner Broadcasting System, Inc.	Atlanta, GA	3,437
31	Comcast Corporation	Philadelphia, PA	3,363
32	Westinghouse/CBS Group	New York, NY	3,333
33	Compagnie Luxembourgeoise pour l'Audio-Visuel et la Finance	Luxembourg, Luxembourg	3,100
34	The Reader's Digest Association, Inc.	Pleasantville, NY	3,069
35	British Broadcasting Corporation PLC	London, UK	3,000
36	The McGraw-Hill Companies, Inc.	New York, NY	2,935
37	Pearson plc	London, UK	2,931
38	Axel Springer Verlag AG	Hamburg, Germany	2,888
39	Knight-Ridder, Inc.	Miami, FL	2,752
40	Carlton Communications PLC	London, UK	2,533
41	Nippon Television Network Corporation	Tokyo, Japan	2,413
42	The New York Times Company	New York, NY	2,409
43	WPP Group plc	London, UK	2,406
44	Tokyo Broadcasting System	Tokyo, Japan	2,386
45	U S WEST Media Group	Englewood, CO	2,374
46	The Hearst Corporation	New York, NY	2,331
47	Dow Jones & Company, Inc.	New York, NY	2,284
48	Omnicom Group Inc.	New York, NY	2,258
49	CEP Communication SA	Paris, France	2,253
50	Tribune Company	Chicago, IL	2,245

* Note: Media revenue only

Advertising Age's 100 Leading Media Companies

1995 Rank	Company	Total Media Revenue ($ mil.)	1995 Rank	Company	Total Media Revenue ($ mil.)
1	Time Warner*	9,884.7	51	Discovery Communications	451.5
2	Disney Capital Cities/ABC*	7,391.5	52	Morris Communications*	438.5
3	Tele-Communications Inc.*	5,118.0	53	Heritage Media Corp.	435.8
4	CBS (Westinghouse Electric Co.)*	4,318.3	54	Gaylord Entertainment Co.	413.2
5	Gannett Co.*	3,998.7	55	Adelphia Communications Corp.	403.6
6	NBC TV (General Electric Co.)	3,919.0	56	Marcus Cable Co.	401.5
7	Advance Publications*	3,217.0	57	Gruner & Jahr USA (Bertelsmann)	400.0
8	News Corp.	2,945.0	58	Copley Newspapers	391.0
9	Cox Enterprises*	2,749.8	59	Journal Register Co.	385.3
10	Hearst Corp.	2,513.0	60	CMP Publications	382.0
11	New York Times Co.	2,409.4	61	New World Communications	376.8
12	Times Mirror Co.	2,307.1	62	Lee Enterprises	375.4
13	Knight-Ridder	2,250.2	63	Clear Channel Communications*	375.0
14	Viacom*	2,136.1	64	Journal Communications	341.7
15	Tribune Co.	2,022.0	65	Charter Communications	338.8
16	Thomson Corp.	1,787.0	66	Donrey Media Group	333.7
17	Comcast Corp.*	1,719.9	67	Century Communications Corp.	331.3
18	US West Media Group (US West)*	1,657.4	68	Outdoor Systems*	328.2
19	Washington Post Co.	1,582.2	69	Univision Holdings	321.3
20	Dow Jones & Co.	1,191.8	70	Blade Communications	318.0
21	Reed Elsevier	1,101.4	71	DirecTV (Hughes Electronics/GM)	313.0
22	America Online	1,093.9	72	Providence Journal Co.	312.5
23	Cablevision Systems Corp.	1,078.1	73	3M Media (3M Co.)	308.0
24	Advo Inc.	1,011.9	74	Jacor Communications*	306.0
25	E.W. Scripps*	935.3	75	National Geographic Society	294.2
26	Ziff-Davis Publishing (Softbank)	868.0	76	Seattle Times Co.	288.0
27	Reader's Digest Association	828.5	77	Forbes Inc.	285.0
28	A.H. Belo Corp.	735.3	78	A&E Television Networks	284.3
29	Meredith Corp.	722.2	79	American Media	280.7
30	K-III Holdings	653.8	80	Sinclair Broadcasting Group*	273.5
31	Valassis Communications	613.8	81	Lifetime Television	270.6
32	International Data Group	606.4	82	Petersen Publishing Co.	270.2
33	Central Newspapers	579.9	83	Lenfest Group	266.2
34	McGraw-Hill	562.0	84	Evergreen Media Corp.*	248.1
35	CompuServe (H&R Block)	561.0	85	Dispatch Printing Co.	246.3
36	Media General	556.4	86	Prodigy Inc.	240.0
37	Hollinger International	538.4	87	Times Publishing Co.	234.0
38	Chronicle Publishing Co.	534.0	88	LIN Television Corp.*	233.5
39	Harte-Hanks Communications	532.8	89	Young Broadcasting*	223.0
40	Media News Group	525.0	90	Eller Media Co.*	218.0
41	McClatchy Newspapers	514.1	91	Wenner Media	210.1
42	Freedom Newspapers	512.0	92	InterMedia	205.6
43	Zuckerman Media Properties**	510.0	93	Int'l Family Entertainment	201.7
44	Hachette Filipacchi Magazines	507.2	94	American Radio Systems Corp.*	194.7
45	Landmark Communications	500.0	95	Penton Publishing (Pittway Corp.)	191.0
46	USA Network	500.0	96	SFX Broadcasting*	190.4
47	Cowles Media Co.	492.6	97	TCA Cable	189.2
48	United News & Media	473.6	98	Ackerley Communications	187.3
49	Pulitzer Publishing Co.	472.3	99	Rodale Press	187.3
50	BHC Communications (Chris-Craft)	454.7	100	Macromedia	186.7

*Media revenue are pro forma. **Includes *U.S. News & World Report*, *Atlantic Monthly*, and *New York Daily News*.
Source: *Advertising Age*; August 19, 1996.

Top 100 US Magazines by Gross Revenue

1995 Rank	Magazine	Revenue ($ thou.)	1995 Rank	Magazine	Revenue ($ thou.)
1	TV Guide	1,068,832	51	Seventeen	99,887
2	People	801,153	52	Vanity Fair	99,646
3	Sports Illustrated	697,381	53	Elle	97,852
4	Time	672,626	54	Woman's World	94,982
5	Reader's Digest	529,742	55	Golf Magazine	93,501
6	Parade	515,591	56	Life	89,698
7	Newsweek	480,535	57	Smithsonian	88,254
8	Better Homes & Gardens	406,573	58	Inc.	86,142
9	PC Magazine	391,341	59	InformationWeek	85,961
10	Good Housekeeping	339,000	60	Travel & Leisure	85,537
11	U.S. News & World Report	316,390	61	Sunset	84,142
12	Business Week	313,478	62	Harper's Bazaar	83,675
13	Woman's Day	288,045	63	Bride's Magazine	80,859
14	Ladies' Home Journal	261,793	64	Architectural Digest	80,476
15	Family Circle	255,199	65	Macworld	79,648
16	Forbes	252,854	66	Ebony	79,340
17	Cosmopolitan	242,065	67	Self	78,797
18	USA Weekend	229,568	68	Travel Weekly	78,613
19	Fortune	225,682	69	House Beautiful	78,068
20	National Geographic	201,508	70	Windows	76,673
21	PC Week	197,640	71	Electronic Engineering Times	76,396
22	National Enquirer	195,646	72	Endless Vacation	75,926
23	Money	176,881	73	The Economist	75,484
24	Computer Shopper	174,408	74	Road & Track	74,373
25	Star Magazine	174,078	75	Mademoiselle	73,981
26	Southern Living	172,645	76	Popular Mechanics	73,712
27	McCall's	171,379	77	Martha Stewart Living	72,649
28	Redbook	171,012	78	Field & Stream	72,012
29	Playboy	165,144	79	New York	70,095
30	Entertainment Weekly	157,654	80	Modern Bride	69,463
31	Vogue	153,472	81	GQ	69,418
32	Glamour	151,359	82	YM	68,811
33	Computerworld	150,379	83	Parenting	67,253
34	PC World	149,577	84	Motor Trend	67,229
35	Golf Digest	138,962	85	Globe	66,592
36	Rolling Stone	137,871	86	Byte	66,436
37	Country Living	131,755	87	Barron's	65,413
38	Cable Guide	129,136	88	Popular Science	65,023
39	PC Computing	129,098	89	Travel Agent	64,505
40	Computer Reseller News	121,229	90	Home	64,133
41	New York Times Magazine	119,321	91	Conde Nast Traveler	63,355
42	Prevention	117,670	92	Highlights for Children	63,352
43	Modern Maturity	113,846	93	Gourmet	63,313
44	The New Yorker	113,354	94	Men's Health	62,973
45	Parents	112,310	95	Discover	60,713
46	InfoWorld	110,772	96	Us	59,187
47	Consumer Reports	110,368	97	Taste of Home	59,111
48	Car and Driver	109,443	98	Allure	58,505
49	Penthouse	107,611	99	Network World	57,681
50	Soap Opera Digest	104,194	100	Essence	57,674

Source: *Advertising Age*; June 17, 1996

Top 25 Daily US Newpapers by Circulation

Reported by Audit Bureau of Circulations for six months ended March 31, 1996

Rank	Newspaper	Parent Company	Circulation
1	*Wall Street Journal* (national edition)	Dow Jones & Company, Inc.	1,841,188
2	*USA Today* (M-Th)	Gannett Co., Inc.	1,617,743
3	*New York Times* (national edition)	New York Times Co.	1,157,656
4	*Los Angeles Times*	Times Mirror Co.	1,021,121
5	*Washington Post*	Washington Post Co.	834,641
6	*New York Daily News*	Daily News, L.P.	758,509
7	*Chicago Tribune*	Tribune Company	667,908
8	*Newsday*	Times Mirror Co.	555,203
9	*Houston Chronicle*	The Hearst Corporation	551,553
11	*Chicago Sun-Times*	Hollinger International, Inc.	501,115
10	*Dallas Morning News* (M-Th)	A. H. Belo Corporation	494,266
12	*San Francisco Chronicle*	The Chronicle Publishing Company, Inc.	493,942
13	*Boston Globe*	The New York Times Co.	486,403
14	*Philadelphia Inquirer*	Knight-Ridder, Inc.	446,842
15	*Newark Star-Ledger*	Newhouse Newspapers Group	433,317
16	*New York Post*	News Corp.	418,255
17	*Phoenix Arizona Republic*	Central Newspapers	399,830
18	*Cleveland Plain Dealer*	Newhouse Newspapers Group	398,398
19	*Minneapolis Star-Tribune* (M-Sat)	Cowles Media Company	388,120
20	*Miami Herald*	Knight-Ridder, Inc.	378,195
21	*San Diego Union-Tribune*	The Copley Press, Inc.	376,511
22	*St. Petersburg Times*	Times Publishing Company	364,810
23	*Orange County Register*	Freedom Communications, Inc.	358,173
24	*Portland Oregonian*	Newhouse Newspapers Group	349,193
25	*Baltimore Sun* (M-Sat)	The Times Mirror Company	337,292

Not filing: *Detroit News* and *Free Press*, in 9th position during same reporting period last year, and *Detroit News*, in 25th position in March 1996 reporting period. Since July 1995, six production and editorial unions have been striking the jointly produced papers, which have continued to publish.

Source: *Editor & Publisher*; May 11, 1996

Top 10 Web Publishers

Based on 1996 first quarter placement revenue

Rank	Advertiser	($ thou.)
1	Infoseek	3,107.5
2	Lycos	2,622.2
3	Yahoo!	2,190.0
4	Netscape	1,908.5
5	CINET, Inc.	1,330.5
6	Excite	1,243.5
7	Zdnet	1,111.0
8	Espnet Sportzone	1,100.0
9	Pathfinder	987.9
10	Webcrawler	925.0

Source: *Inter Ad Monthly*,
　　　Jupiter Communications; May 1996

Top 10 Web Advertisers

Based on 1996 first quarter placement spending

Rank	Advertiser	($ thou.)
1	IBM Corp.	1,528.3
2	Microsoft Corp.	1,010.9
3	Netscape Comm. Corp.	929.0
4	CINET, Inc.	612.3
5	AT&T Corp.	606.7
6	Nynex Corp.	595.8
7	MCI Comm. Corp.	558.1
8	Internet Shopping Network	510.3
9	Saturn Corp.	415.9
10	Excite, Inc.	415.3

Source: *Inter Ad Monthly*,
　　　Jupiter Communications; May 1996

Top Online Services

Service	Parent Company	Subscribers (as of 6/30/96)
Consumer		
America Online	America Online	6,000,000
CompuServe Information Service	CompuServe Inc.	5,000,000
Prodigy	Prodigy Services Co.	*1,400,000
Microsoft Network	Microsoft Corp.	1,200,000
ZD Net	Ziff-Davis Interactive	275,000
TIP, Billboard, CSN, AIA, Schwab	Telescan Inc.	200,000
CRIS, BBS Direct	Concentric Network Corp.	120,000
Wow!	CompuServe Inc.	70,000
The ImagiNation Network	AT&T	65,000
Delphi	Delphi Internet Services Corp.	50,000
Business/Professional		
LEXIS-NEXIS	Reed Elsevier	762,000
Dow Jones News/Retrieval	Dow Jones Information Services	240,000
TRW Information Services	Bain Capital and Thomas H. Lee	205,000
Dialog Worldwide	Knight-Ridder Information	200,000
First!, Heads Up, iNews	Individual Inc.	**175,000
D&B Information Services N.A.	Dun & Bradstreet Corp.	143,000
MEDLARS	National Library of Medicine	125,043
DowVision	Dow Jones & Co.	115,000
Physicians' Online	Physicians' Online Inc.	110,000
NewsEDGE	Desktop Data	98,000
Financial		**Terminals**
Reuters real-time data services	Reuters Holdings plc	345,000
DJ News Services (Broadtape)	Dow Jones Information Services	205,000
Telerate	Telerate Inc.	99,000
Brokerage Services	Automatic Data Processing	96,000
DTN AgDaily, DTNiron, DTNStant, DTN Produce, DTN Weather Center	Data Transmission Network Corp.	79,000
S&P MarketScope	McGraw-Hill/Standard & Poor's	74,800
The Bloomberg	Bloomberg Financial	62,000
ILX	Thomson Financial Services	60,000
Knight-Ridder Financial	Global Financial Information Corp.	50,000
Signal, QuoTrek, SporTRAX	Data Broadcasting Corp.	35,000

* Figure is for households.

** Figure includes lower-priced, ad-supported services.

Source: Electronic Information Report; July 12, 1996, SIMBA Information Inc., Stamford, CT (203-358-9900)

Top 25 Television Groups in the US by Market Coverage

Rank	Group	Headquarters	% Coverage of Nation's 95.3 mil. TV Homes	No. of Stations
1	Westinghouse/CBS	New York	31.0	14
2	Tribune (including Renaissance*)	Chicago	25.0	16
3	NBC	New York	24.6	11
4	Disney/ABC	New York	24.1	10
5	FOX	Los Angeles	22.1	12
6	Silver King	St. Petersburg, FL	20.0	16
7	Paxson Communications	West Palm Beach, FL	18.0	16
8	Chris Craft/BHC/United Television	New York	17.7	8
9	Gannett	Arlington, VA	14.1	15
10	Univision	New York	12.8	11
11	New World	Atlanta	12.8	10
12	Telemundo	Hialeah, FL	10.4	8
13	Viacom (Paramount)	Los Angeles	10.2	12
14	Young Broadcasting	New York	9.1	13
15	Sinclair Broadcasting	Baltimore	8.9	22
16	Scripps Howard	Cincinnati	8.0	9
17	A.H. Belo	Dallas	8.0	7
18	Cox Broadcasting	Atlanta	7.7	7
19	Hearst	New York	7.3	7
20	Post-Newsweek	Hartford, CT	7.0	6
21	LIN Television	Providence, RI	6.3	9
22	Providence Journal	Providence, RI	5.4	11
23	Pulitzer	St. Louis	5.2	10
24	Ellis Acquisitions/Raycom Media	Atlanta	4.0	22
25	Allbritton Communications	Washington	3.9	8

* Acquisition pending FCC and shareholders' approval

Source: *Broadcasting & Cable*; July 8, 1996

Top 20 Radio Groups in the US by Audience

Rank	Company	City	Listeners	No. of Stations
1	CBS/Group W/Infinity	New York	2,568,050	82
2	Clear Channel Communications Inc./ Radio Equity Partners/ U.S. Radio/Heftel	San Antonio	1,011,400	102
3	Evergreen Media Corp.	Irving, TX	815,500	35
4	Disney/ABC	New York	734,400	21
5	Chancellor Broadcasting Co.	Dallas	618,000	39
6	Jacor/Noble/Citicasters	Cincinnati	556,300	51
7	American Radio Systems Corp.	Boston	546,700	57
8	Emmis Broadcasting Corp.	Indianapolis	527,400	8
9	Cox Communications Inc.	Atlanta	519,500	38
10	SFX Broadcasting Inc./Multi-Market Radio	Austin	480,000	59
11	Viacom	New York	423,400	13
12	EZ Communications Inc.	Fairfax, VA	340,000	23
13	Bonneville International Corp.	Salt Lake City	339,500	20
14	Spanish Broadcasting System Inc.	New York	316,600	9
15	Gannett Co. Inc.	Arlington, VA	274,800	11
16	Secret Communications LP	Cincinnati	248,900	13
17	Susquehanna Radio Corp.	York, PA	247,600	17
18	Nationwide Communications Inc.	Columbus, OH	239,300	15
19	Greater Media Inc.	East Brunswick, NJ	206,200	13
20	Sinclair Broadcasting Group Inc./River City	Baltimore	201,800	33

Source: *Broadcasting & Cable*; July 8, 1996

Top 20 US Cable Operators

Rank	Company	Headquarters	Basic Subscriptions
1	Tele-Communications Inc.	Englewood, CO	12,494,000
2	Time Warner Cable	Stamford, CT	11,700,000
3	Continental Cablevision	Boston	4,200,000
4	Comcast	Philadelphia	3,600,000
5	Cox Communications	Atlanta	3,282,080
6	Cablevision Systems Corp.	Woodbury, NY	1,915,000
7	Adelphia Communications	Coudersport, PA	1,651,850
8	Jones Intercable	Englewood, CO	1,476,000
9	Marcus Cable	Dallas	1,245,259
10	Viacom Cable	Pleasanton, CA	1,157,600
11	Century Communications	New Canaan, CT	1,100,000
12	Falcon Cable	Los Angeles	1,085,513
13	Charter Communications	St. Louis	900,000
14	Scripps-Howard Cable	Cincinnati	804,464
15	TKR Cable	Warren, NJ	750,121
16	Prime Cable	Austin	657,508
17	InterMedia Partners	San Francisco	571,000
18	Lenfest Group	Pottstown, PA	563,909
19	TCA Cable TV	Tyler, TX	549,000
20	Post-Newsweek Cable	Phoenix	542,000

Source: *Cablevision*; April 29, 1996

50 Biggest North American Printing Companies

Rank	Name	Sales Most Recent Fiscal Year ($ thou.)	Rank	Name	Sales Most Recent Fiscal Year ($ thou.)
1	R.R. Donnelley & Sons	6,511,786	26	American Banknote Corp	206,164
2	Quebecor Printing	3,003,998	27	Jostens Inc.	203,100
3	Moore Corporation	2,600,000	28	Paxar Corp.	201,436
4	World Color	1,890,000	29	Ivy Hill	193,000
5	Deluxe Corporation	1,857,981	30	Queens Group	193,000
6	Banta Corporation	1,023,000	31	Stevens Graphics	180,500
7	Quad/Graphics	1,000,000	32	Data Business Forms	175,000
8	Treasure Chest Advertising	950,000	33	Perry Graphic Communications	168,000
9	Standard Register	903,204			
10	Wallace Computer Services	712,838	34	Arandell Corp.	145,500
11	Valassis Communications	613,752	35	Ennis Business Forms	142,134
12	Mail-Well Inc.	596,792	36	Judd's Incorporated	141,200
13	John H. Harland	561,617	37	U.S. Playing Card	140,000
14	Transcontinental Printing	546,350	38	Publishers Press	139,000
15	Sullivan Communications	536,342	39	Menasha Corporation	138,855
16	Brown Printing	485,000	40	Miami Systems Corp.	135,000
17	Graphic Industries	417,262	41	Petty Co.,	133,796
18	Bowne & Co.	392,713	42	Anderson Lithograph	127,000
19	Western Graphic Comm.	318,967	43	Fleming Packaging	122,000
20	American Signature	300,000	44	Courier Corporation	120,701
21	Sonoco Engraph	300,000	45	Avanti/Case-Hoyt	120,000
22	Cadmus Communications	280,000	46	Hart Graphics	120,000
23	Duplex Products	275,728	47	Outlook Group Corp.	120,000
24	Bowater Communication Papers	249,000	48	MacNaughton Lithographic	115,000
25	Merrill Corporation	245,306	49	Shade/Allied	114,800
			50	Mack Printing Group	114,727

Source: *Graphic Arts Monthly*, August 1996

Top 10 US Trade Book Publishers

Rank	Publisher	Parent Company	1995 Revenues ($ mil.)
1	Random House	Advance Publications	1,255.0
2	Simon & Schuster	Viacom	832.7
3	Bantam Doubleday Dell	Bertelsmann	670.0
4	Time Warner	Time Warner Inc.	325.0
5	HarperCollins	News Corp.	317.2
6	Penguin USA	Pearson Inc.	317.0
7	Putnam Berkley	MCA Inc.	300.0
8	Holtzbrinck	Holtzbrinck Publishing Group	267.0
9	Hearst Book Group	Hearst Corp.	160.0
10	Thomas Nelson	Thomas Nelson, Inc.	145.7

Source: SIMBA Information Inc., Stamford, CT (203-358-9900)

Top 10 North American Specialty Directory Publishers

Rank	Publisher	Parent Company	1995 Revenues ($ mil.)
1	Information Handling Services	Information Handling Services Group	178.0
2	Martindale-Hubbell	Reed Elsevier plc	138.0
3	Thomas Publishing	Thomas Publishing Company	122.0
4	R.R. Bowker	Reed Elsevier plc	111.0
5	K-III Communications Corp.	K-III Communications Corp.	110.0
6	Official Airline Guides	Reed Elsevier plc	108.0
7	Bernard C. Harris Publishing	Bernard C. Harris Publishing	95.0
8	Gale	Thomson Corp.	90.0
9	R.L. Polk	R.L. Polk & Co.	75.0
10	Sweet's Catalog	The McGraw-Hill Companies, Inc.	66.0

Source: *The SIMBA Report on Directory Publishing*, SIMBA Information Inc., Stamford, CT (203-358-9900)

Publishers Weekly Bestsellers for 1995

Rank	Title	Author	Publisher
Fiction			
1	The Rainmaker	John Grisham	Doubleday
2	The Lost World	Michael Crichton	Knopf
3	Five Days in Paris	Danielle Steel	Delacorte
4	The Christmas Box	Richard Paul Evans	Simon & Schuster
5	Lightning	Danielle Steel	Delacorte
Nonfiction			
1	Men Are from Mars, Women Are from Venus	John Gray	HarperCollins
2	My American Journey	Colin Powell with Joseph Persico	Random House
3	Miss America	Howard Stern	ReganBooks
4	The Seven Spiritual Laws of Success	Deepak Chopra	New World Library
5	The Road Ahead	Bill Gates	Viking

Source: *Publishers Weekly*; March 4, 1996

Top 10 US Motion Picture Distribution Companies in 1995

Rank	Distributor	Parent Company	Box Office Receipts ($ mil.)
1	Buena Vista Pictures Distribution Inc.	The Walt Disney Co.	1,102.7
2	Warner Bros.	Time Warner	867.1
3	Sony Pictures Entertainment	Sony Corporation	683.3
4	Universal Pictures	MCA Inc.	669.0
5	Paramount Pictures	Viacom Inc.	530.9
6	Twentieth Century Fox	Fox Inc.	411.2
7	New Line Cinema	Turner Broadcasting System	347.8
8	MGM/UA Distribution Co.	Crédit Lyonnais	333.0
9	Mirimax Films	The Walt Disney Co.	189.0
10	Savoy Pictures	Savoy Pictures	68.8

Source: *Los Angeles Business Journal*; July 22, 1996

Top 25 Grossing Films Worldwide of 1995

Rank	Film	Distributor	Box Office ($ mil.)
1	*Die Hard With a Vengeance*	Fox/Buena Vista	353.7
2	*Batman Forever*	Warner Bros.	333.6
3	*Apollo 13*	Universal	331.3
4	*Pocahontas*	Buena Vista	317.1
5	*Casper*	Universal	277.2
6	*Waterworld*	Universal	254.6
7	*Goldeneye*	MGM/UA	219.1
8	*Forrest Gump*	Paramount	195.2
9	*Dumb & Dumber*	New Line	187.3
10	*Outbreak*	Warner Bros.	185.9
11	*While You Were Sleeping*	Buena Vista	181.9
12	*The Bridges of Madison County*	Warner Bros.	175.2
13	*Braveheart*	Paramount/Fox	168.5
14	*Disclosure*	Warner Bros.	165.1
15	*Legends of the Fall*	Sony	158.2
16	*Crimson Tide*	Buena Vista	157.4
17	*Toy Story*	Buena Vista	153.4
18	*Congo*	Paramount	151.1
19	*Ace Ventura: When Nature Calls*	Warner Bros./MCI	141.9
20	*Bad Boys*	Sony	139.7
21	*Seven*	New Line	132.3
22	*First Knight*	Sony	127.6
23	*Nine Months*	Fox	122.9
24	*Lion King*	Buena Vista	117.0
25	*Pulp Fiction*	Mirimax	114.4

Source: *Variety*; February 19–25, 1996

20 Largest Advertising Organizations in the World

1995 Rank	Company	Headquarters	Income ($ mil.)
1	WPP Group	London	3,129.7
2	Omnicom Group	New York	2,576.7
3	Interpublic Group of Companies	New York	2,337.2
4	Dentsu	Tokyo	1,998.6
5	Cordiant	London	1,377.8
6	Young & Rubicam	New York	1,197.5
7	Hakuhodo	Tokyo	958.6
8	Havas Advertising	Levallois-Perret, France	909.4
9	Grey Advertising	New York	896.5
10	Leo Burnett Co.	Chicago	803.9
11	True North Communications	Chicago	758.7
12	D'Arcy Masius Benton & Bowles	New York	645.6
13	Publicis Communication	Paris	606.3
14	Bozell, Jacobs, Kenyon & Eckhardt	New York	404.5
15	BDDP Group	Paris	278.5
16	Asatsu Inc.	Tokyo	254.1
17	Tokyu Agency	Tokyo	238.5
18	Daiko Advertising	Tokyo	211.1
19	Dai-Ichi Kikaku Co.	Tokyo	168.4
20	Dentsu, Young & Rubicam Partnerships	Tokyo/Singapore	160.6

Source: *Advertising Age*; April 15, 1996

10 Magazine Ad Page Leaders

Rank	Magazine	Parent Company	Pages
1	*PC Magazine*	Ziff-Davis Publishing Company	6,632.57
2	*Forbes*	Forbes, Inc.	4,542.13
3	*Business Week*	The McGraw-Hill Companies, Inc.	3,816.36
4	*People*	Time Inc.	3,328.21
5	*TV Guide*	News Corp. (The News Corporation Limited)	3,228.84
6	*Fortune*	Time Inc.	3,184.37
7	*PC Computing*	Ziff-Davis Publishing Company	2,993.80
8	*Bride's & Your New Home*	Advance Publications, Inc.	2,931.32
9	*The Economist*	The Economist Group	2,850.92
10	*Modern Bride*	K-III Communications Corporation	2,734.48

Source: *Advertising Age*; January 22, 1996

Top 50 Megabrands by 1995 Ad Spending

Rank	Brand, Product, or Service	Company	Total ($ thou.)
1	AT&T telephone (svcs.)	AT&T Corp.	673,386.9
2	Ford cars & trucks	Ford Motor Co.	564,866.4
3	Sears stores	Sears, Roebuck & Co.	540,052.5
4	McDonald's restaurants	McDonalds Corp.	490,549.9
5	Kellogg breakfast foods	Kellogg Co.	488,205.1
6	Chevrolet car & trucks	General Motors Corp.	477,599.5
7	Dodge cars & trucks	Chrysler Corp.	414,530.6
8	Toyota cars & trucks	Toyota Motor Co.	384,074.0
9	MCI telephone svcs	MCI Communications corp.	320,955.9
10	Warner Bros. movies	Time Warner	294,003.7
11	Circuit City electronic stores	Circuit City Stores	291,558.1
12	Columbia entertainment	Sony Corp.	289,666.4
13	Nissan cars & trucks	Nissan Motor Co.	281,967.6
14	Honda cars & trucks	Honda Motor Co.	278,826.5
15	Disney entertainment	Walt Disney Co.	269,495.1
16	J. C. Penney stores	J. C. Penney Co.	268,748.5
17	IBM computers	IBM Corp.	257,911.7
18	General Mills cereals	General Mills	253,070.7
19	Burger King restaurants	Grand Metropolitan	251,932.7
20	Mazda cars & trucks	Mazda Motor Corp.	241,283.2
21	Chrysler cars & trucks	Chrysler Corp.	240,129.3
22	Paramount entertainment	Viacom	221,327.2
23	Tylenol remedies	Johnson & Johnson	213,729.7
24	Sprint telephone svcs.	Sprint Corp.	212,902.8
25	American Express financial svcs.	American Express Co.	207,380.1
26	Universal Studios movies	Seagram Co.	206,860.5
27	Budweiser beers	Anheuser-Busch Cos.	201,016.8
28	Buick cars	General Motors Corp.	193,322.7
29	Kraft foods	Philip Morris Cos.	192,191.8
30	Post cereals	Philip Morris Cos.	173,072.3
31	Buena Vista movies	Walt Disney Co.	172,072.8
32	Taco Bell restaurants	PepsiCo	172,029.2
33	Saturn cars	General Motors Corp.	169,812.0
34	Kmart stores	Kmart Corp.	167,572.6
35	Pizza Hut restaurants	PepsiCo	164,358.9
36	Miller beers	Philip Morris Cos.	161,544.3
37	Wendy's restaurants	Wendys International	161,184.9
38	Visa credit cards	Visa International	154,595.7
39	KFC restaurants	PepsiCo	149,397.2
40	Mercury cars & trucks	Ford Motor Co.	149,385.9
41	Microsoft software	Microsoft Corp.	147,733.2
42	Macy's stores	Federated Department Stores	144,445.2
43	Nike footwear & apparel	Nike Inc.	142,648.3
44	Wal-Mart stores	Wal-Mart Stores	141,411.6
45	Jeep vehicles	Chrysler Corp.	141,384.6
46	L'Oreal cosmetics	L'Oreal	137,362.0
47	20th Century Fox movies	News Corp.	137,246.2
48	Cadillac cars	General Motors Corp.	135,595.2
49	Pontiac cars & trucks	General Motors Corp.	134,277.6
50	Mitsubishi cars & trucks	Mitsubishi Motor Corp.	130,722.6

Note: Sources for ad spending include consumer magazines; local and national papers; outdoor; network, spot, syndicated, and cable TV; and national spot and network radio.

Source: *Advertising Age*; May 6, 1996

Top Media Companies

ADOBE SYSTEMS INCORPORATED

OVERVIEW

Adobe is making mud pies of the competition. Based in Mountain View, California, the company is the #3 PC software vendor behind Microsoft and Novell. Adobe, whose PostScript language made desktop publishing a reality in the mid-1980s, is hoping to ride its Internet software toward success in the late 1990s. Its Adobe PageMill and Adobe SiteMill programs help users easily create pages for the World Wide Web by translating documents produced with a word-processing-like program into files the computer could use to construct the site.

Adobe's other products enable computer users to create a virtually unlimited range of printable pages. Its Adobe Illustrator and PageMaker software, with advanced editing,

graphics manipulation, and layout capabilities, are used to design books, consumer product packaging, even fine art. Adobe Photoshop gives users a sort of "electronic darkroom" to alter digitized photographs and design original images. Adobe also makes software for "desktop broadcasting," which enables film and video to be edited and manipulated on the computer instead of with traditional production equipment.

Adobe culminated a string of 10 acquisitions with the 1995 purchase of business and technical document software company Frame Technology. Frame has, however, proved hard to digest, depressing the company's earnings in early 1996.

WHEN

When Charles Geschke hired John Warnock as chief scientist for copier king Xerox's new graphics and imaging lab at its Palo Alto Research Center (a place Warnock called "the world's greatest sandbox" for technology research), he set the stage for one of the world's largest software manufacturers. While at Xerox, the pair developed the PostScript computer language, which instructs a printer how to reproduce a computer image on paper. When Xerox refused to market their product, the duo left the company and started Adobe (named after a river near their homes in San Jose, California) in 1982.

Their original plan was to produce a high-end electronic document processing system based on PostScript, but the company changed direction when Apple Computer whiz Steve Jobs hired the firm to co-design the controller board and software for his company's LaserWriter printer, which was introduced in 1985. A year later Adobe went public. Meanwhile, PostScript was pioneering the desktop publishing industry by allowing users to laser-print nearly anything they could create on the computer.

Adobe branched into the European market in 1987 with the establishment of its Adobe Systems Europe subsidiary. That year it entered the PC market by adapting PostScript for IBM's operating system. In 1989 the company started a subsidiary to market its products in the Pacific Rim.

Adobe grew in the early 1990s by acquiring other software companies, including OCR Systems and Nonlinear Technologies (1992) and AH Software and Science & Art (1993). Also in 1993 the company began licensing its

PostScript software to printer manufacturers so they could use it in their products, which upped Adobe's share of the market. (The company kept control of the software that interprets the information, though, so printermakers still have to rely on them for the programs that complete the printing system.) That year it began marketing Acrobat software, which enables users to create and distribute electronic documents over computer networks or online.

In 1994 Adobe acquired the Seattle-based Aldus, whose PageMaker software had been instrumental in establishing the desktop-publishing market. Since PageMaker's success depended on the font and font translator software that Adobe makes, the 2 companies had a history of cooperation predating 1990.

The company announced a deal in 1995 with Internet wunderfirm Netscape to integrate Acrobat's viewing technology into Netscape's Internet software, including the Navigator browser. Also that year Adobe extended its range of publishing software by acquiring Frame Technology, whose FrameMaker software is used to publish long, complex documents such as books.

Adobe forecast in 1996 that sales of its products for the Internet would grow at a rate of 100% per year and would be focused on business-to-business sites. That year it spun off its prepress applications operations to the newly created Luminous Corporation, which planned to continue marketing Adobe's products. Adobe also agreed with imaging software leader FileNet to develop standards that would enable different image file formats to be shared more easily by different computers.

WHO

Chairman and CEO: John E. Warnock, age 55, $668,332 pay
President & Acting CFO: Charles M. Geschke, age 56, $668,322 pay
SVP and COO: David B. Pratt, age 56, $439,282 pay
SVP and General Manager, Adobe Europe: Derek J. Gray, age 46
VP, General Counsel, and Secretary: Colleen M. Pouliot, age 37
Director Human Resources: Rebecca Guerra
Auditors: KPMG Peat Marwick LLP

WHERE

HQ: 1585 Charleston Rd., Mountain View, CA 94043-1225
Phone: 415-961-4400
Fax: 415-961-3769
Web site: http://www.adobe.com

More than 6,000 North American resellers and 300 distributors in Europe and the Pacific Rim offer Adobe products.

	1995 Sales	
	$ mil.	% of total
The Americas	533	69
Europe	134	17
Pacific Rim	107	14
Adjustments	(12)	—
Total	**762**	**100**

WHAT

	1995 Sales	
	$ mil.	% of total
Product sales	579	76
Licensing fees	183	24
Total	**762**	**100**

Selected Products
Acrobat (electronic document management software)
Adobe Acrobat (document formatting software)
Adobe Art Explorer (painting and drawing software for children)
Adobe Fetch (cataloging software)
Adobe Gallery Effects (special-effects software)
Adobe Illustrator (graphics software)
Adobe PageMill (Web-page creation software)
Adobe PhotoDeluxe (personalized photo software)
Adobe Photoshop (photographic image software)
Adobe Premiere (film and video editing software)
Adobe Persuasion (presentation software)
Adobe SiteMill (Internet link repair software)
FrameMaker (document authoring software)
PageMaker (page layout software)
PostScript (page description language and interpreter)

KEY COMPETITORS

Apple Computer
Autodesk
Avid Technology
Corel
Electronics for Imaging
IBM
Interleaf
Linotype-Hell
Macromedia (CA)
Micrografx
Microsoft
Quark
SoftKey

HOW MUCH

Nasdaq symbol: ADBE FYE: November 30	Annual Growth	1986	1987	1988	1989	1990	1991	1992	1993	1994	1995
Sales ($ mil.)	53.5%	16	39	84	121	169	230	266	314	598	762
Net income ($ mil.)	43.6%	4	9	21	34	40	52	44	57	6	94
Income as % of sales	—	22.4%	22.9%	25.3%	27.8%	23.8%	22.5%	16.4%	18.2%	1.1%	12.3%
Earnings per share ($)	32.5%	0.10	0.22	0.49	0.78	0.92	1.13	0.94	1.22	0.10	1.26
Stock price – high ($)	—	3.31	13.50	12.75	14.75	25.38	33.88	34.25	37.00	38.50	74.25
Stock price – low ($)	—	1.66	3.25	6.00	7.75	8.50	13.38	12.63	15.63	20.50	27.25
Stock price – close ($)	39.1%	3.19	7.38	12.25	10.13	14.56	32.75	15.75	22.25	29.75	62.00
P/E – high	—	33	61	26	19	28	30	36	30	—	59
P/E – low	—	17	15	12	10	9	12	13	13	—	22
Dividends per share ($)	—	0.00	0.00	0.04	0.10	0.12	0.15	0.16	0.19	0.20	0.20
Book value per share ($)	44.9%	0.34	0.58	1.07	1.46	2.57	4.13	5.05	6.03	7.47	9.59
Employees	38.4%	—	172	291	383	508	701	887	1,000	1,584	2,319

1995 YEAR-END

Debt ratio: 0.0%
Return on equity: 16.2%
Cash (mil.): $516
Current ratio: 3.72
Long-term debt (mil.): $0
No. of shares (mil.): 73
Dividends
  Yield: 0.3%
  Payout: 15.9%
Market value (mil.): $4,516
R&D as % of sales: 18.2%

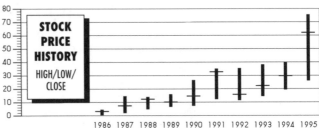

STOCK PRICE HISTORY HIGH/LOW/CLOSE

ADVANCE PUBLICATIONS, INC.

OVERVIEW

It's "Forward, march" for Advance Publications as the publishing conglomerate expands its presence in electronic media and cable communications. Diversification efforts for the book, newspaper, and magazine publisher include a regional news channel in New Jersey and joint venture with Time Warner that combines selected cable operations in Florida, New York, and North Carolina. A new unit, CondéNet, handles new-media operations of its Condé Nast Publications.

But the mainstay of the company, after more than 70 years, is selling words on paper. Newspapers include more than 20 secondary-market newspapers, including the New Orleans *Times-Picayune*, the Cleveland *Plain Dealer*, and 28 local publications gained by the 1995 purchase of American City Business Journals.

Advance also owns Parade Publications, producer of Sunday newspaper supplements *Parade* and *react*.

Condé Nast publishes primarily lifestyle and fashion magazines, including *Vogue*, *Architectural Digest*, *GQ*, *Bride's*, and *Condé Nast Traveler*, along with the general interest offering *Vanity Fair*. The venerable *New Yorker* is a separate division.

The company also owns book publisher Random House, whose imprints include Knopf, Ballantine, the Fodor's travel series, and Crown Publishers.

Advance Publications, controlled by Samuel (Si) Newhouse Jr. and his brother, Donald, is secretive in the extreme. In 1996, however, Si Newhouse revealed the name of his probable successor — cousin Jonathan Newhouse.

WHEN

Solomon Neuhaus (who later became Samuel I. Newhouse) dropped out of school at age 13 because of poverty. He went to work for a lawyer who had taken possession of the *Bayonne* (New Jersey) *Times* as payment for a debt. In 1911, 16-year-old Newhouse was put in charge of the failing newspaper and turned it around. In 1922 he bought his own newspaper, the *Staten Island Advance*, the core of Advance Publications.

Newhouse used profits from the *Advance* to buy other newspapers in the New York area, operating out of a briefcase rather than a headquarters suite. During the 1930s, '40s, and '50s he bought local newspapers in Long Island, Newark, Syracuse, and other middle markets and expanded into Alabama.

In 1959 Newhouse entered magazine publishing when he bought Condé Nast (*Vogue*, *Bride's*, and *House & Garden*) as an anniversary gift for his wife, Mitzi. He joked that she had asked for a fashion magazine, so he bought her *Vogue*. Newhouse continued to build his newspaper empire in the 1960s and expanded into cable television.

Newhouse died in 1979, leaving his sons Si and Donald as trustees of the company's 10 shares of voting stock. They claimed the estate was worth $181.9 million, resulting in inheritance taxes of $48.7 million. The IRS sought more. When the case — the largest until then — was decided in 1990, the IRS lost.

Meanwhile, the sons continued to expand Advance Publications. They entered book publishing in 1980 by buying what was then the largest general interest book publisher,

Random House (founded in 1925 by Bennett Cerf and Donald Klopfer), from RCA.

Si built up the magazine business in the 1980s, resurrecting the roaring '20s standard *Vanity Fair* in 1983 and adding other titles under the Condé Nast banner. Advance bought the *New Yorker* in 1985. Newhouse focused on creating prestigious products never mind the cost. Employee perks such as free food and limousine service became the norm, and editorial decisions were severed from financial considerations — editors were not even informed of their budgets. This '80s approach lasted into the 1990s, despite a recession that brought falling ad revenues and pages. Predictably, profits evaporated at some magazines and management shuffling became common. In 1992 Newhouse moved *Vanity Fair* editor Tina Brown to the *New Yorker*, hoping to give an edge to the eccentric weekly; the next year Condé Nast added Knapp Publications (*Architectural Digest*, *Bon Appetit*) to its stable. The party finally ended when *New Yorker* president Steven Florio was made president of Condé Nast in 1994. He cut excesses and began hard-sell advertising initiatives. Most Condé Nast titles became profitable again in 1995.

As part of an attempt to grab more of its target audience, in 1995 Advance bought American City Business Journals, a producer of local business papers, for $269 million.

Advance also moved into new media, starting a Condé Nast Web site and forming an alliance between New Jersey's *Star Ledger* and Cablevision Systems to produce a regional news channel.

WHO

Chairman and CEO: Samuel I. "Si" Newhouse Jr.
President: Donald E. Newhouse
CFO: Arthur Silverstein
Chairman, President, and CEO, Random House:
Alberto Vitale
President and CEO, Condé Nast Publications: Steven T.
Florio
President, Newhouse Newspapers Metro-Suburbia:
Edwin F. Russell
CEO, American City Business Journals: Ray Shaw
**President, Condé Nast Asia/Pacific; Chairman,
Interculture Communications Ltd. (Taiwan):** Didier
Guerin

WHERE

HQ: 950 Fingerboard Rd., Staten Island, NY 10305
Phone: 718-981-1234
Fax: 718-981-1415

Advance Publications has newspapers and cable TV
groups in the US and book and magazine operations in
New York and Europe.

WHAT

**American City Business
Journals** (28 local
weekly business news-
papers and 3 auto rac-
ing magazines)

**The Condé Nast
Publications Inc.**
Allure
Architectural Digest
Bon Appetit
Bride's
Condé Nast Traveler
Details
Glamour
Gourmet
GQ
Mademoiselle
Vanity Fair
Vogue
The New Yorker

Newhouse Broadcasting
Cable television (1.4 million subscribers)

Parade Publications
Parade
react

Random House, Inc.
Alfred A. Knopf
Ballantine Books
Beginner Books
Crown Publishers
Fawcett Books
Fodor's Travel
Publications
Modern Library
Orion
Pantheon Books
Random Century (UK)
Times Books
Villard Books
Vintage Books

**Selected Newhouse
Newspapers Metro-
Suburbia**
Alabama
Birmingham News
The Mobile Press
*The Mobile Press
Register*
The Mobile Register
Louisiana
The Times-Picayune
(New Orleans)
Massachusetts
*Union-News & Sunday
Republican* (Springfield)
Michigan
The Ann Arbor News
The Flint Times
The Grand Rapids Press
Kalamazoo Gazette
The Saginaw News
Times (Bay City)
Mississippi
Mississippi Press
(Pascagoula)

*Mississippi Press
Register* (Pascagoula)
New Jersey
Jersey Journal (Jersey
City)
Star-Ledger (Newark)
Times (Trenton)
New York
Herald-American
(Syracuse)
The Post-Standard
(Syracuse)
Syracuse Herald-Journal
Ohio
Plain Dealer (Cleveland)
Oregon
The Oregonian
(Portland)
Pennsylvania
The Patriot-News
(Harrisburg)

KEY COMPETITORS

American Express
Bertelsmann
Cablevision Systems
Comcast
Cox Enterprises
Crain Communications
Dow Jones
E.W. Scripps
Gannett
Harcourt General
Hearst
Houghton Mifflin
Knight-Ridder
Lagardère
McClatchy Newspapers
McGraw-Hill
News Corp.
Pearson
Pulitzer Publishing
Time Warner
Times Mirror
Universal Press Syndicate
Viacom
W.W. Norton

HOW MUCH

Private company FYE: December 31	Annual Growth	1986	1987	1988	1989	1990	1991	1992	1993	1994	1995
Sales ($ mil.)	9.2%	2,200	2,482	2,482	2,882	3,040	3,095	4,287	4,416	4,690	4,855
Employees	0.3%	18,500	19,000	19,000	19,000	19,500	19,000	19,000	19,000	19,000	19,000

R A N D O M
H O U S E

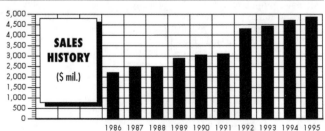

SALES
HISTORY
($ mil.)

AMERICA ONLINE, INC.

OVERVIEW

America Online (AOL) is the world's largest and fastest-growing provider of online services. Through an easy-to-use interface, members are offered access to a variety of information and services, including e-mail, electronic magazines and newspapers, stock quotes, conferences, and online classes, as well as this profile and others published by Hoover's Inc. The Vienna, Virginia-based company hopes to repeat its US success in Canada, Europe, and Japan. Its main obstacles are the competition for content from other online services and the rising popularity of the Internet. Many media providers are creating their own Web sites (which offer a graphical interface to the Internet and links to other sites around the world), and thousands of small service providers offer access to the Internet at a lower cost.

AOL is making moves to better position itself to compete for Internet access business. In one whirlwind week in March 1996, AOL announced major alliances with Netscape Communications, Microsoft, and AT&T. The Netscape and Microsoft deals allow AOL members to use both companies' Web browsers — software for surfing the Internet — and in exchange, Microsoft said it would add AOL access to future versions of Windows 95. The 3rd agreement provides for customers of WorldNet, AT&T's Internet service, to receive discount subscriptions to AOL.

Investors in AOL include Apple Computer and the Tribune Company. Executives and directors own 9.1% of the company.

WHEN

Stephen Case was manager of new pizza development for PepsiCo's Pizza Hut (he researched new pizza toppings) when he first began using an early online service called the Source in the early 1980s. He saw big possibilities in the fledgling technology if it could be made easier to use, and in 1983 he got a chance to get some hands-on experience when he took a marketing job with Control Video, which ran an online service for users of Atari computer games. However, Control Video soon ran into financial trouble, and the company's board fired its management. Entrepreneur Jim Kimsey was named CEO. Case helped Kimsey raise money to resurrect the company, and in 1985 Control Video was rechristened Quantum Computer Services. The company launched an online service called Q-Link for users of Commodore computers.

Q-Link proved to be a success with Commodore users, so in 1987 Quantum expanded its offerings to owners of other types of PCs, signing deals with Apple and Tandy. In 1989 the company launched a nationwide service called America Online for IBM-compatible and Apple computers. In 1991 the company changed its name to America Online.

America Online went public in 1992, the same year Case was named CEO. He focused on expanding AOL's market share. To boost its content (thus making its service more attractive), AOL signed deals with several media companies, adding features from Knight-Ridder newspapers and Time General Media International's *Omni* magazine. Also in 1993 the company began offering a Windows version

of its online software. AOL's attractive and easy-to-use interface, coupled with the growing popularity of Windows, attracted even more users to the online service. In 1994 the company began offering Internet access.

An early investor in the company was Paul Allen, a cofounder of software behemoth Microsoft, who by 1994 had acquired a 24.9% stake in AOL. Allen wanted AOL to work with his other high-tech ventures to develop multimedia software. But he also wanted a seat on the company's board; AOL's board and management turned him down, and Allen sold his shares. It also bought multimedia developer Redgate Communications (bringing the company Ted Leonsis, now president of AOL services), anticipating expansion into CD-ROM and interactive TV formats, and Internet browser software maker Booklink Technologies. By the end of 1994, AOL had more than 1 million subscribers.

In 1995 it teamed up with publishing empire Bertelsmann to offer online services in Europe. AOL also boosted its Internet-related features, buying several Internet-related businesses, including Medior and WAIS. Also that year AOL launched GNN, an Internet-only service for nontechnical users.

By mid-1996 the company had more than 6 million users. The company hired William Razzouk, formerly with Federal Express, as president and COO. He left after 4 months, with Case resuming a more hands-on role as the company adopted design changes and a sharp cut in subscription prices to deal with online competition.

WHO

Chairman Emeritus: James V. Kimsey, age 55
Chairman and CEO: Stephen M. Case, age 36,
$200,000 pay
SVP; President, AOL Technologies: Michael M.
Connors, age 53, $195,000 pay
SVP; President, AOL International: John L. Davies,
age 45, $195,000 pay
SVP, CFO, Treasurer, and Chief Accounting Officer:
Lennert J. Leader, age 40, $188,333 pay
SVP; President, AOL Services: Theodore J. Leonsis,
age 39, $175,025 pay
SVP; President, AOL Enterprises: David Cole, age 42
SVP Corporate Development: Miles Gilburne, age 44
SVP Product Research: Marc S. Seriff, age 47
VP; SVP, AOL Services: Janice Brandt, age 44
VP Investor Relations: Richard Hanlon, age 47
VP, General Counsel, and Secretary: Ellen M. Kirsh,
age 47
VP Operations: Matthew Korn, age 36
VP; President, AOL Productions: Barry Schuler, age 42
VP Corporate Communications: Jean N. Villanueva,
age 35
VP Enterprise Solutions: Mark Walsh, age 41
VP; SVP, AOL Services: Audrey Y. Weil, age 35
VP Human Resources and Facilities: Mark Stavish,
age 40
Auditors: Ernst & Young LLP

WHERE

HQ: 8619 Westwood Center Dr., Vienna, VA 22182-2285
Phone: 703-448-8700
Fax: 703-883-1532
Web site: http://www.aol.com

WHAT

| | 1995 Sales | |
	$ mil.	% of total
Online services	359	91
Other	36	9
Total	**395**	**100**

America Online Channels

Computers & Software	Marketplace
Digital City	MusicSpace
Entertainment	Newsstand
Games	People Connection
Health & Fitness	Personal Finance
The Hub	Reference Desk
International	Sports
Internet Connection	Style Channel
Kids Only	Today's News
Learning & Culture	Travel
Life, Styles & Interests	

KEY COMPETITORS

ASCIINet
AT&T Corp.
CompuServe
Dow Jones
MCI
MFS Communications
Microsoft
NETCOM
News Corp.
PC Van
People World
Prodigy
. PSINet

HOW MUCH

Nasdaq symbol: AMER FYE: June 30	Annual Growth	1986	1987	1988	1989	1990	1991	1992	1993	1994	1995
Sales ($ mil.)	60.4%	—	9	14	15	20	20	26	39	101	395
Net income ($ mil.)	—	—	0	0	(6)	0	1	2	3	6	(34)
Income as % of sales	—	—	0.2%	2.9%	—	0.0%	4.6%	8.4%	8.1%	6.1%	—
Earnings per share ($)	—	—	—	—	—	0.01	0.03	0.05	0.06	0.10	(0.50)
Stock price – high ($)	—	—	—	—	—	—	—	3.66	8.75	14.63	46.25
Stock price – low ($)	—	—	—	—	—	—	—	1.34	2.22	5.97	12.31
Stock price – close ($)	117.2%	—	—	—	—	—	—	3.66	7.31	14.00	37.50
P/E – high	—	—	—	—	—	—	—	73	146	146	—
P/E – low	—	—	—	—	—	—	—	27	37	60	—
Dividends per share ($)	—	—	—	—	—	—	—	0.00	0.01	0.00	0.00
Book value per share ($)	—	—	—	—	—	—	—	0.43	0.50	1.71	2.90
Employees	115.1%	—	—	—	—	—	116	124	236	527	2,481

1995 YEAR-END

Debt ratio: 9.1%
Return on equity: —
Cash (mil.): $45
Current ratio: 1.00
Long-term debt (mil.): $20
No. of shares (mil.): 75
Dividends
  Yield: —
  Payout: —
Market value (mil.): $2,817

STOCK
PRICE
HISTORY
HIGH/LOW/
CLOSE

1986 1987 1988 1989 1990 1991 1992 1993 1994 1995

AXEL SPRINGER VERLAG AG

OVERVIEW

Both highbrows and lowbrows can enjoy Axel Springer Verlag's offerings. Built on the foundations of its serious newspaper *Die Welt* and splashy tabloid *Bild*, the Berlin-based company is a diverse media group with scores of operations in radio, TV, electronic information, books (through its 50%-owned Ullstein-Langen-Müller Verlag subsidiary), and magazines (*Allegra, Auto Bild*), as well as in other newspapers (*Hamburger Abendblatt, Stuttgarter Stadtanzeiger*).

It owns at least a partial stake in more than 30 publishing companies across Europe. Its distribution system includes 109,000 sales outlets in Germany.

Despite boardroom conflicts between family members and current management following the death of the founder, Axel Springer Verlag is expanding with acquisitions in Central Europe. The company is also active in electronic media. It has a stake in the German leader in audiotex (premium telephone services), CompuTel Telefonservice, and also has holdings in DITV, a digital TV company. Axel Springer Verlag has launched *Hörzu Teledisk*, an online program guide distributed on computer diskettes to paid subscribers.

WHEN

The company rose, literally, out of the ashes of WWII Germany. Founder Axel Springer salvaged some equipment from his father's small Hamburg publishing house that had been destroyed in a British bombing raid, and in 1945 he got permission from the occupying authorities to launch his first magazine, *Nordwestdeutsche Hefte*, made up of transcripts of radio broadcasts. In 1948 he started *Hamburger Abendblatt*, and by 1950 it was Hamburg's best-selling newspaper. Two years later Springer launched the tabloid *Bild Zeitung*, later renamed *Bild*. The success of the paper — with its mix of sex, crime, and sports — helped fund his company's move into more serious newspaper publishing. In 1953 Springer acquired the respected daily *Die Welt*, which had been established by British occupation authorities in 1946. He set up a major office in the divided city of Berlin in 1959 to run his newly acquired *Berliner Morgenpost* and *B.Z.* dailies. The company moved its headquarters to Berlin in 1967.

Springer, who as a young man had seen elderly Jews beaten in Berlin, was committed to reconciliation with Jews, the support of Israel, and the reunification of the 2 Germanys — beliefs unpopular at the height of the Cold War.

However, the company itself made headlines in 1966 when allegations emerged about Springer-appointed *Die Welt* editor Herman Starke's pro-Nazi and anti-Semitic past.

In 1972 Axel Springer Verlag built Germany's first offset printing plant for newspapers. During this decade the company expanded into the regional newsletter and magazine market, in 1975 acquiring Gilde-Verlag, the publisher of *Rallye Racing* and *Sportfahrer* magazines, and in 1976 launching *Tennis Magazin* and *Ski Magazin*. Novel publisher Cora Verlag was created that year. Springer also launched women's magazines *Journal für die Frau* (1978) and *Bild der Frau* (1983). Although *Die Welt* had struggled financially since the early 1970s, Springer's company continued to expand. It was part of a German satellite consortium set up in 1983, and in 1985 it also acquired stakes in cable TV and bought 2 Munich radio stations.

Axel Springer's death in 1985 precipitated a long-running series of boardroom disputes that read more like *Bild* than *Die Welt*. Matters came to a head in 1994 when Springer's successor, Bernhard Servatius, appointed 3 new presidents and CEOs. This clear break from the family tradition prompted Springer's son Nicolaus and grandchildren Ariane and Axel-Sven, all shareholders, to write an open letter to the German weekly *Die Zeit* publicly attacking the direction Servatius was taking the company. Springer's wife Friede sided with Servatius.

Despite these internal disputes, the company prospered. Cost cutting and acquisitions in the 1990s mitigated the losses from *Die Welt* and its SAT.1 satellite TV station. In 1994 Axel Springer Verlag introduced a women's magazine, *Pani Domu*, in Poland. The next year it launched another women's title, *Allegra*. In 1995 the company announced that it would acquire a 10% stake in Europe Online, a Luxembourg-based online services consortium. However, it pulled out of the deal later that year, saying that it wanted to review other means of delivering information.

In 1996 Axel Springer entered the Czech and Slovak newspaper markets with the purchase of a 49% stake in Dutch publisher Ringier-Taurus BV.

WHO

Chairman: Bernhard Servatius
Deputy Chairman: Ernst Cramer
Chairman, CEO, and President: Jürgen Richter, age 52
Auditors: C&L Treuhand-Vereinigung Deutsche Revision Aktiengesellschaft

WHERE

HQ: Axel-Springer-Platz 1, D-20350, Hamburg, Germany
Phone: +49-40-347-22884
Fax: +49-40-347-25540
US HQ: Axel Springer Group Inc., 565 Fifth Ave., New York, NY 10017-2413
US Phone: 212-972-1720
US Fax: 212-972-1724
Web site: http://www.asv.de

WHAT

	1995 Sales
	% of total
Newspapers	62
Magazines	26
Print jobs	6
Other	6
Total	**100**

Newspapers
Bild
Bild am Sonntag
Die Welt
Welt am Sonntag

Regional Newspapers
Berliner Morgenpost
B.Z.
B.Z. am Sonntag
Hamburger Abendblatt

Free Sheets and Classified Press
Ahrensburger Wochenblatt
Berliner Wochenblatt
Bille Wochenblatt
Hallo Berlin
Hamburger Wochenblatt
Spandauer Volksblatt

Magazines
Allegra (young women's interests)
Auntiquitaten (antiques)
Auto Bild (car magazine)
Bild der Frau (women's magazine)
Big Sports (sports)
Bildwoche (family interests)
Funk Uhr (TV magazine)
Golf Sport
Hörzu (TV)
Journal für die Frau (women's interests)
Rallye Racing (auto racing)
Rute & Rolle (fishing)

Ski Magazin
Sport Bild (sports)
Tennis Magazin
TVnue (TV)

Selected International Publications
Medical Tribune (medical newssheet, Japan)
Nuevo Estilo (home interior magazine, Spain)
Pani Domu (women's magazine, Poland)
Tiroler Tageszeitung (newspaper, Austria)

Book Publishing Subsidiaries
Cora Verlag (50%, novelette series)
Ullstein-Langen-Müller Verlag (50%)

Other Activities
Interactive media
Radio stations
TV programming and stations

KEY COMPETITORS

Bertelsmann
Burda
Heinrich Bauer Verlag
Holtzbinck
Kirchgruppe
Lagardère
Pearson
Reed Elsevier
United News & Media
VNU
Wolters Kluwer

HOW MUCH

Principal exchange: Frankfurt FYE: December 31	Annual Growth	1986	1987	1988	1989	1990	1991	1992	1993	1994	1995
Sales (DM mil.)	5.5%	—	—	2,843	3,008	3,534	3,681	3,479	3,841	3,961	4,134
Net income (DM mil.)	6.2%	—	—	93	95	65	11	57	73	119	142
Income as % of sales	—	—	—	3.3%	3.2%	1.8%	0.3%	1.6%	1.9%	3.0%	3.4%
Earnings per share (DM)	—	—	—	27.47	26.02	19.10	3.30	16.83	21.35	34.98	41.76
Stock price – high (DM)	—	—	—	625	635	885	748	620	700	695	965
Stock price – low (DM)	—	—	—	428	495	607	449	452	485	610	610
Stock price – close (DM)	5.2%	—	—	515	635	720	473	592	635	623	965
P/E – high	—	—	—	23	24	46	227	37	33	20	23
P/E – low	—	—	—	16	19	32	136	27	23	17	15
Dividends per share (DM)	12.1%	—	—	12.00	12.00	12.00	12.00	0.00	12.00	12.00	15.00
Book value per share (DM)	—	—	—	—	125.41	141.37	148.09	139.09	155.84	164.78	183.16
Employees	2.4%	—	—	—	—	—	12,112	12,620	12,663	14,819	13,331

1995 YEAR-END

Debt ratio: —
Return on equity: —
Cash (mil.): —
Long-term debt: —
No. of shares (mil.): 3
Dividends
  Yield: 1.6%
  Payout: 35.9%
Market value (mil.): $2,282
Sales (mil.): $2,875

Note: $=DM1.44 (December 31, 1995)

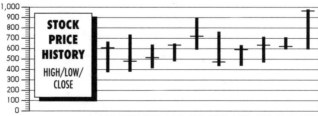

STOCK PRICE HISTORY HIGH/LOW/CLOSE

BARNES & NOBLE, INC.

OVERVIEW

It's in the books! Barnes & Noble is the largest bookseller in the US, with about 1,000 stores in 49 states, the District of Columbia, and Puerto Rico. Key to the success of the New York City-based company have been its superstores. Credited with transforming the way that books are sold at the retail level, Barnes & Noble's superstores (Barnes & Noble, Bookstop, and Bookstar) offer between 60,000 and 175,000 titles and, at some locations, coffee bars and music and software departments. The company's far-ranging titles include books on art, cooking, history, and psychology, as well as children's books and general fiction. It operates about 360 superstores and plans to open approximately 95 a year. Unable to stop the relentless march of the superstores, with their superior selection and inviting, spacious surroundings (now an industry standard), many independent, smaller bookstores have been forced out of the market.

Even Barnes & Noble's mall stores (B. Dalton Bookseller, Doubleday Book Shops, and Scribner's Bookstores) are in decline. The company closed 69 such stores in 1995.

Barnes & Noble also owns a leading direct-mail bookselling business (Marboro Books Corp.) and a publishing company. CEO Leonard Riggio owns 20% of the company and Dutch retailer Vendex International owns 10%.

WHEN

Barnes & Noble dates back to 1873 when Charles Barnes went into the used-book business in Wheaton, Illinois. By the turn of the century he was operating a thriving bookselling business in Chicago. His son, William, took over as president in 1902. William sold his share in the firm in 1917 (to C.W. Follett, who built Follett Corporation into one of Barnes & Noble's biggest competitors) and relocated to New York City, where he purchased an interest in an established textbook wholesalers, Noble & Noble. The company was soon renamed Barnes & Noble.

At that time, the company concentrated on selling to colleges and libraries, providing textbooks to most of the schools in the New York area. During this period it opened a large shop on Fifth Avenue. Over the next three decades Barnes & Noble became one of the leading booksellers in the New York region.

Enter Leonard Riggio. The son of a prizefighter, Riggio worked in a New York University bookstore as a sales clerk to help pay for night school. He was studying engineering, but he got the itch for book retailing. In 1965, at age 24, he borrowed $5,000 and opened a college bookstore of his own in Greenwich Village. Beginning in the late 1960s, he expanded by buying other college bookstores.

He entered the general bookstore business in 1971 when he acquired Barnes & Noble for $1.2 million. With the acquisition of Marboro Books in 1979, the company entered the mail-order and publishing business.

In 1986 Riggio and Dutch retailer Vendex International bought the 754 stores of the B. Dalton mall bookstore chain from retail empire Dayton Hudson. Founded in 1966, B. Dalton focused at first on the shopping malls that were beginning to spring up all over the US. The company eventually shifted its strategy and began placing stores in other heavily trafficked areas such as office complexes.

In 1989 the company acquired the Scribner's Bookstores trade name from Macmillan Publishing and Rizzoli International. That year it beat out Crown Books to buy Bookstop, a chain of 23 Bookstop and Bookstar superstores founded in 1982 by entrepreneur Gary Hoover. With the acquisition of Bookstop, the first book superstore chain, Barnes & Noble began its shift to superstore format. It also began streamlining its operations to integrate Bookstop and Doubleday (acquired in 1990) into its existing business.

Barnes & Noble had planned a public offering for 1992 but withdrew after it got a tepid response from Wall Street because of the company's debt load. Instead, Barnes & Noble raised $100 million from Riggio, Vendex, and private investors. It then embarked on a major expansion of its superstore operation.

With sales at its superstores booming in 1993, the retailer made a 2nd try at going public. This time it had no trouble getting Wall Street's attention. In 1995 Stephen Riggio, Leonard's younger brother, was named COO.

Despite the company's record sales, restructuring charges stemming from the acceleration of its mall store closings led to Barnes & Noble's $53 million loss in fiscal 1996. In June of that year it agreed to buy a 20% stake in Chapters Inc., Canada's only large bookstore chain (375 locations), from majority owner Canadian General Capital, a venture capital firm.

Chairman and CEO: Leonard Riggio, age 55,
  $1,305,000 pay
VC and CFO: Irene R. Miller, age 43, $559,808 pay
COO: Stephen Riggio, age 41, $565,577 pay
EVP; President, Barnes & Noble Development: Mitchell
  S. Klipper, age 38, $575,192 pay
VP; President, Barnes & Noble Superstores: Thomas A.
  Tolworthy, age 41, $355,266 pay
VP; President, Barnes & Noble Distribution: David K.
  Cully, age 43
VP; President, B. Dalton Bookseller: Kristine M. Terrill,
  age 45
VP and Manager General Merchandise: Maureen H.
  Golden, age 45
VP Human Resources: Mike Malone
Secretary: Michael N. Rosen, age 55
Auditors: BDO Seidman LLP

WHERE

HQ: 122 Fifth Ave., New York, NY 10011
Phone: 212-633-3300
Fax: 212-675-0413
Web site: http://www.shareholder.com/bks

	1996 Stores	
	Mall bookstores	Superstores
California	94	56
Texas	48	48
Florida	39	30
Michigan	29	9
Pennsylvania	28	7
Ohio	27	9
New York	26	26
Minnesota	25	12
Illinois	23	14
New Jersey	21	12
Other states	279	135
Total	**639**	**358**

WHAT

	1996 Sales	
	$ mil.	% of total
Superstores	1,350	68
Mall stores	603	30
Other	24	2
Total	**1,977**	**100**

Superstores
Barnes & Noble
Bookstar
Bookstop

Mall Bookstores
B. Dalton Bookseller
Doubleday Book Shops
Scribner's Bookstores

Mail-order Business
Marboro Books Corp.

Publishing
Barnes & Noble Books

KEY COMPETITORS

Blockbuster
Books-A-Million
Borders
Crown Books
Follett
Hastings Books
Lauriat's
MTS
Musicland
Toys "R" Us
Wal-Mart
W H Smith

HOW MUCH

NYSE symbol: BKS FYE: January 31	Annual Growth	1987	1988	1989	1990	1991	1992	1993	1994	1995	1996
Sales ($ mil.)	19.0%	412	661	669	749	880	921	1,086	1,337	1,622	1,977
Net income ($ mil.)	10.3%	(22)	(2)	3	11	7	(5)	(6)	8	26	(53)
Income as % of sales	—	—	—	0.4%	1.5%	0.8%	—	—	—	1.6%	—
Earnings per share ($)	—	—	—	—	—	—	—	0.01	0.30	0.81	(1.70)
Stock price – high ($)[1]	—	—	—	—	—	—	—	—	34.00	31.38	42.25
Stock price – low ($)[1]	—	—	—	—	—	—	—	—	22.63	20.00	26.13
Stock price – close ($)[1]	8.0%	—	—	—	—	—	—	—	24.88	31.25	29.00
P/E – high	—	—	—	—	—	—	—	—	—	113	39
P/E – low	—	—	—	—	—	—	—	—	—	75	25
Dividends per share ($)	—	—	—	—	—	—	—	0.00	0.00	0.00	0.00
Book value per share ($)	30.2%	—	—	—	—	—	—	—	7.03	11.01	11.91
Employees	14.2%	—	—	—	—	—	12,600	17,000	14,700	20,000	21,400

1996 YEAR-END

Debt ratio: 39.6%
Return on equity: —
Cash (mil.): $9
Current ratio: 1.36
Long-term debt (mil.): $262
No. of shares (mil.): 33
Dividends
  Yield: —
  Payout: —
Market value (mil.): $956

STOCK
PRICE
HISTORY[1]
HIGH/LOW/
CLOSE

1987 1988 1989 1990 1991 1992 1993 1994 1995 1996

[1] Stock prices are for the prior calendar year.

BERTELSMANN AG

OVERVIEW

Europe's leading media company, privately owned Bertelsmann, is #3 in the world after US entertainment giants Walt Disney and Time Warner. The Gutersloh, Germany-based company owns leading US book publisher Bantam Doubleday Dell and 75% of newspaper and magazine publisher Gruner + Jahr, which prints magazines in Europe and the US, including *McCall's* and *Family Circle*.

Books (including fiction, reference works, how-to books, and religious publications) account for the largest slice of Bertelsmann's sales. Its book club operation is one of the world's largest, with around 25 million members. The company is also engaged in film, radio, television, and music publishing and production. Its record labels include RCA and Arista in the US, BMG Ariola in Europe, and

BMG Victor in Japan. TV interests include the RTL plus network (Germany, Luxembourg) and the pay channel Premiere (Germany); . Bertelsmann has a paper plant in Italy, and printing plants in Europe, the US, and South America.

The company is moving rapidly into multimedia, including a partnership with electronic information pioneer America Online, and is exploring digital TV. Bertelsmann has also agreed to merge its television interests with those of Compagnie Luxembourgeoise de Télédiffusion (CLT) in a deal that would create the biggest TV company in Europe. It also has plans to expand into China and India. The Bertelsmann Foundation, a nonprofit group, owns about 30% of the company. The Mohn family controls another 8%.

WHEN

Carl Bertelsmann founded the company that bears his name in Gütersloh, Germany, in 1835. One of his first books, a hymnal, was successful enough to allow the company to grow despite the poverty and low literacy rate of the time. It continued to thrive primarily as a religious publisher until WWII, when the Nazis shut it down.

Reinhard Mohn, whose grandfather had married Bertelsmann's granddaughter, was captured by the Allies in North Africa. He spent the rest of the war in a Kansas POW camp, returning to Germany to find Bertelsmann's Gütersloh plant destroyed. The young Mohn took control of the company, rebuilt the plant, and began publishing in 1948.

Bertelsmann started Lesering, Germany's first book club, in 1950, followed by a record club in the late 1950s. The company bought Germany's UFA (TV and film production, 1964) and 25% of Gruner + Jahr (publisher of *Stern* and *Der Spiegel*, 1969; raised to a controlling interest, 1973). In the US, Bertelsmann bought 51% of Bantam Books in 1977 (and the remaining stock in 1981) and Arista Records in 1979.

Mark Wössner succeeded Mohn as CEO in 1981. Under Wössner, Bertelsmann increased its US presence in 1986 when it bought RCA Records and control of Doubleday Publishing. Founded in 1897 by Frank Doubleday, Doubleday was one of America's largest publishers through its strength in hardbacks, Dell paperbacks, and book clubs.

But Bertelsmann's US operations were less successful than had been hoped (the book

clubs that had once provided Doubleday with 35% of its profits had lost thousands of members), prompting the company to develop new activities in the US through joint ventures rather than large acquisitions.

Bertelsmann sold Doubleday Book Shops to B. Dalton in 1990 and shut down its UK book club, Leisure Circle, leaving a near market monopoly to another Bertelsmann affiliate, Book Club Associates. That year Bertelsmann bought eastern Germany's largest book printer, Pössneck.

In 1993 Mohn transferred substantial voting shares in the company to the nonprofit Bertelsmann Foundation (which now controls the media giant). The company absorbed losses in 1994 from the collapse of German television station Vox, in which it was a major shareholder. That year Bertelsmann bought several women's magazines (*Child*, *Family Circle*, *McCall's*) from the New York Times Co.

The company teamed up with America Online in 1995, committing $100 million to create a European online venture in which it holds a 50% stake. In 1996 Bertelsmann joined with British Sky Broadcasting (BSkyB) and French companies Havas and CANAL+ to create digital pay-TV services in Germany. BSkyB dropped out of the venture shortly after it was formed. That year Bertelsmann's joint venture agreement with CLT gave the company a strong presence in advertising-supported TV and eliminated the Luxembourg-based company as a potential competitor in the German pay-TV market.

Chairman of the Supervisory Board: Dieter Vogel
Deputy Chairman: Gerd Schulte-Hillen
President and CEO: Mark Wössner
CFO: Siegfried Luther
Chairman and CEO, BMG Entertainment Group:
Michael Dornemann
President, Bertelsmann Publishing Group
International: Bernhard von Minckwitz
Chairman and CEO, Bantam Doubleday Dell Publishing
Group (US): Jack Hoeft
President and COO, Bantam Doubleday Dell Publishing
Group (US): Erik Engstrom
Auditors: KPMG Peat Marwick LLP

WHERE

HQ: Carl-Bertelsmann-Strasse 270, D-33311, Gütersloh,
Germany
Phone: +49-(0)52-41-80-0
Fax: +49-(0)52-41-7-51-66
US HQ: Bantam Doubleday Dell Publishing Group Inc.,
1540 Broadway, New York, NY 10036
US Phone: 212-354-6500
US Fax: 212-782-9698
Web site: http://www.bertelsmann.de

	1995 Sales
	% of total
Germany	35
Other Europe	33
US	24
Other regions	8
Total	**100**

WHAT

	1995 Sales	
	DM mil.	% of total
Book	6,815	32
BMG Entertainment	6,777	32
Gruner + Jahr	4,384	20
Bertelsmann Industry	3,408	16
Adjustments	(830)	—
Total	**20,554**	**100**

Selected Operations

Book Division
Clubs
Literature and specialized
books
Professional information
Reference books/how-to
books/cartography
Religious publishing
houses

BMG Entertainment
Film
Music
Music publishing
Rights

Storage media
Television
Video

Gruner + Jahr Magazines
Magazines
Newspapers
Printing/Technical services

Industry
Paper production
Printing
Special publishing

New Media
Multimedia

Selected Operating Companies
Arbor TV-Filmproducktion
Arista Records (US)
Bantam Doubleday Dell Publishing Group (US)
Bertelsmann Online France S.N.C.
C. Bertelsmann Verlag
Gruner + Jahr

KEY COMPETITORS

Advance	Lagardère	Thomson Corp.
Publications	MCA	THORN EMI
Axel Springer	McGraw-Hill	Time Warner
CANAL+	News Corp.	Times Mirror
CompuServe	Pearson	Viacom
Harcourt General	Philips	Virgin Group
Hearst	Reader's Digest	VNU
Houghton Mifflin	Reed Elsevier	Walt Disney
John Wiley	R. R. Donnelley	Wolters Kluwer
K-III	Sony	
Knight-Ridder	Thomas Nelson	

HOW MUCH

Private company FYE: June 30	Annual Growth	1986	1987	1988	1989	1990	1991	1992	1993	1994	1995
Sales (DM mil.)	11.7%	7,602	9,160	11,299	12,483	13,313	14,483	15,955	17,170	18,405	20,554
Net income (DM mil.)	10.6%	329	207	362	402	510	540	569	662	759	817
Income as % of sales	—	4.3	2.3	3.2	3.2	3.8	3.7	3.6	3.9	4.1	4.0
Employees	6.9%	31,593	42,013	41,961	43,702	43,509	45,110	48,781	50,437	51,767	57,397

1995 YEAR-END

Debt ratio: 15.4%
Return on equity: 30.2%
Cash (mil.): DM415
Long-term debt (mil.): DM308
Sales (mil.): $14,889

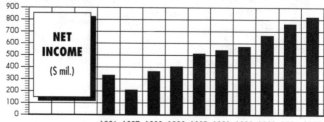

NET
INCOME
($ mil.)

Note: $=DM1.38 (June 30, 1995)

BLOCKBUSTER ENTERTAINMENT GROUP

OVERVIEW

Blockbuster is focused squarely on boxing up the international market for video rentals. The Fort Lauderdale, Florida, subsidiary of entertainment conglomerate Viacom is the nation's leading videotape and video game rental chain, with about 1/4 of the US market. It operates some 4,600 home video and music stores, including 1,000 outside the US. Blockbuster also has interests in TV and film producer Spelling Entertainment and a commercial playground operator, Discovery Zone.

Facing a saturated domestic market and a consumer shift toward purchasing videos rather than renting them, management is expecting foreign markets to support expansion (over half of all VCRs are outside the US).

CEO Steven Berrard, who played a key role in integrating Blockbuster into Viacom after the 1994 takeover, resigned from the company in 1996 to head up national used-car chain AutoNation USA. William Fields, former EVP at discount retailer Wal-Mart, took over, promising to give a new merchandising slant to a company accustomed to offering rentals.

WHEN

In 1982 David Cook founded Cook Data Services in Dallas to sell software and computing services to the oil and gas industries. The company went public the same year. When the energy industry slowed in the mid-1980s, Cook sold these businesses and shifted direction in favor of flashy, computerized video rental stores. The company opened its first store in 1985 and changed its name to Blockbuster Entertainment in 1986.

The company might never have hit the big time had it not attracted the attention of Wayne Huizenga, who was behind the early growth of trash titan Waste Management (now WMX Technologies). Looking for an investment in video rental, he infused $18 million in Blockbuster in 1987 and bought out the company by the end of the year. Huizenga acquired Southern Video Partnership and Movies to Go, increasing the number of Blockbuster stores to 130 by year's end.

Rapid expansion continued in 1988, when the company bought the California-based Video Library chain. By the end of the year, Blockbuster had increased its video chain to 415 stores (stock appreciation was so rapid during 1988 that the company declared two 2-for-1 stock splits in the space of 20 weeks).

During 1989 Blockbuster continued to make acquisitions, including Major Video (a 175-store chain based in Las Vegas) and Video Superstore MLP (its biggest franchise owner). In 1990 it acquired more chains, including Applause Video (Omaha), Video Express (Kansas City), Movie Emporium (Orlando), and units in Arizona, California, and Texas, bringing the store total past the 1,500 mark. That year Blockbuster also added Virginia-based Erol's, the US's 3rd largest video chain, to its expanding empire.

The company became the largest video renter in the UK in 1992 through the purchase of the 875-unit Cityvision chain. It also bought the Sound Warehouse and Music Plus music store chains from Shamrock Holdings. It signed a joint venture with Virgin Retail Group to develop a chain of entertainment superstores in the US (the venture ended after Viacom bought Blockbuster).

In 1993 the company acquired a majority stake in Spelling Entertainment and an interest in movie producer Republic Pictures. It also announced a partnership with IBM, called New Leaf Entertainment, to develop a system allowing music stores to make compact discs on their premises. IBM pulled out of the project in 1995, however, after pressure from major record companies.

The firm acquired software developer Virgin Interactive Entertainment in 1994 and folded it into Spelling. That year Viacom paid $7.6 billion for Blockbuster and formed a new division called Blockbuster Entertainment Group. Following the acquisition, Huizenga (who now serves as CEO of Republic Industries, a waste disposal business, and has interests in AutoNation USA and several major sports franchises in Florida) left the company.

Reflecting the business focus on the international market, Blockbuster announced a plan in 1996 to open more than 1,200 new stores in Europe (it had only 760 there in 1995) by the year 2000. The company also began experimenting with new store concepts, opening an in-store Blockbuster Video department in a Wal-Mart in Denton, Texas.

That year Viacom said it was filing bankruptcy for the struggling Discovery Zone and considering selling Blockbuster Music. It did put Blockbuster's Spelling unit on the block briefly but didn't receive any good offers.

WHO

Chairman and CEO: William R. Fields
President: Gerry Geddis
CEO, Showtime Networks Inc.: Matthew Blank
CEO, Paramount Parks and Live Entertainment: Jane Cooper
EVP Legal, Finance, and Information Systems: Thomas Hawkins
EVP Consumer Strategic Development (HR): Robert Fleetwood
SVP and CFO: Al Detz
SVP International Finance and Administration: Joseph Burke
SVP Business Development: Thomas Byrne
SVP Strategic Systems: Mark T. Gilman
SVP Strategic Marketing: Rich Gabe
President, Domestic Video: H. Scott Barrett
President, Blockbuster Music Division: Jerry M. Comstock
Auditors: Price Waterhouse LLP

WHERE

HQ: One Blockbuster Plaza, 200 S. Andrews Ave., Fort Lauderdale, FL 33301-1860
Phone: 954-832-3000
Fax: 954-832-4086
Web site: http://www.blockbuster.com

Blockbuster operates 4,600 home video and music stores throughout the US and around the world.

WHAT

Selected Operations
Blockbuster Music (retail music outlets)
Blockbuster Video (retail video outlets)
Discovery Zone, Inc. (49%; commercial playgrounds)
Spelling Entertainment Group Inc. (78%; TV and film production)

KEY COMPETITORS

All American Communications
Best Buy
Borders
Camelot Music
Carsey-Werner
Circuit City
DreamWorks SKG
Gymboree
Hastings Books
Hollywood Entertainment
King World
MCA
MTS
Movie Gallery
Musicland
ShowBiz Pizza Time
Time Warner
Trans World Entertainment
Walt Disney
Wherehouse Entertainment
W H Smith

HOW MUCH

Subsidiary FYE: December 31	Annual Growth	1986	1987	1988	1989	1990	1991	1992	1993	1994	1995
Sales ($ mil.)	95.5%	8	43	137	403	633	868	1,201	2,227	3,300	3,333
Employees	66.4%	—	—	1,275	4,151	10,600	12,500	14,750	46,000	40,400	45,000

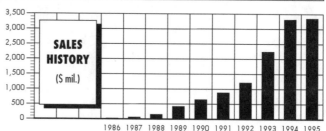

SALES HISTORY ($ mil.)

3,500 / 3,000 / 2,500 / 2,000 / 1,500 / 1,000 / 500 / 0

1986 1987 1988 1989 1990 1991 1992 1993 1994 1995

BORDERS GROUP, INC.

OVERVIEW

Borders Group is trying to cross back into the top spot in the book business. Once the largest bookstore operator in the US, Borders has been 2nd to rival Barnes & Noble since 1992. The Ann Arbor, Michigan-based company operates more than 1,100 retail stores around the US under 3 names: Waldenbooks (the #1 mall-based bookstore chain in the US), Borders (books and music superstores), and Planet Music (CD superstores). The company went public in a 1995 spinoff from reeling discounter Kmart and consolidated its 3 divisions under one roof in Ann Arbor.

Charges incurred in the spinoff led to Borders Group's $211 million loss in 1996. The company also faced fierce industry competition, particularly in its mall-based stores. Both Borders Group and Barnes & Noble have been renegotiating mall contracts to be the sole bookstore tenants, and the US Justice Department is investigating possible collusion between the top 2 chains.

Borders Group is now focusing on its superstores, which average 30,000 square feet and offer a huge selection of books and music. It opened 41 new Borders stores in 1995 and closed 115 Waldenbooks stores. The company will close 50 Waldenbooks stores in 1996 and open 40 Borders superstores. It is planning no further investment in Planet Music.

WHEN

Named for the Massachusetts pond that inspired Thoreau, Waldenbooks was founded in 1933 by Larry Hoyt, who opened a book rental library and rented books for 3 cents a day. By 1948 the company had 250 outlets and began selling books. In 1968 the company opened its first all-retail bookstore in Pittsburgh.

The chain was acquired in 1969 by Carter Hawley Hale (which became Broadway Stores, acquired by Federated in 1995). During the 1970s Waldenbooks expanded rapidly, taking advantage of the growing number of shopping malls sprouting up across the US. By 1979 the company had nearly 550 stores. That same year it hired Harry Hoffman, a former executive with snack food and soap maker Procter & Gamble, to run the company. Hoffman drew the ire of traditionalists in the book retailing industry because he focused on best-sellers, leaving little space for literary works. Hoffman also added nonbook items, including audio tapes, greeting cards, and stuffed toys, to the stores' merchandise mix.

In 1981 Waldenbooks became the first bookseller to operate in all 50 states. Three years later, Carter Hawley Hale sold Waldenbooks to Kmart to raise cash to fight off a takeover attempt by apparel retail giant the Limited.

During the 1980s the company diversified into other retailing concepts, including Waldenbooks & More, larger stores that featured books and gifts. It also opened Waldenkids children's bookstores and Walden Software. By 1988 it had more than 1,300 stores and sold about 100 million books annually.

Hoffman retired in 1991 and was replaced by Charles Cumello. The next year Kmart expanded its bookselling business with the acquisition of Book Inventory Systems, owner of superstore chain Borders Books.

Brothers Louis and Tom Borders founded their first bookstore in Ann Arbor, Michigan, in 1971. The store originally sold only used books but soon began to include new books in the mix. As it added new titles, Louis developed systems to keep track of the growing inventory. In the mid-1970s the Borders brothers formed Book Inventory Systems to market Louis's buying and inventory system to other independent bookstores.

The brothers focused on building the service part of their business through the late 1970s and early 1980s, but by the mid-1980s they were having trouble finding enough large, independent bookstores to buy their services. Returning to their original business, they opened their 2nd store, in Birmingham, Michigan, in 1985. By 1988 they had 3 stores in Michigan, one in Atlanta, and one in Indianapolis. That same year the president of cheeselog chain Hickory Farms, Robert DiRomualdo, was hired to run Borders Books. DiRomualdo continued expanding the company, and when Kmart acquired the company in 1992 Borders Books had 19 superstores.

In 1994 Kmart acquired CD Superstore, which was founded by Paul Mayer in 1986. The company's name was changed to Planet Music.

As part of a larger plan to revive its discounting business, Kmart spun off Borders Group to the public in 1995. It originally planned to retain 48% of the company but ended up selling all but 13%. Later in the year Borders Group bought Kmart's remaining stake in the company.

Chairman and CEO: Robert F. DiRomualdo, age 51, $240,417 pay

VC and President: George R. Mrkonic, age 43, $240,417 pay

President and COO, Walden Book Company: Bruce A. Quinnell, age 47, $169,900 pay

President and COO, Borders: Richard L. Flanagan, age 43, $86,667 pay

VP and Chief Information Officer: Philip C. Semprevivo, age 55, $77,054

VP and General Counsel: Thomas D. Carney, age 49

VP Business Services: James B. Brigham, age 46

VP Group Planning and Resource Management: Cedric J. Vanzura, age 32

VP Distribution: Patrick J. Murphy, age 47

Auditors: Price Waterhouse LLP

WHERE

HQ: 500 E. Washington St., Ann Arbor, MI 48104
Phone: 313-913-1100
Fax: 313-913-1965
Web site: http://www.borders.com

WHAT

	1996 Stores
	No.
Waldenbooks mall bookstores	992
Borders superstores	116
CD stores/Planet Music superstores	9
Total	**1,117**

	1996 Sales	
	$ mil.	% of total
Superstores	717	41
Mall bookstores	1,032	59
Total	**1,749**	**100**

Operations

Borders (superstore with books, videos, and multimedia products)

Borders Press (publishing; classics, special interest books, and calendars)

Planet Music (music superstore)

Waldenbooks (basic bookstore)

KEY COMPETITORS

Barnes & Noble
Best Buy
Blockbuster
Books-A-Million
Camelot Music
Crown Books
Follett
Hastings Books
Lauriat's
MTS

Musicland
Toys "R" Us
Trans World Entertainment
Wal-Mart
W H Smith
Wherehouse Entertainment
The Wiz

HOW MUCH

NYSE symbol: BGP FYE: January 31	Annual Growth	1987	1988	1989	1990	1991	1992	1993	1994	1995	1996
Sales ($ mil.)	10.5%	—	—	—	—	1,064	1,140	1,183	1,370	1,511	1,749
Net income ($ mil.)	—	—	—	—	—	2	17	23	(38)	9	(211)
Income as % of sales	—	—	—	—	—	0.2%	1.5%	1.9%	—	0.6%	1.4%
Earnings per share ($)	—	—	—	—	—	—	—	—	—	0.48	(5.06)
Stock price – high ($)[1]	—	—	—	—	—	—	—	—	—	—	21.88
Stock price – low ($)[1]	—	—	—	—	—	—	—	—	—	—	13.88
Stock price – close ($)[1]	—	—	—	—	—	—	—	—	—	—	18.50
P/E – high	—	—	—	—	—	—	—	—	—	—	—
P/E – low	—	—	—	—	—	—	—	—	—	—	—
Dividends per share ($)	—	—	—	—	—	—	—	—	—	0.00	12.53
Book value per share ($)	(50.4%)	—	—	—	—	—	—	—	—	25.25	12.53
Employees	21.0%	—	—	—	—	—	—	—	13,650	16,700	20,000

1996 YEAR-END

Debt ratio: 12.7%
Return on equity: —
Cash (mil.): $37
Current ratio: 1.36
Long-term debt (mil.): $8
No. of shares (mil.): 38
Dividends
  Yield: —
  Payout: —
Market value (mil.): $697

STOCK PRICE HISTORY[1]
HIGH/LOW/CLOSE

1987 1988 1989 1990 1991 1992 1993 1994 1995 1996

[1] Stock prices are for the prior calendar year.

BRITISH SKY BROADCASTING

OVERVIEW

The sky's the limit for British Sky Broadcasting Group (BSkyB). The Isleworth, Middlesex-based company's Sky Television is the leading UK pay-TV broadcasting service, distributing its programming via cable and satellite to more than 4 million subscribers in the UK and Ireland. BSkyB provides its subscribers with a mix of news, sports, and entertainment programming. Among the heavy servings of American programming dished up (mainly from Rupert Murdoch's Fox channel) for growing British TV appetites are *Beverly Hills 90210*, *The Simpsons*, and *The X-Files*.

The company is partly owned by Murdoch's media group, News Corp. (40%), French TV company Chargeurs (17%), British media firm Pearson (14%), and UK TV programmer Granada (11%).

BSkyB took the innovative route of cable and satellite TV to win an audience in the UK, which is currently limited by law to 4 broadcast TV channels (BBC1, BBC2, ITV, and Channel 4). (State-owned British Broadcasting Corporation (BBC) channels are funded by a license fee levied on all UK homes that own a TV. The other 2 channels are funded by advertising revenues). BSkyB presents TV owners the option of an additional 9 channels (4 basic and 5 premium) paid for by subscription fees. Subscriptions jumped from 3.5 million in 1994 to 4.2 million in 1995.

The company is committed to expanding the number of channels available to British TV viewers. In a move to compete for Europe's digital pay-TV market, the company planned a joint venture with movie and TV programming provider Kirchgruppe.

WHEN

Australian-born media czar Rupert Murdoch (with several British newspapers under his control) moved into satellite television service in the UK in 1989 when his holding company started broadcasting SkyTV. SkyTV used an Astra satellite and cable services to deliver 4 channels of programming. By broadcasting its programs via satellites owned by the Luxembourg-based Astra group, Murdoch was able to gain exemption from the British Broadcasting Act, a law prohibiting owners of national newspapers from owning more than 20% of a TV company. In 1990 a consortium of companies, including Chargeurs, Granada, and Pearson, set up a rival satellite TV service called British Satellite Broadcasting. The rivals faced a consumer market slow to adapt to new technology and a shrinking advertising base due to an economic recession, with both companies posting huge losses (Sky's weekly losses alone grew to over $15 million in 1990). In the wake of such hemorrhaging, the 2 firms merged in 1990 and became BSkyB, a slimmer operation offering only 5 channels.

BSkyB entered into its first joint venture in 1993 by teaming up with US media group Viacom to produce a Nickelodeon (children's programming) channel for the UK market. Later that year the company joined with QVC to launch a British version of the US home shopping channel. By the end of that year the number of UK homes receiving BSkyB's television programs passed the 3 million mark.

In 1994 Murdoch appointed Kelvin MacKenzie, the flamboyant former editor of

leading UK tabloid, the *Sun*, to the top slot as managing director of BSkyB. Seven months later he resigned, allegedly due to a personality clash with the man who later replaced him, Sam Chisholm, the head of Star TV, Murdoch's Asian satellite TV network.

BSkyB sold about 20% of the company to the public in 1994, dropping News Corp.'s stake from 50% to 40%. By 1994 it was offering subscribers 3 movie channels; 2 sports channels; one each of news, soaps, and travel channels; and a general entertainment channel. That year BSkyB also introduced 3 new channels: Sky Sports 2, dedicated to sports coverage; Sky Soap, a soap opera channel; and Sky Travel, featuring geographic shows and travel destinations. In connection with the launch, BSkyB acquired new rights to such sports as soccer, rugby, cricket, and boxing.

As part of its plans to boost ratings, BSkyB teamed up with rival BBC in 1995 to acquire sports programming. It also formed an alliance with international news agency Reuters to increase the content and quality of BSkyB's Sky News Channel.

In 1996 BSkyB joined with Bertelsmann (Europe's #1 media company) and French commercial TV company CANAL+ to develop digital television in Europe. Months later it quit that alliance, then announced a joint venture with Kirch Gruppe (a top European supplier of films, series, classical music, and children's TV programs) to sell digital TV in Germany. BSkyB had pretax profits of $398 million in 1996 on sales of nearly $1.6 billion.

Chairman: Gerry J. Robinson
CEO and Managing Director: Samuel H. Chisholm
Group Finance Director: Richard J. Brooke
Deputy Managing Director: David C. Chance
Company Secretary: C.K. Mackenzie
Auditors: Arthur Andersen & Co, SC

WHERE

HQ: British Sky Broadcasting Group PLC,
  6 Centaurs Business Park, Grant Way, Isleworth,
  Middlesex, TW7 5QD, UK
Phone: +44-(01)71-705-3000
Fax: +44-(01)71-705-3453

BSkyB provides cable and satellite TV services to 4.2 million subscribers in the UK and Ireland.

WHAT

	1995 Sales	
	$ mil.	% of total
Direct-to-home (satellite) subscription	917	75
Advertising	145	12
Cable subscription	118	10
Other	46	3
Total	**1,226**	**100**

TV Channnels
The Movie Channel
Sky Movies
Sky Movies Gold
Sky News
Sky One
Sky Soap
Sky Sports
Sky Sports 2
Sky Travel

Selected Subsidiaries and Affiliates
British Sky Broadcasting Limited (satellite TV services)
BSkyB Finance Ltd.
Nickelodeon UK (children's programming)
QVC (home shopping channel)
Sky Subscribers Services Ltd. (support services)
Sky Television Ltd. (investments)
Tele-Aerials Satellite Ltd. (equipment installation)

KEY COMPETITORS

Anglia
BBC
Comcast
NBC
NYNEX
SBC Communications
TCI
Time Warner
Yorkshire-Tyne Tees Television Holdings

HOW MUCH

NYSE symbol: BSY FYE: June 30	Annual Growth	1986	1987	1988	1989	1990	1991	1992	1993	1994	1995
Sales ($ mil.)	64.1%	—	—	—	—	—	169	408	618	829	1,226
Net income ($ mil.)	—	—	—	—	—	—	(1,376)	(329)	(123)	140	215
Income as % of sales	—	—	—	—	—	—	—	—	—	16.9%	17.6%
Earnings per share ($)	—	—	—	—	—	—	(6.02)	(1.44)	(0.54)	0.61	0.87
Stock price – high ($)	—	—	—	—	—	—	—	—	—	25.25	40.00
Stock price – low ($)	—	—	—	—	—	—	—	—	—	23.75	22.88
Stock price – close ($)	56.8%	—	—	—	—	—	—	—	—	24.00	37.63
P/E – high	—	—	—	—	—	—	—	—	—	41	46
P/E – low	—	—	—	—	—	—	—	—	—	39	26
Dividends per share ($)	—	—	—	—	—	—	—	—	—	—	0.58
Book value per share ($)	—	—	—	—	—	—	—	—	—	(8.00)	(4.26)
Employees	74.5%	—	—	—	—	—	—	575	1,025	2,403	3,054

1995 YEAR-END

Debt ratio: 100%
Cash (mil.): $64
Current ratio: 1.01
Long-term debt (mil.): $1,273
No. of shares (mil.): 286
Dividends
  Yield: 1.5%
  Payout: 66.7%
Market value (mil.): $10,753

STOCK PRICE HISTORY
HIGH/LOW/CLOSE

1986 1987 1988 1989 1990 1991 1992 1993 1994 1995

CABLEVISION SYSTEMS CORPORATION

OVERVIEW

Down is up and bad is good in Cablevision's capital-intensive world. While chairman and founder Charles Dolan isn't king of cable TV Wonderland, he's no Alice either. Cable industry observers consider the high cash flow enjoyed by Woodbury, New York-based Cablevision to outweigh its red ink.

The company is the nation's 6th largest provider, with 2.7 million subscribers, mostly in and around Boston, Cleveland, and New York City. Its Rainbow Programming subsidiary produces programs and operates several cable channels, including American Movie Classics (AMC), Bravo, and the Independent Film Channel. Rainbow's businesses also include 8 regional "SportsChannels" and Madison Square Garden (50%, with hotel and entertainment giant ITT Corporation).

The cable TV industry gauges corporate health by cash flow — not net income. Dolan is using his cash (plus lots of debt) to upgrade Cablevision's system to fiber optic cable, which has a much higher capacity than coaxial. The chairman has a reputation as a "lethal competitor" and seems intent on keeping his company at the leading edge of the much-ballyhooed convergence of cable TV, computer, and voice communications.

As a result, the main thrust of the firm's spending is to ready its system to offer advanced services such as telephony and on-demand digital videos. The company's Cablevision Lightpath subsidiary has more than 175 business telephone customers, but before it can offer voice services to residential customers, Lightpath will need a ton of cash (or a partner). Cablevision and media purveyor U S WEST Media Group have occasionally discussed a merger. Nevertheless, Cablevision has reasserted its financial independence. Dolan and his family own more than 54% of the company's voting stock.

WHEN

The son of a Cleveland inventor, Dolan sold his TV sports editing business in 1954 and helped form Sterling Manhattan Cable, which won the cable TV franchise for Lower Manhattan in 1965. While better reception attracted some customers, Dolan decided that unique programming was the key to a much larger audience. In 1967 he got Madison Square Garden to offer professional basketball and hockey games on his network.

In 1970 Dolan started Home Box Office (HBO, the first nationwide pay-TV channel) and hired Gerald Levin (now Time Warner CEO) to head the enterprise. Dolan took the renamed Sterling Communications public and pulled in media giant Time, Inc., as a partner. However, costs mounted and in 1973 Time (which owned 80% of Sterling) decided to liquidate it but retain HBO. Dolan bought back the New York franchises and formed Long Island Cable Communications Development.

The company changed its name to Cablevision and expanded around the New York and Chicago areas. In 1980 the company formed Rainbow Programming, which soon included AMC and Bravo. In 1983 the firm launched SportsChannel (professional baseball, basketball, and hockey games), which became immensely successful. The next year Cablevision won cable TV franchises in Boston and in Brooklyn and the Bronx, but in 1992 it lost a minority stake in a Sacramento cable system. Cablevision went public in 1986. It bought a Massachusetts cable company and interests in 4 California SportsChannels in 1987. The company's debt shot up as it made these and other acquisitions, including systems in Cleveland and Long Island.

In 1989 Cablevision formed a joint venture with the National Broadcasting Company (NBC) to market a national cable network. In 1992 Dolan's son James became CEO of Rainbow Programming.

To bolster its already powerful sports programming, the company joined with ITT Corp. in 1994 to buy Madison Square Garden, which included the arena, the New York Knickerbockers (basketball), the New York Rangers (hockey), and the Madison Square Garden Network (with more than 5 million subscribers) for $1.1 billion.

Subsidiary Cablevision Lightpath signed a groundbreaking "co-carrier" agreement with Baby Bell NYNEX in 1995. The deal established a way for the 2 firms to compensate each other for calls made between their networks. Also that year Cablevision sold its Chicago cable operations. The company's on-again, off-again merger talks with U S WEST Media stalled over Charles Dolan's high asking price, and late that year, James Dolan became CEO.

In 1996 the company tested an on-demand digital video system and began offering an online version of Rainbow News 12 (a regional news channel) to subscribers via cable modem.

WHO

Chairman: Charles F. Dolan, age 69, $906,667 pay
VC: William J. Bell, age 56, $890,000 pay
VC: Marc A. Lustgarten, age 49, $890,000 pay
CEO: James L. Dolan, age 40, $635,000 pay
CEO, Rainbow Programming Holdings Inc.: Joshua Sapan, age 45
President, Cable Operations: William J. Quinn, age 49, $610,000 pay
EVP, General Counsel, and Secretary: Robert S. Lemle, age 43, $797,000 pay
SVP and Controller: Andrew B. Rosengard, age 38
SVP Finance and Treasurer: Barry J. O'Leary, age 52
SVP Strategic Planning: Joseph W. Cece, age 43
SVP and Chief Information Officer: Thomas C. Dolan, age 43
SVP: Sheila A. Mahoney, age 54
VP News: Patrick F. Dolan, age 44
VP New Business Development: Theodore May
VP Technology: Wilt Hildenbrand
VP Human Resources: Joyce E. Mancini
Auditors: KPMG Peat Marwick LLP

WHERE

HQ: One Media Crossways, Woodbury, NY 11797
Phone: 516-364-8450
Fax: 516-364-4913
Web site: http://www.cablevision.com

Cablevision has 2.7 million subscribers in 19 states, mostly Connecticut, Massachusetts, Michigan, New Jersey, New York, and Ohio.

WHAT

	1995 Basic Service Subscriptions	
	No. (thou.)	% of total
Owned	2,061	76
Managed	662	24
Total	**2,723**	**100**

Selected Services
Cable Television Service
Interactive online version of News 12 (available to Long Island cable subscribers via cable modem)
Telephone service (for business customers in Massachusetts and New York)
Selected Subsidiaries
American Movie Classics Company
Bravo Network
Cablevision Lightpath
Cablevision of Boston
Cablevision of New York City
Independent Film Channel
MSG Holdings (50%)
Much Music
Rainbow Programming Holdings, Inc.

KEY COMPETITORS

AT&T Corp.	King World	United States
Capital Cities/ABC	LIN Broadcasting	Satellite
Century	NBC	Broadcasting
Communications	News Corp.	United Video
Comcast	NYNEX	Satellite
Continental	PRIMESTAR	U S WEST
Cablevision	Rogers	Communications
Cox	Communications	Viacom
Communications	Sprint	Vulcan Video
DIRECTV	TCI	Walt Disney
Echostar	Teledesic	Westinghouse/
International	TeleWest	CBS
Family	Time Warner	
Entertainment	Times Mirror	

HOW MUCH

AMEX symbol: CVC FYE: December 31	Annual Growth	1986	1987	1988	1989	1990	1991	1992	1993	1994	1995
Sales ($ mil.)	24.7%	148	298	489	493	563	603	573	667	837	1,078
Net income ($ mil.)	59.0%	(5)	(59)	(159)	(154)	(271)	(227)	(251)	(247)	(315)	(318)
Income as % of sales	—	—	—	—	—	—	—	—	—	—	—
Earnings per share ($)	50.9%	(0.35)	(2.88)	(7.44)	(7.12)	(12.36)	(10.32)	(11.17)	(10.83)	(13.72)	(14.17)
Stock price – high ($)	—	21.25	32.25	38.00	47.25	38.38	35.50	36.50	72.00	67.88	69.75
Stock price – low ($)	—	13.50	16.00	23.50	29.75	9.88	12.38	24.88	29.38	39.00	48.75
Stock price – close ($)	12.4%	18.88	26.13	31.88	37.13	15.50	35.00	35.00	67.88	50.50	54.25
P/E – high	—	—	—	—	—	—	—	—	—	—	—
P/E – low	—	—	—	—	—	—	—	—	—	—	—
Dividends per share ($)	—	0.00	0.00	0.00	0.00	0.00	0.00	0.00	0.00	0.00	0.00
Book value per share ($)	51.7%	(1.80)	(5.26)	(12.45)	(19.32)	(31.36)	(41.49)	(55.28)	(64.75)	(77.09)	(76.61)
Employees	14.6%	1,700	3,000	3,700	3,400	2,960	3,392	3,444	3,636	4,698	5,801

1995 YEAR-END

Debt ratio: 100%
Return on equity: —
Cash (mil.): $15
Current ratio: —
Long-term debt (mil.): $2,964
No. of shares (mil.): 25
Dividends
  Yield: —
  Payout: —
Market value (mil.): $1,340

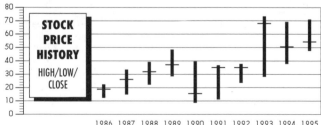

STOCK PRICE HISTORY HIGH/LOW/CLOSE
1986 1987 1988 1989 1990 1991 1992 1993 1994 1995

CANAL+

OVERVIEW

Paris-based CANAL+ is one of the largest pay-television operators in the world. Modeled after US cable pioneer HBO, the company produces TV channels, markets pay-TV channels, and produces and distributes TV programs and movies. It also offers thematic channels such as Canal Jimmy (1960s shows) and Planète (documentaries). About 69% of CANAL+'s subscribers are in France while the rest are mainly in Germany and Spain.

The company owns 59% of Le Studio CANAL+, a film production unit that invests in French and foreign productions and has helped to finance over 300 feature films.

A coalition of 3 large French companies, Havas (advertising), Générale des Eaux (water distribution), and Société Générale (banking), control CANAL+, which is 41% owned by the public.

The firm has hitched its fortunes to a star — a satellite, to be precise. Its proprietary digital-receiver system is meant to give it a lock on the French satellite-TV market. However, a brace of challengers in the US (including PRIMESTAR Partners and DIRECTV) threaten to produce compatible satellite TV receiver equipment that will challenge CANAL+'s stranglehold.

WHEN

When he became head of the Havas advertising agency in 1982, André Rousselet at first rejected the pay-TV concept. But soon after, he agreed that Havas should enter show business and he came on board. Because Havas was under government control, Rousselet went to his golfing partner, President François Mitterrand, for approval (Rousselet had been Mitterrand's chief of staff). To skirt the Socialist influence on early-1980s France, Rousselet used his political connections to the new channel's advantage, easing its entry to the airwaves.

After CANAL+ signed on in November 1984 with 186,000 subscribers, it came to be called "Canal Minus" as subscriptions to the pay-TV service flattened out and the company lost money. Rousselet, who had left Havas to become chairman of the channel, kept CANAL+ out of bankruptcy by putting the fall 1985 season's slate of blockbuster movies on in the spring — reasoning that there might not be a CANAL+ over which to air the films if he waited. Subscribers responded, and by the end of 1986, with former journalist Pierre Lescure (an original CANAL+ director) as CEO, the company broke even.

Over the next 5 years CANAL+ was considered to be a cash factory. The company went public in 1987; in spite of a market crash, its shares sold out. In 1988 its profits were higher than the 3 French networks combined, and the company reduced its debt to zero. However, the firm made a bad investment that year when it joined with Compagnie Générale des Eaux to buy TVS (UK), whose US TV production unit, MTM Entertainment, was losing money and which later lost its license as a franchisee for the ITV television network in the UK.

In 1990 CANAL+ acquired 5% (later increased to 17%) of independent US production company Carolco, investing in a promising movie, *Terminator 2*, and later coproducing *Basic Instinct*. Both became hits, but Carolco soon started losing money and later sought bankruptcy protection.

CANAL+ expanded more successfully into other countries and regions, establishing channels as part owner with others (much like CANAL+ itself is co-owned) in Belgium (1989), Spain (1990), Germany (Premiere, 1991, with media giant Bertelsmann and film supplier Kirch-Beta Taurus), and North Africa (1991).

Thematic channels came on-line as well. CANAL+ and Compagnie Générale des Eaux bought a controlling interest along with US sports channel ESPN in W H Smith Group's UK television holdings in 1991. CANAL+ acquired 15% of MCM-Euromusique in 1992.

Institutional shareholders Havas (23.5%), Générale des Eaux (20%), and Société Générale (5%) merged their interests in 1994 to give the coalition virtual control of the company. Rousselet resigned that year over the increasing influence of the government in the affairs of the company.

In 1995 CANAL+ set up Explore International, a European distribution joint venture with US nonprofit documentary maker National Geographic.

The company acquired the film library of Carolco Pictures in 1996 for $58 million. Also that year it entered into a partnership with Germany's Bertelsmann, British Sky Broadcasting (BSkyB), and Havas to provide digital pay-TV in Germany. BSkyB dropped out of the venture soon after.

WHO

Chairman and CEO: Pierre Lescure
EVP and General Counsel: Marc-André Feffer
EVP and President of Sales and Marketing: Bruno Delecour
Director Finance: Laurent Perpère
Director Human Resources: Françoise Provotelle
CEO, Le Studio CANAL+ (US): Richard Garzilli
CFO, Le Studio CANAL+ (US): Mike Metzer
Manager Human Resources, Le Studio CANAL+ (US): Robert Chamberland
Auditors: Guy Barbier & Autres (Andersen Worldwide); Salustro Reydel

WHERE

HQ: 85-89, Quai André Citroën, 75015, Paris, Cedex 15, France
Phone: +33-1-44-25-10-00
Fax: +33-1-44-25-12-34
US HQ: Le Studio CANAL+, 301 N. Cañon Dr., #228, Beverly Hills, CA 90210
US Phone: 310-247-0994
US Fax: 310-247-0998
Web site: http://www.cplus.fr

CANAL+ is one of the world's largest pay-TV companies, with subscribers in Belgium, France, Germany, Spain, and Africa.

WHAT

	Sales % of total
Subscriptions	78
Advertising & sponsoring	4
Other	18
Total	**100**

Selected Subsidiaries

Cable and Satellite
Canalsatellite SNC (96.7%)
Satellite Service (80%)

Finance
CANAL+ Finance

Foreign CANAL+ Channels
Canal Horizons (34.2%, Africa)

Manufacturing
Antennes Tonna Group (51%)

Movies
Carolco Pictures film library
Le Studio CANAL+ (59%)
Sogepac (29.1%)

Publishing
CANAL+ Editions SNC (51%)

Real Estate
CANAL+ Immobilier SNC

Sport
Data Sport (37.5%)

Television
Docstar SNC
Le Studio Ellipse (61.2%)

Thematic Channels
Canal Jimmy SNC (42.5%)

Video
CANAL+ Video SNC

Other
Explore International (50%)
MCM-Euromusique (15%)

KEY COMPETITORS

Bertelsmann
Cie. Luxembourgeoise de Télédiffusion
France Télécom
Kirchgruppe
Lagardère
Société Télévision Française
TF 1

HOW MUCH

Principal exchange: Paris FYE: December 31	Annual Growth	1986	1987	1988	1989	1990	1991	1992	1993	1994	1995
Sales (FF mil.)	20.6%	1,887	3,402	4,340	5,359	6,130	6,998	7,937	8,675	9,567	10,157
Net income (FF mil.)	76.5%	4	407	619	761	910	1,081	1,104	1,202	626	666
Income as % of sales	—	0.2%	12.0%	14.3%	14.2%	14.8%	15.4%	13.9%	13.9%	6.5%	6.6%
Earnings per share (FF)	4.0%	—	22	33	41	48	57	54	58	30	30
Stock price – high (FF)	—	—	360	659	790	993	1,130	1,329	1,399	1,155	918
Stock price – low (FF)	—	—	320	350	589	738	794	949	1,028	794	586
Stock price – close (FF)	12.5%	—	357	590	765	823	1,023	1,099	1,116	855	918
P/E – high	—	—	—	20	19	21	20	24	24	39	31
P/E – low	—	—	—	11	14	15	14	17	18	27	20
Dividends per share (FF)	(1.1%)	—	—	—	16	18	20	25	25	15	15
Book value per share (FF)	25.7%	—	—	59	85	109	131	259	306	326	292
Employees	19.9%	—	—	584	1,459	1,429	1,550	1,697	2,031	2,082	2,084

1995 YEAR-END

Debt ratio: 17.8%
Return on equity: 9.1%
Cash (mil.): FF3,800
Current ratio: 1.12
Long-term debt (mil.): FF642
No. of shares (mil.): 22
Dividends
 Yield: 1.6%
 Payout: 50.0%
Market value (mil.): $4,136
Sales (mil.): $2,077

Note: $=FF4.89 (December 31, 1995)

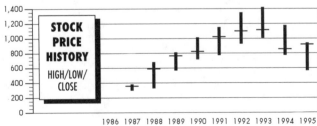

STOCK PRICE HISTORY HIGH/LOW/CLOSE

1986 1987 1988 1989 1990 1991 1992 1993 1994 1995

CAPITAL CITIES/ABC, INC.

OVERVIEW

Capital Cities/ABC's next big hit could be "My So-called Life as a Subsidiary." Headquartered in New York City, the company — now part of entertainment steamroller Walt Disney — operates the ABC Television Network (with 224 affiliates), 10 TV stations, ABC radio networks, and 21 radio stations. It owns stakes in ESPN and other cable TV channels; the subsidiary's broadcasting operations account for about 85% of its revenues. Capital Cities/ABC also publishes newspapers, shopping guides, business periodicals, and books. The Capital Cities/ABC Multimedia Group directs the company's digital TV, interactive TV, pay-per-view, video-on-demand, online, and other non-traditional operations.

Capital Cities/ABC's TV and radio businesses are part of Disney's new broadcasting division, while its distribution, publishing, and other operations have been folded into the parent company's creative content segment. ABC Productions, which had produced *Moonlighting, My So-Called Life,* and the

Commish for the network, was shut down in 1996. The in-house unit was deemed unnecessary in light of the purchase by Disney, which already produced *Home Improvement* and other shows for ABC.

The ABC Television Network ranks 2nd in ratings behind NBC. For the 1995-1996 season, ABC had 8 shows in the top 20: *NFL Monday Night Football, Home Improvement, NYPD Blue, 20/20, Grace Under Fire, Coach, Roseanne,* and *PrimeTime Live.* ABC's new leaders, Disney chairman Michael Eisner and president Michael Ovitz, stepped in to assist ABC president Robert Iger in reconditioning the network's program schedule, reflecting the parent company's hands-on approach following the acquisition. The network is looking to new shows and established stars to help catch NBC, including *Spin City* (Michael J. Fox) and *Townies* (Molly Ringwald). One show that didn't make the cut: a weekly movie hosted by Eisner.

WHEN

Capital Cities/ABC resulted from the 1986 acquisition of the American Broadcasting Companies by much smaller Capital Cities Communications. It was the largest media merger at the time. ABC began as a spinoff from the Blue Network (which, like NBC, was owned by RCA); it was sold in 1943 to LifeSavers candy promoter Edward J. Noble when the FCC prohibited any company from owning more than one network.

In the 1940s and 1950s, ABC was in 3rd place, with 5 TV stations and no daytime programming. Buyout attempts by CBS and 20th Century Fox failed, but ABC and United Paramount Theatres merged in 1953. Leonard Goldenson of United Paramount hired Disney Studios to produce a series for ABC's 1954-55 season. Soon other studios, including Warner Brothers, were producing ABC shows (including *Ozzie and Harriet* and *Wyatt Earp* in 1955). Goldenson was behind the decision in 1954 to broadcast for 36 days the complete Senate hearings staged by Senator Joseph McCarthy.

That same year Hudson Valley Broadcasting hired Thomas Murphy to bail out its struggling TV station in Albany, New York. Hudson Valley bought a Raleigh, North Carolina, station in 1957 and went public, becoming Capital Cities Communications. While Capital Cities founder Frank Smith bought and sold

TV and radio stations and publications, Murphy ran the company.

Smith died in 1966. In 1968 Capital Cities, under Murphy, bought Fairchild Publications (*Women's Wear Daily*). Meanwhile, still in 3rd place in the 1960s, ABC fended off takeover attempts by Norton Simon, General Electric, and Howard Hughes. Programming whiz Fred Silverman defected from CBS, joining ABC in 1975. In 1976 ABC was the #1 network, and it stayed on top until 1979, the year after Silverman went to NBC.

ABC bought cable sports channel ESPN in 1984. Capital Cities also bought cable systems in the 1980s, then sold them in 1986, when, backed by Warren Buffett's Berkshire Hathaway, it bought ABC for $3.5 billion.

The FCC approved Disney's $19 billion purchase of Capital Cities/ABC in 1996. That year the subsidiary's Multimedia Group bought video game maker Spectrum Holobyte's interest in their year-old joint venture, which distributes such games as *NFL Monday Night Football*. Also in 1996 Capital Cities/ABC shelved its plans to start a national 24-hour news channel, saying it would be too costly.

That same year the company brought in former NBC programming executive Jamie Tarses as president of ABC Entertainment. The previous president, Ted Harbert, became chairman.

WHO

President: Robert A. Iger, age 45
EVP: Stephen B. Burke
EVP Walt Disney Television and Telecommunications: Randy Reiss
SVP and CFO: Ronald J. Doerfler
Chairman Disney/ABC International Television: Herbert A. Granath
Chairman Walt Disney Studios: Joe Roth, age 47
Chairman ABC Entertainment: Ted Harbert
President and CEO ESPN: Steven M. Bornstein
President, ABC Television Network Group: David Westin
President ABC Entertainment: Jamie Tarses
President Publishing Group: Phillip J. Meek
President Disney/ABC Cable Networks: Geraldine Laybourne
President Television Creative Services: Stuart Bloomberg
President Capital Cities/ABC Radio: Robert F. Callahan
VP and General Counsel: Alan N. Braverman
VP Corporate Communications: Patricia J. Matson
VP (HR): Jeffrey S. Rosen
Auditors: Ernst & Young LLP

WHERE

HQ: 77 W. 66th St., New York, NY 10023-6298
Phone: 212-456-7777
Fax: 212-456-6850
Web site: http://www.abctelevision.com

WHAT

	1995 Sales		1995 Operating Income	
	$ mil.	% of total	$ mil.	% of total
Broadcasting	5,728	83	1,165	89
Publishing	1,151	17	139	11
Adjustments	—	—	(73)	—
Total	**6,879**	**100**	**1,231**	**100**

Broadcasting

Radio Stations
KABC (AM)/KLOS (FM)/ KMPC (AM), Los Angeles
KQRS (AM/FM)/KEGE (FM), Minneapolis-St. Paul
KSCS (FM)/WBAP (AM), Dallas-Fort Worth
WABC (AM)/WPLJ (FM), New York
WHYT (FM)/WJR (AM), Detroit
WKHX (AM/FM)/WYAY (FM), Atlanta
WLS (AM/FM), Chicago
WMAL (AM)/WRQX (FM), Washington, DC

Selected Television Stations
KABC-TV, Los Angeles
KGO-TV, San Francisco
KTRK-TV, Houston
WABC-TV, New York
WLS-TV, Chicago
WPVI-TV, Philadelphia

Selected Publishing Operations
Diversified publishing (Chilton Publications, Grupo Editorial Expansiun, *Los Angeles* magazine)
Fairchild Publications (*W*, *Women's Wear Daily*)
Institutional Investor
Fort Worth Star-Telegram
The Kansas City Star, Missouri

Other Operations
ABC Distribution
A&E Network (partial interest)
DIC Animation City (children's programs)
ESPN (80%)
Lifetime (50%)

KEY COMPETITORS

Advance Publications
A. H. Belo
Bertelsmann
Cablevision Systems
Chris-Craft
Cox Enterprises
Discovery Communications
Dow Jones
E.W. Scripps

Gannett
Gaylord Entertainment
Hearst
Heritage Communications
Knight-Ridder
Lagardère
Liberty Media
NBC
News Corp.
Nintendo

SEGA
SFX Broadcasting
TCI
Thomson Corp.
Time Warner
Times Mirror
Tribune
Viacom
Washington Post
Westinghouse
Westwood One

HOW MUCH

Subsidiary FYE: December 31	Annual Growth	1986	1987	1988	1989	1990	1991	1992	1993	1994	1995
Sales ($ mil.)	5.8%	4,124	4,440	4,774	4,957	5,386	5,382	5,344	5,674	6,379	6,879
Net income ($ mil.)	16.7%	182	279	387	486	478	375	389	467	680	729
Income as % of sales	—	4.4%	6.3%	8.1%	9.8%	8.9%	7.0%	7.3%	8.2%	10.7%	10.6%
Employees	0.0%	19,960	20,120	19,720	19,860	20,100	19,650	19,250	19,250	20,200	20,000

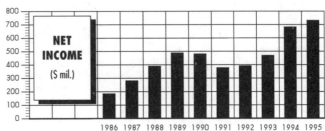

NET INCOME ($ mil.)

CMP PUBLICATIONS, INC.

OVERVIEW

CMP Publications is elbowing its way to the top of the mountain — namely, the mountain of information about computers and technology. The Manhasset, New York-based company publishes 13 magazines and newspapers for technology consumers and professionals, including consumer magazines such as *HomePC* and trade papers such as *Computer Reseller News* and *Electronic Engineering Times*. CMP holds about 24% of its market, putting it neck and neck for the #2 spot with rival Ziff-Davis (*PC Magazine, PC Week*), owned by Japanese software distributor SOFTBANK. Both trail the much larger International Data Group (*InfoWorld, MacWorld*).

CMP "practices what it preaches," embracing computer technology as an adjunct to traditional paper publishing. It launched MAX, a CD-ROM companion to *Computer Reseller News*, in 1994 and the following year established TechWeb, a World Wide Web site where all CMP publications can be viewed online. In early 1996 the company added a Web browser to the MAX CD-ROM, giving its users direct access to the MAX home page and advertisers' Web sites. It also began production of The Newsroom, a daily electronic newsletter for information technology professionals.

The company also organizes trade shows and conferences on high-technology products and issues. Its Looking Glass Consulting service assists advertisers and ad agencies in the development of advertising programs for CD-ROM and the Internet.

CMP is privately held by the founding Leeds family.

WHEN

Husband-and-wife team Gerry and Lilo Leeds founded CMP in 1971 when they began publishing *Electronic Buyers' News*. Gerry, an electronics engineer with experience in marketing, was inspired by a friend's idea to market a specialized mailing list targeted to people involved in high-tech purchasing. However, he was convinced that a newspaper would reach the audience more effectively. Before founding CMP (he had originally wanted to call the company Creative Media Publications), Gerry had started several other companies, including an organization for electronics manufacturers; Lumatron, which made high-speed sampling scopes; and Data Device (later ILC Data Device), which made operational amplifiers.

The Leedses created a prototype for *EBN* modeled after *Newsday* and *Women's Wear Daily*. Dissatisfied with the first issue, they scrapped all 2,000 copies and redesigned it.

As it grew, CMP continued to add trade-oriented tabloids aimed at the computer and telecommunications markets, including *CommunicationsWeek, Computer Reseller News, Electronic Engineering Times*, and *VARBusiness*. It also expanded into travel titles, launching *Tour & Travel News* in 1985. In 1972 CMP's revenues were $1 million; by 1982 annual sales were at $25 million. The company had 10 publications in 1985.

Unsettled by growing pains, in 1986 CMP was restructured into operating groups. The Leedses turned over the operation of the company in 1988 to their oldest son, Michael. He sold most of CMP's health and travel holdings and introduced the *Long Island Monthly*, a lifestyle magazine whose start-up cost the company around $10 million before it ceased publication 2 years later.

CMP consolidated its focus on technology and telecommunications in the early 1990s. It killed its trade titles, *Buildings Journal* and *Manufacturing Week*. The company left the health care market in 1992. With ad sales slowing in the early 1990s, CMP added ancillary products and services such as direct marketing, research services, and trade shows.

In 1991 CMP bought a small, year-old publication called *WINDOWS/OS2* from Silicon Beach Operations, while it pulled the plug on *High Performance Systems* and *Systems & Network Integration*. CMP added *HomePC* and *NetGuide* in 1993.

Early in 1994 CMP sold its 4-title travel publications group (including *Tour & Travel News* and *Business Travel News*) to Miller Freeman for around $20 million. With its focus firmly on high tech, it launched *Interactive Age* (reporting on converging technologies) and *Informatiques*, a publication in French for MIS professionals. It introduced a German edition of *Computer Reseller News* in 1995. Also that year it folded *Interactive Age*, which had competed against Ziff-Davis's *Inter@ctive Week*. In 1996 CMP sold 2 magazines to EMAP Business Communications of London. In 1996 CMP sold Communications Week International and Communications Week International Latinamerica to EMAP Business Communications of London. That year it also became an information provider for the PointCast Network Internet service.

WHO

Cochairperson: Gerard G. Leeds
Cochairperson: Lilo J. Leeds
President and CEO: Michael S. Leeds
President, CMP Publications International: Daniel H. Leeds
President, Publishing: Ken Cron
EVP and Chief Information Officer: Grace Monahan
SVP Enterprise Computing, National Accounts: Jeffrey C. Strief
VP and CFO: Joseph E. Sichler
VP and Treasurer: Pearl Turner
VP and General Counsel: Robert D. Marafioti
VP/Group Publisher, Channel Group: John Russell
VP/Group Publisher, Personal Computing Group: E. Drake Lundell
VP/Group Publisher, OEM Group: Girish Mhatre
VP Customer Services: Georgette Ross
Senior Director Trade Show and Conference Services: Peter Candito

WHERE

HQ: 600 Community Dr., Manhasset, NY 11030-3847
Phone: 516-562-5000
Fax: 516-562-7830
Web site: http://techweb.cmp.com

CMP publishes 13 magazines and trade newspapers and provides marketing and information services to the high-technology consumer and business marketplaces.

WHAT

Selected Publications and Circulation

Channel Group
Computer Reseller News (103,000)
Computer Retail Week (31,000)
VARBusiness (95,000)

Enterprise Computing Group
CommunicationsWeek (175,000)
InformationWeek (325,000)
Informatiques (France, 40,000)
Network Computing (185,550)

OEM Group
Electronic Buyers' News (61,000)
Electronic Engineering Times (131,000)
OEM Magazine (80,000)

Personal Computing Group
HomePC (400,000)
NetGuide (250,000)
WINDOWS Magazine (700,000)

Selected Conferences and Expositions

ATM (Asia/Pacific, Europe)
Client/Server Conference and Exposition
Commercial Parallel Processing Conference
CROSSROADS
Enterprise PC: Desktop Strategies for the '90s
Global Mobile
High-Tech Direct 2000
The Networked Economy Conference (US, Asia/Pacific, Europe)
Programmed Logic Devices Design
TechDecisions

KEY COMPETITORS

C/NET	Modem Media
Cowles Media	Organic Online
Crain Communications	Pittway
Hearst	Reed Elsevier
HyperMedia	T/SF Communications
International Data Group	Walt Disney
Lagardere	Wired
McGraw-Hill	Ziff-Davis
Mecklermedia	

HOW MUCH

Private company FYE: December 31	Annual Growth	1986	1987	1988	1989	1990	1991	1992	1993	1994	1995
Sales ($ mil.)	17.3%	91	111	133	157	174	178	210	259	317	382
Employees	6.7%	—	—	950	—	1,000	1,000	1,045	1,200	1,400	1,500

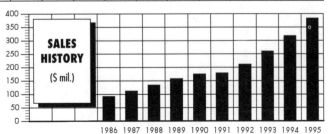

SALES HISTORY ($ mil.)

COMCAST CORPORATION

OVERVIEW

In the vast free-for-all created by the 1996 Telecommunications Act, Comcast is betting on cable. The Philadelphia-based company is the nation's 3rd largest cable operator (after TCI and Time Warner), a major provider of cellular service, and part owner of cable shopping channel QVC. It also provides telephone service and personal communications services and offers other types of cable programming.

Comcast believes that many of its services will soon be available in a bundle over its cable lines, which can handle many times the information of copper phone lines. Though the cable industry has been in a slump in recent years, Comcast agreed to acquire cable provider E.W. Scripps in 1995, raising its total number of cable subscribers to 4.3 million. Most of the new customers are located in Tennessee (Chattanooga and Knoxville) and

California (Sacramento), away from Comcast's traditional market in the Northeast. The company's subscriber base has grown 65% since 1993, largely through acquisitions; for now growth has come at the expense of profits.

In early 1996 Comcast amended an earlier agreement with Sprint, Cox Communications, and TCI. The business, known as Sprint Spectrum, will provide wireless instead of wireline communications services. Comcast has over 600,000 cellular subscribers and owns cellular licenses for 8 million potential users.

In such an unpredictable market Comcast is placing heavier attention on its programming services. The company owns 57% of cable shopping channel QVC and in 1995 introduced a new division, Comcast Content and Communication (known as C3), to develop new cable channels and programs.

WHEN

In 1963, when Ralph Roberts was looking for investments, he came across American Cable Systems, a tiny cable service in Tupelo, Mississippi. Roberts bought the company and expanded it throughout the state before moving into cable operations in Philadelphia. In 1968 he purchased Florida Music Network, the first of several Muzak franchises he would acquire. The next year Roberts gave his company a new name: Comcast (combining *communication* and *broadcast*).

Comcast went public in 1972. Throughout the decade, as the cable industry grew, the company expanded nationwide by purchasing local operations. Comcast's cable business continued growing this way in the early 1980s, even expanding into the UK in 1983. In 1986 Comcast joined 4 other cable providers in acquiring Group W Cable, an operator with 2 million subscribers. Roberts also lent financial support that year to a fledgling home-shopping cable channel called QVC (named after "quality, value, and convenience").

The company's first major step into telecommunications came in 1988 when it bought American Cellular Network. In 1990 Ralph Roberts's 30-year-old son Brian became Comcast's president. The younger Roberts assumed a commanding role in the firm's diversification into communications and programming.

In 1992 Comcast bought Metromedia's Philadelphia-area cellular operations. It also began investing that year in fiber-optic and wireless phone service companies. By then, the

company was a major QVC shareholder. With an eye toward Comcast's programming needs, Brian Roberts convinced former Paramount Pictures and Fox network head Barry Diller to become QVC's chairman. The next year Comcast put up $500 million to support Diller's failed bid to buy Paramount Communications; it also sold Muzak.

In 1994 Diller struck a deal with CBS chairman Larry Tisch for the network to buy QVC. But the agreement would have transformed Comcast from QVC's largest shareholder into a minor player at CBS, and Brian Roberts wasn't interested. He killed the CBS deal (and Diller's chance to head the network) by making a counteroffer for QVC, bringing in TCI as a partner. Also that year Comcast purchased Maclean Hunter's cable and related operations in 3 states. (Comcast's partner in the $1.2 billion deal was CalPERS, the biggest public pension fund in the US.) In addition, the company sold 69% of its UK operations to the public as Comcast UK Cable Partners.

Comcast in 1995 sold its 20% stake in cable company Heritage Communications to TCI to help pay for its share of QVC. Following the completion that year of the QVC deal, Diller left the company. (He now oversees archrival Home Shopping Network.) Also in 1995 QVC began offering online shopping. In 1996 Comcast announced that it would buy a 66% stake in a joint venture that will own and operate the Philadelphia Flyers hockey team and 76ers basketball team, as well as 2 sports arenas, for roughly $500 million.

Chairman: Ralph J. Roberts, age 76, $821,360 pay
VC: Julian A. Brodsky, age 62, $625,000 pay
President: Brian L. Roberts, age 36, $867,000 pay
EVP Accounting and Administration: Lawrence S. Smith, age 48, $661,000 pay
Chairman and CEO, Comcast Content and Communication (C3): Richard Frank
President, QVC: Douglas S. Briggs
SVP and Treasurer: John R. Alchin, age 47, $531,000 pay
SVP; President, Comcast Cable Communications: Thomas G. Baxter
SVP; President, Comcast International: Robert B. Clasen
SVP; President, Comcast Cellular Communications: Donald A. Harris
SVP, General Counsel, and Secretary: Stanley L. Wang, age 55
SVP Human Resources: Paul Gillert
Auditors: Deloitte & Touche LLP

WHERE

HQ: 1500 Market St., 35th Fl., Philadelphia, PA 19102-2148
Phone: 215-665-1700
Fax: 215-981-7790
Web site: http://www.comcast.com

Comcast provides cable service to more than 4.3 million subscribers in the US. The company also provides cellular phone service to more than 600,000 subscribers in Delaware, New Jersey, and Pennsylvania. In addition, it owns more than 31% of Comcast UK Cable, which provides cable television, residential telephone, and business telecommunication services to subscribers in the UK.

WHAT

	1995 Sales	
	$ mil.	% of total
Electronic retailing	1,488	44
Domestic cable communications	1,455	43
Cellular communications	375	12
Corporate & other	45	1
Total	**3,363**	**100**

Selected Operations
Cable television programming
Cable television service
Cellular service
Direct-to-home satellite television
Electronic retailing (QVC)
Personal communications services
Telephone service

KEY COMPETITORS

Advance Publications
AirTouch
ALLTEL
Ameritech
AT&T Corp.
Bell Atlantic
BellSouth
BSkyB
Cable and Wireless
Cablevision Systems
CUC
GTE
Home Shopping Network
MCI
NYNEX
Pacific Telesis
SBC Communications
Sprint
TCI
Time Warner
Times Mirror
United States Satellite Broadcasting
U. S. Cellular
U S WEST Media
ValueVision
Viacom

HOW MUCH

Nasdaq symbol: CMCSK FYE: December 31	Annual Growth	1986	1987	1988	1989	1990	1991	1992	1993	1994	1995
Sales ($ mil.)	43.4%	131	309	450	562	657	721	900	1,338	1,375	3,363
Net income ($ mil.)	—	1	(9)	(48)	(149)	(178)	(156)	(218)	(99)	(75)	(38)
Income as % of sales	—	0.8%	—	—	—	—	—	—	—	—	—
Earnings per share ($)	—	0.01	(0.10)	(0.47)	(0.93)	(1.05)	(0.87)	(1.08)	(0.46)	(0.32)	(0.16)
Stock price - high ($)	—	5.34	7.61	7.63	12.34	11.34	11.59	12.34	26.01	24.01	22.38
Stock price - low ($)	—	4.98	4.40	5.73	7.23	4.92	7.42	8.92	10.51	14.00	13.75
Stock price - close ($)	15.5%	4.98	6.48	7.30	10.84	8.59	11.09	12.09	24.01	15.69	18.19
P/E - high	—	—	—	—	—	—	—	—	—	—	—
P/E - low	—	—	—	—	—	—	—	—	—	—	—
Dividends per share ($)	9.4%	0.04	0.08	0.08	0.07	0.08	0.09	0.19	0.09	0.09	0.09
Book value per share ($)	—	1.89	2.58	2.05	0.99	(0.13)	0.10	(0.89)	(3.93)	(3.04)	(3.24)
Employees	17.8%	2,794	2,798	3,168	3,292	3,478	3,722	5,327	5,391	6,700	12,200

1995 YEAR-END

Debt ratio: —
Return on equity: —
Cash (mil.): $539
Current ratio: 1.47
Long-term debt (mil.): $6,944
No. of shares (mil.): 239
Dividends
  Yield: 0.5%
  Payout: —
Market value (mil.): $4,354

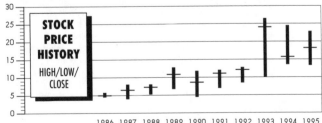

STOCK PRICE HISTORY
HIGH/LOW/CLOSE
1986 1987 1988 1989 1990 1991 1992 1993 1994 1995

COMPUSERVE CORPORATION

OVERVIEW

CompuServe is battling for your cybersoul. The Columbus, Ohio-based company's flagship CompuServe Information Service is the world's #2 online service (after America Online). CompuServe subscribers can access services such as airline reservations, e-mail, online shopping, and stock market information (you may be reading this profile on CompuServe, where Hoover's Company Database is part of its Basic Service). Subscribers can also play computer games, join any of 900 special interest "forums," or search through a variety of online databases and other information. In addition, the company offers SPRYNET, an Internet-only service, and WOW!, a family-oriented, set-fee (about $18 a month) service for novice users.

Through its Network Services Division, CompuServe provides network and Internet services to more than 950 corporate customers. Its corporate networking services include package tracking for FedEx, transmission of credit data to more than 200,000 corporate clients for TRW, and VISA's point-of-sale network for credit card authorizations.

Spun off from its "stodgy" parent, tax prep firm H&R Block, CompuServe is staying on the forefront of online services by adding new features and even winning content from its rivals. It has added online banking services through an agreement with Cardinal Bancshares's Security First Network Bank. Time Warner has moved its live TIME News Center from rival America Online to CompuServe, while WOW! has won the rights to the electronic version of *Sports Illustrated for Kids* from Prodigy.

Overseas presence has also helped keep CompuServe among the online leaders. The company is the leading online service provider in Europe, where its subscribers number more than 650,000. In Japan 1.5 million subscribers use NiftyServe, CompuServe's Japanese counterpart. The company has launched a global campaign to woo more international subscribers, including a major equipment upgrade that will give more people faster access to the network.

WHEN

In 1969, 25-year-old Jeffrey Wilkins started CompuServe to computerize his father-in-law's insurance company. Eight years later he introduced MicroNet, a mainframe computer time-sharing network that eventually became one of the first true online services.

H&R Block acquired CompuServe in 1980, providing the financial support it needed to aggressively develop online technology. Through the 1980s the company expanded globally and initiated several now-standard services, including e-mail and forums. CompuServe Network Services was established in 1982. Wilkins left CompuServe in 1985; he is currently CEO of CD-ROM manufacturer Metatec.

CompuServe was the first online provider to establish an international presence. Through a joint venture with Nissho Iwai and Fujitsu, the company debuted NiftyServe in 1987. During the late 1980s and early 1990s it reached agreements for expansion into Australia, Chile, Hungary, Israel, South Africa, South Korea, and Taiwan. CompuServe established its first European office, in Bristol, England, in 1991. Also that year it added an icon-based, color, graphical user interface. In 1994 the firm joined the rush to commercialize the Internet by acquiring a stake in Network Publishing, a company that established corporate Internet sites.

In 1995 CompuServe purchased SPRY, developer of the popular Internet in a Box software, and in 1996 began supplying World Wide Web access to subscribers via a built-in Web browser. Late in 1995 a German prosecutor said CompuServe was breaking the law by allowing subscribers to view certain sex-related materials. The company responded by banning 200 talk groups. In early 1996 it began offering Cyber Patrol software from Microsystems to control access to "cyberporn."

Under shareholder pressure to maximize share value, H&R Block spun off CompuServe in early 1996. The IPO raised $454 million, much less than analysts had expected. That year the online service firm announced a pact with Netscape that allows CompuServe subscribers to use Netscape's Navigator software to browse the World Wide Web, then said it would abandon its proprietary CompuServe software altogether and restructure itself in the Web's open environment. Also in 1996 the company launched WOW! and said it would offer reduced-rate access to CompuServe for users of AT&T's WorldNet online service.

Chairman: Henry F. Frigon, age 61
President and CEO: Robert J. Massey, age 50, $470,358 pay
EVP and Chief Techology Officer: Alexander B. Trevor, age 50, $470,962 pay
EVP Administration: Herbert J. Kahn, age 55, $285,673 pay
EVP Network Services Division: Peter F. Van Camp, age 40, $247,077 pay
EVP: David Pool
President, International: Steven P. Stanbrook, age 40
President, Online Services: Dennis D. Matteucci, age 57
CFO: Lawrence A. Gyenes, age 45
SVP Marketing, Online Services: Cynthia A. Vahlkamp
Treasurer and Corporate Controller: Ken Marinik
VP Human Resources: Judy Reinhard
Auditors: Deloitte & Touche LLP

WHERE

HQ: 5000 Arlington Centre Blvd., Columbus, OH 43220
Phone: 614-457-8600
Fax: 614-457-0348
Web site: http://www.compuserve.com
CompuServe has more than 60 offices worldwide.

	1996 Sales
	% of total
US	80
Other countries	20
Total	**100**

WHAT

	1996 Sales	
	$ mil.	% of total
Interactive services	561	71
Network services	199	25
Other	33	4
Total	**793**	**100**

Selected Operations

CompuServe Information Service (CIS, consumer online service targeted to experienced home and office users)
Network Services (wide area network applications, connectivity, and systems management services for business clients)
NiftyServe (consumer online service, Japanese counterpart to CIS)
SPRYNET (Internet-access-only service)
WOW! (consumer online service targeted to the home market)

Selected CompuServe Features and Information Providers

Business Database Plus (articles from business publications)
Classified Ads (marketplace for members)
Electronic Mall (products from more than 170 merchants)
Executive News Service (clips from AP, UPI, Dow Jones, Reuters, and others)
Games (including interactive games and trivia)
GO MAPS (weather maps)
Grolier's Academic American Encyclopedia
Hoover's Company Database (business profiles published by Hoover's, Inc.)
IQuest (850 bibliographic and full-text databases)
Knowledge Index (access to the text of more than 50,000 journals and 100 popular databases)
Magazine Database Plus (articles from more than 100 popular magazines)
Movie Reviews (reviews by Roger Ebert)
New Car Showroom (information on current models)
TRAVELSHOPPER (airline schedules, fares, and booking; hotel and car rental information)

KEY COMPETITORS

America Online
ASCIINet
Bertelsmann
Deutsche Telekom
Dow Jones
France Telecom
IBM
Infonautics
Knight-Ridder
La Tribune Defosses
MCI
MFS Communications
Microsoft
NETCOM
PC Van
People World
Prodigy
PSINet
Reed Elsevier
Reuters
Scholastic
Thomson Corp.
UUNET

HOW MUCH

Nasdaq symbol: CSRV FYE: April 30	Annual Growth	1987	1988	1989	1990	1991	1992	1993	1994	1995	1996
Sales ($ mil.)	24.3%	—	—	173	207	252	281	315	430	583	793
Net income ($ mil.)	(11.1%)	—	—	—	—	—	—	—	62	9	49
Income as % of sales	—	—	—	—	—	—	—	—	14.4%	1.5%	6.2%
Employees	61.3%	—	—	—	—	—	1,200	1,500	2,200	2,500	3,650

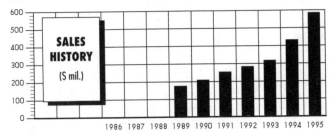

CompuServe

SALES HISTORY
($ mil.)

600
500
400
300
200
100
0

1986 1987 1988 1989 1990 1991 1992 1993 1994 1995

CORDIANT PLC

OVERVIEW

CEO Bob Seelert is doing his best to provide some cohesion at Cordiant (formerly Saatchi & Saatchi). The London-based holding company owns 2 worldwide advertising networks — Saatchi & Saatchi Advertising Worldwide (the UK's #1 ad agency) and Bates Worldwide, which provides a wide range of marketing services. Subsidiary Rowland Worldwide practices public relations in 38 countries through a network of wholly owned and affiliated offices. Cordiant's high-profile clients include Avis, Bell Atlantic, General Mills, IBM, Miller Brewing, Toyota, and Wendy's International.

Cordiant rounds out its marketing services offerings with a variety of subsidiaries that provide media planning, buying, and evaluation services; Internet advertising; and market research. It also provides technical and creative services, such as graphic design, television production, and other artistic services.

When shareholders forced the departure of cofounder and CEO Maurice Saatchi in 1994, he took along his brother Charles, several executive officers, and some major clients. The company was renamed Cordiant shortly thereafter. Seelert joined Cordiant in 1995 with plans to focus on the company's new clients, such as telecommunications concern Bell Atlantic and consumer products company Procter & Gamble.

WHEN

In 1947 Nathan Saatchi, a prosperous Jewish merchant, emigrated from Iraq to London with his wife and 3 sons, David, Charles, and Maurice. Charles left school at 17 and held a series of jobs before becoming a junior copywriter at an advertising agency. Feeling creatively confined, he opened his own consultancy in 1967. Younger brother Maurice finished college and went to work for a publisher that wrote about the advertising industry.

By 1970 Charles wanted to start his own ad agency and recruited the financially oriented Maurice. The agency opened in 1971 with a flashy campaign of self-promotion. It prospered, and in 1973, showing a profit of L90,000, it began to make acquisitions; one of the first failed when its liabilities turned out higher (and assets lower) than expected. Despite this setback and an industry recession, the agency's profits rose steadily. In 1975 the Saatchis completed the takeover of the much larger, publicly held Compton UK Partners, rising from 13th to 5th in size in the UK. Acquisitions and internal growth made it the largest agency in the UK by 1979.

In 1982 the Saatchis set their sights on another much larger firm — Compton Advertising in New York. Its purchase made Saatchi & Saatchi the 9th largest agency in the world. In 1985 the Saatchis acquired the Hay Group, a US consulting firm, for $125 million and the Howard Marlboro sales promotion company for $414 million. The next year the firm bought Backer Spielvogel for $56 million and Ted Bates Worldwide for $450 million, vaulting the firm to #1 in the world. The Bates acquisition caused several key clients with over $250 million in billings to withdraw because of perceived client conflicts among the agencies now part of Saatchi.

In 1987 the company tried unsuccessfully to buy 2 UK banks, but by the end of the year high debt and the lower-than-expected profitability of many of the consulting groups acquired by the Saatchis caused the agency serious financial problems.

A recapitalization in 1991 raised over $100 million and diluted existing shareholders by 84%. Selling off noncore assets was a belated cost-cutting strategy, but Saatchi unloaded its US law consultancy and its UK executive recruiting and financial communications businesses. It sold its Yankelovich Clancy Shulman market research firm in 1992 and its in-store marketing unit, Howard Marlboro Group, in 1993. It consolidated US-based Campbell Mithun Esty and UK-based KHBB into a worldwide network.

In 1994 Saatchi appointed Australian William Muirhead as North American CEO to breathe new life into its unprofitable US operations. However, he resigned the next year after key investors forced Maurice Saatchi's ouster, claiming the latter was destroying shareholder value in the company. After his departure, Saatchi started the M&C Saatchi agency, which promptly targeted clients who had left Cordiant at the time of the Saatchi brothers' departure

Consumer products executive Bob Seelert became CEO of the marketing conglomerate in 1995, rededicating the firm to winning new business in the US and to a stronger focus on such growth markets as telecommunications, information technology, leisure, and over-the-counter drugs.

Chairman: Charles T. Scott, age 47, $360,000 pay
CEO: Robert L. Seelert, age 53, $288,177 pay
EVP Human Resources Worldwide: Albert Pendergast
Group Treasurer: Christopher Bunton
Secretary and General Counsel: Graham Howell
Finance Director: Wendy Smyth, age 42, $180,000 pay
Group Controller: David Weatherseed
Auditors: KPMG Peat Marwick LLP

WHERE

HQ: 83-89 Whitfield St., London, W1A 4XA, UK
Phone: +44-171-436-4000
Fax: +44-171-436-1998
US HQ: 375 Hudson St., New York, NY 10014-3620
US Phone: 212-463-4000
US Fax: 212-463-9855

The company has wholly owned offices and affiliates in 94 countries.

	1995 Sales	1995 Operating Income
	% of total	% of total
US	35	—
Europe (outside UK)	30	47
UK	15	32
Other countries	20	21
Total	**100**	**100**

WHAT

Major Services and Operating Units

Advertising
Bates Worldwide
Saatchi & Saatchi Advertising Worldwide

Media Services
Zenith Media Worldwide

Public Relations
Rowland Worldwide

Other Services
The Facilities Group (technical and creative services)
HP:ICM (presentational communications)
National Research Group (market research)
Siegel & Gale (corporate identity and design)

Selected Major Advertising Clients

Avis	Merck
B.A.T	Miller Brewing
Bell Atlantic	Procter & Gamble
DuPont	Sara Lee
General Mills	Texaco
Hewlett-Packard	Toyota
Hyundai	Warner-Lambert
Johnson & Johnson	Wendy's International

KEY COMPETITORS

Bozell, Jacobs	Interpublic Group
Creative Artists	M&C Saatchi
D'Arcy Masius	Omnicom Group
Dentsu	Publicis
Edelman Public Relations	TMP Worldwide
Grey Advertising	True North
Havas	WPP Group
Heritage Media	Young & Rubicam

HOW MUCH

NYSE symbol: CDA FYE: December 31	Annual Growth	1986	1987	1988	1989	1990	1991	1992	1993	1994	1995
Sales ($ mil.)	6.8%	654	1,204	1,528	1,572	1,514	1,384	1,132	1,203	1,210	1,180
Net income ($ mil.)	—	62	123	142	(30)	14	(162)	(929)	11	22	(58)
Income as % of sales	—	9.5%	10.2%	9.3%	—	—	—	—	0.9%	—	—
Earnings per share ($)	—	16.60	21.40	22.60	(11.20)	(2.50)	(5.10)	(17.59)	0.17	0.76	(0.20)
Stock price – high ($)	—	333.75	343.75	252.50	225.00	137.50	22.50	15.00	8.88	8.63	6.75
Stock price – low ($)	—	184.69	170.00	170.00	112.50	16.25	5.00	4.38	5.50	5.63	3.75
Stock price – close ($)	(36.6%)	242.81	232.50	178.75	127.50	20.00	6.75	7.00	5.88	6.75	4.00
P/E – high	—	20	16	11	—	—	—	—	52	—	—
P/E – low	—	11	8	8	—	—	—	—	32	—	—
Dividends per share ($)	—	0.98	1.11	1.11	1.06	0.11	0.00	0.00	0.00	0.00	0.00
Book value per share ($)	(26.7%)	—	—	(12.17)	(22.11)	(33.38)	(3.35)	(3.88)	(2.63)	(2.43)	(1.38)
Employees	(3.8%)	15,000	15,900	17,400	17,300	13,400	12,400	12,482	11,633	10,913	10,570

1995 YEAR-END

Debt ratio: 100.0%
Return on equity: —
Cash (mil.): $208
Current ratio: 0.99
Long-term debt (mil.): $176
No. of shares (mil.): 232
Dividends
  Yield: —
  Payout: —
Market value (mil.): $798

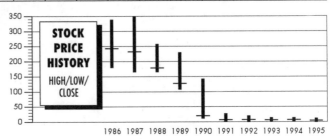

STOCK PRICE HISTORY HIGH/LOW/CLOSE

COX ENTERPRISES, INC.

OVERVIEW

Like an octopus at an all-you-can-eat buffet, Cox Enterprises has its hands full. The family-owned, Atlanta-based company is one of the largest media conglomerates in the US, with interests in newspapers, radio, and broadcast and cable television. With the development of technologies such as wireless communications and fiber optics, Cox is always looking for new ways to deliver the news.

Cox owns about 83% of Cox Communications, which it spun off to the public in 1995. With some 3.2 million subscribers, Cox Communications is the 5th largest cable system in the US. Cox also publishes 19 daily

newspapers (including its flagship, the *Atlanta Constitution*) and 15 weeklies. It owns 6 broadcast TV stations and 19 radio stations. Cox's Manheim Auctions is the world's largest auto auction company.

To profit from the growing interest in the information superhighway, Cox plans to offer access to the Internet using the IBM Global Network through its nationwide collection of local newspaper, TV, and radio stations.

The company is owned by founder James Cox's daughters, Barbara Cox Anthony (mother of CEO James Kennedy) and Anne Cox Chambers.

WHEN

James Middleton Cox dropped out of school in 1886 at age 16 and worked as a teacher, reporter, and congressional secretary before buying the *Dayton Daily News* in 1898. He acquired the nearby *Springfield Press-Republican* in 1905 and soon took up politics. Cox served 2 terms in the US Congress (1909-13) and 3 terms as Ohio governor (1913-15; 1917-21). In 1920 he was the Democratic candidate for president, with Franklin D. Roosevelt as his running mate, but he lost to rival Ohio publisher Warren G. Harding. In 1923 Cox bought the *Miami Daily News* and founded WHIO, Dayton's first radio station. He bought Atlanta's WSB ("Welcome South, Brother"), the South's first radio station, in 1939 and expanded it in 1948 by starting WSB-FM and WSB-TV, the first FM and TV stations in the South. The next year Cox started WHIO-FM and WHIO-TV, the first FM and TV stations in Dayton. The *Atlanta Constitution* joined his collection in 1950. When Cox died in 1957, his company owned 7 newspapers, 3 TV stations, and several radio stations.

Cox Enterprises expanded its broadcasting interests by buying WSOC-AM/FM/TV (Charlotte, 1959) and KTVU-TV (San Francisco-Oakland, 1963). The company became one of the first major broadcasting companies to enter cable TV when it purchased a system in Lewistown, Pennsylvania (1962). The Cox family's broadcast properties were placed in publicly held Cox Broadcasting in 1964; 2 years later, its newspapers were placed into privately held Cox Enterprises; the cable holdings became publicly held Cox Cable Communications. By 1969 Cox was the #2 US cable operator. The broadcasting arm diversified, buying Manheim Services (auto auctions,

1968) and Kansas City Automobile Auction (1969).

Cox Broadcasting bought TeleRep, a TV advertising sales representation firm, in 1972. Cox Cable was in 9 states and had 500,000 subscribers by 1977, when it rejoined Cox Broadcasting. The broadcasting company changed its name to Cox Communications in 1982; the Cox family took the company private again in 1985 and combined it with Cox Enterprises. Kennedy, the founder's grandson, became chairman in 1987.

In 1991 Cox merged its Manheim unit with the auto auction business of Ford Motor Credit and GE Capital and bought Val-Pak Direct Marketing, a direct-mail coupon company.

In 1994 an agreement to form a $4.9 billion cable television joint venture with telephone titan Southwestern Bell (now SBC Communications) fell through after the 2 companies decided that new FCC rules would eat up profits. That year Cox formed Sprint Spectrum LP, a partnership with long-distance operator Sprint and cable leviathans TCI and Comcast to bundle telephone service, cable television, and other communication services. Sprint Spectrum LP acquired the rights to wireless licenses in 29 US markets, covering more than 182 million people, in 1995.

Also in 1995 Cox bought Times Mirror's cable television operations for $2.3 billion in cash and stock and folded those cable systems and its own into a new, publicly traded company, Cox Communications Inc.

Cox agreed in 1996 to acquire 2 direct marketing companies from Donnelley Marketing Inc. and made plans to sell a piece of its radio business, Cox Radio, Inc., to the public in an IPO.

WHO

Chairman and CEO: James Cox Kennedy, age 48
President and COO: David E. Easterly, age 53
SVP and CFO: John R. Dillon, age 54
SVP Administration: Timothy W. Hughes
VP and Controller: John G. Boyette
VP Business Development and Planning: Dean H. Eisner
VP Corporate Security: Charles W. Rochner
VP Internet: David C. Scott
VP Legal Affairs and Secretary: Andrew A. Merdek
VP Planning and Analysis: William L. Killen Jr.
VP Public Policy: Alexander V. Netchvolodoff
VP Tax: Preston B. Barnett
VP Human Resources: Marybeth H. Leamer

WHERE

HQ: 1400 Lake Hearn Dr., Atlanta, GA 30319
Phone: 404-843-5000
Fax: 404-843-5142
Web site: http://www.ajc.com/cox/cox.htm

WHAT

Daily Newspapers
The Atlanta Constitution
The Atlanta Journal
Austin American-Statesman
Chandler Arizonan Tribune
The Daily Reflector (Greenville, NC)
The Daily Sentinel (Grand Junction, CO)
The Daily Sentinel (Nacogdoches, TX)
Dayton Daily News (Ohio)
Gilbert Tribune (Arizona)
Longview News-Journal (Texas)
The Lufkin Daily News (Texas)
Mesa Tribune (Arizona)
Palm Beach Daily News (Florida)
The Palm Beach Post (Florida)
Scottsdale Progress Tribune (Arizona)
Springfield News-Sun (Ohio)
Tempe Daily News Tribune (Arizona)
Waco Tribune-Herald (Texas)
The Yuma Daily Sun (Arizona)

Selected Radio Stations
KACE (FM), Los Angeles
KFI (AM), Los Angeles
KOST (FM), Los Angeles
WCKG (FM), Chicago
WCOF (FM), Tampa/St. Petersburg
WFLC (FM), Miami
WHIO (AM), Dayton
WHKO (FM), Dayton
WHQT (FM), Miami
WIOD (AM), Miami
WRKA (FM), Louisville
WRVI (FM), Louisville
WSB (AM), Atlanta
WSB (FM), Atlanta
WSUN (AM), Tampa/St. Petersburg
WWRM (FM), Tampa/St. Petersburg
WYSY (FM), Aurora-Chicago

Television Stations
KTVU, San Francisco/Oakland
WFTV, Orlando
WHIO-TV, Dayton
WPXI, Pittsburgh
WSB-TV, Atlanta
WSOC, Charlotte

Cable and Television Operations
Cox Communications, Inc. (83%, 5th largest operator of cable television systems in the US)
Harrington, Righter & Parsons (sales representation)
Rysher Entertainment (production and distribution)
TeleRep, Inc. (television sales representation)

Manheim Auctions
52 auto auctions in the US and Canada

Other
Clarendon Farms, Inc. (farming and timber)
Cox Target Media (direct mail advertising and auto advertising)
Hualalai Land Corporation (cattle ranch and flower plantation)
InfoVentures of Atlanta (50%)
Longstreet Press
Nine Bar Ranch Texas, Inc. (cattle ranch)
Southeast Paper Manufacturing Co. (33%)
Trader Publishing Co. (50%)
Val-Pak Direct Marketing Systems, Inc.

KEY COMPETITORS

Advance Publications
AT&T Corp.
Cablevision Systems
Comcast
Dow Jones
Dun & Bradstreet
E.W. Scripps
Gannett
General Electric
Hearst
Heritage Media
King Ranch
Knight-Ridder
Media General
New York Times
News Corp.
TCI
Thomson Corp.
Time Warner
Tribune
U S WEST Media
Viacom
Walt Disney
Washington Post
Westinghouse/ CBS

HOW MUCH

Private company FYE: December 31	Annual Growth	1986	1987	1988	1989	1990	1991	1992	1993	1994	1995
Sales ($ mil.)	10.3%	1,569	1,665	1,816	1,973	2,094	2,323	2,495	2,675	2,939	3,806
Employees	7.4%	20,000	20,766	21,612	22,487	24,864	29,943	30,865	31,000	37,000	38,000

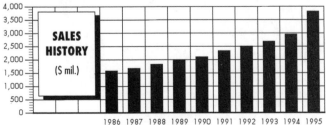

SALES HISTORY ($ mil.)

DAI NIPPON PRINTING CO., LTD.

OVERVIEW

Dai Nippon Printing (DNP) is Japan's largest printing company, with about 12% of the market. The Tokyo-based company's main lines of business are commercial and specialty printing. It produces advertising materials, books, magazines, and catalogs at 17 plants in Japan. DNP also operates a plant in Denmark that makes TV projection screens.

Other products include packaging, decorative interiors, and software (mainly CD-ROMs and electronic books for its client publishers). DNP operates a Central Research Institute (CRI) and a number of laboratories focused on the development of packaging materials, information media, business forms, materials development, and microprocessing.

The company has a majority stake in Hokkaido Coca-Cola Bottling, which accounts for about 6% of DNP's total revenues. It also sells photomasks (used in making semiconductors). Specialty printing and packaging account for about 31% of sales.

By focusing on its noncyclical businesses (printing and packaging), DNP has avoided steep slumps in sales, but it has not grown rapidly either.

WHEN

In 1876 Shueisha, the predecessor to Dai Nippon Printing, was established in central Tokyo. As the only modern printing firm in Japan, it was well positioned to attract the business of the emerging newspaper and book industries. Originally a movable-type hand printer, the company became the first private industry to use steam power in Japan when it updated its presses in 1884. By 1894 Japan made 36 million pounds of paper, up from only 35,000 pounds in 1874. In 1900 rival printer Toppan was established.

Following Japanese victories over China and Russia at the turn of the century, Japan embarked on a period of military and economic expansion. This was matched by a growing demand for printing. In 1927 Japan published 20,000 new book titles and 40 million magazines. The country's first 4-color gravure printing system was inaugurated the following year. In 1935 Shueisha changed its name to Dai Nippon Printing following its merger with Nisshin Printing.

The 1930s and 1940s were a lean time for printers, as a repressive military government suppressed publishers and banned books. WWII devastated the publishing industry along with the rest of the Japanese economy, but the industry recovered quickly after the end of the war. DNP was assisted in its recovery by government contracts; in 1946 it was designated by the Ministry of Finance to print 100-yen notes. In 1949 the company entered the securities printing business, and in 1951 it expanded into packaging and decorative interiors production. DNP reemerged in 1958 as Japan's largest printing firm.

In 1963 DNP followed Toppan in setting up an office in Hong Kong. Both Hong Kong and Singapore had become centers of overseas Chinese publishing after Shanghai printing entrepreneurs emigrated in the face of the Communist takeover of China in 1949. Hong Kong and Singapore became centers for low-cost, high-quality color printing for British and American book publishers. In 1973 DNP overtook R. R. Donnelley as the world's largest printer. The next year the company set up a subsidiary in the US, DNP (America), Inc.

DNP moved into the information processing business in the 1980s, developing a credit card-sized calculator in 1985, a digital color printer system in 1986, and a Japanese-language word processor in 1987. The company launched Hi-Vision Static Pictures in 1989 to market a process that converted data into a form used by high-definition TV. In 1990 DNP bought a controlling stake in Tien Wah Press, the #1 printer in Singapore.

The next year DNP completed the first construction stage of its Okayama plant, dedicated to information media supplies (mainly transfer ribbons for color printers). The 2nd stage, specializing in interior decorative materials, was completed in 1993.

The company is expanding its array of electronic products from audiovisual displays to color filters for liquid crystal displays, a database for the newly formed Japanese professional soccer league, and CD-ROM products. In 1994 the company launched its Let's Go to an Amusement Park! virtual reality software system. BNP acquired a 3% stake in French computer maker Machines Bull in 1995. In 1996 the company announced that it had produced an integrated circuit card for about 1/10 of current costs, giving it a major competitive edge in the magnetic card market.

Chairman and President: Yoshitoshi Kitajima
Managing Director: Michiji Sato
Managing Director: Yasuo Yamaji
Managing Director: Jitsuo Okauchi
Managing Director: Ryozo Kitami
Executive Director: Satoshi Akiyama
Executive Director: Isamu Hirabayashi
Executive Director: Nobuo Iitsuka
Executive Director: Ken-ichi Nakamura
Executive Director: Taira Takahashi
Executive Director: Kousuke Hirabayashi
Executive Director: Koichi Takanami
President and COO, DNP (America): Hideki Fuchigami
CFO, DNP (America): Tadashi Sato
Personnel Assistant, DNP (America): Lisa Moynihan
Auditors: Meiji Audit Corporation

WHERE

HQ: 1-1, Ichigaya Kagacho 1-chome, Shinjuku-ku, Tokyo, 162-01, Japan
Phone: +81-3-3266-2111
Fax: +81-3-3266-2119
US HQ: DNP (America), Inc., 2 Park Ave., Ste. 1405, New York, NY 10016
US Phone: 212-686-1919
US Fax: 212-686-3250
Web site: http://www.dnp.co.jp

WHAT

	1996 Sales
	% of total
Commercial printing & other	63
Packaging & special printing	31
Soft drinks	6
Total	**100**

Selected Products and Services
Audiovisual displays
Books and magazines
Business forms
Commercial printing
Decorative interiors
Hi-Vision software
Information media supplies
Multimedia software
Packaging
Photomasks
Soccer database
Specialty printing
TV projection screens
Virtual reality system

Selected Subsidiaries and Affiliates
Dai Nippon Printing Co. (Australia) Pty. Ltd.
Dai Nippon Printing Co. (Hong Kong) Ltd.
DNP (America), Inc.
P.T. Dai Nippon Printing Indonesia
Tien Wah Press (Pte.) Ltd. (85%, Singapore)
TWP Sendirian Berhad (Malaysia)

KEY COMPETITORS

C & C
Graphic Industries
International Imaging
 Materials
Mitsui High-Tec
Photronics
Quebecor

R. R. Donnelley
Scitex
Shinko Electric
Sing Tao
Toppan Printing
Toyo Seikan

HOW MUCH

Principal exchange: Tokyo FYE: March 31	Annual Growth	1987	1988	1989	1990	1991	1992	1993	1994	1995	1996
Sales (Y bil.)	4.5%	839	758	1,011	1,075	1,170	1,244	1,192	1,146	1,193	1,245
Net income (Y bil.)	7.3%	28	27	35	41	43	44	42	41	49	53
Income as % of sales	—	3.3%	3.6%	3.5%	3.8%	3.7%	3.5%	3.5%	3.6%	4.1%	4.3%
Earnings per share (Y)	6.0%	42	39	48	54	51	56	56	54	66	71
Stock price – high (Y)[1]	—	1,905	2,419	2,629	2,667	2,400	1,710	1,540	1,790	2,020	1,860
Stock price – low (Y)[1]	—	1,210	1,600	2,286	2,143	1,250	1,260	1,180	1,240	1,560	1,260
Stock price – close (Y)[1]	(0.8%)	1,886	2,190	2,581	2,390	1,450	1,460	1,260	1,590	1,700	1,750
P/E – high	—	45	62	55	49	47	31	28	33	31	26
P/E – low	—	29	41	48	40	25	23	21	23	24	18
Dividends per share (Y)	5.4%	10	9	10	10	13	13	13	14	15	16
Book value per share (Y)	7.5%	542	590	645	777	809	856	902	934	985	1,040
Employees	3.1%	—	—	—	—	—	—	30,092	30,000	33,000	33,000[2]

1996 YEAR-END

Debt ratio: —
Return on equity: 7.0%
Cash (bil.): Y606
Current ratio: 1.62
Long-term debt (bil.): —
No. of shares (mil.): 750
Dividends
 Yield: 0.9%
 Payout: 22.7%
Market value (mil.): $12,234
Sales (mil.): $11,611

STOCK PRICE HISTORY[1]
HIGH/LOW/CLOSE

1987 1988 1989 1990 1991 1992 1993 1994 1995 1996

[1] Stock prices are for the prior calendar year. [2] Estimate. Note: $ = Y107.26 (March 31, 1996)

DENTSU INC.

OVERVIEW

Privately held Dentsu may not be a household word, but it works hard to ensure its clients are. The Tokyo-based advertiser is one of the world's largest advertising organizations. The company operates worldwide through wholly owned local agencies and alliances serving multinational clients like Apple, Federal Express, Hitachi, Matsushita, and Toyota.

Although Dentsu dominates the Japanese advertising business (it has more than twice the sales of its nearest competitor), its market share has shrunk as Japanese advertising styles have changed. Contrary to US custom, which holds that it is a conflict of interest for individual agencies to serve competing customers, Japanese agencies frequently have competing clients. In recent years, however, advertisers have grown suspect of such arrangements and Dentsu has lost clients to other agencies that don't also pitch their rivals.

The company's foreign alliances are shifting as well. Recently the company restructured its alliance with US agency Young & Rubicam to take control of the Los Angeles office as part of its effort to seek automotive accounts in the US. And Dentsu is expanding its presence in new areas of Asia, following its clients as they venture outside Japan.

The Kyodo and Jiji news services own about 28% and 20% of Dentsu, respectively.

WHEN

Sino-Japanese war correspondent Hoshiro Mitsunaga wanted to set up a Japanese wire service for faster reporting. In 1901 he founded Telegraphic Service Co. (news wire service) and Japan Advertising Ltd. Mitsunaga let newspapers pay their wire service bills with advertising space, which the advertising agency resold. In 1907 the companies merged as Nihon Denpo-Tsushin Sha (Japan Telegraphic Communication Company), shortened to Dentsu. After gaining Japanese rights to the United Press wire in 1908, Dentsu extracted even more favorable advertising rates from its clients.

In 1936 Japan's government consolidated all news services into Domei, a propaganda machine it controlled, and gave Domei half of Dentsu's stock. In 1943 the government combined all advertising agencies into 12 entities. Future Dentsu president Hideo Yoshida managed to gain control of 4 of them.

After WWII, US occupation forces dismantled Domei, but instead of regaining full control of itself, Dentsu saw Domei's 50% of its stock transferred to 2 new news agencies, Kyodo and Jiji. Yoshida became president in 1947. He established Dentsu's successful formula of building personal connections and loyalty by hiring executives previously purged from their companies by occupation forces and employing sons of politicians and business leaders.

Under Yoshida, Dentsu essentially created the Japanese TV industry by investing in start-up broadcasters, whose gratitude translated into preferential treatment for the influential agency. This led to its decades-long domination of Japanese TV advertising.

In 1973 Dentsu became the world's largest advertising agency. But by the early 1980s, growth had slowed along with Japan's economy. Having failed to follow its clients as they expanded overseas, Dentsu derived only 1% of its revenue from foreign advertising in 1980. The agency teamed with Young & Rubicam in a 1981 joint venture, but by 1986 foreign billings still amounted to only 7% of revenues, and the next year Saatchi & Saatchi passed Dentsu as the world's #1 advertising group. In 1987 Young & Rubicam/Dentsu joined with Eurocom, a French agency, to form HDM Worldwide in hopes of expanding its European penetration.

Dentsu's results soared along with the Japanese economy during the boom times of the late 1980s, but the company continued to struggle abroad as Eurocom pulled out of HDM Worldwide in 1990. The newly named Dentsu, Young & Rubicam Partnerships reorganized to focus on North America, Asia, and Australia, and Dentsu joined with Collett Dickenson Pearce to remain in Europe after HDM's withdrawal.

In 1995 Dentsu announced the foundation of a subsidiary to handle accounts in other parts of Asia and the opening of an office in Canada, in partnership with Cadence Advertising. The next year the company bought out Young & Rubicam's interest in their joint Los Angeles office and renamed it Rogge Effler & Partners.

Chairman: Gohei Kogure
President: Yutaka Narita
EVP: Toshiro Toyota
Senior Managing Director: Kaushiko Yamashita
Senior Managing Director: Yuzo Irie
Senior Managing Director: Mutso Fuji
Senior Managing Director: Fumio Suzuki
Senior Managing Director: Shuzo Ishikawa
President and CEO, DCA Advertising (US):
  Kiyoshi Eguchi
Treasurer, DCA Advertising (US): Masaki Yaegashi
SVP and Director Administration (Personnel), DCA
  Advertising (US): Diane Dennis
Auditors: KPMG Peat Marwick LLP

WHERE

HQ: 1-11 Tsukiji, Chuo-ku, Tokyo 104, Japan
Phone: +81-3-5551-5111
Fax: +81-3-5551-2013
US HQ: DCA Advertising, 666 Fifth Ave., 9th Fl.,
  New York, NY 10103
US Phone: 212-397-3333
US Fax: 212-397-3322
Web site: http://www.dentsu.co.jp/DHP

Dentsu and its subsidiaries have offices in 34 countries.

	1995 Sales
	% of total
Japan	91
Europe	2
US	1
Other countries	6
Total	**100**

WHAT

	1995 Billings
	% of total
Television	42
Newspapers	17
Promotion	14
Creative services	9
Magazines	4
Radio	3
Other	11
Total	**100**

Selected Subsidiaries
AD Dentsu Tokyo, Inc. (advertising)
cdp europe (44.8%, advertising, UK)
DCA Advertising (US)
Dentsu Actis Inc. (printing and premium production)
Dentsu Cotec Inc. (typesetting and engraving)
Dentsu Deutschland GmbH (advertising, Germany)
Dentsu EYE Inc. (advertising)
Dentsu Institute for Human Studies (think tank)
Dentsu PR Center Ltd. (public relations)
Dentsu Prox Inc. (media production)
Dentsu Research, Inc. (market research)
Dentsu, Sudler & Hennessy Inc. (advertising)
Dentsu Wunderman Direct Inc. (direct marketing)
Dentsu, Young & Rubicam Inc. (50% advertising)
Information Services International-Dentsu, Ltd. (joint
  venture with General Electric, information services)

Selected Clients

All Nippon Airways	Hitachi
Apple	Matsushita
Bridgestone	Nestlé
Canon	Royal/Dutch Shell
Central Japan Railway	Sanyo
Dai-Ichi Kangyo	TDK
Daimler-Benz	Toshiba
Dole	Toyota
Federal Express	VF

KEY COMPETITORS

Bozell, Jacobs	Havas	Omnicom Group
Cordiant	Interpublic Group	Publicis
D'Arcy Masius	Leo Burnett	True North
Grey Advertising	New Saatchi	WPP Group
Hakuhodo	Agency	

HOW MUCH

Private company FYE: March 31	Annual Growth	1986	1987	1988	1989	1990	1991	1992	1993	1994	1995
Sales ($ mil.)	16.2%	524	755	1,055	1,274	1,166	1,423	1,481	1,385	1,622	2,026
Net income ($ mil.)	10.2%	30	38	62	102	96	140	134	55	24	72
Income as % of sales	—	5.7%	5.0%	5.9%	8.0%	8.2%	9.9%	9.1%	4.0%	1.5%	3.5%
Employees	0.3%	5,759	5,844	5,867	5,896	5,893	6,000	5,811	5,834	5,972	5,910

Debt ratio: 29.5%
Return on equity: 4.4%
Cash (mil.): $1,069
Current ratio: 1.40
Long-term debt (mil.): $434

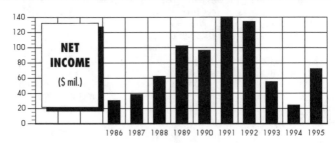

NET INCOME ($ mil.)

DOW JONES & COMPANY, INC.

OVERVIEW

Business is the top story at Dow Jones. The company remains the US's dominant source for business information with such products as its flagship, the *Wall Street Journal*, and Dow Jones News/Retrieval service. However, competition is intense in the financial news market, and despite an array of new information products, the New York City-based publisher still trails far behind the market leader, Reuters, in world penetration.

Dow Jones's operations are organized along business lines. Subscription-based financial information services, which include Telerate (provider of real-time market data for financial professionals) and financial news services, are supplied by its Dow Jones News Service. The company also carries archival news articles and federal corporate filings. The *Wall Street Journal* heads up Dow Jones's publishing operations, which also include Asian and European editions, *Barron's*, *Far Eastern Economic Review*, the company's financial television broadcasting operations, and the *Wall Street Journal* Interactive Division (an Internet-based financial news service). The Community Newspapers segment consists of Ottaway Newspapers, 19 general-interest daily newspapers published in 11 states.

Dow Jones also invests in related businesses, including other publications (*Texas Monthly* and Germany's *Handelsblatt*) and newsprint mills.

Heirs of early owner Clarence Barron own 42% of the company.

WHEN

Edward Jones, Charles Dow, and Charles Bergstresser (the latter 2 related by marriage), all financial reporters, left the Kiernan News Agency and founded Dow Jones & Company in 1882. Working out of an office next door to the NYSE, the company delivered handwritten bulletins of stock and bond trading news to subscribers in New York's financial districts. In 1883 Dow Jones started summarizing the trading day in the *Customers' Afternoon Letter*, which evolved into the *Wall Street Journal* (1889). Dow Jones's reports became even more timely with the commencement of an electric ticker service acquired in 1897 from Kiernan.

Jones sold out to his partners in 1899; three years later Dow and Bergstresser sold the company to Clarence Barron, who owned the Boston News Bureau. In 1921 the company introduced *Barron's National Business and Financial Weekly* for investors. The company suffered along with the financial industry during the Depression as circulation dropped from 50,000 in 1928 to 28,000 a decade later.

WWII brought an increased emphasis on news, but the paper remained a trade paper for the financial industry. It was a big trade paper, though, with editions in New York, Dallas, and San Francisco in the 1950s. The 1960s and 1970s saw increased business diversification. In 1962 Dow Jones started a general interest weekly called the *National Observer* (shuttered in 1977) and in 1975 it bought a textbook publisher, Richard D. Irwin. The company also automated its operations (Dow Jones began transmitting copy via satellite to regional printing plants for nationwide same-day delivery in 1975). By 1980 the company had 7 divisions.

Circulation of the *Wall Street Journal* peaked at over 2 million in 1983 (1995 circulation was 1.8 million). In the 1980s the company sought new outlets, increasingly in the electronic arena. Between 1985 and 1990 it gradually acquired all of Telerate, a real-time financial data network. But while the electronic business grew, print circulation remained essentially flat. In 1991 Dow Jones bought an interest in Minex, a Japanese consortium developing automated foreign exchange trading information.

Other initiatives have been less successful; a 1992 alliance with regional Bell operating company BellSouth to provide telephone access to Dow Jones reports was discontinued in 1995 as the Internet gained prominence. In 1993 the company teamed with publisher Hearst Corp. to launch the financial magazine *Smart Money*.

Dow Jones is attempting to crash the increasingly crowded financial television field. In 1994 the company started the European Business News television network in London.

A new service offered in 1995 was Personal Journal; it allows online subscribers to customize the subject matter they receive. In 1996 the company joined with ITT Corp. in buying New York television WNYC (renamed WBIS+) for $207 million in order to convert it to an all-financial news station. Telerate also launched new foreign services, one focused on Latin America and the other on Italy.

Chairman and CEO; Publisher, *The Wall Street Journal*: Peter R. Kann, age 53, $1,125,000 pay
President and COO: Kenneth L. Burenga, age 51, $830,000 pay
SVP: Carl M. Valenti, age 57, $642,000 pay
SVP, General Counsel, and Secretary: Peter G. Skinner, age 51, $586,000 pay
VP Finance and CFO: Kevin J. Roche, age 61
VP Employee Relations: James A. Scaduto
Auditors: Coopers & Lybrand L.L.P.

WHERE

HQ: World Financial Center, 200 Liberty St., New York, NY 10281
Phone: 212-416-2000
Fax: 212-732-8356
Web site: http://www.dowjones.com

	1995 Sales		1995 Operating Income	
	$ mil.	% of total	$ mil.	% of total
US	1,589	70	172	53
Europe, Middle East, Africa	383	17	54	17
Asia/Pacific	262	11	96	29
Other regions	50	2	3	1
Adjustments	—		(21)	—
Total	**2,284**	**100**	**304**	**100**

WHAT

	1995 Sales		1995 Operating Income	
	$ mil.	% of total	$ mil.	% of total
Business publications	1,050	46	95	29
Financial information	961	42	197	61
Community papers	273	12	33	10
Other	—	—	(21)	—
Total	**2,284**	**100**	**304**	**100**

HOW MUCH

Selected Business Publication
The Asian Wall Street Journal (Hong Kong)
Barron's
Far Eastern Economic Review (Hong Kong)
National Business Employment Weekly
SmartMoney, The Wall Street Journal Magazine of Personal Business (with Hearst Corp.)
The Wall Street Journal
The Wall Street Journal Europe (Belgium)

Selected Information Services
AP-Dow Jones News Service (economic, business, and financial news wire, with the Associated Press)
Dow Jones News/Retrieval (online business and financial news and information)
Dow Jones Telerate (market information)
DowVision (customized online news service)
Federal Filings (government and court news wire)
Personal Journal (electronic publication; personalized business news, world news, weather, and sports)
The Wall Street Journal Interactive Edition (Internet-based financial news service)
The Wall Street Journal Report (radio and TV programs)

Community Newspapers
Ottaway Newspapers, Inc. (19 newspapers in 11 states)

Other Investments
America Econima (South American business magazine)
Mediatex Communication Corp. (*Texas Monthly*)
Newsprint mills

KEY COMPETITORS

Advance Publications	Pearson
Bloomberg	Reed Elsevier
CompuServe	Reuters
Forbes	Times Mirror
Gannett	Thomson Corp.
Knight-Ridder	Time Warner
McGraw-Hill	Tribune
New York Times	Value Line
News Corp.	Washington Post

HOW MUCH

NYSE symbol: DJ FYE: December 31	Annual Growth	1986	1987	1988	1989	1990	1991	1992	1993	1994	1995
Sales ($ mil.)	8.1%	1,134	1,314	1,603	1,687	1,720	1,725	1,817	1,931	2,091	2,284
Net income ($ mil.)	0.4%	183	203	228	317	107	72	118	148	181	190
Income as % of sales	—	16.2%	15.4%	14.2%	18.8%	6.2%	4.2%	6.5%	7.6%	8.7%	8.3%
Earnings per share ($)	0.4%	1.89	2.10	2.35	3.15	1.06	0.71	1.17	1.48	1.83	1.96
Stock price – high ($)	—	42.13	56.25	36.50	42.50	33.75	30.63	35.38	39.00	41.88	40.13
Stock price – low ($)	—	28.09	28.00	26.75	29.25	18.13	21.63	24.50	26.75	28.13	30.63
Stock price – close ($)	0.2%	39.00	29.88	29.50	33.25	24.00	25.88	27.00	35.75	31.00	39.88
P/E – high	—	22	27	16	14	32	43	30	26	23	21
P/E – low	—	15	13	11	9	17	31	21	18	15	16
Dividends per share ($)	5.9%	0.55	0.64	0.68	0.72	0.76	0.76	0.76	0.80	0.84	0.92
Book value per share ($)	9.1%	7.52	8.80	11.51	13.94	14.23	14.20	14.41	14.96	15.33	16.47
Employees	5.2%	7,069	9,014	9,080	9,818	9,677	9,459	9,860	10,006	10,300	11,200

1995 YEAR-END

Debt ratio: 13.9%
Return on equity: 12.3%
Cash (mil.): $14
Current ratio: 0.64
Long-term debt (mil.): $254
No. of shares (mil.): 97
Dividends
  Yield: 2.3%
  Payout: 46.9%
Market value (mil.): $3,878
R&D as % of sales: 2.9%

STOCK PRICE HISTORY HIGH/LOW/CLOSE
1986 1987 1988 1989 1990 1991 1992 1993 1994 1995

THE DUN & BRADSTREET CORPORATION

OVERVIEW

This year, business fashion decrees divestiture, and Wilton, Connecticut-based Dun & Bradstreet (D&B) means to obey. After more than 2 decades of acquisitions, the company announced in 1996 that it would follow ITT, AT&T and others in a return to "core competencies" with the announcement that it intends to split up in 1996 into 3 separate public companies. This will allow D&B to concentrate on its financial businesses, and offer investors a clear choice of industries to invest in.

Dun & Bradstreet Corp., headed by EVP Volney Taylor, will slim down to its traditional financial specialties: Dun & Bradstreet Information Services, the world's largest corporate credit reporting agency, which reports on over 38 million businesses in more than 30 countries; Moody's Investors Service, a leading publisher of financial information; and R. H. Donnelley, a publisher of telephone directories (*Yellow Pages*).

The financially troubled A.C. Nielsen will now face global competition on its own. The world's #1 market research company A.C. Nielsen offers consumer-purchasing behavior analysis and other market research. It has recently moved into Asia with the acquisition of the Survey Research Group, Asia's leading market research company. D&B's current CFO, Nicholas Trivisonno, will lead this spinoff.

D&B chairman Robert Weissman will head a new information services entity, Cognizant, which will be created with health care marketing research firm IMS International, broadcasting analyzer Nielsen Media Research (which produces TV ratings), and Dun & Bradstreet's 53% interest in information technology advisor Gartner Group. The breakup will also result in the sale of some problematic businesses: Dun & Bradstreet Software and American Credit Indemnity.

WHEN

Dun & Bradstreet originated in Lewis Tappan's Mercantile Agency, established in 1841 in New York City. The Mercantile Agency was one of the first commercial credit reporting agencies, and it supplied wholesalers and importers with written reports on the creditworthiness of their customers. Some of the company's credit reporters included 4 men who became US presidents (Lincoln, Grant, Cleveland, and McKinley). In the 1840s Tappan opened offices in Boston, Philadelphia, and Baltimore and in 1857 established operations in Montreal and London. In 1859 Robert Dun took over the agency and changed its name to R.G. Dun & Co. The first edition of the *Dun's Book* (1859) contained information on 20,268 businesses; by 1886 the number had risen to over one million. John M. Bradstreet, a rival company founded in Cincinnati in 1849, merged with Dun in 1933; the company adopted the Dun & Bradstreet name in 1939.

In 1961 D&B bought Reuben H. Donnelley Corp., a direct-mail advertiser and publisher of the *Yellow Pages* (first published in 1886) and 10 trade magazines. In 1962 Moody's Investors Service (founded 1900) and Official Airline Guides (guides first published in 1929; sold in 1988) became part of D&B.

D&B computerized its records in the 1960s and eventually developed the largest private business database in the world. By 1975 the firm had a national network with a centralized database. Sales boomed when D&B created

new products by repackaging information from its vast database (such as Dun's Financial Profiles, first published in 1979).

In the 1970s the company began buying up other information, data, and publishing companies, including Technical Publishing (trade and professional publications, 1978), and National CSS (computer services, 1979). This trend continued in the 1980s with the purchase of McCormack & Dodge (software, 1983), A.C. Nielsen (1984), and IMS International (pharmaceutical sales data, 1988). In 1989 it bought Management Science America. That year reports surfaced that D&B was overcharging customers for credit reports; it settled the resulting class-action suit in 1994.

The tide turned in the 1990s as D&B sold its specialty industry and consumer database companies and IMS's communications unit. But it still hoped to cash in on the medical information industry by forming D&B HealthCare Information and on information technology by buying a majority interest in high-tech consulting firm the Gartner Group. In 1993 the company began a restructuring program to improve efficiency in its information services businesses. It consolidated 27 data centers worldwide into 4 automated centers and cut its headquarters staffing.

But these measures did not jumpstart D&B's performance, and in 1996, after its 2nd earnings decline in 3 years, management decided to dismember the company.

Chairman and CEO: Robert E. Weissman, age 55, $1,632,095 pay
EVP Finance and CFO: Nicholas L. Trivisonno, age 48
EVP: Dennis G. Sisco, age 49, $805,516 pay
EVP: Volney Taylor, age 56, $798,615 pay
EVP: Robert J. Lievense, age 50, $676,688 pay
EVP: William G. Jacobi, age 52, $654,872 pay
SVP Communications and Government Affairs: Michael F. Brewer, age 52
SVP and General Counsel: Earl H. Doppelt, age 42
Chief Information Officer: Clifford L. Bateman, age 50
Chief Communications Officer: William F. Doescher, age 58
Chief Human Resources Officer: Peter J. Ross, age 50

WHERE

HQ: 187 Danbury Rd., Wilton, CT 06897
Phone: 203-834-4200
Fax: 203-834-4201
Web site: http://www.dnb.com

	1995 Sales		1995 Operating Income	
	$ mil.	% of total	$ mil.	% of total
US	3,016	56	359	69
Europe	1,561	29	91	17
Other regions	838	15	72	14
Total	**5,415**	**100**	**522**	**100**

WHAT

	1995 Sales		1995 Operating Income	
	$ mil.	% of total	$ mil.	% of total
Information services	2,388	44	126	15
Risk management business marketing	1,734	32	450	54
Software services	457	8	(10)	—
Directory information	424	8	186	23
Other	412	8	61	8
Adjustments	—	—	(291)	—
Total	**5,415**	**100**	**522**	**100**

Services
Dun & Bradstreet Information Services (credit information and insurance, receivables management)
Moody's Investors Service, Inc. (financial information, bond rating)
Reuben H. Donnelley (directories)

KEY COMPETITORS

ADP
American Business Information
Dow Jones
Equifax
Hoover's, Inc.
IBM
Information Resources
M/A/R/C Group
McGraw-Hill
Morningstar, Inc.
Pearson
PeopleSoft, Inc.
Thomson Corp.
TRW
Value Line

HOW MUCH

NYSE symbol: DNB FYE: December 31	Annual Growth	1986	1987	1988	1989	1990	1991	1992	1993	1994	1995
Sales ($ mil.)	6.3%	3,113	3,359	4,267	4,321	4,817	4,642	4,750	4,710	4,895	5,415
Net income ($ mil.)	(0.6%)	340	393	499	586	508	509	554	429	630	321
Income as % of sales	—	10.9%	11.7%	11.7%	13.6%	10.5%	11.0%	11.7%	9.1%	12.9%	5.9%
Earnings per share ($)	(1.9%)	2.24	2.58	2.67	3.14	2.80	2.85	3.10	2.42	3.70	1.89
Stock price – high ($)	—	60.19	71.75	57.50	60.25	48.63	58.00	59.13	68.50	64.00	65.50
Stock price – low ($)	—	40.38	44.50	45.88	41.25	36.13	39.13	50.63	55.75	51.88	48.50
Stock price – close ($)	2.3%	52.63	54.75	53.63	46.00	42.13	57.50	57.75	61.63	55.00	64.75
P/E – high	—	27	28	22	19	17	20	19	28	17	35
P/E – low	—	18	17	17	13	13	14	16	23	14	26
Dividends per share ($)	8.7%	1.24	1.45	1.68	1.94	2.09	2.15	2.25	2.40	2.56	2.63
Book value per share ($)	(3.7%)	9.79	10.95	11.18	11.80	11.65	12.11	12.10	6.53	7.77	6.98
Employees	(1.8%)	58,352	62,000	69,500	71,500	62,900	58,500	52,400	50,400	47,000	49,500

Debt ratio: 27.3%
Return on equity: 25.7%
Cash (mil.): $438
Current ratio: 0.81
Long-term debt (mil.): $445
No. of shares (mil.): 169
Dividends
  Yield: 4.1%
  Payout: 139.2%
Market value (mil.): $10,968

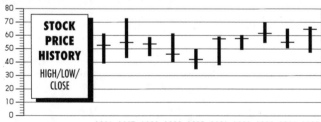

STOCK PRICE HISTORY HIGH/LOW/CLOSE

ENCYCLOPÆDIA BRITANNICA, INC.

OVERVIEW

The Encyclopædia Britannica sales staff won't knock at your door any more, but they may try to reach out of your computer. Headquartered in Chicago, the publisher of the "oldest and largest English-language general encyclopædia" (according to the text itself) has stopped its in-home sales effort in North America. Instead, the company is peddling its books along the Information Superhighway, hoping that this approach will revive its precarious fortunes.

The company's stable of print products includes the *Young Children's Encyclopedia*, the 32-volume *Encyclopædia Britannica*, and *Webster's* dictionaries. Electronic products include the Britannica CD, a CD-ROM version of the *Encyclopædia Britannica*; Britannica Online, a database accessible on the Internet; and a CD-ROM complement to the printed French-language *Encyclopædia Universalis*.

In addition to online marketing, Britannica relies on direct mail and broadcast advertising to sell its products. The company believes these methods allow customers to learn about and buy its reference materials more easily. They are also less expensive than in-home sales. An investment group led by Swiss financier Jacob Safra, nephew of banking king Edmund Safra (one of the world's richest men), purchased the suffering company from the University of Chicago's nonprofit William Benton Foundation in 1995 for an undisclosed amount.

Increased competition in the market for reference materials has brought down the price consumers are willing to pay. Instead of purchasing an entire set of encyclopedias for around $2,000, customers want to pay for only the amount of information they actually use. Such pay-as-you-go methods make products such as Britannica's online service more important for building future profits.

WHEN

Encyclopædia Britannica was founded in Scotland in 1768 by engraver Andrew Bell and printer and bookseller Colin Macfarquhar. The first edition of the *Encyclopædia Britannica*, edited by William Smellie of the University of Edinburgh, was released volume-by-volume between 1768 and 1771. It included articles by Benjamin Franklin (on electricity) and John Locke (on human understanding). From the late 1700s to the mid-1800s, the encyclopedia grew from 10 to 22 volumes and developed a reputation for quality and scholarship.

The *Britannica's* Ninth Edition (1870) included ideas inspired by Charles Darwin's controversial *Origin of Species*, in which he espoused his theories of evolution. American businessmen Horace Hooper and Walter Jackson purchased the company in 1901 and established the encyclopædia britannica Company in the US. The company published the first *Britannica Book of the Year* in 1913. (It was discontinued until 1938, then published continually ever since.) Hooper's golfing partner, Sears chairman Julias Rosenwald, bought the company in 1920. After a failed attempt to market the *Britannica* through Sears's mail-order catalog and retail stores, Rosenwald assembled a national sales force to market the books door-to-door. Ex-piano salesman Louis Schoenewald led the effort.

In 1934 the company began printing the *Britannica Junior* (later the *Children's Britannica*) for school children. Ownership was transferred in 1943 to the University of Chicago and university VP William Benton (of Benton and Bowles Advertising Agency fame). Benton built up a nationwide sales force with a hard-sell reputation. Britannica released its first foreign-language encyclopedia in 1957, the *Enciclopedia Barsa*, in Spanish.

In 1964 it acquired G. & C. Merriam Co., publisher of *Webster's Third New International Dictionary*. Britannica bought out rival *Compton's Encyclopedia* in the mid-1970s. In 1987 it published the *Concise Encyclopædia Britannica*, in Chinese. The firm moved into software with the 1989 release of Compton's MultiMedia Encyclopedia. Declining sales led the firm to sell Compton's NewMedia division to Chicago's Tribune Co. in 1993. This move took the company completely out of the CD-ROM business just before the market exploded. It belatedly reentered electronic publishing in 1994 when it released Britannica CD, which provides access to the entire 32-volume encyclopedia on a single CD-ROM for half the price of the printed version.

In 1995 Jacob Safra's group purchased the company. That year it launched Britannica Online, a version of its encyclopedia, on the World Wide Web. Joseph Esposito departed in 1996 after only 9-months as president and CEO. COO James Goulka has taken over until a new CEO is found.

WHO

Chairman and CEO: [position vacant]
COO and CFO: James E. Goulka
EVP International: Thomas A. Gies
EVP, Secretary, and General Counsel: William J. Bowe
VP and Controller: Nancy Wilke
VP Human Resources: Karl Steinberg
Treasurer: Thomas B. Digan

WHERE

HQ: 310 S. Michigan Ave., Chicago, IL 60604
Phone: 312-347-7000
Fax: 312-347-7135
Web site: http://www.eb.com

WHAT

	1995 North American Sales
	% of total
Print encyclopedias & other	84
CD-ROM encyclopedias	16
Total	**100**

***The Encyclopædia Britannica* (Fifteenth Edition)**
32 volumes
7,000 contributors
23,000 illustrations
32,000 pages
65,000 articles
720,000 citations
44 million words
300 megabytes of text

Selected Current and Past Contributors
Isaac Asimov
Marie Curie
Michael Ellis DeBakey
W.E.B. Du Bois
Albert Einstein
Benjamin Franklin
Sigmund Freud
Milton Friedman
Lillian Gish
Thor Heyerdahl
Thomas Henry Huxley
John Locke
John Muir
Linus Pauling
Carl Sagan
George Bernard Shaw
Lorado Taft
Leon Trotsky
Alfred North Whitehead

Selected Publications
The Annals of America
Britannica Atlas
Britannica Book of the Year
Children's Britannica
Children's Britannica Yearbook
Enciclopedia Hispánica (Spanish)
The Encyclopædia Britannica
Encyclopædia Universalis (French)
Great Books of the Western World
Libro del Año (Spanish)
Medical Health Annual
Merriam-Webster's Collegiate Dictionary, Tenth Edition
Webster's New Geographical Dictionary
Webster's Third International Dictionary, Unabridged
Yearbook of Science and the Future
Young Children's Encyclopedia

Other Selected Products and Services
Britannica CD (CD-ROM)
Britannica Online (Internet)

KEY COMPETITORS

Advance Publications
Berkshire Hathaway
Houghton Mifflin
K-III
Lagardère
Microsoft
Oxford University Press
Rand McNally
SoftKey

HOW MUCH

Private company FYE: September 30	Annual Growth	1986	1987	1988	1989	1990	1991	1992	1993	1994	1995
Sales ($ mil.)	(7.0%)	—	—	—	625	650	627	586	540	453	405
Employees	11.6%	—	—	—	1,193	1,247	1,260	2,000	2,350	2,350	2,300

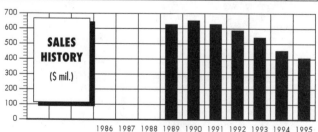

SALES HISTORY ($ mil.)

THE E.W. SCRIPPS COMPANY

OVERVIEW

E.W. Scripps has chosen substance over systems. The Cincinnati-based media conglomerate has signaled a strategic sea change by agreeing to sell its cable TV franchises to cable maven Comcast for about $1.58 billion of the latter's stock. Scripps will return its attention to editorial content and programming of its newspapers (including its flagship *Rocky Mountain News* in Denver), TV production companies, and TV stations.

The company publishes 24 daily and weekly newspapers throughout the US, which accounted for 62% of its 1995 revenues. It owns 9 television stations in the Midwest, Southeast, and Southwest (29% of revenues). The firm's entertainment segment includes Cinetel Productions (cable TV programming), Home & Garden Television (cable TV network), Scripps Howard Productions (TV programming), and United Media, which syndicates comic strips (including "Dilbert" and "Peanuts") and news features. Scripps is seeking to produce a variety of prime time and niche TV programs and has launched a World Wide Web site.

The Edward W. Scripps family trust owns 61% of the firm. The trust will expire with the death of the last of 4 Scripps grandchildren, the youngest of whom is 72.

WHEN

Edward Wyllis Scripps started the first US newspaper chain by launching the *Penny Press* (Cleveland, 1878) and the *Cincinnati Post* (1883). A pioneer of the "people's papers," Scripps described his papers as "schoolrooms" for the barely educated working classes of the day. In 1890, at age 36, Scripps moved to his California ranch, Miramar, from which he conducted business from then on.

In 1907 the company combined 3 wire services to form United Press (UP), later headed by Roy Howard, a Scripps newspaper executive. By WWI the Scripps-McRae League, formed with business manager Milton McRae, had 30 newspapers in 15 states. In 1922 the newspaper groups and news operations were named the E.W. Scripps Company, with Howard as chairman and CEO, and the chain became the Scripps Howard League. The United Feature Service, a UP offshoot, was incorporated in 1923.

The company acquired Denver's *Rocky Mountain News* in 1926. When Scripps died that year, most of the firm's stock went into a trust for his heirs. His son Robert gradually ceded editorial control to the conservative Howard.

In 1931 the company bought the *New York World* and merged it to create the *New York World-Telegram* (later, the *World-Telegram and Sun* and then the *World Journal Tribune*; closed, 1967). Scripps entered broadcasting by buying Cincinnati radio station WCPO in 1935, and in 1937 the radio section of the company became Scripps Howard Radio, Inc.

Ernie Pyle, who died on the battlefield in WWII, was a Scripps Howard reporter. UP employed Walter Cronkite, assigned to London during WWII, and Merriman Smith, dean of White House correspondents for 30 years.

UP absorbed Hearst's International News Service to form United Press International in 1958. Scripps sold the wire service in 1982.

In 1986 and 1987 Scripps sold nondaily papers, business journals, and magazines and bought TV stations and cable systems. In 1986 Scripps bought a newspaper group of 7 California dailies developed independently by a grandson of the founder. The company went public in 1988.

Extensive changes in *Pittsburgh Press* circulation systems led to a delivery employees' strike in 1992; the company sold the paper that year.

Jack Howard, son of Roy Howard and one-time president of both Scripps Howard (1937-1974) and E.W. Scripps (1953-1975), retired in 1993. That year the company sold its book publishing operations and its radio stations.

Scripps's cable channel, Home & Garden TV, won placement on cable systems in exchange for the systems' transmission rights to Scripps TV stations. In 1994 Charles E. Scripps retired as chairman after 41 years at the post. He was succeeded by Lawrence Leser, who retained his role as CEO.

In 1995 United Media signed worldwide licensing agreements with the National Geographic Society and with the Public Broadcasting System. Late that year Scripps's Home & Garden Television division gained access to 4.6 million cable TV subscribers through an affiliation agreement with the National Cable Television Cooperative (an association of 4,100 cable TV systems). In March 1996 Scripps agreed to acquire the *Vero Beach (Florida) Press-Journal*, which has a daily circulation of 33,000.

Chairman: Lawrence A. Leser, age 61, $1,215,000 pay
President and CEO: William R. Burleigh, age 60, $682,500 pay (prior to promotion)
SVP Broadcasting: Paul F. "Frank" Gardner, age 53, $486,400 pay
SVP Finance and Administration: Daniel J. Castellini, age 56, $469,000 pay
SVP Corporate Development: Craig C. Standen, age 53, $455,000 pay
SVP Newspapers: Alan M. Horton, age 52, $455,000 pay
VP and Controller: J. Robert Routt, age 41
VP Human Resources: Gregory L. Ebel, age 40
Auditors: Deloitte & Touche LLP

WHERE

HQ: 312 Walnut St., Ste. 2800, Cincinnati, OH 45202
Phone: 513-977-3000
Fax: 513-977-3721
Web site: http://www.scripps.com

Scripps has information and entertainment properties in 16 states and the District of Columbia.

WHAT

	1995 Sales		1995 Operating Income	
	$ mil.	% of total	$ mil.	% of total
Newspapers	640	62	126	59
Broadcast TV	295	29	87	41
Entertainment	95	9	(15)	—
Adjustment	—	—	(17)	—
Total	**1,030**	**100**	**181**	**100**

Selected Daily Newspapers and Circulation
The Albuquerque Tribune (30,000)
Birmingham Post-Herald (Alabama, 58,200)
The Cincinnati Post (87,400)
The Commercial Appeal (Memphis, 190,200)
El Paso Herald Post (22,300)

The Knoxville News-Sentinel (124,900)
Naples Daily News (Florida, 47,800)
Rocky Mountain News (Denver, 331,000)
The Sun (Bremerton, WA; 35,900)
The Ventura County Star (California, 96,300)

Selected Nondaily Newspapers
Bonita Banner (Bonita Springs, FL)
Sun-Bulletin (Morro Bay, CA)

Scripps Howard News Service (wire service; Washington, DC)

Broadcast Television
KJRH-TV, Tulsa
KNXV-TV, Phoenix
KSHB-TV, Kansas City
WCPO-TV, Cincinnati
WEWS-TV, Cleveland
WFTS-TV, Tampa
WMAR-TV, Baltimore
WPTV-TV, West Palm Beach, FL
WXYZ-TV, Detroit

Entertainment
Cinetel Productions (cable TV programming)
Home & Garden Television (cable TV network)
Scripps Howard Productions (TV programming)
SportSouth (12%, cable TV network)
United Media (licensing and syndication of comics, feature and news)

KEY COMPETITORS

A. H. Belo	Media General
Associated Press	MediaNews
Citicasters	New York Times
Copley Press	News Corp.
Dow Jones	Reuters
Freedom Communications	Times Mirror
Gannett	Tribune
Hearst	Washington Post
Knight-Ridder	Westinghouse/CBS

HOW MUCH

NYSE symbol: SSP FYE: December 31	Annual Growth	1986	1987	1988	1989	1990	1991	1992	1993	1994	1995
Sales ($ mil.)	(0.1%)	1,036	1,147	1,214	1,266	1,296	1,299	1,263	1,205	1,220	1,030
Net income ($ mil.)	16.4%	34	45	70	89	48	65	106	129	123	133
Income as % of sales	—	3.3%	3.9%	5.8%	7.1%	3.7%	5.0%	8.4%	10.7%	10.1%	12.9%
Earnings per share ($)	14.6%	0.49	0.62	0.93	1.14	0.63	0.87	1.43	1.72	1.61	1.67
Stock price – high ($)	—	—	—	18.00	26.50	24.00	24.50	29.00	30.88	31.00	40.63
Stock price – low ($)	—	—	—	14.63	17.00	13.00	14.75	22.13	22.88	23.00	26.75
Stock price – close ($)	12.6%	—	—	17.13	24.00	17.00	24.13	24.75	27.50	30.25	39.38
P/E – high	—	—	—	19	23	38	28	20	18	19	24
P/E – low	—	—	—	16	15	21	17	16	13	14	16
Dividends per share ($)	—	0.00	0.00	0.15	0.35	0.40	0.40	0.40	0.44	0.44	0.50
Book value per share ($)	10.2%	6.20	6.72	7.98	8.43	8.57	9.04	9.83	11.50	13.57	14.88
Employees	(7.3%)	—	—	11,400	9,900	10,000	9,700	8,200	7,600	7,700	6,700

1995 YEAR-END

Debt ratio: 6.4%
Return on equity: 11.7%
Cash (mil.): $30
Current ratio: 1.26
Long-term debt (mil.): $2
No. of shares (mil.): 80
Dividends
  Yield: 1.3%
  Payout: 29.9%
Market value (mil.): $3,153

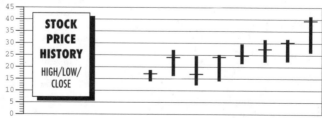

STOCK PRICE HISTORY HIGH/LOW/CLOSE

1986 1987 1988 1989 1990 1991 1992 1993 1994 1995

GANNETT CO., INC.

OVERVIEW

The biggest bird in a flock of US newspaper publishers, Gannett (with 92 daily newspapers under its control) has swallowed the electronic media fish whole. The Arlington, Virginia-based company joined 8 other large newspaper companies in 1995 to create New Century Network, a national online newspaper service. In 1996 it teamed up with newspaper publisher Knight-Ridder and media firm Landmark Communications to form InfiNet, a similar system. Its flagship daily, *USA Today* (with the nation's largest daily circulation), is also published on the Internet and a weekend edition is available on America Online. However, despite Gannett's flight into cyberspace, newspapers (in 38 states, Guam, and the Virgin Islands) still generate most of the company's revenues.

Gannett's other properties include 15 TV stations and 13 radio stations (7 FM and 6 AM), all in major markets, and Gannett News Service. It planned to sell off its billboard group (Mediacom in Canada and Outdoor Network in the US), the largest in North America, to focus on television and newspapers.

Gannett's gullet was large enough to accommodate South Carolina-based Multimedia, Inc. (and its 10 papers, 5 TV stations, and 2 radio stations) in a $2.3 billion deal. The purchase gave Gannett additional print and broadcast properties as well as an entry into cable TV (airing syndicated TV shows for 458,000 subscribers in 5 states) and an alarm security business.

WHEN

In 1906 Frank Gannett started building a newspaper empire when he and his associates purchased a half-interest in the *Elmira* (New York) *Gazette*. The small company expanded slowly, purchasing 2 additional newspapers by 1912. In 1918 the company moved to Rochester, where it acquired 2 more newspapers, and in 1923 Gannett bought out his associates' interests and formed the Gannett Company. In 1929 Frank Gannett invested in the development of the teletypesetter. His company continued to buy small- and medium-size dailies in the Northeast, and by 1947 operated 21 newspapers and 7 radio stations. By the time of Gannett's death in 1957, the company had accumulated 30 newspapers.

In the 1960s Gannett continued its acquisitions, becoming a national newspaper chain. It was not until 1966, however, that Gannett started its own newspaper, *TODAY*, in Cocoa Beach, Florida. Gannett went public in 1967.

The company went through its greatest expansion during the 1970s and 1980s under the direction of Allen Neuharth, who became CEO in 1973 and chairman in 1979. Gannett captured national attention in 1979 when it merged with Phoenix-based Combined Communications Corporation (CCC), another media conglomerate whose holdings included TV and radio stations, an outdoor advertising business (2nd largest in the US), the Louis Harris polling business, the *Cincinnati Enquirer*, and the *Oakland Tribune*. Gannett's revenues passed the $1 billion mark that year.

In 1982 Gannett started *USA TODAY*, a national newspaper whose splashy format and short articles made it an industry novelty. In

1986 it bought the Evening News Association for $717 million, gaining 5 more papers, including the *Detroit News*, and 2 TV stations.

Neuharth retired as chairman of Gannett in 1989. During his 16-year tenure as the company's leader, the outspoken Neuharth had spent approximately $1.5 billion on acquisitions and increased the combined circulation of Gannett's newspapers to 6.3 million. The next year, Gannett's sequence of 89 consecutive quarters of earnings gains was broken.

In 1991 Gannett sold 5 Washington, DC-area newspapers to comply with FCC rules and sold the assets of Little Rock's *Arkansas Gazette* to the *Arkansas Democrat*.

USA TODAY-On-Demand, a fax service for such information as corporate earnings and news, began in 1992. In 1993 *USA TODAY* recorded its first annual profit. That year Gannett sold 4 Missouri radio stations. It sold a TV station in Boston in 1994 and bought one in Little Rock, Arkansas.

In 1995 Gannett bought the *Daily Commercial* (Leesburg, Florida) from the New York Times Co. That year, the company purchased Multimedia Inc., a newspaper, TV, cable, and program syndication company. Gannett also debuted its USA TODAY ONLINE, an electronic complement to *USA TODAY*.

In 1996 Gannett sold its Louis Harris & Associates polling and public policy research firm to Gordon S. Black Corp., a research and consulting company. It also announced it would sell its outdoor advertising operations to Outdoor Systems for $690 million.

WHO

Chairman, President, and CEO: John J. Curley, age 57, $1,650,000 pay
VC, CFO, and Chief Administrative Officer: Douglas H. McCorkindale, age 56, $1,425,000 pay
President, Gannett Newspaper Division: Gary L. Watson, age 50, $780,000 pay
President, Broadcasting Division: Cecil L. Walker, age 59, $600,000 pay
President and Publisher, USA TODAY: Thomas Curley, age 47, $575,000 pay
President, Gannett Outdoor Group: Donald W. Davidson, age 57
SVP Personnel: Richard L. Clapp, age 55
SVP, General Counsel, and Secretary: Thomas L. Chapple, age 48
Auditors: Price Waterhouse LLP

WHERE

HQ: 1100 Wilson Blvd., Arlington, VA 22234
Phone: 703-284-6000
Fax: 703-558-3506
Web site: http://www.gannett.com

Gannett has facilities in 44 states, the District of Columbia, Guam, the US Virgin Islands, Canada, Germany, Hong Kong, Switzerland, and the UK.

WHAT

	1995 Sales	
	$ mil.	% of total
Newspaper advertising	2,220	55
Newspaper circulation	869	22
Broadcasting	466	12
Cable	15	0
Other	437	11
Total	**4,007**	**100**

Selected Daily Newspapers
The Cincinnati Enquirer (204,924 daily circulation)
The Courier-Journal (Louisville; 238,515 daily circulation)
The Des Moines Register (178,330 daily circulation)
The Detroit News (312,093 daily circulation)
The Tennessean (Nashville; 148,856 daily circulation)
USA TODAY (2,072,973 daily circulation)

Selected Nondaily Publications
USA TODAY Baseball Weekly
USA WEEKEND (weekly magazine in 452 newspapers)
Publications (33 states, DC, Guam)

Selected Radio Stations
KHKS (FM), Dallas
KIIS (AM/FM), Los Angeles
KKBH (FM), San Diego
KKBQ (AM/FM), Houston
KSDO (AM), San Diego
WDAE (AM), Tampa-St. Petersburg
WGCI (AM/FM), Chicago

Selected Television Stations
KARE-TV, Minneapolis-St. Paul
KPNX-TV, Phoenix
KSDK-TV, St. Louis
KUSA-TV, Denver
KVUE-TV, Austin
WKYC-TV, Cleveland
WLWT-TV, Cincinnati
WTLV-TV, Jacksonville, FL
WUSA-TV, Washington, DC
WXIA-TV, Atlanta

Selected Other Businesses
Gannett Direct Marketing Services, Inc.
Gannett Media Technologies International (software and other products for publishing industry)
Gannett New Media
Multimedia Cablevision Co.
Multimedia Entertainment Co. (syndicated TV programming)

KEY COMPETITORS

Advance Publications	E.W. Scripps	McClatchy Newspapers
A. H. Belo	Freedom Communications	Media General
Associated Press	Hearst	New York Times
Central Newspapers	Heritage Media	News Corp.
Clear Channel	Hollinger Inc.	Times Mirror
Cox Enterprises	Journal Communications	Tribune
Dow Jones	Knight-Ridder	Washington Post
		Westinghouse

HOW MUCH

NYSE symbol: GCI FYE: Last Sunday in December	Annual Growth	1986	1987	1988	1989	1990	1991	1992	1993	1994	1995
Sales ($ mil.)	4.1%	2,801	3,079	3,314	3,518	3,441	3,382	3,469	3,641	3,824	4,007
Net income ($ mil.)	6.3%	276	319	365	398	377	302	346	398	465	477
Income as % of sales	—	9.9%	10.4%	11.0%	11.3%	11.0%	8.9%	10.0%	10.9%	12.2%	11.9%
Earnings per share ($)	8.0%	1.71	1.98	2.26	2.47	2.36	2.00	2.40	2.72	3.23	3.41
Stock price – high ($)	—	43.56	56.25	39.88	49.88	44.50	47.00	54.00	58.25	59.00	64.88
Stock price – low ($)	—	29.63	26.00	29.25	34.50	29.50	35.13	41.25	46.75	46.13	49.50
Stock price – close ($)	6.1%	36.06	39.13	35.63	43.50	36.13	45.50	50.75	57.25	53.25	61.38
P/E – high	—	26	28	18	20	19	24	23	21	18	19
P/E – low	—	17	13	13	14	13	18	17	17	14	15
Dividends per share ($)	5.6%	0.84	0.92	1.00	1.08	1.20	1.24	1.25	1.29	1.33	1.37
Book value per share ($)	6.2%	8.88	9.94	11.09	12.40	12.98	10.71	10.94	12.98	13.04	15.26
Employees	0.9%	36,000	36,000	37,000	36,650	36,600	36,700	36,700	36,500	36,000	39,100

1995 YEAR-END

Debt ratio: 57.1%
Return on equity: 24.1%
Cash (mil.): $47
Current ratio: 1.05
Long-term debt (mil.): $2,768
No. of shares (mil.): 141
Dividends
  Yield: 2.2%
  Payout: 40.2%
Market value (mil.): $8,628

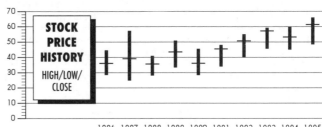

STOCK PRICE HISTORY HIGH/LOW/CLOSE

GRANADA GROUP PLC

OVERVIEW

There is more to Granada than television programming and broadcasting. The London-based company also operates leisure businesses (including nightclubs, theme parks, and hotels), rents out electronic equipment (TVs, mobile phones, VCRs, and PCs), and is the largest independent provider of computer maintenance in Europe. Granada, which is licensed to broadcast in London and the northwest of England by the UK's commercial Independent Television Network, is the 2nd largest provider of original TV programming in the UK (after the state-owned British Broadcasting Corporation, or BBC). It is also an 11% shareholder of media maven Rupert Murdoch's satellite TV company, British Sky Broadcasting. The company's leisure and ser-

vices businesses include contract catering, clothing rental, and travel services.

Granada is expanding the 2 areas of business it is historically most familiar with — television and leisure services. Having acquired a TV station (LWT) a year earlier, it went on the road again in 1995 with the $190 million acquisition of Pavilion freeway services (gas stations and restaurants). Pavilion's service sites in Northwest England and Wales complement Granada's freeway service centers in other parts of the country. In a major expansion move, the company acquired the Forte hotel group for roughly $6 billion in 1996 and subsequently made plans to sell some hotels to pay down debt.

WHEN

The Bernsteins, the founding family of Granada, began their involvement in show business in England in the early years of this century. In 1908 Alexander Bernstein opened the Edmonton Empire music hall. During the 1920s sons Cecil and Sidney set up a chain of movie theaters. The company was incorporated as Granada Theatres Ltd. in 1934 and went public the next year. Between 1936 and 1938 it opened a cinema every 3 months.

Following WWII, the company moved into commercial television, applying for a TV broadcasting license in 1948. After the passing of the 1954 Broadcasting Act, which authorized commercial broadcasting and broke the state monopoly of the BBC, Granada was granted a license to broadcast in the north of England. The company launched its first TV programs in 1956. The next year the firm changed its corporate name to Granada Group Ltd. Among the early original programming were the regional soap opera *Coronation Street* (1960), which later emerged as a long-running series and is currently viewed around the world, and current affairs show *World in Action* (1963).

The company diversified its activities in the 1960s, opening its first TV rental showroom in 1961, Granada Motorway Services (food and gas) in 1964, and a bowling center in 1965. By 1967 it was operating over 200 TV rental showrooms nationwide, and by 1973 it had 65 non-UK showrooms in operation. Lord Sidney Bernstein retired in 1979 and nephew Alex took over the top slot.

Granada moved into the travel business in 1982 with the acquisition of MCH, a travel

firm that provided mobile home- and self-catering vacations around the Mediterranean. The next year it launched Granada Microcomputer Services and Granada Cable and Satellite to cater to the emerging computer and telecommunications markets. The company's TV programs in the 1980s included *Brideshead Revisited* (1982) and *The Jewel in the Crown* (1984), both of which were met with international acclaim. In 1990 a group of media companies, including Granada and Pearson, merged with Rupert Murdoch's rival Sky cable station to form satellite service British Sky Broadcasting.

The company ran into trouble in the early 1990s when, overextended and facing a recession, it experienced stagnant sales and dropping profits. In 1991 Granada sold its bingo businesses (part of its leisure group activities) and its Canadian rental business to pay down debt. That year the firm hired Irish-born Gerry Robinson, a former executive of large diversified food company Grand Metropolitan, as chief executive. The new broom swept clean; Robinson fired nearly all of the senior management his first year in office.

Granada acquired the Sutcliffe Group, a major catering firm, from cruise operators P & O in 1993. In 1995 the company purchased Direct Vision Rentals, a TV and video recorder rental business.

In 1996 Alex Bernstein stepped down and Robinson replaced him as chairman. Granada TV head Charles Allen was appointed as chief executive.

Chairman: Gerry J. Robinson, age 47
CEO; Chairman, Granada Media Group: Charles Allen, age 38
Chief Executive, UK Rental; Chairman, Computer Services and International Rental: Graham Wallace, age 47
Finance Director: Henry Staunton, age 47
Commmercial Director: Graham Parrott, age 47
Personnel Director: Stephanie Monk, age 52
Auditors: KPMG Peat Marwick LLP

WHERE

HQ: 36 Golden Square, London, W1R 4AH, UK
Phone: +44-71-734-8080
Fax: +44-71-494-2893

WHAT

	1995 Sales
	% of total
Rental & computer services	32
Leisure & Services	
Services to business	21
Leisure	16
Workplace services	4
Television	
London Weekend Television	14
Granada Television	13
Total	**100**

Rental and Computer Services
Granada Computer Services International Ltd.
Granada Computer Services (UK) Ltd.
Granada Hospital Group Inc. (US)
Granada Hospital Services Inc. (Canada)
Granada Insurance Ltd.
Granada UK Rental and Retail Ltd.
Telerent Fernseh-Mietservice GmbH & Co. KG (Germany)

UK Consumer Electronics Ltd.
UK Retail Ltd.

Leisure and Services
Granada Contract Services Ltd.
Granada Hospitality Ltd.
Granada Services Group Ltd.
Granada Studios Tours Ltd.
Granada Theme Park & Hotels Ltd.
Granada Travel PLC
Granada Vending Services Ltd.
Spring Grove Services Group Ltd.
Sutcliffe Catering Group Ltd.

Television
Granada LWT International Ltd.
Granada Television Ltd.
London Weekend Television Ltd.
LWT (Holdings) plc

KEY COMPETITORS

Acal	ICL PLC
Accor	Johnson Group Cleaners
Amstrad	NYNEX
Anglia	Pearson
BBC	Rank
Carlton	SBC Cablecomms
Comcast	TCI
Danka	THORN EMI
Davis	Time Warner
Dixons Group	Yorkshire-Tyne Tees
Heath	Television Holdings
HTV Group	

HOW MUCH

Principal exchange: London FYE: September 30	Annual Growth	1986	1987	1988	1989	1990	1991	1992	1993	1994	1995
Sales (L mil.)	11.8%	841	1,020	1,468	1,636	1,392	1,392	1,340	1,615	2,098	2,301
Net income (L mil.)	22.7%	40	82	101	121	67	10	77	126	192	253
Income as % of sales	—	4.7%	8.0%	6.9%	7.4%	4.8%	0.7%	5.7%	7.8%	9.2%	11.0%
Earnings per share (p)	8.3%	20	24	27	29	22	12	15	25	32	41
Stock price – high (p)	—	309	375	337	393	351	212	383	542	600	710
Stock price – low (p)	—	190	222	266	266	122	124	186	388	472	475
Stock price – close (p)	9.6%	283	286	313	327	174	192	376	520	510	645
P/E – high	—	15	15	12	14	16	18	26	22	19	17
P/E – low	—	9	9	10	9	6	11	12	16	15	12
Dividends per share (p)	(1.3%)	9	10	11	12	12	7	8	9	10	8
Book value per share (p)	(2.2%)	12	14	15	17	17	13	13	10	9	10
Employees	8.8%	18,331	19,800	27,977	27,782	25,257	22,562	18,385	28,025	42,878	39,085

1995 YEAR-END

Debt ratio: 48.7%
Return on equity: 46.5%
Cash (mil.): L181
Current ratio: 0.76
Long-term debt (mil.): L456
No. of shares (mil.): 585
Dividends
  Yield: 1.2%
  Payout: 19.3%
Market value (mil.): $5,978
Sales (mil): $3,647

Note: L = $1.58 (September 30, 1995)

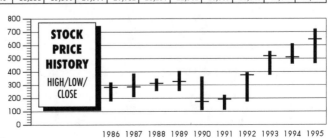

STOCK PRICE HISTORY
HIGH/LOW/CLOSE
1986 1987 1988 1989 1990 1991 1992 1993 1994 1995

HARCOURT GENERAL, INC.

OVERVIEW

Harcourt General believes in the basics: reading, writing, and retail. Based in the Boston suburb of Chestnut Hill, the company has redefined its core businesses as scholarly publishing (Harcourt Brace and Holt, Rinehart and Winston) and upscale department stores (Neiman Marcus and Bergdorf Goodman). The company also offers professional services (Drake Beam Morin).

Harcourt Brace is among the world's largest publishing houses, publishing books, scholarly journals, and related materials in print and electronic forms. The company is involved in a joint venture with educational software publisher Edmark to develop new lines of software for the elementary school market. The

Psychological Corporation, Harcourt's publisher of assessment exams, acquired Assessment Systems, a provider of electronic testing and licensing services, in 1995.

The Neiman Marcus Group, 67% of which is owned by Harcourt, focuses on the upscale retail market. In 1995 Neiman Marcus abandoned the junior retail market by selling its ailing Contempo Casuals subsidiary to Wet Seal for 250,000 shares of Wet Seal stock and $100,000 cash.

The company also owns Drake Beam Morin, which helps employers provide job search and placement services to laid-off employees. This unit has been hit hard by heavy competition in the outplacement services business.

WHEN

In 1919 Alfred Harcourt and Donald Brace, former classmates at Columbia University, quit their jobs at Henry Holt & Company and joined Will Howe to begin their own publishing firm in New York. The company was called Harcourt, Brace and Howe. Howe left in less than a year, and Harcourt and Brace changed the company's name to Harcourt, Brace and Company. In the following years, the company published such notable works as *The Economic Consequences of Peace* by John Maynard Keynes, and *Main Street* and *Arrowsmith* by Sinclair Lewis. In the 1920s Harcourt, Brace diversified into other areas of publishing, including religious works and high school and college textbooks.

In 1942 Alfred Harcourt turned over the company's operations to Donald Brace. William Jovanovich joined the company in 1947 as a $50-per-week salesman. Eight years later, after the deaths of Alfred Harcourt and Donald Brace (1954 and 1955, respectively), Jovanovich was elected president of the firm.

During the 1960s and 1970s, Jovanovich diversified Harcourt, Brace into other publishing and nonrelated areas. Merging with World Book Company in 1960, the company became the largest publisher of elementary, secondary, and college materials in the US and changed its name to Harcourt, Brace & World, Inc. Also in 1960 Jovanovich took the company public. The 1967 purchase of Harvest Publishing Co., which sold farm journals and life insurance, provided Harcourt, Brace its entry into the insurance business. In 1970 Jovanovich became chairman, and the company became Harcourt Brace Jovanovich (HBJ). The company bought

the Psychological Corporation in 1970 and Sea World in 1976.

Throughout the 1980s HBJ continued its acquisitions, including theme parks, publishers, and insurance companies. In 1984 HBJ moved its headquarters from New York City to Orlando, Florida. Three years later the company tripled its debt fighting a hostile takeover from British Printing and Communications Corp. Jovanovich retired as chairman in 1990.

In 1991 HBJ was acquired by General Cinema for $1.5 billion. The movie-theater pioneer had been founded in 1922 as Philip Smith Theatrical Enterprises. Smith's son, Richard, took over in 1961, and the company was renamed General Cinema in 1964. In 1984 General Cinema bought 37% of Carter Hawley Hale, which controlled Neiman Marcus.

Neiman Marcus was founded in 1907 by the Neiman and Marcus families and popularized many new retailing and fashion concepts, including gift wrapping (1928) and his-and-hers gifts (1960).

In 1993 General Cinema was renamed Harcourt General and its General Cinema theaters were spun off as GC Companies. In 1994 Drake Beam Morin, Harcourt's consulting firm, bought its UK affiliate. That year Harcourt sold its insurance companies to GNA Corp., GE Capital's affiliate, for $410 million.

In 1995 publishing unit Academic Press announced plans to make its journals available on the Internet. Harcourt Brace International closed its Orlando-based export operations and opened its new headquarters in London that year in an effort to increase its international presence.

Chairman: Richard A. Smith, age 71, $1,275,000 pay
President, CEO, and COO: Robert J. Tarr Jr., age 52, $2,625,000 pay
President and CEO, Harcourt Brace & Co.: Brian J. Knez, age 38, $454,306 pay
Chairman and CEO, Neiman Marcus Stores: Burton Tansky
Chairman and CEO, Bergdorf Goodman: Stephen C. Elkin
President and COO, Drake Beam Morin: Charles F. Albrecht Jr.
SVP and CFO: John R. Cook, age 54, $506,250 pay
SVP, General Counsel, and Secretary: Eric P. Geller, age 48, $438,750 pay
Group VP: Robert A. Smith, age 36
VP Corporate Relations: Peter Farwell, age 52
VP and Treasurer: Paul F. Gibbons, age 44
VP General Auditor: Michael F. Panutich, age 47
VP and Controller: Stephen C. Richards, age 40
VP Planning and Analysis: Craig B. Sawin, age 39
VP Human Resources: Gerald T. Hughes, age 39
Auditors: Deloitte & Touche LLP

HQ: 27 Boylston St., Chestnut Hill, MA 02167
Phone: 617-232-8200
Fax: 617-278-5397

Harcourt General has publishing operations in Australia, Canada, Japan, the UK, and the US. Drake Beam Morin provides outplacement consulting services worldwide. The company also operates 28 Neiman-Marcus stores in 25 US cities and 2 Bergdorf Goodman stores in New York City.

	1995 Revenues		1995 Operating Income	
	$ mil.	% of total	$ mil.	% of total
Retailing	1,888	62	162	46
Publishing	1,018	34	177	50
Professional services	129	4	13	4
Adjustments	—	—	(34)	—
Total	**3,035**	**100**	**318**	**100**

Retail
Bergdorf Goodman
Neiman Marcus
NM Direct (direct mail catalog sales)

Selected Publishing
Academic Press
Assessment Systems
Harcourt Brace & Co.
Harcourt Brace Professional Publishing
Holt, Rinehart and Winston
The Psychological Corp.
WB Saunders

Professional Services
Drake Beam Morin

Advance Publications	Houghton Mifflin	Reed Elsevier
Barneys	J. Crew	Saks
Bertelsmann	John Wiley	Scholastic
Brown Group	Lands' End	Spiegel
Dayton Hudson	The Limited	Steck Vaughn
Dillard	May	Tiffany
Federated	McGraw-Hill	Time Warner
Golden Books	News Corp.	Tribune
Hearst	Nordstrom	Viacom
	Pearson	

NYSE symbol: H FYE: October 31	Annual Growth	1986	1987	1988	1989	1990	1991	1992	1993	1994	1995
Sales ($ mil.)	13.2%	997	1,038	2,323	1,913	2,149	3,587	3,716	3,655	3,154	3,035
Net income ($ mil.)	3.1%	126	69	88	972	111	(293)	114	171	178	166
Income as % of sales	—	12.6%	6.7%	3.8%	50.8%	5.2%	—	3.1%	4.7%	5.6%	5.5%
Earnings per share ($)	2.6%	1.72	0.94	1.19	13.16	1.51	(3.88)	1.44	2.15	2.22	2.16
Stock price – high ($)	—	29.50	31.75	25.75	28.50	27.00	24.75	36.63	46.13	39.50	45.75
Stock price – low ($)	—	18.31	13.75	15.75	23.13	16.50	16.50	18.00	31.25	30.25	32.38
Stock price – close ($)	7.3%	22.13	19.38	25.50	25.75	19.50	19.00	36.50	36.25	35.25	41.88
P/E – high	—	17	34	22	2	18	—	25	22	18	21
P/E – low	—	11	15	13	2	11	—	13	15	14	15
Dividends per share ($)	10.7%	0.26	0.32	0.37	0.41	0.45	0.49	0.53	0.57	0.61	0.65
Book value per share ($)	6.6%	7.25	7.87	8.75	22.28	23.35	6.24	12.08	13.58	13.43	12.93
Employees	2.2%	12,500	14,900	27,714	24,200	25,500	32,641	33,090	30,166	15,430	15,219

1995 YEAR-END

Debt ratio: 46.1%
Return on equity: 16.7%
Cash (mil.): $607
Current ratio: 2.05
Long-term debt (mil.): $749
No. of shares (mil.): 73
Dividends
  Yield: 1.6%
  Payout: 30.1%
Market value (mil.): $3,045

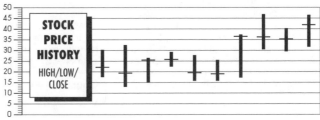

STOCK PRICE HISTORY HIGH/LOW/CLOSE
1986 1987 1988 1989 1990 1991 1992 1993 1994 1995

HAVAS S.A.

OVERVIEW

Havas's web of diversified subsidiaries gets top marks for its intricacy. The company, the world's 5th largest communications group, has organized its vast holdings into 5 general departments: advertising, audiovisual, directories and billboards, publishing and news, and travel and recreation.

The advertising arm, Havas Advertising, is Europe's #1 agency (the world's 8th largest), with 200 affiliates in 60 countries. In the audiovisual sector, Havas has operations in radio, TV, film production, and in-cinema advertising. Its CANAL+ affiliate is one of the world's largest pay-TV operators, and its CLT subsidiary is Europe's #1 commercial TV and radio venture, with 30 television and radio stations.

The company's Havas Media Communication subsidiary is France's leading publisher of directories and circulars, its #1 home delivery press distributor, and the leader in ad sales for regional publications. Havas Media Communication is also Europe's leading billboard advertising agency. With about 50 book imprints and ownership of several of France's leading newsmagazines (*L'Express*, *Le Point*), Havas's C.E.P Communication subsidiary is one of Europe's largest publishers.

Havas Tourisme, the company's travel and recreation subsidiary, is France's largest travel agent. Havas Voyages American Express, a business-travel joint venture concluded with American Express France in 1996, extends Havas's reach into the international travel market. Havas Edition Electronique produces and distributes CD-ROMs and researches new electronic technologies.

WHEN

Charles-Louis Havas, a former banker, importer, and newspaper publisher, launched a news publication in 1832, 2 years after King Louis-Philippe allowed freedom of the press in France. The bulletin provided French newspapers with translations of foreign publications. In 1835 Havas began providing translations of French newspapers for foreign publications and changed the company's name to Agence Havas. The company expanded to become a full-fledged news agency.

In 1852 Havas added France's first publicity agency. Charles died in 1858, 5 years after turning control of the business over to his sons. To further expand its news gathering abilities, the company signed agreements with news agencies in Britain and Germany (Reuters and Wolff, respectively, whose founders were former Havas employees) to divide up territories and share information.

While it was expanding its reach geographically, the company also got a solid grip on its home territory. In 1862 it signed a deal with the French minister of the interior to be France's official news agency. It began trading on the Paris Stock Exchange in 1879.

Havas continued to grow and increase its powerful position in the French media, thanks to its dual operations of news and publicity. Businesses and foreign governments hired the company to place favorable news stories to tilt public opinion. During WWI Havas distributed propaganda for the French government.

Following the war, the company began to sign exclusive agreements to place advertising in newspapers. By 1930 Havas had exclusive rights to over 200 newspapers.

During WWII the Germans took control of Havas, and it became a propagandist for the Vichy government. After the war the company was accused of collaboration with the Germans, and it was nationalized.

Havas continued to expand, entering the leisure and tourism industry through Havas Tourisme. In 1973 the company reorganized and placed its advertising operations under a newly formed company, Eurocom.

The company entered the television broadcasting business in 1984 when it launched CANAL+, a pay-television service. In 1987 the French government privatized Havas. That year Eurocom expanded into management consulting when it acquired Bernard Juilhet.

Eurocom merged with publicity group RSCG in 1992 to form EURO RSCG. In 1994 Havas formed a joint venture, NHL Partners, with Turner Broadcasting's New Line Cinema to develop interactive software. In 1995 the company acquired telecommunication giant Alcatel Alsthom's publishing operations in exchange for a 21% stake in Havas.

In 1996 an expected TV alliance with British Sky Broadcasting, Germany's Bertelsmann, and CANAL+ to form Newco, a European digital pay TV network, soured when BSkyB announced it was pulling out of the agreement.

Chairman and CEO: Pierre Dauzier
EVP: Jean-François Meaudre
EVP: Nicolas Duhamel: Nicolas Duhamel
EVP: Philippe Sahut d'Izarn
CEO and President, Havas Media Communication:
Michel Boutinard Rouelle
CEO and President, Groupe C.E.P Communication:
Christian Bregou
CEO and President, Havas Tourisme:
Christophe Charpentier
CEO and President, Havas Intermediation: Guy Gervais
CEO and President, CANAL+: Pierre Lescure
CEO and President, Havas Advertising:
Alain de Pouzilhac
CFO: Guy Saigne
Legal Director: Arnaud Ingen-Housz
Communications Director: Anne Brucy
EVP and CFO, EURO RSCG Holdings (US):
Robert W. Parker
VP Administration (HR), EURO RSCG Holdings (US):
James Fuller
Auditors: Cabinet Constantin; Salustro Reydel;
KPMG Audit

WHERE

HQ: 136, Avenue Charles de Gaulle, 92522,
Neuilly-sur-Seine Cédex, France
Phone: +33-1-47-47-30-00
Fax: +33-1-47-47-32-32
US HQ: EURO RSCG Holdings, 350 Hudson St.,
New York, NY 10014
US Phone: 212-886-2000
US Fax: 212-886-4428
Web site: http://www.havas.fr

	1995 Sales
	% of total
France	66
Other countries	34
Total	**100**

WHAT

	1995 Pretax Income	
	FF mil.	% of total
Information & publishing	888	38
Audiovisual	743	32
Directories & billboards	524	23
Advertising	88	4
Travel & recreation	71	3
Adjustments	(102)	—
Total	**2,212**	**100**

Selected Subsidiaries and Affiliates

Adways (50%)	Havas Media
Audiofina (52%)	Communication
Avenir	Havas Media Hebdos
CANAL+ (24%)	Havas Régies
CANAL+ DA (25%)	Havas Tourisme
C.E.P Communication	Havas Voyages American
(73%)	Express (81%)
CLMM (40%)	IP
CLT (96%)	Maeva (50.1%)
Comareg	Mediavision (33%)
Europoster	Métrobus (50%)
Groupe de la Cité (98%)	MK2 (20%)
Havas Advertising (39%)	Oda
Havas DOM	Peaktime
Havas Intermediation	Pearl & Dean
	Télé Images (44%)

KEY COMPETITORS

Bertelsmann	Lagardère	Time Warner
Bozell, Jacobs	McGraw-Hill	Viacom
Carlson	News Corp.	VNU
Cordiant	Omnicom Group	Wolters Kluwer
Dentsu	Pearson	WPP Group
Harcourt General	Reed Elsevier	Young &
Houghton Mifflin	Thomson Corp.	Rubicam
Interpublic		
Group		

HOW MUCH

Principal exchange: Paris FYE: December 31	Annual Growth	1986	1987	1988	1989	1990	1991	1992	1993	1994	1995
Sales (FF mil.)	16.5%	11,299	13,709	15,796	18,870	23,661	26,497	28,183	34,957	37,751	44,626
Net income (FF mil.)	7.6%	458	551	751	975	1,154	1,083	823	708	936	886
Income as % of sales	—	4.1%	4.0%	4.8%	5.2%	4.9%	4.1%	2.9%	2.0%	2.5%	2.0%
Earnings per share (FF)	(6.3%)	—	—	22	28	30	28	19	16	19	14
Stock price – high (FF)	—	221	221	281	555	710	574	552	500	494	500
Stock price – low (FF)	—	78	150	139	259	420	361	355	402	398	402
Stock price – close (FF)	9.7%	193	150	265	527	437	444	433	445	417	445
P/E – high	—	—	—	13	20	24	20	28	32	26	36
P/E – low	—	—	—	6	9	14	13	18	26	21	29
Dividends per share (FF)	20.4%	1.60	3.00	4.10	5.80	6.90	8.00	8.00	8.00	8.00	8.50
Book value per share (FF)	18.4%	43	64	139	148	171	220	190	196	199	196
Employees	10.3%	—	—	9,407	11,383	11,904	12,462	12,430	18,628	18,324	18,628

1995 YEAR-END

Debt ratio: 25.2%
Return on equity: 8.0%
Cash (mil.): FF3,489
Long-term debt (mil.): FF4,150
No. of shares (mil.): 64
Dividends
Yield: 1.9%
Payout: 61.0%
Market value (mil.): $5,808
Sales (mil.): $9,091

Note: $ = FF4.9 (December 31, 1995)

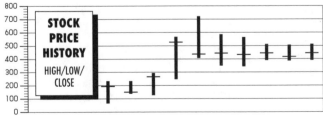

STOCK PRICE HISTORY HIGH/LOW/CLOSE 1986 1987 1988 1989 1990 1991 1992 1993 1994 1995

THE HEARST CORPORATION

OVERVIEW

Like legendary founder William Randolph Hearst's castle, Hearst Corporation is BIG. New York City-based Hearst has its fingers in many media pies, including newspaper, magazine, book, and business publishing; TV and radio broadcasting; cable network programming; and online services. The family owned company owns 11 daily newspapers (including the *San Antonio Express-News* and *Houston Chronicle*) and 6 weeklies; 16 US consumer magazines (including *Cosmopolitan, Popular Mechanics, Good Housekeeping*, and *Redbook*); stakes in 5 cable TV networks (in-cluding A&E and ESPN); 6 TV and 6 radio stations; and major book and business publishers. While it no longer owns Hearst Castle (deeded to the State of California in 1951), the company has extensive real estate holdings.

Hearst has joined 8 other large newspaper companies to create New Century Network, a national online newspaper service. It also teamed up with Knight-Ridder, Times Mirror, Adobe Systems, and TCI, to acquire a stake in Netscape Communications, a leading Internet software provider. Hearst also bought a stake in KidSoft, an educational software company.

WHEN

William Randolph Hearst, son of a California mining magnate, started his empire as a reporter, having been expelled from Harvard in 1884 for playing jokes on professors. He became editor of the *San Francisco Examiner*, which his father had obtained as payment for a gambling debt, in 1887. Hearst's sensationalist style brought financial success to the paper. In 1895 he bought the *New York Morning Journal* and competed against the *New York World*, owned by Joseph Pulitzer, Hearst's first employer. The "yellow journalism" resulting from that rivalry characterized American-style reporting at the turn of the century. Hearst used his newspapers as a forum for his personal and political views for more than 30 years.

The company branched out into magazines (1903), film (1913), and radio (1928). The Hearst organization owned 13 newspapers and 7 magazines by 1920 and pioneered film journalism throughout the 1920s with the Hearst-Selig News Pictorial. In 1935 the company was at its peak, with newspapers in 19 cities (nearly 14% of total US daily and 24% of Sunday circulation), the largest syndicate (King Features), international news and photo services, 13 magazines, 8 radio stations, and 2 motion picture companies. Two years later Hearst had to relinquish control of the company to avoid bankruptcy, selling movie companies, radio stations, magazines, and, later, most of his San Simeon estate to reduce debt. (Hearst's rise and fall inspired Orson Welles's 1941 film *Citizen Kane*.)

In 1948 Hearst became the owner of one of the first TV stations in the US, WBAL-TV in Baltimore. When he died in 1951, Richard Berlin, in charge of the company since 1940,

became CEO. During his tenure Berlin sold off failing newspapers but also moved into television and acquired more magazines. The Hearst family retained control through a family trust.

Frank Bennack Jr., president and CEO since 1979, expanded the company, acquiring daily and weekly newspapers in several major cities, publishing companies (notably William Morrow, 1981), 3 TV stations (in 1981, 1982, and 1986), magazines (*Redbook*, 1982; *Esquire*, 1986), and 20% of cable sports network ESPN (1991). Hearst branched into video via a joint venture with Capital Cities/ABC (1981) and helped launch the Lifetime and Arts & Entertainment cable channels (1984). It closed the Los Angeles *Herald Examiner* in 1989.

Hearst teamed up with *Izvestia* (1990) to start a newspaper in Russia and with Dow Jones (1992) to publish *SmartMoney*, a personal finance magazine. Also in 1992 the company closed the *Light* in San Antonio after buying its competitor, the *Express-News*, and launched a New England news network with Continental Cablevision. The following year Hearst brought on board former FCC chairman Alfred Sikes, who quickly moved the company onto the information superhighway. It also bought a stake in a California electronic publisher to put Hearst magazines online.

The company opened the Hearst New Media Center at its New York headquarters in 1994 to orient its employees in electronic media and the creation of digital products. In 1996 Randolph A. Hearst (the sole surviving son of the founder) passed the title of chairman, a position he held for 23 years, to George Hearst Jr., his nephew.

WHO

Chairman: George R. Hearst Jr., age 68
President and CEO: Frank A. Bennack Jr.
EVP and COO: Gilbert C. Maurer
President, Hearst Magazines: Cathleen P. Black
SVP, CFO, and Chief Legal Officer; Group Head, Hearst Books/Business Publishing: Victor F. Ganzi
VP; General Manager, Hearst Broadcasting: John G. Conomikes
VP; General Manager, Hearst Newspapers: Robert J. Danzig
VP; President, Hearst New Media and Technology: Alfred C. Sikes
VP and Director Human Resources: Kenneth A. Feldman

WHERE

HQ: 959 Eighth Ave., New York, NY 10019
Phone: 212-649-2000
Fax: 212-765-3528
Web site: http://www.hearstcorp.com

WHAT

Selected Businesses

Book Publishing
Avon Books
William Morrow & Co.

Broadcasting

KMBC-TV, Kansas City	WISN-TV, Milwaukee
WBAL (AM) Baltimore	WIYY (FM), Baltimore
WBAL-TV, Baltimore	WLTQ (FM), Milwaukee
WCVB-TV, Boston	WTAE (AM), Pittsburgh
WDTN-TV, Dayton, OH	WTAE-TV, Pittsburgh
WISN (AM), Milwaukee	WVTY (FM), Pittsburgh

Business Publishing
American Druggist
Diversion
Electronic Products
First DataBank Blue Book (drug database)
Motor

Entertainment and Syndication
A&E Network (minority stake)
ESPN and ESPN2 (20%)
Hearst/ABC Video Services (joint venture)
Hearst Animation Productions
Hearst Entertainment Distribution
Hearst Entertainment Productions
The History Channel (minority stake)

King Features Syndicate
Lifetime Television (minority stake)
New England Cable News (joint venture with Continental Cablevision)

Magazines

Colonial Homes	*Motor Boating & Sailing*
Cosmopolitan	*Popular Mechanics*
Country Living	*Redbook*
Esquire	*SmartMoney* (joint venture
Good Housekeeping	with Dow Jones)
Harper's Bazaar	*Sports Afield*
House Beautiful	*Town & Country*
Marie Claire	*Victoria*

Major Newspapers
Albany (NY) Times Union
Houston Chronicle
San Antonio Express-News
San Francisco Examiner
Seattle Post-Intelligencer

New Media and Technology
Books That Work (minority stake, home-improvement software)
Hearst New Media Center (orientation of employees in new technologies)
HomeArts (online home and garden information)
KidSoft (minority stake, educational software)
The Multimedia Newsstand (Internet service)
Netscape Communications (minority stake)
New Century Network (minority stake, online newspaper services)

Other
Real estate (agricultural operations in California, timberlands in Canada and California, and commercial properties in New York City and San Francisco)

KEY COMPETITORS

Advance Publications	MediaNews
Bertelsmann	New York Times
Bloomberg	News Corp.
Chronicle Publishing	Reader's Digest
Cox Enterprises	Reed Elsevier
E.W. Scripps	Time Warner
Freedom Communications	Times Mirror
Gannett	Tribune
K-III	Viacom
Knight-Ridder	Walt Disney
Lagardère	Washington Post
McGraw-Hill	Westinghouse

HOW MUCH

Private company FYE: December 31	Annual Growth	1986	1987	1988	1989	1990	1991	1992	1993	1994	1995
Sales ($ mil.)	4.8%	1,529	1,886	1,986	2,094	2,138	1,888	1,973	2,174	2,299	2,331
Employees	1.3%	12,000	15,000	15,000	14,000	13,950	14,000	13,000	13,500	14,000	13,500

The Hearst Corporation

SALES HISTORY ($ mil.)

HOLLINGER INC.

What's led by Black and read all over? Toronto-based Hollinger, which is piloted by Conrad Black and invests in and owns newspapers around the globe. Its main subsidiary, Hollinger International, publishes daily and nondaily newspapers, with a total circulation of 4.3 million.

Hollinger International operations include the Telegraph plc, which publishes the *Daily Telegraph* (the largest nontabloid daily in the UK, with a readership of 2.6 million), other UK publications, and the Electronic Telegraph, the most popular European site on the World Wide Web. The Telegraph has a stake in John Fairfax Holdings, which prints Australia's *Sydney Morning Herald*, the (Melbourne) *Age*, and the country's only business daily, the *Australian Financial Review*. The Telegraph also has a stake in Southam Inc., Canada's largest publisher of daily papers.

Through the Sun-Times Company, Hollinger International publishes the *Chicago Sun-Times*, the *Daily Southtown*, and 69 paid nondaily community papers in the greater Chicago area. American Publishing Company, Hollinger International's community group, publishes 188 paid daily and nondaily newspapers and 176 free papers in rural communities of 29 states. Hollinger International also owns Jerusalem Post Publications, which prints Israel's #1 English-language daily and 3 nondailies. In addition to Hollinger International, Hollinger Inc. owns Sterling Newspaper Group (more than 50 papers) and UniMedia Inc. (3 dailies in Quebec).

Hollinger focuses on acquiring financially unstable papers and others that are performing poorly due to bad management. By cutting costs, refinancing debt, and making other changes, the company tries to return them to profitability. With this strategy, Hollinger has expanded its empire around the world. Chairman Black owns 49% of the company.

Conrad Black was a born entrepreneur. He bought his first share of stock, in carmaker General Motors, at age 8. Six years later, he was selling exams to his classmates at a prominent Toronto private school. (He was expelled, his ingenuity unappreciated.) Black started in the publishing business in 1969 when he and his associate, Peter White, founded Sterling Newspapers and bought the *Sherbrooke Record*. The 2 added a group of small daily papers in British Columbia and extensions in Quebec and Prince Edward Island. In 1975 Black bought his father's 22% of the Ravelston Corporation, which owned Argus, a company formed in 1945 by E. P. Taylor to invest in breweries, malting and bottling operations, and a chemical business. In the late 1970s Black was able to take out a large enough loan (in Sterling's name) to buy control of Ravelston.

After assuming the leadership of Argus (through Ravelston), Black set about selling off chunks of the business to increase the value of his investment and refine the company's holdings to a few key businesses. In 1981 he began liquidating Argus's Dominion Stores grocery chain, primarily to the A&P chain. The company adopted the Hollinger name (left over from Argus's early investment in Hollinger Consolidated Gold Mines) in 1985 and gained control of London's struggling *Daily Telegraph* newspaper, which it turned around by drastically cutting staff and modernizing the publishing process. The next year Black brought his Sterling Newspapers company under the Hollinger umbrella. The firm's newspaper holdings increased again in 1989 with the purchase of Jerusalem Post Publications.

Hollinger continued this M.O. in the 1990s, acquiring struggling papers and turning them around. It bought its stake in Southam in 1992 and two years later acquired Sun-Times Co., publisher of the *Chicago Sun-Times* and a group of smaller area papers. Also in 1994 Hollinger launched the Electronic Telegraph, an online version of the *Daily Telegraph*.

In 1995 Hollinger purchased 2 dailies (the *Regina Leader-Post* and the *Saskatoon StarPhoenix*) and 12 nondaily papers from Armadale, a closely held Canadian firm. It also bought 19 paid-circulation papers (12 dailies and 7 weeklies) and several free publications from Canadian publisher Thomson Corporation. That year, in a move to shift more power to Hollinger International for future acquisitions, the parent company sold the subsidiary its interests in the Telegraph plc, John Fairfax, and Southam.

John Fairfax Holdings purchased magazine publisher Australian Geographic in 1996 and began distributing its Australian newspapers on CD-ROM. Also that year Hollinger announced plans to increase its stake in Southam from about 20% to at least 50%.

WHO

Chairman and CEO: Conrad M. Black, age 51,
C$2,049,741 pay
Deputy Chairman; CEO, The Telegraph plc: Daniel W.
Colson, age 49, C$1,334,074 pay
Deputy Chairman: Dixon S. Chant, C$1,126,551 pay
President and COO: F. David Radler, age 54,
C$1,912,603 pay
Chairman, UniMedia Inc.: Peter G. White,
C$660,725 pay
VP and Secretary: Charles G. Cowan
VP Finance and Treasury: J. A. Boultbee, age 52
VP Editorial: Barbara A. Black, age 55
VP and General Counsel: Peter Y. Atkinson
VP Strategic and Corporate Development:
Marianne Godwin
President and CEO, Hollinger International (US):
Jerry Strader
EVP and CFO, Hollinger International (US):
J. David Dodd
**Director Human Resources, Hollinger International
(US):** Roland McBride
Auditors: KPMG Peat Marwick LLP

WHERE

HQ: 1827 W. Fifth Ave., V6J 1P5, Vancouver, BC, Canada
Phone: 416-363-8721
Fax: 416-364-0832
US HQ: Hollinger International Inc., 401 N. Wabash
Ave., Chicago, IL 60611
US Phone: 312-321-2492
US Fax: 312-321-0629

	1995 Sales	
	C$ mil.	% of total
US	738	49
UK	575	38
Canada	170	11
Other countries	30	2
Total	**1,513**	**100**

WHAT

	1995 Newspaper Circulation
	No. (mil.)
Paid daily	4.7
Others	8.7
Total	**13.4**

Selected Operations
American Publishing Co. (US community newspapers)
Electronic Telegraph (online version of *The Daily
Telegraph*)
Hollinger International Inc. (newspapers outside
Canada)
Jerusalem Post Publications Ltd.
John Fairfax Holdings Ltd. (25%, newspapers in
Australia)
Southam Inc. (19.5%, newspapers in Canada)
Sterling Newspaper Group (newspapers in Canada)
The Sun-Times Company (*Chicago Sun-Times* and other
Chicago-area papers)
The Telegraph plc (64%, *The Daily Telegraph* and other
UK papers)

Selected Newspapers
The Age (Melbourne, Australia)
The Gazette (Montreal)
The Sydney Morning Herald (Australia)
The Vancouver Sun (Canada)

KEY COMPETITORS

Central Newspapers	McClatchy Newspapers
Copley Press	MediaNews
Cox Enterprises	New York Times
Dow Jones	News Corp.
E.W. Scripps	Pearson
Freedom Communications	Publishing & Broadcasting
Gannett	Thomson Corp.
Hearst	Tribune
Knight-Ridder	Washington Post
Lee Enterprises	

HOW MUCH

Principal exchange: Montreal FYE: December 31	Annual Growth	1986	1987	1988	1989	1990	1991	1992	1993	1994	1995
Sales (C$ mil.)	20.9%	275	525	691	755	790	780	857	873	1,271	1,513
Net income (C$ mil.)	—	(90)	22	30	58	34	31	74	25	118	10
Income as % of sales	—	—	4.3%	4.4%	7.6%	4.3%	4.0%	8.6%	2.9%	9.3%	0.7%
Earnings per share (C$)	—	(1.63)	0.29	0.60	1.01	0.24	0.30	1.14	0.31	1.96	0.03
Stock price – high (C$)	—	7.38	12.38	15.50	15.25	14.00	14.50	13.50	14.38	17.50	13.25
Stock price – low (C$)	—	4.50	7.00	9.50	10.75	10.00	9.88	9.75	8.50	12.13	9.38
Stock price – close (C$)	3.6%	7.38	10.00	14.50	12.50	11.38	11.63	10.63	13.75	12.63	10.13
P/E – high	—	—	43	26	15	58	48	12	46	9	—
P/E – low	—	—	24	16	11	42	33	9	27	6	—
Dividends per share (C$)	22.0%	0.10	0.18	0.20	0.20	0.40	0.40	0.40	0.40	0.50	0.60
Book value per share (C$)	6.0%	3.47	3.89	3.67	3.94	4.37	4.15	5.26	4.57	6.89	5.85
Employees	13.6%	—	—	—	—	4,600	4,600	4,800	5,700	8,700	8,700

1995 YEAR-END

Debt ratio: 68.7%
Return on equity: 2.0%
Long-term debt (mil.): C$707
No. of shares (mil.): 56
Dividends
  Yield: 5.9%
  Payout: 2,000%
Market value (mil.): $415
Sales (mil.): $1,109

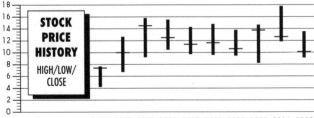

STOCK PRICE HISTORY
HIGH/LOW/CLOSE

Note: $ = C$1.36 (December 31, 1995)

HOME SHOPPING NETWORK, INC.

OVERVIEW

In an effort to turn around the ailing Home Shopping Network (HSN), chairman Barry Diller is leaving no stone unturned. The St. Petersburg, Florida-based company closed its Reno, Nevada, distribution center and its celebrity marketing division, fired 100 workers, cut its inventory 47%, and reshuffled management in an attempt to transform the television retailer and its new parent (and former subsidiary), Silver King Communications, into a significant broadcast network.

Silver King acquired an 80% interest in HSN in a stock swap with cable giant TCI late in 1995. After former CEO David Dyer's ill-fated campaign in 1994 to move HSN mer-

chandise upscale, Diller wants to return to a more traditional line of goods. James Held was appointed HSN president and CEO in 1995. Diller hopes that some of Held's experience as an executive at rival QVC will benefit HSN.

HSN is a holding company whose primary source of income is the Home Shopping Club (HSC), which sells jewelry, cosmetics, and other items through its live programming. HSC beams its programming 24 hours a day, 7 days a week via satellite to cable companies, broadcast TV stations, and satellite dish owners, reaching more than 69 million households. HSN also sells via the Internet, mail order, and infomercials.

WHEN

Lowell Paxon, who had spent years working in radio, owned an AM radio station in Clearwater, Florida, in the mid-1970s that began losing listeners to its FM competitors. Paxon decided in 1977 to begin selling merchandise over the air. He bought distressed and overstocked merchandise from local merchants and sold it on a program he called Suncoast Bargaineers. The show was a hit, and Paxon began giving it more airtime.

By the early 1980s the Clearwater area was wired for cable, and Paxon teamed with Roy Speer, a Florida assistant attorney general, to found the Home Shopping Club in 1982. They soon expanded to other cable services in the Tampa Bay area. In 1985 the jump was made to become a national network. The company's name changed to Home Shopping Network, which offered live 24-hour-a-day shopping (called the Home Shopping Club) on cable services across the nation.

The network was a success, as viewers embraced the bargain-basement prices coupled with game-show-type entertainment. Products were displayed one at a time, for 2-10 minutes, and could only be bought while on screen. Shoppers never knew what was going to come up next, so some of the more rabid fans stayed riveted for hours just to see what would come up for sale. The network's rotating collection of hosts gained cult followings.

HSN went public in 1986 in one of the hottest IPOs of the year. That year the company moved into broadcast TV, paying $226 million for 12 UHF stations. The deal gave it broadcast and cable programming in several major markets, including New York, Los Angeles, and Boston.

The luster began to wear off when a host of competitors entered the TV retail fray. HSN's competitors were given a boost when the company's phone system became overloaded in 1987. HSN sued GTE for $1.5 billion, claiming it lost half of its incoming calls because of the phone problems.

HSN, led by CEO Speer, made unsuccessful attempts to diversify into other businesses, including financial services and mail-order pharmaceuticals, but in 1989 decided to focus solely on electronic retailing. That year HSN lost its case against GTE, and it was forced to pay $4.5 million in legal fees and damages from a countersuit for libel. Despite these setbacks, its core shopping business continued to grow, and by 1990 HSN reached $1 billion in sales. Paxon retired as president of the company that year.

HSN spun off its television stations unit, Silver King, in 1992. Speer sold his controlling interest in the company the next year to Liberty Media, a subsidiary of TCI. He left the company amid allegations of corruption, including vendor kickbacks, but the investigation was dropped in 1994.

In 1995 Hollywood mogul Barry Diller acquired Silver King, which owns or has interests in some 40 TV stations that carry HSN programming. Diller (who built the Fox network and had previously run HSN's archrival QVC) and TCI head John Malone were named that year to the company's board.

Also in 1995 HSN and Sumitomo Corp., one of Japan's largest trading companies, agreed to start a television shopping business in Japan.

Chairman: Barry Diller, age 54
President and CEO: James G. Held, age 45, $44,230 pay
EVP Broadcast and Cable Affiliate Sales: Honore A. Le Brun III, age 50, $316,870 pay
EVP, Secretary, and General Counsel: Barry S. Augenbraun, age 56, $275,000 pay
EVP, CFO, and Treasurer: Kevin J. McKeon, age 39, $164,711 pay
EVP Broadcasting: Mark Bozek, age 36
EVP Administration (HR): Mary Ellen Pollin, age 50
Chief Administrative Officer and SVP Strategic Development and Corporate Finance: Peter M. Kern, $195,480 pay
VP and Controller: Brian J. Feldman, age 36
Auditors: KPMG Peat Marwick LLP

WHERE

HQ: 2501 118th Ave. North, St. Petersburg, FL 33716-1900
Phone: 813-572-8585
Fax: 813-539-6505
Web site: http://www.internet.net

WHAT

	1995 Sales
	% of total
Jewelry	39
Hardgoods	37
Softgoods	14
Cosmetics	10
Total	**100**

	1995 Programming by Category	
	No. households (mil.)	% of total
Cable	44.2	64
Broadcast	21.2	31
Satellite	3.7	5
Total	**69.1**	**100**

Subsidiaries

Home Shopping Club, Inc. (live, interactive retail sales programming via broadcast and cable television)
HSN Direct Joint Venture (infomercials, majority-owned)
HSN Insurance, Inc. (life, health, auto, homeowners, and commercial insurance for HSC members and the public)
HSN Mail Order, Inc. (mail-order merchandise via 5 catalogs)
Internet Shopping Network, Inc. (interactive shopping service specializing in small office and computer equipment, merchandising via digital interactive television and other new digital retailing vehicles)
Vela Research, Inc. (audio and video compression/decompression products)

KEY COMPETITORS

Amway
Comcast
CUC International
DAMARK International
Fingerhut
Integrated Communication Network
J. Crew
Lands' End
Lillian Vernon
L. L. Bean
Positive Response Television
Roll International
Ronco
Sears
Service Merchandise
Sharper Image
Solo Serve
Spiegel
Stanhome
TDX
ValueVision
Zale

HOW MUCH

NYSE symbol: HSN FYE: December 31	Annual Growth	1986	1987	1988	1989	1990	1991	1992	1993	1994	1995
Sales ($ mil.)	22.8%	160	582	730	774	1,008	1,078	1,097	1,046	1,126	1,018
Net income ($ mil.)	—	17	30	18	(22)	33	(10)	37	(16)	18	(62)
Income as % of sales	—	10.6%	5.1%	2.5%	—	3.2%	—	3.4%	—	1.6%	—
Earnings per share ($)	—	0.22	0.33	0.21	(0.25)	0.35	(0.11)	0.42	(0.18)	0.19	(0.69)
Stock price – high ($)	—	19.69	47.00	7.75	7.63	9.25	7.63	9.00	15.38	15.13	10.88
Stock price – low ($)	—	6.34	5.00	3.38	3.00	2.88	3.50	4.25	4.13	9.50	6.50
Stock price – close ($)	(7.7%)	18.56	5.38	4.50	7.25	4.00	5.88	8.25	14.88	10.00	9.00
P/E – high	—	90	142	37	—	26	—	21	—	80	—
P/E – low	—	29	15	16	—	8	—	10	—	50	—
Dividends per share ($)	—	0.00	0.00	0.00	0.00	0.00	0.00	0.00	0.00	0.00	0.00
Book value per share ($)	10.5%	0.56	1.36	1.65	1.56	1.97	1.86	1.94	2.10	2.22	1.38
Employees	17.8%	982	4,400	4,400	5,341	6,394	5,966	5,967	5,018	5,064	4,295

1995 YEAR-END

Debt ratio: 52.3%
Return on equity: —
Cash (mil.): $25
Current ratio: 1.04
Long-term debt (mil.): $136
No. of shares (mil.): 91
Dividends
 Yield: —
 Payout: —
Market value (mil.): $817

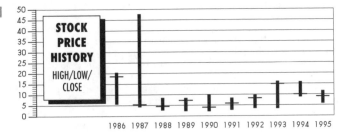

STOCK PRICE HISTORY
HIGH/LOW/CLOSE

INGRAM INDUSTRIES INC.

OVERVIEW

Breaking up is hard to do, but Nashville-based Ingram Industries has chosen to do just that. One of the top 10 privately held businesses in the nation, Ingram Industries has decided to break itself into 3 separate chunks by the start of 1997.

After the split, Ingram Industries will be made up of wholesaler Ingram Book Co., Ingram Materials Co., insurer Permanent General Cos., and shipping concern Ingram Barge. The US's leading wholesale distributor of trade books, Ingram Book supplies titles from more than 2,000 publishers to major bookstores. Current Ingram head, Martha Ingram, will run this company.

Two new companies will emerge from the reorganization: Ingram Entertainment, the US's largest video distributor, and Ingram Micro, the world's largest distributor of microcomputer products. Ingram heir David Ingram will run the former company, while the management picture at the latter remains unclear in the wake of Ingram Micro CEO Chip Lacy's sudden departure. The company plans to take Ingram Micro public as part of the reorganization.

As Ingram's chairman, Martha Ingram heads the largest woman-owned business in the US. She is the principal shareholder in the company, which was built by her late husband, Bronson.

WHEN

Bronson Ingram's great-grandfather, Orrin Ingram, was a New York farm boy who, in the late 1840s, took a job at a sawmill. By age 21 he was designing and operating mills in Ontario, Canada. In 1857 Ingram and 2 partners founded the Dole, Ingram & Kennedy sawmill in Eau Claire, Wisconsin, on the Chippewa River, about 50 miles upstream from the Mississippi River. By the 1870s the company, renamed Ingram & Kennedy, was selling lumber as far downstream as Hannibal, Missouri.

Ingram's success was noticed by Frederick Weyerhaeuser, a German immigrant in Rock Island, Illinois, who, like Ingram, had worked in a sawmill before buying one of his own. In 1881 Ingram and Weyerhaeuser negotiated the formation of Chippewa Logging (35%-owned by up-river partners, 65%-owned by down-river interests), which controlled the white pine harvest of the Chippewa Valley. In 1900 Ingram paid $216,000 for 2,160 shares in the newly formed Weyerhaeuser Timber Company. Ingram let his sons and grandsons handle the investment and formed O.H. Ingram Co. to manage the family's interests. He died in 1918.

In 1946 Ingram's descendants founded Ingram Barge, which hauled crude oil to the company's refinery near St. Louis. After buying and then selling other holdings, in 1962 the family formed Ingram Corp., consisting solely of Ingram Barge. Brothers Bronson and Fritz Ingram bought the company from their father, Hank, before he died in 1963. In 1964 they bought half of Tennessee Book, a textbook distributing company founded in 1935, and in 1970 they formed Ingram Book to sell trade books to bookstores and libraries.

In 1971 Ingram Barge won a $48 million sludge-hauling contract in Chicago, but later the company was accused of bribing city politicians with $1.2 million in order to land the contract. The brothers stood trial in 1977 for authorizing the bribes; Bronson was acquitted, but the court convicted Fritz on 29 counts. Before Fritz entered prison (he served 16 months of a 4-year sentence), he and his brother split their company. Fritz took the energy operations and went bust in the 1980s. Bronson took the barge and book businesses and formed Ingram Industries.

This new company formed computer products distributor Ingram Computer in 1982 and between 1985 and 1989 bought all the stock of Micro D, a computer wholesaler. Ingram Computer and Micro D merged to form Ingram Micro. In 1992 Ingram acquired Commtron, the world's #1 wholesaler of prerecorded videocassettes, and merged it into Ingram Entertainment.

Ingram created its Ingram Publisher Services division in 1995 to oversee the anticipated growth in order-fulfillment services for medium-sized and large publishers. When Bronson Ingram (at the time Tennessee's only billionaire) died in mid-1995, his wife, Martha, became chairman; she had been the company's PR director. Late that year the company closed Ingram Merchandising, which had provided nonbookstore rack distribution for about 50 customers.

In 1996 Ingram sold its Cactus Co. oil-and-gas machinery subsidiary for $100 million. Also that year Chip Lacy, who had guided Ingram Micro's rise to market dominance, left the company after butting heads with Martha Ingram.

WHO

Chairman and Public Relations Director: Martha Ingram
Co-president, Ingram Industries; Interim CEO, Ingram Micro: John Ingram
President and COO, Ingram Micro: Jeff Rodek
Co-chairman, Ingram Micro: David R. Dukes
Chairman and CEO, Ingram Book Co.: Lee Synnott
President, Ingram Publisher Services: Steven Little
VP and Treasurer: Robert W. Mitchell
President, Ingram Entertainment: David Ingram
Co-president, Ingram Industries: Orrin H. Ingram
Auditor: Price Waterhouse

WHERE

HQ: One Belle Meade Place, 4400 Harding Rd., Nashville, TN 37205-2244
Phone: 615-298-8200
Fax: 615-298-8242

Ingram Book and Ingram Entertainment are headquartered in Nashville, and Ingram Micro is headquartered in Santa Ana, California.

WHAT

Ingram Book Group
Ingram Library Services Inc.
Ingram Periodicals Inc.
Publisher Resources Inc. (distribution services for publishers, wholesalers, and retailers)
Tennessee Book Co. (textbook distribution)
White Bridge Communications (promotional programs)

Ingram Entertainment Inc. (prerecorded videocassette distribution)

Ingram Micro Inc. (microcomputer products)
Ingram Alliance Reseller Co.
Ingram Dicom S.A. de C.V. (Mexico)
Ingram Micro Europe
Ingram Micro Inc. (Canada)

Inland Marine Group
Ingram Barge Co. (custom fuel services)
Ingram Materials Co.

Insurance Group
Permanent General Cos. (auto insurance)
Tennessee Insurance Co. (insures Ingram affiliates)
Advanced Marketing

KEY COMPETITORS

Allstate
Baker & Taylor
Bookazine
Chas. Levy
CIGNA
CompuCom
East Texas Distributing
Handleman
Inacom
Intelligent Electronics
Merisel
MicroAge
Navarre
SAFECO
Southern Electronics
State Farm
Wal-Mart

HOW MUCH

Private company FYE: December 31	Annual Growth	1986	1987	1988	1989	1990	1991	1992	1993	1994	1995
Sales ($ mil.)	30.5%	1,000	1,170	2,090	2,640	2,677	3,422	4,657	6,163	8,010	11,000
Employees	20.6%	2,400	3,000	3,425	4,600	5,400	6,526	8,407	9,658	10,000	13,000

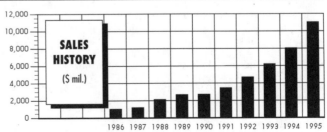

SALES HISTORY ($ mil.)

1986 1987 1988 1989 1990 1991 1992 1993 1994 1995

INTERNATIONAL DATA GROUP

OVERVIEW

A million dollars says Microsoft king Bill Gates has at least one International Data Group (IDG) magazine on his coffee table. Through its print products, Internet magazines, e-mail newsletters, and other media, the Boston-based company is the world's leading provider of computer information. Subsidiary IDG Communications is the world's #1 publisher of computer-related periodicals, with more than 275 magazines (including *Macworld* and *PC World*) and newspapers in 78 countries. Its publications are read by more than 90 million people each month. IDG Books Worldwide prints some 350 titles (including the *For Dummies* series and *InfoWorld*) in 28 languages. Subsidiary International Data Corporation leads the industry in computer market research and analysis. IDG World

Expositions sponsors conferences, trade shows, and other events for the computer industry.

IDG's strategy is to develop computer publications in markets throughout the world. It is also starting online-only "webzines," such as JavaWorld Magazine (introduced in 1996), which features techie news and programming tips. IDG and Internet search service Infoseek announced in 1996 that *Macworld* would be the exclusive sponsor and content provider for Infoseek's Macintosh Directory.

Founder Patrick McGovern owns about 65% of IDG, while the employees own the rest. McGovern, known as "Chairman Pat," is one of the 400 richest Americans in *Forbes* and has been known to dress up like Ben Franklin for employees in Boston and as Confucius for employees in China. He hands out Christmas bonuses personally — in cash.

WHEN

Patrick McGovern began his publishing career at the *Philadelphia Bulletin* as a paper boy. As a teenager in the 1950s he was inspired by Edmund Berkeley's book *Giant Brains; or Machines That Think*. He built a computer impressive enough to win a scholarship to MIT. While there he edited the first computer magazine, *Berkeley's Computers and Automation*.

In 1964 McGovern was interviewing the president of computer pioneer UNIVAC for *Computers and Automation* when he was inspired to start a market research service, International Data Corporation. Three years later he began International Data Group with the launch of an 8-page tabloid, *Computerworld*. At that time, according to McGovern, computer products had a 7-year life cycle, and over 75% of the computer market was in the US. (Today product life cycles are measured in months, and less than 35% of the market is US based.) McGovern introduced his new paper at a computer trade show. Within a few weeks it had 20,000 subscribers; advertisers soon started to seek out the publication. By 1968 IDG had $1 million in annual revenues.

Since its modest beginning IDG has set out to conquer the computer world. It began publishing in Japan in 1971, then expanded to Germany in 1975 and to Brazil in 1976. By 1988 the company had established a presence in Russia. Two years later, after the collapse of Communism, it started 10 publications in Russia and Eastern Europe.

Two teen hackers, angry because they didn't receive a free poster with the IDG publication

Gamepro, broke into the company's voice-mail system in 1990 and erased orders from customers and messages from writers. The prank cost IDG roughly $2.4 million.

Beset by competition from the mushrooming computer magazine marketplace in 1993, several of IDG's magazines, including *InfoWorld*, *Macworld*, and *PC World*, began losing ad pages. The company began an incentive program tied in to its new online service to help stem advertiser attrition.

In 1994 IDG traded a 4% stake in its *Multimedia World* magazine and $110,000 cash for the assets of Mecklermedia's *CD-ROM World*. The 2 publishers said they would collaborate on future projects. The following year the company said it would cease publication of *AmigaWorld*, started in 1985.

Also in 1995, as part of IDG's move away from closed systems and toward Internet-based services, it purchased a stake in online software companies Architext Software (now Excite) and Netscape. That year IDG and a former IDG officer, Axel Leblois, bought Boston-based publisher World Times.

The company started producing a free e-mail weekly newsletter, *infusion*, in 1996 on the networking industry. That year it purchased *PC Advisor*, the UK's fastest-growing computer magazine, and laid plans to launch *Intranet Magazine* as a tabloid-size supplement to *Network World* before spinning it off as a stand-alone publication.

WHO

Chairman and CEO: Patrick J. McGovern, age 58
President: Kelly P. Conlin, age 35
COO: James Casella, age 47
EVP Finance: William P. Murphy
VP Human Resources: Martha Stephens
Director Information Systems: Jeff Debalko
Director Corporate Communications: Chris McAndrews
Auditors: Deloitte & Touche LLP

WHERE

HQ: One Exeter Plaza, 15th Fl., Boston, MA 02116
Phone: 617-534-1200
Fax: 617-262-2300
Web site: http://www.idg.com

IDG publishes more than 275 computer magazines and newspapers in 78 countries.

WHAT

Divisions

IDG Communications
Books
Magazines
Newsletters
Newspapers
Online services

IDG Research Companies
Advisory services

Consulting
Research reports
Technology briefings

IDG World Expositions
Conferences
Special events
Trade shows

Selected Periodicals

United States
CD Review
CIO Magazine
Computerworld
Computerworld
   Client/Server Journal
DOS World
Federal Computer Week
GamePro
InfoWorld
Macworld
Network World
PC World
Video Event
WebMaster

Foreign
China Infoworld
Computerworld Brazil
East African Computer
   News (Kenya)
InfoCanada
Le Monde Informatique
   (France)
Macworld Denmark
PC Advisor
PC World Hong Kong
PC World Israel
PC World Vietnam
Telecom Romania
Windows World Japan

Selected Books
Computerworld ... For Dummies
Heavy Metal
InfoWorld
Macworld
Multimedia World
Network World
PC World
SECRETS
Type and Learn

KEY COMPETITORS

CMP Publications
GP Publications
HyperMedia
McGraw-Hill
Mecklermedia
Pittway
Seybold
Upside Publishing
Wired Ventures
Wolff New Media

HOW MUCH

Private company FYE: September 30	Annual Growth	1986	1987	1988	1989	1990	1991	1992	1993	1994	1995
Sales ($ mil.)	17.7%	—	—	—	—	620	780	840	880	1,100	1,400
Employees	17.4%	—	—	—	—	3,812	4,200	4,500	5,000	7,200	8,500

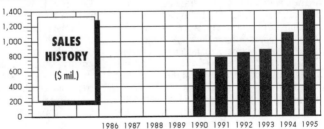

SALES HISTORY ($ mil.)

INTERPUBLIC GROUP

OVERVIEW

Interpublic is "inter" public relations in a big way — as well as product, retail, and corporate image advertising, market research, ad placement, direct mail, and related promotional services. The New York City-based advertising conglomerate is a one-stop shopping center for ad services. Its main subsidiaries include McCann-Erickson Worldwide, Ammirati Puris Lintas, the Lowe Group, and Western International Media. Interpublic is one of the world's 3 largest advertising businesses (with WPP and Omnicom).

The acquisitive company operates as a cluster of competing agencies within a holding company; its subsidiaries serve rival clients while using the resources and worldwide connections of the parent. The group concept has been an effective way for Interpublic to allow creative independence while keeping financial control.

Through most of its history, Interpublic has collected advertising agencies. In recent years, however, it has also focused on ancillary service companies that specialize in areas such as interactive technology, media planning and buying, graphic design, and brand consultancy. In 1995 Interpublic united several of these companies (which are used by its advertising agencies) into a new subsidiary, Allied Communications Group.

WHEN

The Interpublic Group's history began in 1911 with Harrison McCann, an advertising executive for Standard Oil who opened his own agency after the petroleum trust was split up. Standard Oil of New Jersey (now Exxon) was his first client, and as the automobile and petroleum products became integral parts of American life, McCann's ad business boomed.

In 1930 McCann's firm merged with Alfred Erickson's agency (founded in 1902), forming the McCann-Erickson Company. At the end of the decade, the ad firm hired Marion Harper, a top Yale graduate, as a mail room clerk. He quickly rose through the ranks, and by 1948 he had become president of the agency.

Harper used social science techniques to determine what motivated people to buy. He also began acquiring other ad agencies and by 1961 controlled more than 20 companies. That year he unveiled his concept of an advertising holding company for various subsidiaries that would use the parent company's financial and informational resources but operate separately, allowing them to work on accounts for competing products. He named the company the Interpublic Group, after a German research company for various subsidiaries that was owned by the former H. K. McCann Co.

The advertising conglomerate continued expanding, buying Afamal (the largest ad firm in Africa) in 1962 and Erwin, Wasey, Ruthrauff & Ryan in 1963, making it the biggest agency in the world. But Harper's management capabilities weren't up to the task. With the company facing bankruptcy, the board of directors replaced Harper with Robert Healy in 1967. (Harper died in 1990, having lived his last 20 years as a recluse.) By borrowing from employees, securing advance payments from clients, and cutting costs, Healy was able to save the company and return it to profitability. In 1971 Interpublic went public.

The 1970s were fruitful years for the company, whose ad teams created memorable campaigns for Coke ("It's the Real Thing" and "Have a Coke and a Smile") and Miller Beer ("Miller Time" and Miller Lite ads).

After Philip Geier became chairman in 1980, the company's acquisitions included Lintas International and Dailey & Associates. With 60% of its billings coming from overseas, Interpublic was sufficiently diversified to withstand declines in regional businesses or even the loss of major clients.

Interpublic bought UK-based Lowe Group and sailed through the global recession of the early 1990s with few problems until 1993, when Coca-Cola (a client since 1942) hired Creative Artists Agency to develop a new image. But growth did not stop. Interpublic bought Western International Media, the largest independent media buyer in the US, and Ammirati & Puris, a New York firm respected for its creativity. In 1995 Interpublic teamed up with All American Communications (in which it owns an approximate 25% interest) to purchase game show producer Mark Goodson. However, it sold its interest to its partner a few months later.

As the pace of industry consolidation picked up, in 1996 Interpublic made 4 acquisitions in 3 months, buying Angotti, Thomas, Hedge (a creative shop), William Douglas McAdams (health industry advertising), Jay Advertising (retail advertising), and a minority interest in Accentmarketing (which targets the US Hispanic market).

Chairman, President, and CEO: Philip H. Geier Jr.,
age 61, $1,833,600 pay
VC Finance and Operations and CFO: Eugene P. Beard,
age 60, $1,250,745 pay
Chairman, McCann-Erickson Worldwide: John J.
Dooner Jr., age 47, $1,235,000 pay
Chairman and CEO, Ammirati Puris Lintas Worldwide:
Martin F. Puris, age 57, $1,187,500 pay
Chairman, Lowe Group: Frank B. Lowe, age 54,
$1,135,000 pay
SVP Financial Operations: Thomas J. Volpe, age 60
SVP Human Resources: C. Kent Kroeber, age 57
VP, General Counsel, and Secretary: Nicholas J. Camera,
age 49
Auditors: Price Waterhouse LLP

WHERE

HQ: The Interpublic Group of Companies, Inc.,
1271 Avenue of the Americas, New York, NY 10020
Phone: 212-399-8000
Fax: 212-399-8130

Interpublic provides advertising services in 106 countries.

	1995 Sales	
	$ mil.	% of total
Europe	837	38
US	755	35
Asia/Pacific	282	13
Latin America	152	7
Other regions	68	3
Other	86	4
Total	**2,180**	**100**

WHAT

Services
Advertising
Direct marketing
Market research
Media buying
Media placement
Product development
Sales promotion
Telemarketing

Selected Clients
AT&T
Continental Airlines
Flagstar
General Motors
Hanson
Johnson & Johnson
Kmart
L'Oréal
Microsoft
Motoroloa
Nestlé

SEGA
Unilever
U S WEST

Selected Subsidiaries
Allied Communications
Group (New York)
Ammirati Puris Lintas
Inc. (New York)
Campbell Mithun Esty
LLC (Minneapolis)
Campbell-Ewald Co.
(Detroit)
Dailey & Associates (Los
Angeles)
Lowe & Partners Inc.
(New York)
McCann-Erickson USA,
Inc. (New York)
Western International
Media (Los Angeles)

KEY COMPETITORS

Ackerley Communications
Bozell, Jacobs
Cordiant
D'Arcy Masius
Dentsu
Grey Advertising
Leo Burnett
Omnicom Group
Publicis
True North
WPP Group
Young & Rubicam

HOW MUCH

NYSE symbol: IPG FYE: December 31	Annual Growth	1986	1987	1988	1989	1990	1991	1992	1993	1994	1995
Sales ($ mil.)	11.6%	814	943	1,191	1,256	1,368	1,677	1,804	1,793	1,984	2,180
Net income ($ mil.)	13.6%	41	49	60	71	80	95	112	125	115	130
Income as % of sales	—	5.0%	5.2%	5.0%	5.6%	5.9%	5.6%	6.2%	7.0%	5.8%	6.0%
Earnings per share ($)	11.4%	0.63	0.75	0.91	1.05	1.19	1.30	1.50	1.67	1.53	1.66
Stock price – high ($)	—	10.17	14.50	12.34	18.94	19.00	28.63	35.75	35.63	35.88	43.38
Stock price – low ($)	—	7.00	7.59	3.30	12.17	14.63	16.88	25.75	23.88	27.50	31.75
Stock price – close ($)	18.9%	9.13	10.59	12.25	16.31	17.50	28.63	34.88	32.00	32.13	43.38
P/E – high	—	16	19	14	18	16	22	24	21	24	26
P/E – low	—	11	10	4	12	12	13	17	14	18	19
Dividends per share ($)	13.2%	0.20	0.22	0.26	0.32	0.37	0.41	0.45	0.49	0.55	0.61
Book value per share ($)	11.1%	3.65	4.23	4.77	5.32	6.94	7.78	6.81	7.53	8.36	9.42
Employees	5.1%	12,600	13,300	14,700	14,700	16,800	16,800	16,800	17,600	18,200	19,700

1995 YEAR-END

Debt ratio: 37.3%
Return on equity: 18.6%
Cash (mil.): $418
Current ratio: 1.05
Long-term debt (mil.): $284
No. of shares (mil.): 80
Dividends
Yield: 1.4%
Payout: 36.7%
Market value (mil.): $3,454

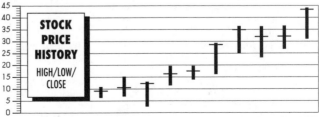

STOCK PRICE HISTORY HIGH/LOW/CLOSE

JOHNSON PUBLISHING COMPANY, INC.

OVERVIEW

Johnson Publishing has built its diversified business empire by minding the business of black America. The Chicago-based company is the nation's 2nd largest black-owned enterprise (after TLC Beatrice) and the leading US publisher of black-oriented magazines. Publications include *Ebony*, the cornerstone of the Johnson empire, with a circulation of 2 million; *Jet*, a weekly newsmagazine, which has a circulation of one million; and *EM* (Ebony Man), a magazine for men that has a circulation of 250,000. It also produces hair care products (Supreme Beauty) and cosmetics (Fashion Fair and Ebone) for the black con-sumer market. The book division features titles by black authors. Since 1978 Johnson Publishing has sponsored the *American Black Achievement Awards*, a nationally syndicated TV special, and each year it hosts the Ebony Fashion Fair, a traveling fashion show that visits more than 100 US cities.

Johnson Publishing is owned and controlled by company founder John Johnson and his family. Johnson's daughter and heir apparent, Linda Rice, handles the day-to-day operations and was listed by Crain's as one of Chicago's 100 most influential women in 1996.

WHEN

John Johnson launched his publishing business in 1942 while still in college in Chicago. The idea for a magazine oriented to blacks came to him while he was working part-time for Supreme Life Insurance Co. of America, where one of his jobs was to clip news articles about the black community from magazines and newspapers. With $500 his mother raised by mortgaging family furniture, Johnson mailed a $2 charter subscription offer to potential subscribers. He got 3,000 replies and with that $6,000 printed the first issue of *Negro Digest*, patterned after *Reader's Digest*. Within a year circulation was 50,000.

In 1945 Johnson started *Ebony* magazine, which was immediately popular and is still the company's premier publication. *Ebony* (like *Life*, but focusing on black culture and achievements) and *Jet* (a celebrity-oriented magazine started in 1951) were the only publications for US blacks for 20 years.

In the early days Johnson was unable to obtain advertising, so he formed his own mail-order business called Beauty Star and advertised its products (dresses, wigs, hair care products, and vitamins) through his magazines. He won his first major account, Zenith Radio, in 1947; Johnson landed Chrysler in 1954 after he sent a salesman to Detroit every week for 10 years.

By the 1960s Johnson had become one of the most prominent black men in America. In 1963 he posed with John F. Kennedy to publicize a special issue of *Ebony* celebrating the Emancipation Proclamation. In 1972, US magazine publishers named Johnson Publisher of the Year. His first magazine, *Negro Digest* (renamed *Black World*), became known for its provocative articles, but its circulation dwindled from 100,000 to 15,000, and Johnson retired the magazine in 1975.

Unable to find the proper makeup for his *Ebony* models, Johnson founded his own cosmetics business, Fashion Fair Cosmetics, in 1973. Fashion Fair competed successfully against Revlon (which introduced cosmetic lines for blacks) and another black cosmetics company, Johnson Products (unrelated) of Chicago. By 1982 the sales for the Fashion Fair division alone were more than $30 million.

In 1973 Johnson also launched *Ebony Jr!* (since discontinued), a black preteens magazine, designed to provide "positive black images." Johnson bought radio stations WJPC (Chicago's first black-owned station; sold in 1995) and WLOU (Louisville) in 1974 and WLNR (Lansing, Illinois) in the mid-1980s (merged into WJPC in 1992). In 1984 Johnson Publishing became the largest black-owned business in America. *Black Enterprise* magazine selected John Johnson in 1987 as Entrepreneur of the Decade.

Johnson and the company sold their controlling interest in Supreme Life Insurance to Unitrin, a Chicago-based life, health, and property insuror, in 1991. That year the company and catalog retailer Spiegel announced a joint venture to develop black women's fashions. The 2 companies launched a mail-order catalog, called *E Style*, in 1993, and a credit card to go with it (1994). Johnson Publishing teamed up with South African companies Publico, a specialty magazine publisher, and Real Africa Investments, a black-owned media conglomerate, in 1995 with plans to launch its South African edition of *Ebony*. In early 1996 company VP Willie Miles Burns died. She was one of the first women named a major executive of a national magazine.

WHO

Chairman and CEO: John H. Johnson
President and COO: Linda Johnson Rice, age 37
Secretary and Treasurer: Eunice W. Johnson
Controller: Gregory Robertson
Editor, *Ebony*: Lerone Bennett Jr.
Director Personnel: La Doris Foster

WHERE

HQ: 820 S. Michigan Ave., Chicago, IL 60605
Phone: 312-322-9200
Fax: 312-322-0918

WHAT

Business Lines

Beauty Aids
Eboné Cosmetics
Fashion Fair Cosmetics
Supreme Beauty Products Co.
Duke (hair care for men)
Raveen (hair care for women)

Books
Johnson Publishing Co. Book Division

Fashion
E Style (women's apparel, accessories, and home
    fashions catalog;
joint venture with Spiegel)
Ebony Fashion Fair (traveling fashion show)

Magazines
Ebony
EM (Ebony Man)
Jet

Television Production
American Black Achievement Awards

KEY COMPETITORS

Advance Publications
Alberto-Culver
Amway
Avon
BET
Chattem
Essence Communications
Estée Lauder
Forbes
Gannett
Hearst
Helene Curtis
Knight-Ridder
Lagardère
L'Oréal
Mary Kay
New York Times
Perrigo
Playtex
Procter & Gamble
Reader's Digest
Revlon
Soft Sheen Products
Time Warner

HOW MUCH

Private company FYE: December 31	Annual Growth	1986	1987	1988	1989	1990	1991	1992	1993	1994	1995
Sales ($ mil.)	6.9%	174	202	217	241	252	261	274	294	307	316
Employees	4.3%	1,828	1,903	2,364	2,370	2,382	2,710	2,785	2,600	2,662	2,680

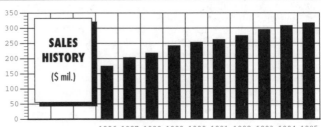

SALES HISTORY ($ mil.)

K-III COMMUNICATIONS CORPORATION

OVERVIEW

"Shop 'Til You Drop" seems to be the motto at K-III Communications. Headquartered in New York City, the company is a media conglomerate built by former executives at publisher Macmillan with backing from investment firm Kohlberg Kravis Roberts (KKR). Since its founding in 1989, the company has made more than 40 acquisitions, and it now owns leading publishing companies in educational, business, and special-interest consumer magazines; trade and technical publications; and database products.

K-III's best-known products include Channel One News (whose TV broadcasts reach 40% of middle schools and high schools in the US); *The World Almanac* (the #1 English-language almanac), *Funk & Wagnalls* (general reference encyclopedias), the *Daily Racing Form* (thoroughbred horseracing), and several

consumer magazines (including *Seventeen*, *Soap Opera Digest*, and *New York*). The company also is a leading publisher of database directories that are targeted at specific industries (such as financial services, transportation, construction, and public relations), trade magazines for markets such as agriculture and automobiles, service manuals, and newsletters.

A 1995 IPO lowered KKR's stake in K-III from 96% to 83%. Going public means K-III can reduce its huge debt load and gives the company flexibility to seek new acquisitions. However, its coming-out party was less successful than K-III had hoped (the offering price was dropped from $11-$13 to $10). Some analysts say the company's media holdings are too varied to be run efficiently, but CEO William Reilly continues to search for niche properties that are leaders in their markets.

WHEN

In 1989, with several publishing properties up for grabs and most potential buyers burdened by heavy debt, Kohlberg Kravis Roberts zeroed in on the publishing industry as a solid investment opportunity. So KKR and several publishing executives, including future K-III CEO Reilly, president Charles McCurdy, and VC and general counsel Beverly Chell, set up K-III Holdings to acquire Intertec Publishing and Newbridge Communications. The total price for Intertec (acquired from JW Corporation) and Newbridge (bought from Macmillan) was $320 million.

Reilly and KKR had been buddies since KKR backed him in his bid to buy Macmillan in 1988, a battle he lost to Robert Maxwell. But Reilly did get something from Macmillan: he brought 45 of the company's executives with him to K-III, including his entire management team. Reilly and his crew set about making K-III a major media player.

In 1991 K-III paid $162 million for *Weekly Reader*, Newfield Publications (sold in 1995), and Funk & Wagnalls. The deal doubled K-III's number of operating divisions. Later that year the group beat out a passel of rival bidders, including Condé Nast and Hearst, to pick up several publications from Rupert Murdoch's News Corp. K-III paid $675 million for 9 publications, including *Soap Opera Digest*, *Seventeen*, and the *Daily Racing Form*.

In 1992 the group paid $44 million for medical information publisher Krames Communications. It also changed its name to

K-III Communications that year. By the end of 1992, K-III had spent $1.3 billion on acquisitions.

In 1993 the group was outbid by Conde Nast when it tried to buy *Bon Appetit* and *Architectural Digest*. K-III also had trouble starting its own magazines: 2 publications test-marketed in 1993, *Soap Opera Illustrated* and *True News* (celebrity and tabloid news), failed to win consumer support. *True News* was dropped, and *Soap Opera Illustrated* was turned into a quarterly.

Those setbacks didn't curb K-III's appetite for promising companies. In 1993 Funk & Wagnalls acquired *The World Almanac* and the World Almanac Education division of United Media Publishing. K-III also bought directory publisher Nelson Publications that year.

In 1994 the firm acquired Channel One News cable TV education network, office-skills trainer Katharine Gibbs Schools, and Haas Publishing, a publisher of apartment rental guides. K-III sold its *Premiere* magazine to a joint venture of Hachette and New World Communications in 1995.

The company bought 14 magazines (including *Modern Bride*, *Power & Motoryacht*, and *Sail*) from the Anglo-Dutch publisher Reed Elsevier in 1996 for $180 million. That year the company announced plans to pay $422 million for Westcott Communications, which provides educational and career training programs via satellite and videotape.

Chairman and CEO: William F. Reilly, age 57
VC, General Counsel, and Secretary: Beverly C. Chell, age 53
President: Charles G. McCurdy, age 40
EVP; President, K-III Media Group: Harry A. McQuillen, age 49
VP; President, K-III Information Group: Jack L. Farnsworth, age 50
VP; President, K-III Education Group: Pedro F. Mata, age 51
VP; President, Reference and School Group: George Philips, age 65
VP Human Resources: Michaelanne C. Discepolo, age 43
VP and Controller: Curtis A. Thompson, age 44
Auditors: Deloitte & Touche LLP

WHERE

HQ: 745 Fifth Ave., New York, NY 10151
Phone: 212-745-0100
Fax: 212-745-0169
Web site: http://www.k3.com

WHAT

	1995 Sales		1995 Operating Income	
	$ mil.	% of total	$ mil.	% of total
Media	452	43	32	—
Education	330	32	(32)	—
Information	264	25	(8)	—
Adjustments	—	—	(18)	—
Total	**1,046**	**100**	**(26)**	**—**

Selected Holdings and Products

Education
Channel One News (school TV broadcasts)
The Classroom Channel
Current Events
Current Science
Films for the Humanities and Sciences (6,000 educational videos and CD-ROMs)
Katharine Gibbs Schools (7 business schools)
Krames Communications (patient information materials)
Read
Weekly Reader (elementary and secondary school newspaper)

Media
Consumer magazines
American Baby
Automobile
Chicago
Modern Bride
New Woman
New York
Power & Motoryacht
Sail
Seventeen
Soap Opera Digest
Soap Opera Weekly
Special interest publications
Crafts
Dog World
Sew News
Truckin'
Trade and technical magazines

Information
Apartment Guides
Daily Racing Form
Directories
Nelson's Directory of Investment Managers
Nelson's Directory of Investment Research
Reference materials
Facts on File News Services
Funk & Wagnalls' New Encyclopedia
The World Almanac
World Almanac for Kids
Trade and technical newsletters and database products
Aircraft Bluebook
The Electronics Sourcebook
Market Reports
Ward's Automotive Reports
Waterway Guides

KEY COMPETITORS

Advance Publications
American Media
Apollo Group
Berkshire Hathaway
Bertelsmann
DeVry
Dun & Bradstreet
Educational Insights
Encyclopaedia Britannica
ITT Educational
Lagardère
McGraw-Hill
Meredith
New York Times
News Corp.
Pearson
Pittway
Random House
Reader's Digest
Reed Elsevier
Scholastic
Simon & Schuster
Thomson Corp.
Time Warner
Times Mirror

HOW MUCH

NYSE symbol: KCC FYE: December 31	Annual Growth	1986	1987	1988	1989	1990	1991	1992	1993	1994	1995
Sales ($ mil.)	9.2%	—	—	565	714	795	779	778	845	964	1,046
Net income ($ mil.)	—	—	—	23	(23)	(24)	(87)	(145)	(86)	(41)	(104)
Income as % of sales	—	—	—	4.0%	—	—	—	—	—	—	—
Earnings per share ($)	—	—	—	—	—	—	—	—	—	—	(0.91)
Stock price – high ($)	—	—	—	—	—	—	—	—	—	—	12.63
Stock price – low ($)	—	—	—	—	—	—	—	—	—	—	10.25
Stock price – close ($)	—	—	—	—	—	—	—	—	—	—	12.13
P/E – high	—	—	—	—	—	—	—	—	—	—	—
P/E – low	—	—	—	—	—	—	—	—	—	—	—
Dividends per share ($)	—	—	—	—	—	—	—	—	—	—	0.00
Book value per share ($)	—	—	—	—	—	—	—	—	—	—	0.88
Employees	13.8%	—	—	—	—	3,300	3,473	3,445	3,600	4,550	6,300

1995 YEAR-END

Debt ratio: 92.5%
Return on equity: —
Cash (mil.): $27
Current ratio: 0.84
Long-term debt (mil.): $1,135
No. of shares (mil.): 105
Dividends
  Yield: —
  Payout: —
Market value (mil.): $1,277

STOCK PRICE HISTORY HIGH/LOW/CLOSE

KING WORLD PRODUCTIONS, INC.

OVERVIEW

King World is one of the world's leading makers of couch potatoes. The New York City-based company distributes the US's 3 highest-rated syndicated daily shows: *Wheel of Fortune*, *Jeopardy!*, and the *Oprah Winfrey Show*. It also produces and distributes *Inside Edition* (ranked #5), *American Journal* (ranked #10), and *Rolonda*. King World's distribution system covers some 400 stations in more than 200 TV markets.

Other operations include subsidiary Camelot Entertainment Sales, which sells television time to national advertisers. King World Direct, the direct marketing division, manages direct-response marketing campaigns for retailers Sears and Sharper Image and for National Geographic Television. King World International markets the company's shows outside the US and develops new shows for foreign markets. The firm also owns more than 60 movies and 200 TV shows, which it distributes to domestic TV stations for broadcast.

The King family, including chairman Roger and several executive officers, owns 24% of the company. Talk show host Oprah Winfrey and Jeffrey Jacobs, president of her production company, Harpo Entertainment, together own 5% of King World.

WHEN

Charles and Lucille King established King World Productions in 1964 to syndicate films and TV programs to TV stations. The Kings started by acquiring rights to distribute reruns, including those of the *Little Rascals*. The King family often discussed the television industry at home, and after Charles's death in 1973, sons Roger and Michael took over. In lean times they worked out of their kitchen, and Michael parked cars for extra cash.

In 1978 the Kings bought subdistribution rights to the game shows *Joker's Wild* and *Tic Tac Dough*. After a 1982 failed attempt to distribute a talk show, *Soap World*, the Kings returned to game shows. They paid Merv Griffin a $50,000 advance for the rights to syndicate *Wheel of Fortune* in evening time slots, and they sold the show aggressively, signing up 59 stations. The brothers picked up rights to Griffin's *New Jeopardy* in 1983, a few months before *Wheel* began an astounding climb to the top, backed by heavy advertising support and a careful promotion of the show's letter-turner, Vanna White.

In 1984 King World nearly tripled its fees for *Wheel*, by then broadcast over 181 stations, and launched *Jeopardy!*, a remake of the successful network game show, which proved to be another smash hit. The company went public the same year and acquired rights to the Leo A. Gutman library of films and TV series, which included *Branded* and the *Charlie Chan* and *Mr. Moto* film series.

Heavy spending on market research paid off, helping the company customize sales pitches to TV stations, select shows for syndication, and build confidence among TV program producers. Consequently, WLS-TV of Chicago, then producer of the *Oprah Winfrey Show*, chose King World to launch *Oprah* nationally in 1986. By the end of the year, *Wheel* and *Jeopardy!* had become the top 2 syndicated TV shows and *Oprah* had entered the top 10. In 1988 King World bought CBS-TV affiliate Buffalo (New York) Broadcasting.

Along with its successes were several minor failures, including *Headline Chasers* and *Instant Recall*. King World wrote off its 1990 investment in Financial News Network in 1991, when FNN failed.

King World launched its first in-house production in 1989 with *Inside Edition*. Other productions had limited runs: *Arts & Entertainment Revue* (1990-92) and a new *Candid Camera* series (1991-92). The company entered children's programming in 1992 with the cartoon *Wild West C.O.W.-Boys of Moo Mesa*. The next year it agreed to produce infomercials for Sears and launched *Inside Edition* spin-off *American Journal* and the *Les Brown Show* (soon replaced by *Rolonda*).

During 1995 media master Turner Broadcasting talked about, then decided against, acquiring King World. That year Oprah Winfrey (whose show accounted for 1/3 of King World's sales) renewed her contract for 2 more years. Also in 1995 the firm sold its CBS-TV affiliate and announced a deal with entertainment and electronics conglomerate Sony to launch 2 game shows.

In 1996 King World started an alliance with Chicago publisher and broadcaster Tribune by taking over distribution of the *Geraldo Rivera Show*. Later that year a deal that would have seen the company acquired by broadcaster New World Communications for $1.5 billion fell through when New World was itself purchased by Rupert Murdoch's News Corp.

WHO

Chairman: Roger King, age 51, $1,810,000 pay
President and CEO: Michael King, age 47, $1,810,000 pay
EVP and COO: Stephen W. Palley, age 50, $1,395,000 pay
President, Camelot Entertainment Sales, Inc.: Steven R. Hirsch, age 46, $730,000 pay
President, King World International: Fred Cohen
President, King World Direct, Inc.: Burl Hechtman
President, Domestic Television Sales: Scott Towle
SVP Business Affairs and General Counsel: Jonathan Birkhahn
SVP Programming and Development: E. V. DiMassa Jr.
SVP Corporate Research and Marketing: Moira Farrell
SVP Strategic Planning and Acquisitions: Robert King
VP, Interim CFO, and Controller: Steven A. LoCascio, age 37, $190,000 pay
VP Special Projects and Secretary: Diana King, age 46
VP Public Relations: Allyson Kossow Felix
VP Corporate Administration (HR): Patsy Bundy
Auditors: Andersen Worldwide

WHERE

HQ: 1700 Broadway, 33rd Fl., New York, NY 10019
Phone: 212-315-4000
Fax: 212-582-9255
Web site: http://www.kingworld.com

King World distributes programming in the US and Canada and several other foreign countries.

WHAT

	1995 Sales
	% of total
The Oprah Winfrey Show	37
Wheel of Fortune	21
Jeopardy!	18
Inside Edition	8
American Journal	4
Other operations	12
Total	**100**

First-run Syndicated Programs
American Journal
Inside Edition
Jeopardy!
The Oprah Winfrey Show
Rolonda
Wheel of Fortune

Program Library
Selected TV series
  Branded
  The Guns of Will Sonnett
  Topper

Selected film series
  Charlie Chan
  The Little Rascals
  Mr. Moto
  Sherlock Holmes

Other Operations
Camelot Entertainment Sales, Inc. (advertising sales)
King World Direct, Inc. (infomercials, telemarketing)
King World International (foreign distribution)

KEY COMPETITORS

All American Communications
Carsey-Werner
CST Entertainment
DreamWorks SKG
Gannett
Hearst
International Family Entertainment
Katz Media
Kushner-Locke
New World
News Corp.
Sony
Spelling Entertainment
Time Warner
Tribune
Viacom
Walt Disney

HOW MUCH

NYSE symbol: KWP FYE: August 31	Annual Growth	1986	1987	1988	1989	1990	1991	1992	1993	1994	1995
Sales ($ mil.)	16.5%	146	241	280	396	454	476	503	474	481	574
Net income ($ mil.)	21.9%	20	34	61	73	84	93	95	102	88	117
Income as % of sales	—	13.6%	14.1%	21.7%	18.5%	18.5%	19.6%	18.95	21.5%	18.4%	20.4%
Earnings per share ($)	24.7%	0.43	0.74	1.52	1.94	2.15	2.38	2.43	2.65	2.33	3.14
Stock price – high ($)	—	12.61	22.18	17.76	27.10	30.02	34.50	35.25	43.75	44.13	44.50
Stock price – low ($)	—	6.77	8.67	10.59	15.26	18.13	21.50	22.13	31.75	32.50	32.50
Stock price – close ($)	17.2%	9.34	11.84	15.84	25.43	24.50	24.75	33.63	38.38	34.50	38.88
P/E – high	—	29	30	12	14	14	15	15	17	19	14
P/E – low	—	16	12	7	8	8	9	9	12	14	10
Dividends per share ($)	—	0.00	0.00	0.00	0.00	0.00	0.00	0.00	0.00	0.00	0.00
Book value per share ($)	36.5%	0.95	0.89	(0.19)	1.65	3.87	6.35	9.01	10.57	12.49	15.66
Employees	18.5%	93	94	106	319	449	474	246	405	430	430

1995 YEAR-END

Debt ratio: 0.0%
Return on equity: 22.7%
Cash (mil.): $447
Current ratio: 5.30
Long-term debt (mil.): $0
No. of shares (mil.): 37
Dividends
  Yield: —
  Payout: —
Market value (mil.): $1,429

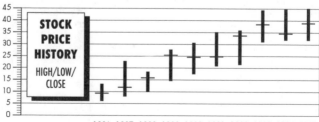

STOCK PRICE HISTORY
HIGH/LOW/CLOSE

1986 1987 1988 1989 1990 1991 1992 1993 1994 1995

KNIGHT-RIDDER, INC.

OVERVIEW

Media Goliath Knight-Ridder tangled with several would-be Davids and did some horse trading to continue building its word empire. The Miami-based company prints 38 papers (which account for about 80% of its revenues), including the *Detroit Free Press*, the *Miami Herald*, and the *Philadelphia Inquirer*. The 2nd largest US newspaper chain (after Gannett), the firm also has a significant presence online: its Knight-Ridder Information subsidiary offers information retrieval services such as DataStar and Dialog, which provide abstracts and full text of more than 4,000 business, news, and science publications. The company is also seeking to publish World Wide Web versions of most of its newspapers.

Knight-Ridder has been wrestling with several challenges, including a lengthy Teamsters strike (contributing to losses of at least $46 million at the *Detroit Free Press*) and newsprint costs that skyrocketed 40% in one year. However, the company added to its print holdings with the purchase of Lesher Communications (which owns the *Contra Costa Times* in California and 3 other journals). It also withdrew from the cable television market by selling its half-interest in TKR Cable (with 350,000 subscribers) to partner and king-of-the-(cable)-hill Tele-Communications, Inc. (TCI) for $420 million.

CEO Anthony Ridder (great-grandson of Ridder Publications founder Herman Ridder) and president Jack Fontaine are struggling to cut "costs" (jobs) and shed marginal operations such as Knight-Ridder Financial, while maintaining growth in the company's core newspaper and online segments. The firm is also wooing additional acquisition candidates.

WHEN

Knight-Ridder began as a 1974 merger between Knight Newspapers, the #2 newspaper group by circulation, and #3 Ridder Publications (both companies had gone public in 1969). Knight dominated the new board of directors.

Knight Newspapers had begun in 1903 when Charles Knight, a lawyer turned editor, purchased the *Akron Beacon Journal* and became a publisher. He died in 1933, leaving the paper to his sons, Jack and Jim. With their guidance the company grew to include 16 metropolitan dailies, including the *Miami Herald* (1937), *Detroit Free Press* (1940), and *Philadelphia Inquirer* (1969).

Ridder Publications had begun in 1892 when Herman Ridder bought a New York German-language newspaper, the *Staats-Zeitung*. He expanded in 1926 with the purchase of the *Journal of Commerce*, a New York shipping daily founded in 1827. Over the next 5 decades, the company grew to 19 dailies and 8 weeklies, mostly in the West.

After the Knight-Ridder merger, Knight's Lee Hills became chairman and CEO. Ridder's Bernard Ridder Jr. became VC.

During the 1970s and 1980s, the company expanded into television, radio, and book publishing. In 1978 it purchased VHF stations in 3 states. The company bought HP Books in 1979 (sold in 1987) and formed TKR Cable with TCI in 1981. A year later Knight-Ridder launched VU/TEXT (on-line news retrieval, now a provider of library systems to newspapers), followed in 1983 by Viewtron, America's first consumer videotext system. In 1988 the company bought DIALOG, the world's largest on-line, full-text service, from Lockheed. Broadcast properties were sold in 1989.

During the 1980s Knight-Ridder's *Detroit Free Press* lost over $90 million in a newspaper war against Gannett's *Detroit News*. After a 43-month court battle, the 2 papers signed a joint operating agreement in 1989.

In 1992 the *San Jose Mercury News*, working with America Online, became the first newspaper to integrate online services with the daily paper. Also in 1993 Knight-Ridder bought DataStar (European online service), Equinet (Australian online service), the Dataline Asia-Pacific Database (Hong Kong), and EFECOM (Spain, financial news; renamed KRF/Iberia).

In 1995 the company sold the 168-year-old *Journal of Commerce*, along with its print and electronic products and bought a small stake in Internet software developer Netscape Communications. It also purchased Lesher Communications, its first newspaper acquisition in 9 years, and sold its interest in TKR Cable for $420 million. Chairman and CEO James Batten died of cancer that year and was succeeded by Anthony Ridder.

In 1996 Knight-Ridder formed MediaStream, a new digital products subsidiary that will be the home of PressLink Online (online information service for the news media) and Vu/Text division. In 1996 the company sold its financial news unit, Knight-Ridder Financial, to Global Financial Information for $275 million.

WHO

Chairman and CEO: P. Anthony Ridder, age 55, $797,996 pay (prior to promotion)
President: John C. Fontaine, age 64, $613,834 pay (prior to promotion)
SVP and CFO: Ross Jones, age 53, $508,905 pay
VP; President, Knight-Ridder Information, Inc.: Patrick J. Tierney, age 50, $613,873 pay
VP Human Resources: Mary Jean Connors, age 43, $346,795 pay
VP Operations: Frank McComas, age 50
VP Operations: Peter E. Pitz, age 54
VP News: Clark Hoyt, age 53
VP News: Marty Claus, age 47
VP Marketing: Jerome S. Tilis, age 53
VP New Media: Robert D. Ingle, age 56
VP Technology: Larry D. Marbert, age 42
VP and General Counsel: Cristina Lagueruela Mendoza, age 49
Auditors: Ernst & Young LLP

WHERE

HQ: One Herald Plaza, Miami, FL 33132-1693
Phone: 305-376-3800
Fax: 305-376-3828
Web site: http://www.phillynews.com

Knight-Ridder has newspaper printing and publishing facilities in 30 cities in 16 states and maintains news bureaus and business information service offices worldwide.

WHAT

	1995 Sales	
	$ mil.	% of total
Advertising	1,673	61
Circulation	495	18
Business information svcs.	502	18
Other	82	3
Total	**2,752**	**100**

	Selected Newspapers	Daily Circulation (Average)
	Detroit Free Press	537,353
	Philadelphia Inquirer	475,090
	Miami Herald	386,316
	San Jose Mercury News (California)	288,558
	Charlotte Observer (North Carolina)	239,304
	St. Paul Pioneer Press (Minnesota)	209,519
	Philadelphia Daily News	197,998
	Lexington Herald-Leader (Kentucky)	121,034
	Biloxi Sun Herald (Mississippi)	47,832
	Boulder Daily Camera (Colorado)	34,820
	Aberdeen American News (South Dakota)	18,325

Selected Information Services
Knight-Ridder Information, Inc. (fax and online delivery of business, general news, legal, and science abstracts and articles; includes DataStar and Dialog online services)
Technimetrics (investor information)

Selected Investments and Joint Ventures
Netscape Communications Corp. (Internet browsers and server software)
Newspapers First (50%, advertising sales)
Ponderay Newsprint Co. (13.5%, newsprint mill)
Seattle Times Co. (49% voting interest, newspapers)
Southeast Paper Manufacturing Co. (33%, newsprint mill)

KEY COMPETITORS

Advance	E.W. Scripps	Thomson Corp.
Publications	Gannett	Time Warner
Associated Press	Hearst	Times Mirror
Bertelsmann	McGraw-Hill	Tribune
Bloomberg	Media General	Viacom
Capital	NBC	Washington Post
Cities/ABC	New York Times	West Publishing
Cox Enterprises	News Corp.	Westinghouse/
Dow Jones	Reed Elsevier	CBS
Dun & Bradstreet	Reuters	Wolters Kluwer

HOW MUCH

NYSE symbol: KRI FYE: Last Sunday in December	Annual Growth	1986	1987	1988	1989	1990	1991	1992	1993	1994	1995
Sales ($ mil.)	4.1%	1,910	2,072	2,083	2,268	2,305	2,237	2,329	2,451	2,649	2,752
Net income ($ mil.)	2.0%	140	155	156	180	149	132	146	148	171	167
Income as % of sales	—	7.3%	7.5%	7.5%	7.9%	6.5%	5.9%	6.3%	6.0%	6.5%	6.1%
Earnings per share ($)	3.7%	2.41	2.65	2.76	3.44	2.94	2.55	2.65	2.68	3.15	3.34
Stock price – high ($)	—	57.88	61.25	47.75	58.38	58.00	57.50	64.13	65.00	61.00	66.63
Stock price – low ($)	—	37.50	33.25	35.75	42.88	37.00	43.75	51.50	50.63	46.50	50.50
Stock price – close ($)	3.2%	46.88	40.13	45.38	58.38	45.75	52.88	58.00	59.75	50.50	62.50
P/E – high	—	24	23	17	17	20	23	24	24	19	20
P/E – low	—	16	13	13	13	13	17	19	19	15	15
Dividends per share ($)	5.9%	0.88	1.00	1.12	1.22	1.32	1.40	1.40	1.40	1.44	1.48
Book value per share ($)	5.4%	14.28	15.85	15.47	17.83	18.09	21.44	21.50	22.66	23.15	22.86
Employees	(0.6%)	24,000	24,000	22,000	21,000	21,000	20,000	20,000	20,000	21,000	22,800

1995 YEAR-END

Debt ratio: 47.7%
Return on equity: 14.3%
Cash (mil.): $26
Current ratio: 1.15
Long-term debt (mil.): $1,001
No. of shares (mil.): 49
Dividends
  Yield: 2.4%
  Payout: 44.3%
Market value (mil.): $3,037

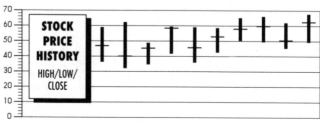

STOCK PRICE HISTORY
HIGH/LOW/CLOSE

LAGARDÈRE GROUPE

OVERVIEW

By George, Lagardère is making money through the global expansion of its magazine businesses. The Paris-based limited partnership's media and publishing interests account for 57% of total revenues. Through its Hachette Filipacchi subsidiary, Lagardère publishes more than 100 magazines and newspapers (including *Woman's Day* and *Car and Driver*) in over 15 languages. In 1995 Lagardère bankrolled political scion John F. Kennedy Jr.'s *George*, a new political magazine, in one of the most closely watched US magazine launches in years. The company also owns Grolier, a world leader in encyclopedias (CD-ROM and print versions).

The company, through its advanced technologies subsidiary Matra, is a leader in smart missile weapon technology in Europe, and a major player in satellite technology. Matra

Automobile makes cars in collaboration with Renault. Other concerns range from the construction of transit systems to telecommunications, film, broadcasting, and banking.

French entrepreneur Jean-Luc Lagardère is both a managing partner of the Lagardère Groupe and CEO of Matra Hachette, its 94%-owned operating company.

In 1995, Lagardère formed a joint venture with American financier Ron Perelman to buy the US edition of movie magazine *Premiere* and launched a Chinese version of *Woman's Day*, the first market outside the US for the title. The company has its sights set on launching *Woman's Day* editions in Hong Kong and Taiwan and *Premiere* editions in South Korea, Spain, and Taiwan, as well as expanding the vernacular versions of *Car and Driver* and *Elle*.

WHEN

The Lagardère Groupe's flagship publishing business, Hachette, traces its origins back to 1826, when schoolteacher Louis Hachette bought a small book publishing and selling business in Paris. He published his first periodical, a journal for teachers, in 1827 and began buying rights to primary school texts in 1831. Business took off when France enacted a law in 1833 calling for free primary schooling. Librairie Hachette received an enormous order from the Ministry of Public Education, including orders for 500,000 alphabet primers.

An 1851 visit to British bookseller W H Smith in London convinced Hachette that rail passengers would buy books from stores in stations. The next year he began signing contracts with French railroads and soon had a virtual monopoly on bookselling in French train stations. In 1853 Hachette started the Bibliothèque de Chemins de Fer (Railway Library) series of books and travel guides. In 1862 French novelist Emile Zola began a 4-year stint in press relations with Hachette.

Louis Hachette died in 1864. Around the turn of the century, Hachette bought France's leading newspaper distributors, and it acquired major French printing and binding companies in 1920. Hachette launched fashion magazine *Elle* in 1945, and the company acquired control of French publishers Grasset, Fayard, and Stock in the 1950s.

Jean-Luc Lagardère, the director general of defense contractor Matra since 1963, gained control of Hachette in 1980. He launched international spinoffs of its magazines, including

a successful US *Elle* in 1985 in partnership with media maven Rupert Murdoch.

In the late 1980s Hachette bought an interest in the #2 French radio station, Europe 1; helped start another, Europe 2; purchased the 2nd largest magazine distributor in the US, Curtis Circulation. In 1988, it spent over $1.1 billion on Grolier (encyclopedias) and US publisher Diamandis Communications and bought out Murdoch's share of *Elle*.

The company purchased 25% of a money-losing French TV network, La Cinq, in 1990. The station collapsed a year later, causing Hachette to write off $643 million. To cover the huge debt, Lagardère merged Matra with Hachette in 1993.

Lagardère had taken over Matra at the age of 35 and steered the company on a path of rapid diversification and growth. In the 1960s Matra entered the space systems market (satellites and space launchers) and also produced a series of Le Mans-winning cars. In the 1970s Matra began developing transit systems and telecommunications products. Lagardère united the disparate companies under the holding company that bears his name when it gained control of Matra Hachette in 1994.

The US publishing unit, buoyed by a successful expansion in the early 1990s, continued its acquisitive ways in 1995 with the purchase of *Family Life* (founded by *Rolling Stone* publisher Jann Wenner) and *Video* magazines. That year Lagardère acquired UCS, the largest network of media publications in Canada. In 1996 launched *Elle* in Russia.

Chairman: Raymond H. Lévy
General Partner and Managing Partner; Chairman and CEO, Matra Hachette: Jean-Luc Lagardère
Chairman of Group Finance Committee; President, Matra Hachette: Philippe Camus
Chairman and CEO, Grolier; Chairman and CEO, Matra Hachette Multimedia: Arnaud Lagardère
Deputy Chairman, President and CEO, Hachette Filipacchi Presse: Gérald de Roquemaurel
President and CEO, Hachette Filipacchi Magazines, Inc. (US): David J. Pecker, age 44
General Counsel and Secretary; Chairman, Lagardère Sociétés: Pierre Leroy
Spokesman of the Managing Partner and EVP Communications and Human Resources: Thierry Funck-Brentano
Auditors: Barbier Frinault et Autres (Andersen Worldwide)

WHERE

HQ: 4, rue de Presbourg, 75116, Paris, France
Phone: +33-1-40-69-16-00
Fax: +33-1-47-23-01-92
US HQ: Lagardère Groupe North America, 1633 Broadway, New York, NY 10019
US Phone: 212-767-6753
US Fax: 212-767-5635
Web site: http://www.lagardere.com

	1995 Sales % of total
France	48
Other Europe	29
US	17
Middle East/Far East	3
Other regions	3
Total	**100**

WHAT

	1995 Sales % of total
Distribution services	24
Print media	16
Space	11
Automobile	11
Telecommunications	11
Defense	9
Book publishing	8
Broadcast, film & display	5
Multimedia & Grolier	4
Other	1
Total	**100**

Selected Matra Hachette Operating Companies
Banque Arjil (42%, investment bank)
Europe 1 Communication (45%; broadcast, film, display)
Grolier (encyclopedias)
Hachette Filipacchi Presse (66%, print media)
Hachette Livre (book publishing)
Matra Automobile (in collaboration with Renault)
Matra Cap Systèmes (50%, defense)
Matra Communication (50%, telecom and CAD-CAM)
Matra Datavision (74%, telecom and CAD-CAM)
Matra Défense
Matra Hachette Multimedia (online and other media)
Matra Marconi Space (51%)

KEY COMPETITORS

Advance Publications	Encyclopaedia Britannica	Grumman Pearson
Alcatel Alsthom	Hearst	Reader's Digest
Bertelsmann	K-III	Siemens
Bombardier	Lockheed Martin	Thyssen
British Aerospace	Meredith	Time Warner
CANAL+	New York Times	United News &
Chas. Levy	News Corp.	Media
Chrysler	Northrop	Viacom

HOW MUCH

Principal exchange: Paris FYE: December 31	Annual Growth	1986	1987	1988	1989	1990	1991	1992	1993	1994	1995
Sales (FF mil.)	0.7%	—	—	—	—	—	53,111	55,102	53,981	53,018	54,695
Net income (FF mil.)	—	—	—	—	—	—	(448)	96	155	615	630
Income as % of sales	—	—	—	—	—	—	—	0.2%	0.3%	1.2%	1.2%
Earnings per share (FF)	—	—	—	—	—	—	(31.42)	4.51	5.05	8.74	8.95
Stock price – high (FF)	—	—	—	—	—	—	134	100	152	168	128
Stock price – low (FF)	—	—	—	—	—	—	55	66	84	108	83
Stock price – close (FF)	6.5%	—	—	—	—	—	70	82	149	124	90
P/E – high	—	—	—	—	—	—	—	22	30	19	14
P/E – low	—	—	—	—	—	—	—	15	17	12	9
Dividends per share (FF)	(1.7%)	—	—	—	—	—	3.00	1.50	2.20	2.50	2.80
Book value per share (FF)	(10.8%)	—	—	—	—	—	96	69	80	62	61
Employees	11.3%	—	—	—	—	—	28,460	44,394	41,394	40,326	43,622

1995 YEAR-END

Debt ratio: 62.0%
Return on equity: 7.6%
Cash (mil.): FF10,164
Current ratio: 1.13
Long-term debt (mil.): FF9,911
No. of shares (mil.): 86
Dividends
  Yield: 2.0%
  Payout: 31.3%
Market value (mil.): $1,573
Sales (mil.): $11,142

Note: $=FF4.9 (December 31, 1995)

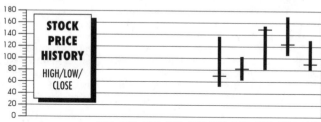

STOCK PRICE HISTORY
HIGH/LOW/CLOSE

1986 1987 1988 1989 1990 1991 1992 1993 1994 1995

LEO BURNETT COMPANY, INC.

OVERVIEW

The original Marlboro Man may be long dead of lung cancer, but the "Marlboro Man" campaign rides on. Thirty years after the ads' introduction by Chicago ad agency Leo Burnett, the Marlboro brand was inducted into the Marketing Hall of Fame because of its "enduring success in the marketplace." This campaign illustrates 2 key factors in Leo Burnett's success — vivid imagery (the Jolly Green Giant, Tony the Tiger, and the Pillsbury Doughboy) and client loyalty.

Many of its biggest clients have been with the company for decades. Its longest relationship is with Green Giant, which has been with Leo Burnett for 60 years. Other long-term clients include Pillsbury (now Green Giant's

parent), Kellogg, and of course, Philip Morris (which makes Marlboro). As these companies have expanded their global operations, Leo Burnett has followed, and its reach now extends to more than 60 countries.

The advertising business is changing, and Leo Burnett is keeping up. It has become increasingly involved with creating interactive media sites for some of its clients (including McDonald's and Kelloggs), and is flexible enough to adopt new performance-based billing arrangements which are becoming increasingly common in the industry, instead of sticking with percentage fees.

Burnett is a private company whose stock is held by its employees.

WHEN

In 1935 Leo Burnett left Erwin Wasey & Company, then one of America's top advertising agencies, to form his own firm. He opened his office in Chicago with 8 staffers, 3 clients (the Minnesota Valley Canning Company, Hoover, and Realsilk Hosiery), and a bowl of red apples on the receptionist's desk as a gesture of hospitality. Early on, a journalist summed up the prevailing attitude about the agency's chances of success during the Depression by saying, "It won't be long 'til Leo Burnett is selling apples on the street corner instead of giving them away." But Burnett soon rewarded Minnesota Valley's loyalty by creating the Jolly Green Giant campaign, and the apples have remained a symbol of his success.

The agency's national success was not immediate. Not until 1949, when it landed the Pillsbury Family Flour account (then worth $7 million), did Burnett hit the big time. It soon acquired accounts for Kellogg and the New York-based Tea Council.

Burnett shunned the flashy sophistication used by many New York firms and instead tried to convey the "inherent drama" of a product. This strategy proved itself repeatedly in ads such as United Airlines's "Fly the Friendly Skies," but it was most successful with Philip Morris, which hired the agency in the 1950s to boost sales of one of its minor brands — Marlboro. Burnett repositioned the brand, transforming its distinctly feminine image into one of rugged masculinity, culminating in the rollout of the Marlboro Country campaign in

1964. Sales soared and Marlboros became (and still are) the world's most popular smokes.

By 1962 the agency had offices in Detroit, Hollywood, New York, and Toronto. That year it expanded overseas, buying an interest in British firm Legget Nicholson and Partners. In 1967 Burnett merged with D. P. Brother & Co. of Detroit, which brought with it GM's Oldsmobile account. In 1971 Leo Burnett died.

The agency grew throughout the 1970s, not by adding many new clients but by helping improve the sales of its existing clients, many of which were large, consumer-oriented companies that constantly introduced new products. In the 1980s the agency adopted a slightly more aggressive approach, wresting the McDonald's account from Needham. The firm's client list remained relatively short (only 31 clients for its US operations) but stable.

Leo Burnett has been pressured in the 1990s by competition from a handful of advertising conglomerates (like Interpublic and Omnicom), which are able to offer a wider range of services. In response, the agency has added services, particularly in the electronic area. In 1996 it bought an interest in Giant Step Productions, with which it has worked since 1994 to create online and Web site home pages and advertising. The company has also sought new clients. Leo Burnett's Italian office has designed an ad campaign for a Vatican devotional product, *The Pope of the Rosary*, which features Pope John Paul II reciting the Rosary on CD and cassette tape and includes a picture of the Pope and a set of Rosary beads.

Chairman and Chief Creative Director: Richard B.
Fizdale
President and CEO: William T. Lynch
Group President and Deputy Chief Creative Officer:
Michael B. Conrad
Group President and CFO: Roger A. Haupt
Group President, The Americas: James M. Jenness
Group President, Asia/Pacific: James G. Oates
Group President, Europe/Middle East/Africa: Kerry M.
Rubie
Corporate VC and Director Corporate Planning:
Albert C. M. Winninghoff
EVP Human Resources and Law, Worldwide: Michael
Breslin

WHERE

HQ: 35 W. Wacker Dr., Ste. 2200, Chicago, IL 60601
Phone: 312-220-5959
Fax: 312-220-3299
Web site: http://www.leoburnett.com

	1995 Billings	
	$ mil.	% of total
US	2,902	54
Other countries	2,485	46
Total	**5,387**	**100**

Selected Countries

Argentina	Norway
Australia	Pakistan
Brazil	Peru
Canada	Philippines
China	Poland
Czech Republic	Russia
Egypt	Saudi Arabia
France	Singapore
Germany	South Africa
Hong Kong	Spain
Hungary	Sweden
India	Switzerland
Israel	Syria
Italy	Taiwan
Japan	Thailand
Korea	Turkey
Malaysia	UK
Mexico	US
Netherlands	Venezuela
	Vietnam

WHAT

Selected Services
Advertising
Brand consulting
Direct mail
Interactive media services
Market research
Media buying
Promotional services
Public relations

**Selected Clients (year
signed)**
Allstate Insurance Cos.
(1957)
Ameritech (1994)
Amoco (1996)
Andersen Worldwide
(1994)
The Coca-Cola Company
(1995)
Commonwealth Edison
Co. (1954)
Dairy Management Inc.
(1995)
Dean Witter Discover &
Co. (1988)
First Brands Corp. (1961)
Fruit of the Loom (1992)
Hallmark Cards (1988)

J. M. Smucker Co. (1994)
Keebler Co. (1968)
Kellogg Co. (1949)
Kraft Foods (1984)
Maytag (1955)
McDonald's (1982)
Miller Brewing (1982)
National Cattleman's Beef
Association (1991)
New York Stock Exchange
(1996)
Nintendo (1991)
Oldsmobile division of
General Motors (1967)
Philip Morris (1954)
The Pillsbury Co. (1944)
Procter & Gamble (1952)
Reebok (1993)
Rockport (1994)
Samsonite (1983)
Sealy (1990)
True Value Hardware
Stores (1994)
United Airlines (1965)
United Distillers North
America (1968)
Walt Disney (1994)

KEY COMPETITORS

Ackerley Communications
Bozell, Jacobs
Cordiant
Creative Artists
D'Arcy Masius
Dentsu
Grey Advertising
Interpublic Group
Omnicom Group
True North
WPP Group
Young & Rubicam

HOW MUCH

Private company FYE: December 31	Annual Growth	1986	1987	1988	1989	1990	1991	1992	1993	1994	1995
Sales ($ mil.)	11.5%	293	338	430	487	538	577	560	622	677	780
Employees	2.1%	1,697	1,775	1,908	2,045	2,198	2,270	2,440	2,438	1,979	2,049

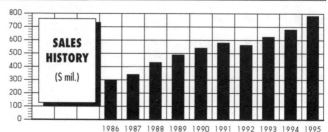

SALES
HISTORY
($ mil.)

MCA INC.

OVERVIEW

MCA's executive offices must have have seemed like the epicenter of an earthquake zone. Since Seagrams paid consumer electronics monarch Matsushita about $5.7 billion for 80% of MCA in 1995 (Matsushita retains the remaining 20%), Edgar Bronfman, CEO of the Canadian beverage giant, has been shaking up headquarters to try to awaken the sleepy company. Heads of almost every major division have been replaced, and MCA is aggressively seeking new talent. Bronfman tapped Frank Biondi Jr., former president and CEO of entertainment empire Viacom, to become chairman and CEO at MCA.

Universal City, California-based MCA produces and distributes films, TV programming, and records; publishes books; produces concerts; owns or operates 6 amphitheaters; operates 2 Universal Studios theme parks; and licenses and markets products from films and TV. MCA also owns a 50% interest in USA Network and about 40% of Cineplex Odeon, one of the largest movie theater chains in North America.

To invigorate the company's movie unit, Universal Studios, the company has signed deals with a number of major stars, including Sylvester Stallone, Danny DeVito, and Demi Moore. MCA also has Stephen Spielberg on board to direct the sequel to *Jurassic Park*. Spielberg has directed some of MCA's biggest hits (*E.T.*, *Jurassic Park*), but he has formed his own studio, DreamWorks SKG, with Jeffrey Katzenberg and David Geffen. MCA does have a distribution deal with DreamWorks, however.

The company is also working to pump up its television business, which has barely registered more than a test pattern lately. In 1996 it bought a $100 million stake in producer Brad Grey's TV and film production operations (*NewsRadio*).

WHEN

In the early 1920s Jules Stein earned his way through Rush Medical College in Chicago by organizing bands to play one-night stands. A year after becoming an ophthalmologist, he formed the Music Corporation of America (MCA). By 1927 his sideline had become so big that he left his practice. MCA grew into the biggest agency of bands in the US. Stein expanded by signing up singers, dancers, and comedians and selling whole "packages" of groups. Later he expanded to include radio, motion pictures, and TV.

MCA moved to Hollywood in 1937 and began buying out other talent agencies, acquiring such famous clients as Betty Grable, Greta Garbo, Henry Fonda, Jimmy Stewart, and Ronald Reagan. MCA did a better job than the competition, broke the old studio contract system, and invented the percentage deal by which the company and client received a percentage of the profits of a picture. Eventually MCA handled 60% of all Hollywood talent.

Stein retired from active control in 1946, becoming chairman of the board and promoting Lew Wasserman, then 33, to president and CEO. In 1952 the company began producing television films. The Screen Actors Guild didn't like the idea of a talent agency producing its own films because it would be negotiating contracts between its clients and itself; however, MCA negotiated with the Guild for a waiver to produce TV programs.

In 1959 MCA bought Universal's 410-acre film lot in the San Fernando Valley to provide room for its TV production. The company absorbed Decca Records, which owned nearly 90% of Universal Pictures, in 1961. The studio, which had been producing movies as Universal-International since 1946, reverted to its original name in 1962.

MCA expanded into retailing in 1968 when it acquired Spencer Gifts. In 1975 it added book publishing to its list of activities with the acquisition of G. P. Putnam's Sons. With videocassettes emerging as a new way to deliver entertainment, the company formed MCA Home Entertainment Group in 1980. In 1986 MCA bought a stake in Cineplex Odeon. In 1990 MCA opened Universal Studios Florida (owned jointly with Britain's Rank Organisation). The next year Matsushita acquired MCA for about $6.1 billion.

After Seagram bought the company from Matsushita, CAA executive Ron Meyer was picked as president by Bronfman after a deal fell through with CAA head (now Walt Disney president) Michael Ovitz. Longtime chairman Lew Wasserman was named chairman emeritus in 1995.

In 1996 MCA's Music Entertainment Group bought 50% of Interscope Records for $200 million. Interscope is the controversial rock and rap label that distributes Death Row Records, the gangsta rap label.

WHO

Chairman and CEO: Frank J. Biondi Jr., age 51
President and COO: Ron Meyer, age 50
Chairman, Universal Pictures: Casey Silver, age 40
Chairman and CEO, MCA Music Entertainment: Doug Morris, age 56
Chairman, Universal Televison: R. Gregory Meidel, age 42
EVP Corporate Operations: Howard Weitzman, age 55
EVP: Sanford R. Climan, age 39
SVP and General Counsel: Karen Randall, age 42
CFO: Bruce Hack
Treasurer: Pamela Cherney
Director Human Resources: Ken Khars
Auditors: Price Waterhouse LLP

WHERE

HQ: 100 Universal City Plaza, Universal City, CA 91608
Phone: 818-777-1000
Fax: 818-733-1402
Web site: http://www.mca.com

WHAT

Business Units

MCA Development (commercial real estate development on Universal City complex; real estate services to MCA divisions worldwide)

MCA Enterprises (business development)

MCA Home Entertainment Group
MCA Home Video
MCA/Universal Home Video
Universal Pay Television

MCA Motion Picture Group
United Cinemas International (joint venture with Paramount Pictures operating movie theaters in Austria, Germany, Ireland, Spain, and the UK)
Universal Pictures Distribution
Universal Pictures Marketing
Universal Pictures Production

MCA Music Entertainment Group
Geffen Records
GRP Records
Interscope Records (50%)
MCA Concerts
MCA Music Entertainment International
MCA Music Publishing
MCA Records

Uni Distribution
Winterland Productions

MCA Publishing Group
The Putnam Berkley Group

MCA Recreation Services Group
Universal Studios Florida (theme park)
Universal Studios Hollywood (theme park)

MCA Television Group
MCA Television Entertainment
MCA TV
MCA TV International
Universal Family Entertainment/Cartoon Studios
Universal Television

MCA/Universal Merchandising (licensing and marketing)

Spencer Gifts (retail gift chain)

Universal Studios Operations Group

Other Holdings
Brillstein-Grey Communications (minority stake, TV show production)
Brillstein-Grey Entertainment (approximately 50%, film production)
Cineplex Odeon Corporation (approximately 40%, North American movie theaters)
USA Networks (50%)
Sci-Fi Channel
USA Network

KEY COMPETITORS

Advance Publications
All American Communications
AMC Entertainment
Anheuser-Busch
Bertelsmann
Carsey-Werner
GC
International Family Entertainment
Liberty Media
King World
LucasArts
MGM

National Amusements
New World Communications
News Corp.
PolyGram
Samuel Goldwyn
Savoy Pictures
Sony
Spelling Entertainment
THORN EMI
Time Warner
United Artists Theatre
Viacom
Walt Disney

HOW MUCH

Subsidiary FYE: December 31	Annual Growth	1986	1987	1988	1989	1990	1991	1992	1993	1994	1995
Sales ($ mil.)	10.0%	2,441	2,590	3,024	3,272	—	—	5,290	5,730	5,571	5,772
Employees	(3.7%)	—	—	—	17,000	—	—	—	—	—	13,564

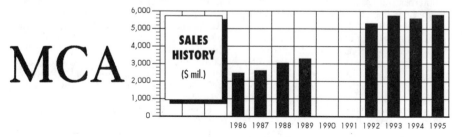

MCA

SALES HISTORY
($ mil.)

THE MCGRAW-HILL COMPANIES, INC.

OVERVIEW

One and one can make three — at least for McGraw-Hill. The New York City-based publishing company has found that its financial and corporate information print products create demand for comparable electronic products and that its electronic products whet customers' appetites for more print sources. Operations in McGraw-Hill's media, financial, and information segments range from mainstream broadcasting at 4 ABC-affiliated stations to trade journals to specialized financial data and corporate credit ratings to *Business Week*, one of the US's premier business journals. The company is increasingly offering these products in electronic form via software, CD-ROMs, online services, and the Internet.

McGraw-Hill is also the US's leading textbook publisher for elementary and secondary schools. Here, too, the company is making its materials available in new media to serve the growing number of schools that use computers. Other educational products include texts and supplements for vocational education and college and university courses. In addition, the company publishes specialized resource materials for a variety of professions, including engineering, law, and medicine.

In the 1990s McGraw-Hill has been restructuring by cutting staff and consolidating warehouse and distribution facilities. At the same time, the company is expanding its international services, sometimes through alliances (including one with Indian conglomerate Tata), as well as entering new markets at home. McGraw-Hill announced that it would enter the consumer market with interactive educational products.

WHEN

In 1909 magazine publishers James McGraw (*Street Railway Journal*) and John Hill (*American Machinist, Locomotive Engineer*) formed the McGraw-Hill Book Company to publish scientific and technical books. Initially the 2 kept their magazines separate from the company, but following Hill's death in 1916, the magazine segments were merged with McGraw-Hill.

In the 1920s the company pioneered the risky but successful "send-no-money" plan, giving customers a free 10-day examination of its books. In 1929, 2 months before the stock market crash, McGraw-Hill started *Business Week* magazine, in which it expressed concerns about the economy's health—a view contrary to general opinion.

McGraw-Hill continued to expand during the next 3 decades, publishing trade journals and college textbooks. It entered trade publishing in 1930 under the Whittlesey House name (changed to McGraw-Hill in 1950), but it was not until the 1950s that the trade division earned some distinction. Its greatest early commercial success was *Betty Crocker's Picture Cook Book* (1947), which sold 2.3 million copies in its first 2 years.

The company later diversified into financial information services, acquiring Standard & Poor's (S&P, corporate credit ratings and other financial services) in 1966 and Data Resources Inc. (DRI) in 1979; into broadcasting with the 1972 purchase of 4 TV stations from Time Inc.; and into product information services with the addition of Datapro Research Corp. in 1976.

Three years later it successfully fended off American Express's attempt to take it over.

Expanding its electronic information services businesses in the 1980s, McGraw-Hill acquired small, industry-specific publishing and information service operations. In 1989 it sold its trade books division, prompting subsidiary S&P to downgrade the parent's credit rating to A- because of a restructuring charge associated with reorganization. McGraw-Hill also began a partnership with imaging pioneer Kodak and megaprinter R. R. Donnelley to produce customized college textbooks based on the contents of McGraw-Hill's Primis database. It also formed a textbook and educational software joint venture, Macmillan/McGraw-Hill School Publishing.

During the 1990s the company continued to refine its financial information segment, buying J.J. Kenny, a provider of municipal securities information (1990), and 25% of Liberty Brokerage, Inc. (New York, 1993), which gave McGraw-Hill access to US Treasury securities pricing information. On the educational front, in 1991 the Macmillan/ McGraw-Hill joint venture acquired Computer Systems Research and its integrated learning system for instruction in basic mathematics, reading, and writing. Two years later Macmillan's parent, Maxwell Communications, went bankrupt and McGraw-Hill bought Macmillan's share of the venture.

The company has introduced new Internet-related products, including *tele.com Magazine* (started in 1996) to cover the networking industry.

WHO

Chairman and CEO: Joseph L. Dionne, age 62, $1,528,181 pay
President and COO: Harold W. "Terry" McGraw III, age 47, $942,973 pay
EVP and CFO: Robert J. Bahash, age 50, $634,487 pay
EVP Administration: Thomas J. Sullivan, age 60, $608,457 pay
EVP Corporate Development: Robert E. Evanson, age 59
SVP Taxes: Frank J. Kaufman, age 51
SVP Corporate Affairs: Barbara A. Munder, age 50
SVP Treasury Operations: Frank D. Penglase, age 55
SVP and General Counsel: Kenneth M. Vittor, age 46
SVP Human Resources: Barbara B. Maddock, age 45
Auditors: Ernst & Young LLP

WHERE

HQ: 1221 Avenue of the Americas, New York, NY 10020-1095
Phone: 212-512-2000
Fax: 212-512-4871
Web site: http://www.mcgraw-hill.com
McGraw-Hill operates worldwide.

WHAT

	1995 Sales		1995 Operating Income	
	$ mil.	% of total	$ mil.	% of total
Educational & professional publishing	1,235	42	163	32
Information & media services	913	31	115	23
Financial services	787	27	231	45
Total	**2,935**	**100**	**509**	**100**

Selected Subsidiaries

Educational and Professional Publishing
Educational Publishing (Macmillan/McGraw-Hill, McGraw-Hill School Systems)
International publishing (McGraw-Hill Interamericana, Tata McGraw-Hill)
Professional Publishing (Professional Book Group, Shepard's/McGraw-Hill)

Information and Media Services
Broadcasting group (KMHG-TV, Denver; KGTV, San Diego)
Business Week Group (*Business Week* magazine and related operations)

Construction Information Group (*Architectural Record, Engineering News-Record*)
Publication Services Group (*Aviation Week & Space Technology, BYTE, Chemical Engineering, Hospital Practice*)
Tower Group International (import/export business)

Financial Services
Financial Information Services Group (Standard & Poor's Compustat, DRI/McGraw-Hill, J.J. Kenny Drake)
Standard & Poor's Ratings Services

KEY COMPETITORS

Advance Publications
American Financial
Bertelsmann
Bloomberg
Dow Jones
Dun & Bradstreet
Forbes
Harcourt General

Houghton Mifflin
Hoover's, Inc.
John Wiley
Knight-Ridder
Media General
Morningstar, Inc.
News Corp.
Pearson
Primark
Reed Elsevier

Reuters
Scholastic
Thomson Corp.
Time Warner
Times Mirror
TRW
Value Line
Viacom
West Publishing
Wolters Kluwer

HOW MUCH

NYSE symbol: MHP FYE: December 31	Annual Growth	1986	1987	1988	1989	1990	1991	1992	1993	1994	1995
Sales ($ mil.)	7.1%	1,576	1,751	1,818	1,789	1,938	1,943	2,050	2,195	2,760	2,935
Net income ($ mil.)	4.4%	154	165	186	40	173	148	153	11	203	227
Income as % of sales	—	9.8%	9.4%	10.2%	2.2%	8.9%	7.6%	7.5%	0.5%	7.4%	7.7%
Earnings per share ($)	4.6%	1.52	1.64	1.92	0.41	1.77	1.52	1.57	0.12	2.05	2.28
Stock price – high ($)	—	32.00	42.25	38.00	43.06	30.56	32.38	33.25	37.63	38.63	43.81
Stock price – low ($)	—	23.25	21.50	23.38	26.75	19.94	24.88	26.50	27.63	31.25	31.81
Stock price – close ($)	5.3%	27.31	24.13	31.13	28.38	26.31	28.69	30.69	33.81	33.44	43.56
P/E – high	—	21	26	20	105	17	21	21	—	19	19
P/E – low	—	15	13	12	65	11	16	17	—	15	14
Dividends per share ($)	5.2%	0.76	0.84	0.92	1.03	1.08	1.10	1.12	1.14	1.16	1.20
Book value per share ($)	2.2%	8.52	8.17	8.97	9.04	9.75	10.18	9.29	8.33	9.19	10.34
Employees	12.4%	5,232	15,892	16,255	14,461	13,868	13,539	13,393	15,661	15,339	15,004

1995 YEAR-END

Debt ratio: 37.8%
Return on equity: 23.3%
Cash (mil.): $10
Current ratio: 1.18
Long-term debt (mil.): $557
No. of shares (mil.): 100
Dividends
  Yield: 2.8%
  Payout: 52.6%
Market value (mil.): $4,362

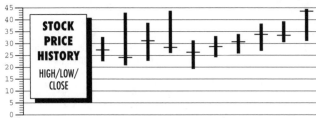

STOCK PRICE HISTORY HIGH/LOW/CLOSE

1986 1987 1988 1989 1990 1991 1992 1993 1994 1995

METRO-GOLDWYN-MAYER, INC.

OVERVIEW

Maybe the 3rd time will be the charm for financier Kirk Kerkorian and Metro-Goldwyn-Mayer (MGM). In mid-1996 Kerkorian and a group led by MGM chairman Frank Mancuso and Australian broadcastor Seven Network have agreed to acquire MGM. French bank Credit Lyonnais received $1.3 billion for the Hollywood studio. Kerkorian appears ready to resuscitate the studio many accuse him of ruining during the 1980s.

Fortunately, MGM has some recent hits under its belt, including 1996 Academy Award honoree *Leaving Las Vegas* (for which Nicholas Cage received the best actor Oscar), *Get Shorty, GoldenEye* (the most successful James Bond adventure in years), and 1996's surprise mainstream hit *The Birdcage* (a gay drawing room farce). Not bad for a studio with no actual production facilities — it's based in an office building in Santa Monica, California.

In addition to MGM Pictures, the company also operates United Artists Pictures (which owns the James Bond franchise), MGM Worldwide Television, MGM/UA Telecommunications Group, MGM/UA Distribution Co., MGM/UA Home Entertainment, MGM/UA Music, and MGM Interactive. These operations make and distribute movies and television shows, soundtracks, cartoons, and interactive products.

WHEN

Louis B. Mayer, a Russian emigrant, came to Haverhill, Massachusetts, in 1907 and began showing movies in a rundown vaudeville theater. His venture was a success despite not having enough movies to meet viewer demand. To help solve the shortage, in 1915 Mayer and several other theater owners and distributors formed Metro Pictures to make movies. In 1919 Mayer began producing his own movies and dropped out of Metro, which was bought by theater chain-owner Marcus Loew. In 1922 Samuel Goldwyn was ousted from Goldwyn Studios (which Goldwyn, born Goldfish, had formed with Edgar Selwyn in 1916) and joined United Artists (formed by Charlie Chaplin, Mary Pickford, and other stars in 1919).

In 1924 Loew's Inc. bought Goldwyn Studios, merged it with Metro Pictures, and then bought Mayer's production company, uniting production, distribution, and theater operations. MGM was instantly profitable and remained consistently so, despite the upheavals of the conversion to sound and declining attendance during the Depression. It did not lose money until WWII interrupted international sales in 1940. This did not stop Mayer from leading an industry-wide attempt to halve salaries, which was beaten back by the unions. Throughout the 1930s MGM was known for its prestige "literary" titles, like *A Tale of Two Cities, Gone with the Wind*, and *Wizard of Oz* and its sheer star power. Actors under contract included Fred Astaire, Joan Crawford, Clark Gable, Judy Garland, Greta Garbo, Katharine Hepburn, and Spencer Tracy.

The decline began after WWII, when changing tastes and television kept people away from the theaters. More seriously, federal antitrust action forced movie companies to disconnect from their theater chains. MGM fought back with a series of lavish musicals (including *Singin' in the Rain*) but financial problems continued. Mayer resigned under pressure in 1951; he died in 1957.

By 1969 the company was on the ropes. Financier Kirk Kerkorian bought the beleaguered firm and sold off assets, including the accumulated props and costumes of 45 years. Under the management of amateurs, production in the 1970s slowed to 3 or 4 films a year. Kerkorian used the MGM name and its Leo the Lion logo (first used by Goldwyn in 1921) for a new Las Vegas casino, the MGM Grand.

United Artists, meanwhile, had never achieved the first rank in movie production but struck it rich with the James Bond series in the 1960s and 1970s. In 1973 UA (then owned by Transamerica) bought MGM's distribution rights. Kerkorian bought United Artists in 1981 and formed MGM/UA (the name was changed back to Metro-Goldwyn-Mayer in 1992). In 1986 he sold it to Ted Turner, who sold most of it back to him, keeping the MGM film library for his cable TV operations.

Kerkorian put industry professional Alan Ladd Jr. in charge and went looking for a new buyer. In 1990 he found Pathe Communications. Pathe went bankrupt in 1992, leaving Credit Lyonnais in charge of a US national icon. The bank infused money and installed new management, which got MGM back on a sound enough footing to be attractive to potential buyers.

MGM invested $18 million in 1995 to market and distribute *Cutthroat Island* — the biggest box office bomb in the history of moviedom, surpassing previous titleholder *Heaven's Gate*, which UA released in 1980.

Chairman and CEO: Frank G. Mancuso
SVP Financial Operations: Daniel Rosett
SVP Financial Planning and Analysis: Charles Cohen
VP Corporate Communications: Ann H. Corley
VP Human Resources: Steven Shaw
VP Management Information Systems: Edward Altman
Auditors: Price Waterhouse LLP

WHERE

HQ: 2500 Broadway, Santa Monica, CA 90404
Phone: 310-449-3000
Fax: 310-449-3100
Web site: http://www.mgmua.com

WHAT

Production and Distribution
Home video
Interactive entertainment
Movies
Television shows

Retail
Movie theme stores

Selected 1996 Releases
A Family Thing (Robert Duvall and James Earl Jones)
All Dogs Go to Heaven 2 (cartoon)
The Birdcage (Robin Williams, Gene Hackman)
It's My Party (Eric Roberts, Marlee Matlin, Olivia
    Newton-John)
Large as Life (Bill Murray)
Moll Flanders
Mulholland Falls (Nick Nolte, John Malkovich)
Unforgettable (Ray Liotta)

KEY COMPETITORS

3DO
7th Level
Acclaim Entertainment
Broderbund
CANAL+
Cinergi Pictures
COMSAT
CST Entertainment
DreamWorks SKG
Hasbro
Kushner-Locke
LIVE Entertainment
LucasFilm
Nintendo
Producers Entertainment
Samuel Goldwyn
Seagram
SEGA
Sony
Spelling Entertainment
Viacom
Walt Disney

HOW MUCH

Private Company FYE: December 31	Annual Growth	1986	1987	1988	1989	1990	1991	1992	1993	1994	1995
Sales ($ mil.)	(3.0%)	355	428	675	877	715	922	892	937	937	861
Employees	(3.1%)	—	900	770	830	—	650	900	—	—	700

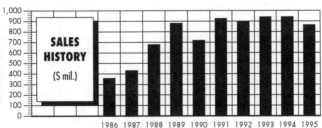

SALES HISTORY
($ mil.)

1986 1987 1988 1989 1990 1991 1992 1993 1994 1995

MICROSOFT CORPORATION

OVERVIEW

With Microsoft's operating systems controlling an estimated 80% of the PCs sold in the world, the Redmond, Washington-based company is the 800-pound gorilla of the computer world. However, Microsoft CEO Bill Gates can't thump his chest for long because an even bigger beast is now roaming the jungle — the Internet. Microsoft is the world's #1 independent software company, and the release (and marketing hype) of Windows 95, its upgraded operating system, increased its dominance. The company offers a variety of other software, including networking systems (Windows NT), database products (Access), spreadsheets (Excel), word processing (Word), and personal finance (Money), as well as games and reference products.

Gates is trying to make sure the burgeoning popularity of the Internet doesn't make a monkey out of Microsoft. To stave off competition from rivals such as Web browser maker Netscape and Internet software language developer Sun Microsystems, it has developed an Internet-intensive strategy. It has realigned its online service, the Microsoft Network, to allow Internet access and some free information. It has signed deals with other major online services, including America Online and CompuServe, to make Microsoft's Web browser, Internet Explorer, their primary browser. And it is releasing software that allows users to develop pages easily for the Web.

Microsoft is also expanding into other media. The company operates MSNBC, cable TV and online news service, with NBC; it has a deal with movie studio DreamWorks SKG to develop interactive games; it is developing interactive digital video systems and is publishing a series of computer books.

Gates, the richest person in the world, owns about 24% of Microsoft. Cofounder Paul Allen owns about 10% of the company's stock and still serves on its board.

WHEN

Microsoft (originally Micro-soft) was founded in 1975 after 19-year-old William Gates dropped out of Harvard and teamed with high school friend Paul Allen to sell a version of the programming language BASIC. While Gates was at Harvard, the pair had written the language for the Altair, the first commercial microcomputer (sold by Albuquerque-based MITS, a maker of electronic kits). Gates and Allen moved to Albuquerque and set up Microsoft in a hotel room to produce the program. Although MITS folded in 1979, Microsoft continued to grow by modifying its BASIC program for other computers.

Microsoft moved to Gates's native Seattle area in 1979 and developed software that enabled others to write programs for PCs. Microsoft's big break came in 1980, when it was chosen by IBM, over Gary Kildall's Digital Research, to write the operating system (software that controls a computer's basic functions) for IBM's new PC. Faced with a complex task and a tight deadline, Microsoft bought the rights to QDOS (short for "quick and dirty operating system") for $50,000 from Seattle programmer Tim Paterson and renamed it the Microsoft Disk Operating System (MS-DOS).

The popularity of IBM's PC made MS-DOS an instant monopoly because other PC makers wanted to be compatible with IBM. It became the standard PC operating system in the 1980s. Microsoft went on to develop software for IBM, Apple, and Radio Shack computers. In the meantime, Allen fell ill with Hodgkin's disease; he left Microsoft in 1983. Allen later started his own software company, Asymetrix, and acquired or invested in several other companies, including Starwave, Telescan, and Ticketmaster.

In the mid-1980s Microsoft introduced Windows. When the company went public in 1986, Gates retained 45% of the shares, becoming, in 1987, the PC industry's first billionaire. In 1992 Microsoft acquired Fox Software (database management system) and released Access, a database program.

In 1993 Microsoft introduced Windows NT, a client/server product. Microsoft agreed in 1994 to modify its marketing practices in order to settle an antitrust investigation by the US Department of Justice. When the settlement moved to judicial review, it was ruled unconducive to the public good and set aside. In a victory for Microsoft, a federal appeals court in mid-1995 reinstated the 1994 antitrust settlement between Microsoft and the Justice Department. Also in 1995, after several delays, the company released Windows 95, the latest version of its operating system.

In 1996 Microsoft introduced Slate (http://www.slate.com), an Internet-based magazine edited by former CNN pugilist Michael Kinsley. Microsoft's sales jumped to almost $8.7 billion in 1996 as earnings neared $2.2 billion.

Chairman and CEO: William H. Gates III, age 39, $415,580 pay
EVP and COO: Robert J. Herbold, age 53, $740,133 pay
EVP Worldwide Sales and Support: Steven A. Ballmer, age 39, $411,974 pay
SVP; President, Microsoft Europe: Bernard P. Vergnes, age 50, $526,445 pay
SVP Law and Corporate Affairs and Secretary: William H. Neukom, age 53
SVP Consumer Systems: Craig J. Mundie, age 46
SVP Personal Systems: Brad A. Silverberg
SVP Business Systems: James E. Allchin, age 44
SVP Worldwide OEM Sales: Joachim Kempin, age 53
Group VP Applications and Content Group: Nathan P. Myhrvold, age 36
Group VP Applications and Content Group: Frank M. Pete Higgins, age 37
VP Research: Richard Rashid
VP Finance and CFO: Michael W. Brown, age 49
VP Human Resources and Administration: Michael R. Murray
Auditors: Deloitte & Touche LLP

WHERE

HQ: One Microsoft Way, Redmond, WA 98052-6399
Phone: 206-882-8080
Fax: 206-883-8101
Web site: http://www.microsoft.com

Microsoft has subsidiaries in nearly 50 countries.

	1995 Sales		1995 Operating Income	
	$ mil.	% of total	$ mil.	% of total
US	4,495	68	1,709	77
Europe	1,575	24	412	19
Other regions	558	8	91	4
Adjustments	(691)	—	(174)	—
Total	**5,937**	**100**	**2,038**	**100**

WHAT

	1995 Sales	
	$ mil.	% of total
Applications & content	3,581	60
Platforms	2,356	40
Total	**5,937**	**100**

Selected Products

Business Systems
Microsoft Mail
Microsoft Project
Microsoft Schedule+
Microsoft SQL Server
Microsoft Windows NT Server
Microsoft Windows NT Workstation

Consumer Products
Microsoft Bookshelf
Microsoft Flight Simulator
Microsoft Mouse
Microsoft Works

Desktop Application Software
Microsoft Excel
Microsoft Office
Microsoft PowerPoint
Microsoft Word

Developer Products
Microsoft Access
Microsoft FoxPro
Microsoft Visual Basic & C++

Personal Systems
Microsoft MS-DOS
Microsoft Windows
Microsoft Windows 95
Microsoft Windows for Workgroups

Other
Computer books
Microsoft Network
MSNBC (24-hour cable news channel and Internet site)
Slate (Internet-based magazine)

KEY COMPETITORS

America Online
Apple Computer
AT&T Corp.
Borland
CompuServe
Computer Associates
DEC

Electronic Arts
Informix
Netscape
NeXT
Novell
Oracle
Prodigy
Silicon Graphics

SoftKey
Sun Microsystems
Sybase
Symantec
Time Warner
Tribune

HOW MUCH

Nasdaq symbol: MSFT FYE: June 30	Annual Growth	1986	1987	1988	1989	1990	1991	1992	1993	1994	1995
Sales ($ mil.)	46.0%	197	345	590	803	1,183	1,843	2,758	3,753	4,649	5,937
Net income ($ mil.)	49.4%	39	72	124	171	279	463	708	953	1,146	1,453
Income as % of sales	—	19.9%	20.8%	21.0%	21.2%	23.6%	25.1%	25.7%	25.4%	24.7%	24.5%
Earnings per share ($)	43.5%	0.09	0.15	0.25	0.34	0.52	0.82	1.21	1.58	1.88	2.32
Stock price – high ($)	—	2.84	8.79	7.74	9.84	17.96	37.35	47.50	49.00	65.13	109.25
Stock price – low ($)	—	1.42	2.66	5.12	5.17	9.34	16.24	32.75	35.19	39.00	58.25
Stock price – close ($)	47.3%	2.68	6.03	5.92	9.68	16.74	37.10	42.69	40.31	61.13	87.75
P/E – high	—	32	59	31	29	35	46	39	31	35	47
P/E – low	—	16	18	21	15	18	20	27	22	21	25
Dividends per share ($)	—	0.00	0.00	0.00	0.00	0.00	0.00	0.00	0.00	0.00	0.00
Book value per share ($)	46.2%	0.30	0.50	0.78	1.14	1.80	2.59	4.03	5.75	7.88	9.18
Employees	35.5%	1,153	1,816	2,793	4,037	5,635	8,226	11,542	14,430	15,257	17,801

1995 YEAR-END

Debt ratio: 0.0%
Return on equity: 29.7%
Cash (mil.): $4,750
Current ratio: 4.17
Long-term debt (mil.): $0
No. of shares (mil.): 581
Dividends
  Yield: —
  Payout: —
Market value (mil.): $50,983

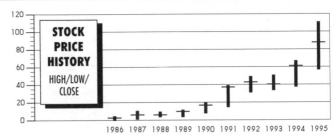

STOCK PRICE HISTORY HIGH/LOW/CLOSE

MUSICLAND STORES CORPORATION

OVERVIEW

The nation's #1 specialty retailer of recorded music and videos is singing the blues. Several years of rapid growth have yielded to disappointing results, leading Minnetonka, Minnesota-based Musicland to put the brakes on new store openings. Instead, Musicland is moving beyond its roots in music retail toward offering a variety of media, including books and CD-ROMs.

Musicland operates more than 800 mall stores under the names Musicland and Sam Goody. It also operates over 400 Suncoast Motion Picture Company mall stores, which sell prerecorded videos, movie-themed apparel, gifts, and accessories. Mall stores have been getting the squeeze from discount stores and consumer electronics superstores (such as Best Buy) that sell CDs and prerecorded tapes

and videos at low cost. Same-store mall sales were down 4.9% in 1995. Flat sales throughout the music industry contributed to the poor performance.

The company's main push in the past several years has been outside the malls through its Media Play and On Cue stores. Media Play superstores average 49,000 square feet and feature a huge assortment of prerecorded music, books, computer software, prerecorded videos, comic books, and related items. On Cue stores are aimed at smaller markets (towns with populations of 10,000-30,000) and offer a range of products similar to Media Play's, but with less selection. In 1996 the company planned to slow expansion with only 10 new Media Play stores, 10 On Cue stores, 4 music stores, and 10 Suncoast stores in the works.

WHEN

Musicland was founded in Minneapolis in 1956 by Terry Evenson and Grover Sayre, who had played in a dance band together. The 2 expanded the business, and by 1963 they had a chain of 6 stores. That year they sold the company to brothers Amos and Dan Heilicher, who owned a record distribution business. Evenson went on to found a chain of greeting card stores, which he sold to Hallmark, and Sayre worked for Musicland until 1981.

Under the Heilichers, Musicland grew to 48 stores by 1968. That year it merged with music and book producer, distributor, and merchandiser Pickwick International. In 1977 American Can (a diversifying canning company later absorbed by insurance megalith Travelers) acquired Pickwick and Musicland for $103 million. By that time Musicland had grown to about 230 stores. In 1978 it acquired the Sam Goody chain of 28 record stores.

Musicland began to lose money during the late 1970s when the record industry as a whole hit a slump. In 1980 Jack Eugster, a former executive with the Gap and Dayton Hudson's Target stores, was hired to run the company. Eugster closed poorly performing stores, centralized distribution, and installed a state-of-the-art computer system to track inventory. He also got the company out of record pressing, wholesaling, and other operations in order to focus on record retailing.

The company continued to expand through acquisitions, buying the Harmony Hut chain for $7 million (1984), the Licorice Pizza chain of 34 music and home entertainment stores for $6.8 million, the leases to 26 record stores

held by Record Bar for $5.3 million (1986), and Musicden Retail's chain of 21 stores (1987).

In 1986 Musicland opened its first video retail store, under the name of Paramount Pictures (now Suncoast Motion Picture Company). By 1987 Musicland had more than 550 stores in 47 states. That year American Can sold 19% of the company to the public. In 1988 Eugster led a group of investors, including Donaldson, Lufkin & Jenrette, who bought the company in a leveraged buyout (LBO) for $410 million. Eugster continued to expand the company, and by 1990 it had more than 900 record and video stores. Also in 1990 Musicland opened its first 2 music stores in the UK, under the name Sam Goody.

In 1992 Musicland began its expansion out of the malls and into multimedia stores, opening its first Media Play and On Cue stores. The company went public that year. It used the money to pay down the debt left over from the LBO.

The company embarked on a major expansion plan in 1993, doubling its investment in new stores that year to $60 million and opening Readwell's bookstore in Minnesota.

Musicland opened a new 715,000-square-foot distribution center in Franklin, Indiana, in 1995. That year it opened 43 Media Play stores, 76 On Cue stores, 34 Suncoast stores, and 15 new music stores. The company announced in 1995 that it would change the name of some of its Musicland stores to Sam Goody. The company announced in 1996 that it would close 50 underperforming Sam Goody and Musicland stores and focus on existing stores.

WHO

Chairman, President, and CEO: Jack W. Eugster, age 50, $507,500 pay
President, Suncoast Division: Gary A. Ross, age 49, $319,827 pay
President, Music Stores: Keith A. Benson, age 51, $293,012 pay
President, Media Play: Larry C. Gaines, age 48, $245,369 pay
EVP Finance and Administration and CFO: Reid Johnson, age 53, $278,808 pay
SVP Real Estate: Bruce B. Bausman, age 53
SVP and General Merchandise Manager: Robert A. Henderson, age 51
SVP Distribution: Douglas M. Tracey, age 42
VP Human Resources: Jay Landauer
Auditors: Andersen Worldwide

WHERE

HQ: 10400 Yellow Circle Dr., Minnetonka, MN 55343
Phone: 612-931-8000
Fax: 612-931-8300

Musicland has operations in 49 states, the District of Columbia, Puerto Rico, the Virgin Islands, and the UK.

WHAT

	1995 Sales	
	$ mil.	% of total
Compact discs	610	35
Prerecorded videocassettes	506	29
Audiocassettes & other prerecorded music	285	17
Computer software, accessories & apparel	215	13
Books	107	6
Total	**1,723**	**100**

	1995 Stores
	No.
Sam Goody & Musicland	820
Suncoast	412
On Cue	153
Media Play	89
UK stores	21
Readwell's	1
Total	**1,496**

Selected Stores

Sam Goody (music, video, and home entertainment products through mall stores)
Musicland (music, video, and home entertainment products through mall stores)
Suncoast Motion Picture Company (video, apparel, gifts, and other movie-related products through mall stores)
On Cue (music, books, video, computer software, and other products for smaller markets)
Media Play (books, music, video, computer software, magazines, comic books, and other products through superstores)
Readwell's (books, CD-ROMs, travel videos, audiobooks, and related items)

KEY COMPETITORS

Barnes & Noble	Hollywood	Time Warner
Best Buy	Entertainment	Toys "R" Us
Blockbuster	J & R Music	Trans World
Books-A-Million	World	Entertainment
Borders	Kmart	Venture Stores
Camelot Music	Movie Gallery	Viacom
Circuit City	MTS	Virgin Group
CompUSA	NeoStar	Wal-Mart
Crown Books	Supercom	Walt Disney
Dayton Hudson	Tandy	Wherehouse
Egghead	Corporation	Entertainment
Hastings Books		

HOW MUCH

NYSE symbol: MLG FYE: December 31	Annual Growth	1986	1987	1988	1989	1990	1991	1992	1993	1994	1995
Sales ($ mil.)	16.2%	—	—	603	695	836	932	1,020	1,181	1,478	1,723
Net income ($ mil.)	—	—	—	—	5	7	9	24	31	17	(136)
Income as % of sales	—	—	—	—	0.8%	0.9%	1.0%	2.4%	2.7%	1.2%	—
Earnings per share ($)	—	—	—	—	0.26	0.37	0.38	0.83	1.03	0.51	(4.00)
Stock price – high ($)	—	—	—	—	—	—	—	17.13	23.38	22.50	11.00
Stock price – low ($)	—	—	—	—	—	—	—	10.13	11.13	8.75	3.75
Stock price – close ($)	(28.2%)	—	—	—	—	—	—	11.50	20.75	9.00	4.25
P/E – high	—	—	—	—	—	—	—	21	23	44	—
P/E – low	—	—	—	—	—	—	—	12	11	17	—
Dividends per share ($)	—	—	—	—	—	—	0.00	0.00	0.00	0.00	0.00
Book value per share ($)	12.4%	—	—	—	—	—	3.58	7.42	9.42	9.94	5.71
Employees	15.6%	—	—	—	—	—	—	11,000	13,000	16,000	17,000

1995 YEAR-END

Debt ratio: 45.4%
Return on equity: —
Cash (mil.): $2
Current ratio: 0.90
Long-term debt (mil.): $110
No. of shares (mil.): 34
Dividends
  Yield: —
  Payout: —
Market value (mil.): $146

STOCK PRICE HISTORY
HIGH/LOW/CLOSE
1986 1987 1988 1989 1990 1991 1992 1993 1994 1995

NBC

OVERVIEW

Boosted by hit TV shows like *ER*, *Friends*, and *Seinfeld*, NBC's multicolored peacock is strutting its stuff. According to research firm Nielsen's network pecking order, New York City-based NBC (wholly owned by industrial behemoth General Electric) rules the roost, drawing more viewers than Westinghouse's CBS, Walt Disney's ABC, and News Corp.'s Fox. In addition to the NBC Television Network, which serves 9 company-owned stations and more than 200 US affiliate stations, NBC operates two 24-hour cable channels (including CNBC) and has part ownership in 17 other cable channels (such as Court TV).

NBC has established a presence outside the US via cable and satellite. It operates CNBC Asia, a 24-hour business channel, and is planning to launch NBC Asia, a general entertainment channel. The company has expanded its interactive media lines, adding NBC Digital Publishing (CD-ROMs) and NBC Online Ventures (sites for news, sports, and entertainment on the World Wide Web) and launching NBC SuperNet, an online joint venture with multimedia maven Microsoft. In 1996 it again worked with Microsoft to launch another venture, MSNBC, a 24 hour all-news cable channel and Internet site that replaced its America's Talking talk-show channel.

Although the company let *Baywatch* slip through its fingers (it dropped and subsequently sold the lifeguard/cheesecake action/adventure show — now shown in more than 110 countries — in 1991), its show selection has been surefooted in recent years. The current roster includes *Dateline NBC*, *Frasier*, *Mad About You*, and *Meet the Press*, TV's longest running show.

NBC accounts for roughly 6% of parent GE's total revenues.

WHEN

In 1919 General Electric and Westinghouse formed Radio Corporation of America (RCA) to acquire the American radio assets of Marconi, a British company that through its US subsidiary had a monopoly on transatlantic radio and telegraph communications. In 1924 RCA pioneered television with the transmission of the first radio-photo. Led by inventor-cum-entrepreneur David Sarnoff, RCA set up the National Broadcasting Company (NBC) in 1926 to develop quality radio programs. Its first broadcast, that year, was a musical comedy show. Its first coast-to-coast broadcast was the 1927 Rose Bowl game in California. RCA bought out GE's and Westinghouse's interests in the company in 1930.

The demand for radio network programming grew rapidly. The company split its programming into 2 networks to give listeners a choice of formats. In 1941 the Federal Communications Commission (FCC) ruled that companies could own only one network. NBC subsequently sold one of its networks, which formed the nucleus of rival American Broadcasting Company (ABC).

Sarnoff also pursued the development of television. In 1939 NBC began the first regular TV service with coverage of President Roosevelt inaugurating the New York World's Fair. In 1941 NBC obtained a commercial TV license from the FCC, and its WBNT-TV (New York) became the world's first commercial TV station. NBC launched current affairs program *Meet the Press* in 1947. The company beat rival CBS in winning FCC approval for its color TV system in 1953 and presented the first nationwide color broadcast that year.

NBC aired the presidential debates between John Kennedy and Richard Nixon in 1960. The Peacock Network's popular series in the 1960s included *Rowan and Martin's Laugh-In* and *The Man from U.N.C.L.E.*

Network founder Sarnoff died in 1971. NBC launched sketch-comedy groundbreaker *Saturday Night Live* in 1975. During the 1970s NBC's radio business slumped, and despite a number of attempts to revive radio's popularity, the company decided to exit the business (it sold 7 of its 8 stations in 1988).

Returning the network to its roots, GE bought RCA for $6.4 billion in 1986. Led by NBC Entertainment's president Brandon Tartikoff, the network staged a TV ratings comeback with a string of successful programs. Hit TV shows in that decade included the *Cosby Show* and *Cheers*.

In 1992 the company acquired the Financial News Network, which it merged with CNBC. The following year it slipped to last in the Nielsen ratings and CBS lured away late-night host David Letterman (for $14 million a year). But NBC bounced back. It acquired control of the UK-based European television service Super Channel in 1993 and launched a slew of new programs in 1994 and 1995 to win back the top ratings position. In 1996 NBC launched CNBC Europe, a 24-hour business cable and satellite channel.

WHO

President and CEO: Robert C. Wright
EVP and General Counsel: Richard Cotton
EVP Employee Relations (HR): Edward L. Scanlon
SVP Finance: Warren C. Jenson
President, CNBC: William Bolster
President, Television Network: Neil Braun
President, Sports: Dick Ebersol
President, News: Andrew R. Lack
President, NBC-West Coast: Donald W. Ohlmeyer Jr.
President, NBC Cable and Business Development:
   Thomas S. Rogers
President, Television Stations: John H. Rohrbeck
Auditors: KPMG Peat Marwick LLP

WHERE

HQ: National Broadcasting Company, Inc., 30
   Rockefeller Plaza, New York, NY
   10112-0002
Phone: 212-664-4444
Fax: 212-664-6193
Web site: http://www.nbc.com

WHAT

Selected Programs and Services

NBC Television Network
NBC News
NBC Sports
NBC Shows
3rd Rock from the Sun
Dateline NBC
ER
Frasier
Friends
Homicide
Law & Order
Mad About You
Saturday Night Live
Seinfeld
Tonight Show
Wings

TV Stations (9 owned, plus more than 200 affiliates)

Cable Channels
Canal de Noticias NBC (South America)
CNBC, MSNBC, and part ownership in 17 other cable
   channels including Court TV and American Movie
   Classics
CNBC Asia
CNBC Europe
NBC Super Channel (Europe)

NBC Supernet (multimedia joint venture with
   Microsoft)

KEY COMPETITORS

All American	News Corp.
Communications	Seagram
BET	Sony
BSkyB	TCI
Comcast	Time Warner
Cox Enterprises	Tribune
Corporation for Public	Viacom
Broadcasting	Walt Disney
Gannett	Washington Post
Hearst	Westinghouse
International Family	
Entertainment	
Knight-Ridder	

HOW MUCH

Subsidiary FYE: December 31	Annual Growth	1986	1987	1988	1989	1990	1991	1992	1993	1994	1995
Sales ($ mil.)	8.5%	1,888	3,241	3,638	3,392	3,236	3,121	3,363	3,102	3,361	3,919
Employees	—	—	—	—	—	—	—	—	—	—	5,000

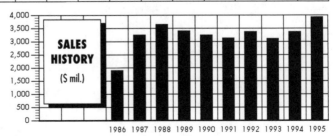

SALES
HISTORY
($ mil.)

NATIONAL GEOGRAPHIC SOCIETY

OVERVIEW

The name may not ring a bell, but Gilbert Grosvenor, the National Geographic Society's chairman, is the great-grandson of inventor Alexander Graham Bell. He's also the great-great-grandson of the first president of the Washington, DC-based organization, which, led by its flagship *National Geographic* magazine, is the world's largest not-for-profit educational society. The society promotes geographic knowledge through research and exploration, magazines, maps, books, videos, TV programs, and games. *National Geographic*, which has established a reputation for stunning photography, boasts 8.9 million subscribers worldwide. Higher

subscription costs have trimmed the magazine's subscriber base, resulting in the society's first layoffs. However, an increase in advertising revenues reversed the recent declines in revenue.

The society's for-profit TV subsidiary, NGV, Inc., is increasing its production of TV specials, documentaries, and syndicated series. In addition, it has joined with Sony to produce films; formed a partnership with the Discovery Channel, Turner Broadcasting, and interactive media start-up daVinci Time & Space to create an interactive children's TV channel; and is working with Japanese TV network NHK to produce specials in that country.

WHEN

On January 13, 1888, a group of prominent scientists and explorers gathered at the Cosmos Club in Washington, DC, to form the National Geographic Society. Gardiner Hubbard was its first president. The society mailed the first edition of its magazine, dated October 1888, to 165 members. The magazine was clothed in a dull terra-cotta cover and contained a few esoteric articles (such as *The Classification of Geographic Forms by Genesis*). Regular monthly issues didn't appear until the January 1896 issue, which was sold on newsstands in an attempt to boost sales.

Following Hubbard's death in 1897, his son-in-law, inventor Alexander Graham Bell, became president. Bell wanted to make the magazine as popular as *Harper's Weekly*. To do the job, he hired the current chairman's grandfather, Gilbert Grosvenor, as editor. Grosvenor, who later married Bell's daughter, turned the magazine from a dry, technical publication to one of more general interest. It was Bell's idea to send the magazine to "members only," a marketing concept still in use today (other National Geographic Society magazines are sold on newsstands).

Under Grosvenor the magazine pioneered the use of photography, including rare photographs of remote Tibet (1905), the first hand-tinted colored photos (1910), the first underwater color photos (1920s), and the first color aerial photographs (1930).

The society sponsored Robert Peary's trek to the North Pole in 1909 and Hiram Bingham's 1912 exploration of Machu Picchu in Peru. Members raised $100,000 in 1915 to save what is now Sequoia National Park. Grosvenor became president in 1920.

The 1900 circulation of 2,200 had risen to 1.2 million by 1930. Grosvenor's policy of printing only "what is of a kindly nature ... about any country or people" resulted in 2 articles that were criticized for their kindly portrayal of prewar Nazi Germany (however, society maps and photographs were used by the US government for WWII intelligence). That policy eased over the years, and in 1961 a *National Geographic* article described the growing US involvement in Vietnam.

Grosvenor retired in 1954 after 55 years with the society. His son Melville Bell Grosvenor, who became president and editor in 1957, accelerated book publishing and created a film unit. Its first TV show, *Americans on Everest*, aired in 1965. Melville retired in 1967.

Melville's son Gilbert Melville Grosvenor took over as president in 1970. Since then the magazine has increasingly covered important social and political events as well as scientific and environmental subjects.

Wilbur Garrett, editor since 1980, resigned in 1990 after a dispute with Grosvenor over the magazine's direction. In 1993 the society, which had sold its books only by mail to its members for 75 years, agreed to have Random House distribute them in bookstores.

In 1995 William Allen was named as editor of *National Geographic*, succeeding William Graves. A Japanese-language edition of *National Geographic*, published in a joint venture with Nikkei Business Publications, was launched in 1995.

Veteran newspaper publisher Reg Murphy (a top company executive since 1993) was appointed president in 1996.

WHO

Chairman: Gilbert M. Grosvenor, age 64
President: Reg Murphy, age 62
Editor, *National Geographic*: William L. Allen, age 54
Associate Editor, *National Geographic*:
Elizabeth A. Moize
Associate Editor, *National Geographic*: Robert M. Poole
SVP Fulfillment and Membership Services: Gene
Ferrone
SVP Publications: Nina Hoffman, age 42
SVP Communications and Advertising: Robert Sims
President, NGT Inc.: Timothy T. Kelly, age 40
President, NGV, Inc.: John Fahey, age 44
**VP; Chairman, Committee for Research and
Exploration:** George E. Stuart
VP and Treasurer: H. Gregory Platts
VP and Corporate Counsel: Suzanne K. Dupre, age 54
VP Human Resources: John Blodger

WHERE

HQ: 1145 17th St. NW, Washington, DC 20036
Phone: 202-857-7000
Fax: 202-775-6141

The National Geographic Society has almost 9 million
members in 190 countries.

WHAT

Magazines
National Geographic (8,980,000 circulation; Japanese-
language edition, 157,000 circulation)
National Geographic Traveler (735,538 circulation)
National Geographic World (1,135,000 circulation)

Selected Publications
Atlas of the World
The Blue and the Gray
Geisha
The Great Apes: Between Two Worlds
Lost Kingdoms of the Maya
The Photographs
Picture Atlas of the World (CD-ROM)
Star-Spangled Banner
Whales

Children's Publications
Animal Acrobats
Mammals
Reptiles & Amphibians
Secret Treasures

Educational Programs
Committee for Research and Exploration
Geography Education Program (sponsor; teacher educa-
tion and public awareness programs)
GTV (interactive videodiscs)
International Geography Olympiad
National Geographic Kids Network
National Geographic Society Education Foundation
National Geography Bee
National Geography Standards (student curriculum for
grades 4, 8, and 12)
Teaching Geography Project (teacher workshops)

Games
Global Pursuit
On Assignment with National Geographic
ZipZapMap! (computer game)

TV Programs and Videos
Best of National Geographic (syndicated)
GeoKids (children's home videos)
National Geographic Explorer (TBS SuperStation)
National Geographic Horizons (PBS)
National Geographic on Assignment
National Geographic Specials (NBC)

Subsidiaries
NGT Inc. (not-for-profit TV, video, and film production)
NGV, Inc. (for-profit TV, video, and film production)

KEY COMPETITORS

A&E Networks
Advance Publications
American Express
Brøderbund
Cox Communications
Discovery Communications
Rand McNally
Smithsonian
Time Warner
Viacom
Walt Disney

HOW MUCH

Not-for-profit organization FYE: December 31	Annual Growth	1986	1987	1988	1989	1990	1991	1992	1993	1994	1995
Sales ($ mil.)	(7.1%)	—	—	—	426	437	436	453	423	419	456
Employees	(5.0%)	—	—	—	2,628	2,526	2,293	2,231	2,022	1,721	1,551

NATIONAL GEOGRAPHIC SOCIETY

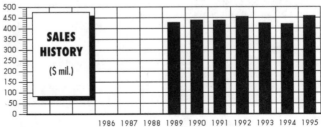

SALES HISTORY ($ mil.)

THE NEW YORK TIMES COMPANY

OVERVIEW

All the News That's Fit to Print, Broadcast, and Post Online would be a more accurate motto for this New York City-based media titan. The New York Times Company publishes the *New York Times* (#3 in circulation after *USA Today* and the *Wall Street Journal*), the *Boston Globe*, and 21 other newspapers in 6 states. It also has a 1/2 interest in the *International Herald Tribune* (with rival *Washington Post*). The firm owns 9 magazines (such as *Golf Digest* and *Cruising World*), 6 television stations, and 2 radio stations and publishes online on America Online and its own web site.

The company gets some of its newsprint from mills it partially owns. At the other end of the production spectrum, the New York Times News Service licenses its articles, graphics, and

photographs to about 650 newspapers and magazines worldwide, and to online computer database firms (such as Lexis-Nexis and Dow Jones Business Information Services) and archiving companies (such as UMI) to create and sell microform copies.

CEO Arthur Ochs Sulzberger (whose family effectively controls the company) is prudently hedging his bets: the *New York Times* is nearing completion of a 10-year capital investment program that will let it hit the streets with later-breaking news, daily color, and more sections. While the company was able to raise advertising rates and circulation prices to cover a surge in newsprint costs, its readership has continued to decline. So it continues to seek other avenues to widen its audience, such as cyberspace.

WHEN

In 1851 George Jones and Henry Raymond, 2 former *New York Tribune* staffers, started the *New York Times*. The paper began a long tradition of political coverage during the Civil War and of investigative reporting with the Tammany Hall scandals, but by the late 1800s it had lost popularity to the yellow journalism of the Hearst and Pulitzer papers.

In 1896 Adolph Ochs, a newspaperman from Chattanooga, bought the *Times*. Continuing hard news and business coverage and eschewing diversification, Ochs added the newspaper's now-famous slogan, "All the News That's Fit to Print." Ochs's son-in-law Arthur Hays Sulzberger, who ran the paper from 1935 to 1961, diversified the company with the purchase of 2 New York City radio stations (1944). Sulzberger's son-in-law Orvil Dryfoos was publisher until his death in 1963, leaving Adolph's grandson Arthur Ochs "Punch" Sulzberger in charge.

In the 1960s declining ad revenues and a newspaper strike sent the company into the red. To regain strength Punch built the largest news-gathering staff of any newspaper. The *Times*'s coverage of the Vietnam War helped change public sentiment, and the newspaper won a Pulitzer Prize in 1972 for publishing the Pentagon Papers.

In the meantime Punch had taken the company public (1967), though the family retained solid control through ownership of most of the Class B stock. In the 1970s the Times Co. bought magazines, publishing houses, television stations, smaller newspapers, and cable TV systems and began co-publishing the

International Herald Tribune. To contain costs the company invested in 3 pulp and paper companies.

In the 1980s the *Times* added feature sections to compete with suburban papers. The company bought *Golf World* in 1988, and in 1989 it bought women's magazine *McCall's* and sold its cable systems. In 1990 the company started TimesFax, a summary of the *Times* sent to subscribers' fax machines worldwide.

Family members are still active on the board and in publishing activities. In 1992 Arthur Ochs Sulzberger Jr. succeeded his father as *Times* publisher.

In 1993 the Times Co. bought Affiliated Publications, owner of the *Boston Globe*, for $1.1 billion; the next year it sold the 1/3 interest in BPI Communications (specialty magazines) that had come with the Affiliated purchase.

In 1994 the company sold its women's magazines and 3 UK golf publications. In 1995 it acquired a majority stake in Video News International, a news-gathering company, launched 2 cable news channels in Arkansas, and invested in OVATION, a performance arts cable TV network set to premiere the next year. The company continued to sell off some of its holdings, including 7 smaller papers. Also in 1996 the firm said it would buy 2 TV stations in Des Moines, Iowa, and Oklahoma City from Palmer Communications for $226 million, and the *Times* launched a Web site.

WHO

Chairman and CEO: Arthur Ochs "Punch" Sulzberger, age 70, $1,377,200 pay
President and COO: Lance R. Primis, age 49, $1,125,800 pay
Publisher, *New York Times*: Arthur Ochs Sulzberger Jr., age 44, $938,200 pay
Publisher, *Boston Globe*: William O. Taylor, age 63, $568,796 pay
SVP and CFO: Diane P. Baker, age 41
SVP and Deputy COO: David L. Gorham, age 63, $722,000 pay
SVP Broadcasting, Corporate Development, and Human Resources: Katharine P. Darrow, age 52
VP and General Counsel: Soloman B. Watson IV, age 51
Auditors: Deloitte & Touche LLP

WHERE

HQ: 229 W. 43rd St., New York, NY 10036
Phone: 212-556-1234
Fax: 212-556-4011
Web site: http://www.nytimes.com

WHAT

	1995 Sales	
	$ mil.	% of total
Newspapers & information services	2,161	90
Magazines	163	7
Broadcasting	85	3
Total	**2,409**	**100**

Selected Daily Newspapers
Boston Globe
Dispatch (Lexington, NC)
Gainesville Sun (Florida)
International Herald Tribune (50%, with the Washington Post Co.; Paris)
Ledger (Lakeland, FL)
New York Times
Santa Barbara News-Press (California)
Spartanburg Herald-Journal (South Carolina)
Star-Banner (Ocala, FL)
Tuscaloosa News (Alabama)

Selected Information Services
@times (America Online site)
The New York Times Electronic Media Company (online services)
The New York Times Index
The New York Times Syndication Sales Corp.
The New York Times News Service (650 newspaper and magazine customers)
NYT Business Information Services
The Times on the Web (web site)
TimesFax (fax-, satellite-, and PC-delivered Times summary)

Magazines
Cruising World
Golf Digest
Golf Shop Operations
Golf World
Sailing World
Snow Country
Snow Country Business
Tennis
Tennis Buyer's Guide

Broadcasting
KFSM-TV, Fort Smith, AR
NYT Video Productions
NYT Video News International
WHNT-TV, Huntsville, AL
WNEP-TV, Wilkes-Barre/Scranton, PA
WQAD-TV, Moline, IL
WQEW (AM), New York
WQXR (FM), New York
WREG-TV, Memphis
WTKR-TV, Norfolk, VA

Forest Products
Donohue Malbaie Inc. (49%, Canada)
Madison Paper Industries (partnership, Maine)

KEY COMPETITORS

Advance Publications
Associated Press
Bloomberg
Capital Cities/ABC
Cox Enterprises
Dow Jones
E.W. Scripps
Gannett
Hearst
Knight-Ridder
Lagardère
Media General
Meredith
NBC
News Corp.
Pearson
Reuters
Rodale Press
Thomson Corp.
Time Warner
Times Mirror
Tribune
Viacom
Washington Post
Westinghouse

HOW MUCH

AMEX symbol: NYTA FYE: December 31	Annual Growth	1986	1987	1988	1989	1990	1991	1992	1993	1994	1995
Sales ($ mil.)	4.9%	1,564	1,689	1,700	1,768	1,776	1,703	1,773	2,019	2,357	2,409
Net income ($ mil.)	0.3%	132	160	168	267	65	47	(11)	213	136	136
Income as % of sales	—	8.4%	9.5%	9.9%	15.1%	3.6%	2.8%	—	0.3%	9.0%	5.6%
Earnings per share ($)	(1.7%)	1.63	1.96	2.08	3.39	0.85	0.61	(0.14)	0.07	2.05	1.40
Stock price – high ($)	—	42.00	49.63	32.75	34.75	27.50	25.25	32.13	31.25	29.50	30.88
Stock price – low ($)	—	23.31	24.75	24.38	24.50	16.88	18.25	22.63	22.38	21.25	20.13
Stock price – close ($)	(2.0%)	35.50	31.00	26.88	26.50	20.63	23.63	26.38	26.25	22.13	29.63
P/E – high	—	26	25	16	10	32	41	—	—	14	22
P/E – low	—	14	13	12	7	20	30	—	—	10	14
Dividends per share ($)	6.4%	0.32	0.38	0.45	0.49	0.67	0.42	0.70	0.56	0.56	0.56
Book value per share ($)	7.5%	8.64	10.04	10.44	13.63	13.68	13.70	12.53	14.94	15.71	16.50
Employees	2.3%	10,000	10,500	10,700	10,600	10,400	10,100	10,100	13,000	12,800	12,300

1995 YEAR-END

Debt ratio: 28.4%
Return on equity: 8.6%
Cash (mil.): $91
Current ratio: 0.89
Long-term debt (mil.): $638
No. of shares (mil.): 98
Dividends
  Yield: 1.9%
  Payout: 40.0 %
Market value (mil.): $2,892

STOCK PRICE HISTORY
HIGH/LOW/CLOSE

THE NEWS CORPORATION LIMITED

OVERVIEW

At the News Corporation, news is just the beginning. Headquartered in Sydney, Australia, Rupert Murdoch's planetary media empire spans newspapers, books, magazines, movies, and television, with a paper mill, a record company, an airline, and a sheep farm thrown in for good measure. It ranks 4th in sales behind media supernovas Time Warner, Walt Disney, and Bertelsmann.

News Corp. publishes 4 major UK newspapers and produces about 100 Australian daily and nondaily papers. (Its main US paper is the *New York Post*.) It also publishes the ever-popular *TV Guide* (behind only *Reader's Digest* in paid US circulation), numerous newspaper ad-vertising inserts, and general interest magazines. Subsidiary Twentieth Century Fox produces movies and TV programs and maintains a large programming library, and its Fox TV network broadcasts to more than 200 US affiliates. Subsidiary HarperCollins publishes educational texts and general-interest and religious books throughout the world. News Corp. also has a 40% interest in UK satellite pay-TV service British Sky Broadcasting and has moved into the TV market in China. Murdoch's family owns about 30% of the company through Cruden Investments (named for his boyhood home), and long-distance telephone bigwig MCI owns 13.5%.

WHEN

Murdoch started in the newspaper business in 1952 when he inherited 2 Adelaide, Australia, newspapers from his father. After launching the *Australian*, the country's first national daily, in 1964, Murdoch bought *News of the World*, a London Sunday paper, in 1968. In 1969 he bought London's *Sun*, which he transformed into a sensationalist tabloid featuring lurid headlines and topless women. Murdoch entered the US media market in 1973 with the purchase of the *San Antonio Express-News*. The next year he created the US supermarket tabloid *Star*. He bought the *New York Post* in 1976 and again used sensationalist tactics to boost circulation. Three years later Murdoch incorporated the company in Australia under the name News Corporation.

Murdoch bought London's highly respected *Times* and a 40% stake in Collins Publishers, a London book publisher, in 1981. After buying the *Chicago Sun-Times* in 1983 (sold in 1986), Murdoch bought 13 US travel, hotel, and aviation trade magazines from Ziff-Davis, as well as film producer Twentieth Century Fox in 1985. He became a US citizen to comply with FCC rules on broadcast ownership and in 1986 bought 6 Metromedia TV stations; the publisher of Hong Kong's *South China Morning Post* (sold in 1993); and Australia's #1 media company, the Herald & Weekly Times Group.

Also in 1986 Murdoch launched Fox Broadcasting, the first new US TV network since 1948. The next year he bought US book publisher Harper & Row. News Corp. purchased Triangle Publications, publisher of *TV Guide*, the *Daily Racing Form*, and *Seventeen*, and religious publisher Zondervan in 1988.

Also that year the company sold the *New York Post* to comply with federal regulations prohibiting companies from owning a TV station and paper in the same city. In 1989 it bought textbook publisher Scott, Foresman and acquired the rest of Collins Publishers.

News Corp. started Sky Television, a British satellite TV network, in 1989. After 18 months of intense competition, Sky joined with rival network British Satellite Broadcasting to form British Sky Broadcasting.

In 1990 Murdoch sold the *Star* to *Enquirer* publisher G. P. Group and the next year sold the *Daily Racing Form* and his US magazine holdings (except *Mirabella* and *TV Guide*) to K-III Holdings.

Murdoch sold the *Express-News* to Hearst in 1991, and after federal media ownership rules were relaxed, bought back the *New York Post* in 1993. That year News Corp. acquired 64% of STAR TV, an Asian satellite TV network. In 1994 Murdoch shelled out $1.6 billion to outbid other broadcasters for the rights to show NFL games for 4 years on Fox.

News Corp. joined with cable TV monolith TCI and 2 Latin American TV concerns to offer satellite TV service in Latin America in 1995, bought the remaining 36% of STAR TV, and sold *Mirabella* to magazine publisher Hachette Filipacchi. In addition, the company formed new film production units, including Fox 2000 (general entertainment) and Fox Searchlight Pictures (art films for mass audiences). In 1996 News Corp. announced plans to start a 24-hour Fox news channel and offered cable operators $10 per subscriber to carry it on their service.

WHO

Chairman, Managing Director, and CEO; Chairman, President, and CEO, News America Holdings Incorporated: Keith Rupert Murdoch, age 64
COO: August A. Fischer
CFO and Finance Director; EVP, News America Holdings Incorporated: David F. DeVoe, age 48
EVP: Richard A. Sarazen
EVP and Group General Counsel: Arthur M. Siskind, age 57
EVP Human Resources; EVP Human Resources, News America Holdings Incorporated: William A. O'Neill, age 55
Chairman, Fox, Inc.: Chase Carey
Auditors: Andersen Worldwide

WHERE

HQ: 2 Holt St., 2010, Sydney, New South Wales, Australia
Phone: +61-(02)288-3000
Fax: +61-(02)288-2300
US HQ: News America Holdings, Inc., 1211 Avenue of the Americas, New York, NY 10036
US Phone: 212-852-7000
US Fax: 212-852-7145
Web site: http://www.fox.com

News Corp. operates principally in the US, the UK, Australia, and the Pacific Basin.

	1995 Sales	
	$ mil.	% of total
US	6,037	70
UK	1,502	17
Australia & Pacific Basin	1,102	13
Total	**8,641**	**100**

WHAT

	1995 Sales
	% of total
Filmed entertainment	26
Newspapers	24
Television	21
Magazines/inserts	14
Books & other	15
Total	**100**

Selected Holdings
The Australian (national)
Australian Newsprint Mills Limited (46.2%, newsprint production)
British Sky Broadcasting (40%, satellite TV service)
Fox Broadcasting Company
Fox Studios Australia
HarperCollins Publishers
New York Post
News of the World (UK)
STAR TV (satellite TV in Asia)
The Sun (UK)
The Times and The Sunday Times (UK)
TV Guide (US)
Twentieth Century Fox Film Corporation (US)
The Weekly Standard (US)

KEY COMPETITORS

Advance Publications	Knight-Ridder	Time Warner
Bertelsmann	Lagardère	Times Mirror
Cablevision Systems	Liberty Media	United News & Media
Cox Enterprises	McGraw-Hill	Viacom
Dow Jones	NBC	VNU
Gannett	New York Times	Walt Disney
Havas	Pearson	Westinghouse/
Hearst	Reed Elsevier	CBS
Hollinger Inc.	Silver King	
	Sony	
	Thomson Corp.	

HOW MUCH

NYSE symbol: NWS FYE: June 30	Annual Growth	1986	1987	1988	1989	1990	1991	1992	1993	1994	1995
Sales ($ mil.)	14.4%	2,575	3,503	4,354	5,957	6,947	6,550	7,625	7,124	8,468	8,641
Net income ($ mil.)	21.7%	163	241	336	375	224	(211)	397	653	883	952
Income as % of sales	—	6.3%	6.9%	7.7%	6.3%	3.2%	—	5.2%	9.2%	10.4%	11.0%
Earnings per share ($)	18.5%	0.40	0.56	0.74	0.80	0.54	(0.87)	0.74	1.07	0.93	1.84
Stock price – high ($)	—	8.05	11.90	7.28	9.03	7.78	8.62	14.15	21.06	20.31	25.13
Stock price – low ($)	—	3.79	4.08	4.95	5.54	2.21	1.79	7.08	11.99	15.00	14.38
Stock price – close ($)	11.8%	7.83	5.62	5.49	7.41	2.62	7.70	13.57	17.57	15.63	21.38
P/E – high	—	20	21	10	11	14	—	19	20	22	14
P/E – low	—	10	7	7	7	4	—	10	11	16	8
Dividends per share ($)	—	0.00	0.02	0.03	0.09	0.05	0.03	0.07	0.05	0.05	0.07
Book value per share ($)	21.3%	2.65	5.01	8.89	6.30	19.00	4.30	14.11	13.98	10.46	15.03
Employees	2.1%	22,100	29,800	28,300	30,900	38,400	30,700	—	24,700	25,845	26,600

1995 YEAR-END

Debt ratio: 33.7%
Return on equity: 9.1%
Cash (mil.): $860
Current ratio: 1.42
Long-term debt (mil.): $5,690
No. of shares (mil.): 482
Dividends
  Yield: 482.0%
  Payout: 3.8%
Market value (mil.): $10,845

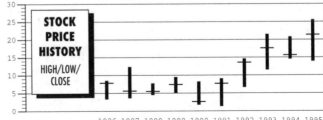

STOCK PRICE HISTORY HIGH/LOW/CLOSE

1986 1987 1988 1989 1990 1991 1992 1993 1994 1995

NIPPON TELEVISION NETWORK

OVERVIEW

Tokyo-based Nippon Television Network Corporation (NTV) is one of Japan's leading commercial broadcasters. The company is part of the diversified Yomiuri Group, whose many companies include the *Yomiuri Shimbun* newspaper, the Yomiuri Giants baseball team, and the Yomiuri Nippon Symphony Orchestra. Its primary operating business is Channel 4, one of 5 commercial stations in Tokyo. (There are also 2 publicly funded channels.) The company is the core of NNN, a nationwide news network. NTV's activities include motion picture and home video production, event and fund-raising promotion, publishing and merchandising, and sports-event production, one of it's specialties.

NTV is also well established outside Japan, with 16 news bureaus around the world and subsidiary companies that serve as liaisons for its global sales and marketing activities (NTV International Corporation [New York, Los Angeles] and Nippon Television Network Europe B.V. [Amsterdam]).

Ratings competition is fierce in Japan, where viewers constantly demand innovative programs. Because of this, many Japanese shows have a short life span. One exception to this is *Show by Shobai*, NTV's fast-paced weekly quiz show. Spinoffs of this commercially successful program are seen in Hong Kong, Italy, Thailand, and even China.

The company is a strong advocate of state-of-the-art technology and in 1996 claimed the first transmission of full-frame high-definition TV pictures via satellite.

WHEN

Broadcasting began in Japan in the wake of the disastrous 1923 earthquake that hit the Tokyo area, as a response to the chaos and lack of publicly accessible information that followed the catastrophe. The first Japanese radio broadcast occurred in 1925. A year later 3 radio stations in Nagoya, Osaka, and Tokyo were merged to form Nippon Hoso Kyokai (NHK), a privately managed but government-controlled national broadcaster. NHK became a propaganda vehicle of the military until after WWII.

In 1950 the Radio Law and Broadcast Law were passed calling for the reorganization of NHK as a public corporation and the establishment of commercial broadcasting companies. To prevent media monopolies, the government banned newspaper companies from owning more than 10% of a broadcasting station. In practice many of the commercial TV stations that emerged were de facto extensions of the newspaper companies, with key personnel from the newspapers taking top positions in the broadcast companies.

Created in 1952 by the management of the leading Tokyo daily *Yomiuri Shimbun* (founded in 1874), NTV was Japan's first commercial broadcaster to operate a TV station. Founder Matsutaro Shoriki, who had guided the newspaper's rise and prosperity since 1924 and helped organize Japan's first professional baseball team in 1934 (which later became the Yomiuri Giants), was an early advocate of TV. Shoriki would later say that TV helped motivate the Japanese after their defeat in WWII

and spurred technological innovation and economic growth; early sponsors — automobile, camera, and watch companies — were transformed over the next decades into major exporters. NTV was one of the first Japanese networks to offer all-day programming and color transmissions. One early success was its coverage of the 1965 Beatles Japan Tour, which set a record for viewers (56.5% rating).

In 1981 company veteran Yosoji Kobayashi became chairman of NTV and president of *Yomiuri Shimbun*. Continuing Shoriki's heritage of technological innovation and promotional flair, NTV arranged a live satellite transmission from the top of Mt. Everest in 1988 to celebrate the 35th anniversary of its first broadcast. The company established an R&D center in 1989 (the largest laboratory for commercial broadcasters in Japan) to investigate new technologies.

NTV teamed up with US network NBC in 1991 to form a joint news gathering venture. The company paid $11 million to clean and restore Michelangelo's famous frescoes in Rome's Sistine Chapel (completed in 1994) in return for exclusive coverage of the activities. In 1995 NTV produced 4 computer-animated programs (*CG Drama Series*) on its *Neo Hyper Kids* show. They were the first Japanese TV programs produced entirely by use of computer graphics.

In 1996 the company announced plans to launch a Japanese-language satellite service for Asian countries such as China, India, and South Korea.

WHO

Chairman: Yosoji Kobayashi
President: Seiichiro Ujiie
CEO, NTV International Corp. (US): Takas Sumii
Manager Human Resources, NTV International Corp. (US): Eric Levine

WHERE

HQ: Nippon Television Network Corporation,
14, Niban-cho, Chiyoda-ku, Tokyo, 102-40, Japan
Phone: +81-3-5275-4139
Fax: +81-3-5275-4008
US HQ: NTV International Corporation, 50 Rockefeller
Plaza, New York, NY 10020
US Phone: 212-765-5076
US Fax: 212-489-8395
Web site: http://www.ntr.co.jp/

NTV has news bureaus in Atlanta, Bangkok, Beijing,
Bonn, Cairo, Hong Kong, London, Los Angeles, Manila,
Moscow, New York, Paris, Sao Paulo, Seoul, Vladivostok,
and Washington.

WHAT

	1996 Sales
	% of total
TV spot advertising	41
TV programs	29
TV time sales	21
Program sales	4
Other	5
Total	**100**

Selected TV Programs

Animation
Acchi, Kocchi, Socchi
Kickers

Documentaries
Human Talent
   Backstage Maestro
   The Challenge of the
   Deep
   Mika's Miracle
Japanese Restaurants,
   Inns, and Cuisine
   A Hotel is Born
   The Ultimate Service
   in Cantonese
   Cuisine

Wildlife and Nature
   The Backstreet Cats of
   Tokyo
   Between Two Worlds
   Diving with Dad

Drama
After the Children Have
   Gone to Bed
Alumni Reunion
Can't Help Loving You
Forbidden Fruit

Other
Show by Shobai

Subsidiaries

Nippon Television Network Europe BV (The Netherlands)
NTV International Corp. (US)

KEY COMPETITORS

Asahi National Broadcasting
Fuji Telecasting Company
Kinki Broadcasting System
NHK
Television Saitama
Tokyo Broadcasting System

HOW MUCH

Principal exchange: Tokyo FYE: March 31	Annual Growth	1987	1988	1989	1990	1991	1992	1993	1994	1995	1996
Sales (Y mil.)	6.6%	130,021	146,545	164,532	183,807	196,039	206,500	199,795	196,830	208,873	230,230
Net income (Y mil.)	15.4%	3,422	5,461	7,805	9,011	10,176	10,519	2,813	2,697	5,813	12,385
Income as % of sales	—	2.6%	3.7%	4.7%	4.9%	5.2%	5.1%	1.4%	1.4%	2.8%	5.4%
Earnings per share (Y)[1]	12.8%	330	515	683	754	808	834	223	213	459	977
Stock price – high (Y)[1]	—	15,064	20,696	26,667	37,238	37,400	28,900	21,200	21,500	27,700	28,500
Stock price – low (Y)[1]	—	8,425	9,982	17,619	18,762	20,000	18,400	12,300	12,800	18,500	17,700
Stock price – close (Y)[1]	9.3%	12,363	18,223	23,429	36,762	20,000	18,500	12,900	18,500	23,900	27,600
P/E – high	—	46	40	39	49	46	35	95	101	60	29
P/E – low	—	26	19	26	25	25	22	55	60	40	18
Dividends per share (Y)	5.2%	70	80	100	110	100	120	85	100	95	110
Book value per share (Y)	7.7%	5,422	6,150	6,920	8,044	8,389	9,130	9,230	9,357	9,719	10,599
Employees	0.0%	—	—	—	—	—	1,358	—	1,368	—	1,360

1996 YEAR-END

Debt ratio: —
Return on equity: 9.6%
Cash (mil.): Y109
Long-term debt (mil.): —
No. of shares (mil.): 13
Dividends
   Yield: 0.4%
   Payout: 11.3%
Market value (mil.): $3,260
Sales (mil.): $2,147

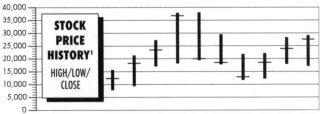

STOCK PRICE HISTORY[1]
HIGH/LOW/CLOSE

1987 1988 1989 1990 1991 1992 1993 1994 1995 1996

[1] Stock prices are for the prior calendar year. Note: $ = Y107.26 (March 31, 1996)

OMNICOM GROUP INC.

OVERVIEW

If Omnicom can bring Ivana and the Donald back together again (for a Pizza Hut commercial), then uniting a wide variety of agencies in the fast-consolidating advertising industry ought to be a snap. And it appears to be, for Omnicom. The New York City-based company, whose #1 position in the US advertising business is hotly contested by Interpublic Group, consistently wins awards for creativity.

Omnicom's group of firms includes BBDO Worldwide, DDB Needham, TBWA International, and Diversified Agency Services (DAS), which provide marketing services such as public relations, direct marketing, and specialty advertising. Each of these groups in turn owns all or portions of hundreds of agencies throughout the world, forming an international web that can handle the needs of even the largest multinationals. Like other advertising conglomerates, Omnicom manages its

group of agencies with a relatively small holding-company staff, providing overall strategic direction, financial resources, and worldwide connections. But the agencies are operated independently, which often allows firms under the Omnicom umbrella to work for rival clients.

Despite an agency purchasing spree that began in the 1980s, Omnicom has avoided the mistakes of other ad agency holding companies that accumulated heavy debt burdens in their acquisition binges (such as Saatchi & Saatchi and the WPP Group). The company remains on the lookout for new acquisition prospects and for other new opportunities. However, it is taking a cautious approach to the phenomenon of Internet advertising, believing that for the time being there is more danger of losing money by rushing into the field than there is opportunity.

WHEN

Omnicom Group was created in 1986 to combine 3 leading creative ad agencies into a single group capable of competing in the worldwide market. BBDO Worldwide, originally formed in New York in 1928 as Batten, Barton, Durstine & Osborn, had the huge PepsiCo account and developed the "Pepsi Generation" campaign. Doyle Dane Bernbach Group (DDB), which had come up with the fahrvergnügen ads for Volkswagen, had strong ties in Europe. Needham Harper Worldwide, which had served up the "You Deserve a Break Today" commercials for McDonald's, had connections in the Far East. The merger also offered administrative economies of scale and the ability to provide all of a client's marketing needs under one roof.

BBDO remained separate, while DDB and Needham Harper were merged to form DDB Needham Worldwide. The specialty service units (e.g., public relations firms and direct marketers) of each of these companies were put into a unit called the Diversified Agency Services (DAS).

Bruce Crawford, a previous chairman of BBDO who had just finished a stint of 3-1/2 years running New York's Metropolitan Opera, became CEO in 1989. He transformed DAS from a chaotic group of shops into a smooth-running marketing giant by selling off pieces that didn't fit or that were losing money. Crawford ran Omnicom as a holding company of independent operating units, jettisoning

lofty ideas of synergy through cross-referrals. By keeping costs low, especially interest expenses, Omnicom did not suffer during the 1990-91 recession.

Omnicom acquired Goodby, Berlin & Silverstein in 1992. The next year TBWA Advertising was added to Omnicom's roster. Started in Paris in 1970 by American Bill Tragos, TBWA was creator of the imaginative Absolut Vodka ads and a driving force behind the popularity of Evian water in the US.

The merger spree continued in 1994 when Omnicom purchased WWAV Group, the largest direct marketing agency in the UK, and Interbrand, an international branding agency, which was merged into the Schecter Group (acquired in 1989). Events in 1995 included the merger of TBWA with Chiat/Day (which was founded in 1968 by Jay Chiat and Guy Day and was the creator of the Energizer Bunny) to form TBWA International Network. This merger united automaker Nissan's European advertising with its US Nissan and Infiniti accounts.

In late 1995 Omnicom acquired Michigan-based Ross Roy Communications, which is one of the largest full-service marketing communication services companies. Continuing its acquisition binge into early 1996, the company agreed to acquire Pittsburgh-based Ketchum Communications Holdings, which has a highly respected corporate public relations operation.

WHO

Chairman and CEO: Bruce Crawford, age 67, $2,505,000 pay
President: John D. Wren, age 43, $1,300,000 pay
CFO: Fred J. Meyer, age 65, $1,737,500 pay
Chairman and CEO, DDB Needham Worldwide Communications Group: Keith L. Reinhard, age 61, $1,427,806 pay
Chairman and CEO, BBDO Worldwide Network: Allen Rosenshine, age 57, $1,425,000 pay
Secretary and General Counsel: Barry J. Wagner, age 55
Director Human Resources and Benefits: Leslie Chiocco
Auditors: Andersen Worldwide

WHERE

HQ: 437 Madison Ave., New York, NY 10022
Phone: 212-415-3600
Fax: 212-415-3530

	1995 Sales	
	$ mil.	% of total
International	1,141	51
US	1,117	49
Total	**2,258**	**100**

Omnicom operates in more than 60 countries worldwide.

WHAT

Selected Services
Ad design and production
Ad placement
Advertising campaigns
Corporate image services
Direct mail
Marketing consulting and research
Public relations

Selected Agencies
BBDO Worldwide Newtork
DDB Needham Worldwide Network
Diversified Agency Services
Goodby, Silverstein & Partners
TBWA International Network

Selected Clients
Anheuser-Busch
Banco Real (Brazil)
Bayer AG
Chrysler
Gillette
GTE
Hasbro
Johnson & Johnson
McDonald's
Mobil
Nissan
PepsiCo
Seagram
US Department of Housing and Urban Development
Visa
Volkswagen

KEY COMPETITORS

Bozell, Jacobs
Cordiant
Creative Artists
D'Arcy Masius
Dentsu
Edelman Public Relations
Grey Advertising
Heritage Media
Interpublic Group
Leo Burnett
Publicis
TMP Worldwide
True North
WPP Group
Young & Rubicam

HOW MUCH

NYSE symbol: OMC FYE: December 31	Annual Growth	1986	1987	1988	1989	1990	1991	1992	1993	1994	1995
Sales ($ mil.)	13.0%	753	811	881	1,007	1,178	1,236	1,385	1,516	1,756	2,258
Net income ($ mil.)	—	(4)	35	39	47	52	57	66	85	108	140
Income as % of sales	—	—	4.3%	4.4%	4.6%	4.4%	4.6%	4.7%	5.6%	6.2%	6.2%
Earnings per share ($)	—	(0.09)	0.71	0.78	0.86	0.97	1.01	1.10	1.31	1.54	1.85
Stock price – high ($)	—	13.50	14.31	10.94	12.88	13.75	17.00	20.94	23.75	26.88	37.50
Stock price – low ($)	—	8.63	7.88	8.94	9.69	8.06	10.50	15.63	18.50	21.88	24.94
Stock price – close ($)	15.7%	10.06	9.81	9.81	12.88	11.56	15.94	20.63	23.13	25.88	37.25
P/E – high	—	—	20	14	15	14	17	19	18	18	20
P/E – low	—	—	11	12	11	8	10	14	14	14	14
Dividends per share ($)	4.3%	0.44	0.49	0.49	0.49	0.52	0.55	0.59	0.62	0.62	0.64
Book value per share ($)	8.5%	3.55	3.90	4.15	4.53	5.63	6.68	5.43	6.06	7.48	7.39
Employees	9.7%	—	—	10,174	11,400	11,800	12,300	12,500	14,400	16,100	19,400

1995 YEAR-END

Debt ratio: 36.1%
Return on equity: 25.6%
Cash (mil.): $314
Current ratio: 0.84
Long-term debt (mil.): $290
No. of shares (mil.): 75
Dividends
  Yield: 1.7%
  Payout: 34.6%
Market value (mil.): $2,781

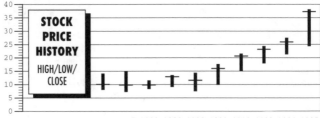

STOCK PRICE HISTORY HIGH/LOW/CLOSE

PEARSON PLC

OVERVIEW

Pearson is picking its media operations to bring in a juicier slice of the green. The London-based conglomerate is vying to become a global media force by focusing more on such holdings as the *Financial Times* business newspaper and Penguin, a publisher of consumer books, maps, audio books, and CD-ROMs, than on such operations as the Tussauds Group, which manages tourist attractions in Europe.

Other media operations include educational book publisher Addison Wesley Longman (AWL; the #1 publisher of English-language teaching books); TV broadcaster and producer Pearson Television; Westminster Press,

publisher of more than 100 UK newspapers; and Pearson New Entertainment, which prints special-interest magazines. Pearson also has a majority interest in Recoletos, which is among the leading newspaper and magazine publishers in Spain, and a 50% stake in corporate bank Lazard Brothers.

Pearson is counting on its emphasis on the information, education, and entertainment markets to help it reach additional consumers in worldwide markets. It is advancing its objectives by acquiring complementary businesses (HarperCollins Educational Publishing and Interactive Data Corporation) and divesting noncore operations (Eden Toy).

WHEN

In 1844 Samuel Pearson became a partner in a small Yorkshire building firm. When he retired in 1879, his grandson Weetman took over, moving the company to London in 1884, 2 years after it had won its first London contract. The business enjoyed extraordinary success, winning numerous contracts, including one to build the first tunnel under New York's Hudson River and another to construct the main drainage system in Mexico City. By the 1890s the company (incorporated as S. Pearson & Son in 1897) was the world's #1 contractor. Weetman Pearson was knighted in 1894 and later received the title of lord.

In 1901 Weetman Pearson missed a railroad connection in Laredo, Texas, and, during his 9-hour wait, heard about the Spindletop oil gusher. Recalling reports of oil seepages in Mexico, he bought drilling rights to huge tracts of Mexican land. Pearson sank $25 million into his Mexican Eagle Oil Company. In turn, it made him a very wealthy man before he sold it to Shell Oil in 1919.

That year Pearson, by then Lord Cowdray, restructured S. Pearson & Son as a holding company separate from the construction business. In the 1920s the company bought newspapers and a stake in Lazard Brothers, and engaged in oil exploration (including the startup and sale of US-based Amerada). Cowdray died in 1927 and, without him, so did the construction business. His heirs took over S. Pearson & Son and added unrelated businesses to a company that has since been called "a collection of rich men's toys."

In 1935 Pearson helped form British Airways (merged into British Overseas Airways Corporation, the predecessor of today's British Airways, in 1939). In 1957 Pearson bought

control (it now owns 100%) of the *Financial Times* newspaper. Later the company bought stakes in Chateau Latour (wine, 1963), Longman (books, 1968), and, after going public in 1969, Penguin Books (1971), Royal Daulton (1971), Madame Tussaud's (1978), and Camco (1987).

After a takeover scare in 1986, when Hong Kong's Hutchison Whampoa bought 4.9% of the company, Pearson's Lazard Frères affiliate bought a block of Pearson's stock to discourage the would-be suitor. Rupert Murdoch's Australian media company News Corp. bought 20% of Pearson in 1987 but later sold his stake. Taking steps to improve profitability, Pearson in 1988 and 1989 sold Chateau Latour and Camco and bought Addison-Wesley (publisher, US) and *Les Échos* (financial newspaper, France). The company bought Cuisenaire (teaching materials, US) in 1990 and sold Royal Daulton in 1993.

The company began its push to become an international media enterprise in 1993; the next year it entered the US educational software market with the purchase of Software Toolworks for $462 million and paid $484 million for software and video game publisher Mindscape. In 1995 Pearson sold most of its stake in BSkyB, a satellite television company. Pearson grew its television business that year with the purchase of Grundy Worldwide, producer of game shows and soap operas for foreign markets.

Pearson bought financial information services provider Interactive Data Corp. for $201 million in 1995 and News Corp.'s HarperCollins Educational Publishing subsidiary for $580 million in 1996. It also put its Westminster Press newspaper unit up for sale.

Chairman: Lord Michael Blakenham, age 58
Managing Director and COO: Frank Barlow, age 66
Finance Director: John Makinson, age 41
CEO, Pearson New Entertainment: Nick Alexander, age 40
CEO, Financial Times Group: David Bell, age 49
CEO, Pearson Television: Greg Dyke, age 48
CEO, The Tussauds Group: Michael Jolly, age 43
CEO, Addison Wesley Longman: J. Larry Jones, age 54
CEO, Mindscape: John Moore
CEO, Penguin: Peter Mayer, age 59
CEO, Westminster Press: Will Gibson
CEO, Pearson Professional: Peter Warwick, age 44
Supervisor Human Resources: Melanie Zebler
Auditors: Coopers & Lybrand L.L.P.

WHERE

HQ: 3 Burlington Gardens, London W1X 1LE, UK
Phone: +44-71-411-2000
Fax: +44-71-411-2390
US HQ: Pearson Inc., 30 Rockefeller Plaza, 50th Fl., New York, NY 10112-5095
US Phone: 212-641-2400
US Fax: 212-641-2500
Web site: http://www.ft.com

	1995 Sales	
	L mil.	% of total
UK	687	38
North America	591	32
Continental Europe	352	19
Asia/Pacific	163	9
Other regions	37	2
Total	**1,830**	**100**

WHAT

	1995 Sales		1995 Operating Income	
	L mil.	% of total	L mil.	% of total
Information	759	41	105	36
Entertainment	712	39	111	39
Education	359	20	32	11
Investment banking	—	—	40	14
Adjustments	—	—	(28)	—
Total	**1,830**	**100**	**260**	**100**

Selected Subsidiaries and Affiliates
Addison Wesley Longman (English-language books)
Financial Times Ltd. (*The Financial Times* and FT Information)
Lazard Brothers & Co., Ltd. (50%, merchant bank)
Les Echos SA (newspapers, France)
Mindscape Inc. (software and video games)
Pearson New Entertainment Ltd. (special-interest magazines and new media ventures)
Pearson Professional Ltd. (professional materials)
Pearson Television Ltd. (Thames Television, Grundy Worldwide, and ACI)
Penguin (books, CD-ROMs, audio books, maps)
Recoletos Compañia Editorial SA (57%, newspapers and magazines, Spain)
The Tussauds Group Ltd. (visitor attractions)
Westminster Press Ltd. (newspapers)

KEY COMPETITORS

Advance Publications	K-III	Rank
Berkshire Hathaway	Kidder, Peabody	Reader's Digest
Bertelsmann	Knowledge Adventure	Reed Elsevier
BBC	Lagardère	Reuters
Brøderbund	Lloyd's of London	SEGA
Daily Mail Group	Matsushita	Thomson Corp.
Dow Jones	McGraw-Hill	THORN EMI
Electronic Arts	News Corp.	Time Warner
	Nintendo	Times Mirror
		Viacom

HOW MUCH

Principal exchange: London FYE: December 31	Annual Growth	1986	1987	1988	1989	1990	1991	1992	1993	1994	1995
Sales (L mil.)	7.5%	953	952	1,195	991	1,045	1,078	1,145	1,320	1,550	1,830
Net income (L mil.)	15.0%	74	98	127	233	88	134	105	148	223	261
Income as % of sales	—	7.8%	10.3%	10.6%	23.5%	8.4%	12.4%	9.2%	11.2%	14.4%	14.3%
Earnings per share (p)	4.8%	19	24	26	29	25	18	17	28	34	29
Stock price – high (p)	—	309	507	398	415	403	379	459	614	735	690
Stock price – low (p)	—	192	262	310	310	299	295	302	356	551	534
Stock price – close (p)	8.2%	308	342	323	368	328	349	390	608	555	624
P/E – high	—	16	21	11	14	16	21	27	22	22	24
P/E – low	—	10	11	12	11	12	16	17	13	16	19
Dividends per share (p)	12.3%	6.0	7.5	9.0	10.8	11.6	11.6	12.0	13.0	15.0	17.0
Book value per share (p)	(7.2%)	—	—	—	—	—	—	193	181	187	154
Employees	(3.9%)	27,800	23,250	26,017	27,915	29,410	28,492	27,966	15,514	17,215	19,422

1995 YEAR-END

Debt ratio: 46.3%
Return on equity: 27.4%
Cash (mil.): L672
Long-term debt (mil.): L476
No. of shares (mil.): 556
Dividends
 Yield: 2.6%
 Payout: 57.3%
Market value (mil.): $5,537
Sales (mil.): $2,920

Note: L = $1.60 (December 31, 1995)

POLYGRAM N.V.

OVERVIEW

Whether you listen to U2, Leonard Bernstein, or Herbie Hancock, PolyGram delivers the goods. The Baarn, Netherlands-based company is one of the largest music enterprises in the world, with operations in more than 40 countries. It is the #2 music company in the US, after Time Warner. Two-thirds of its sales are generated by international and national pop labels, including A&M, Mercury, Def Jam, and Island. PolyGram also holds 40% of the classical music market worldwide via labels such as Deutsche Grammophon, Decca/London, and Philips Classics. The company is the 3rd largest music publisher worldwide, owning over 320,000 copyrights.

PolyGram has diversified by focusing more of its attention on the big screen in recent years, acquiring independent film companies and libraries such as actress Jodie Foster's Egg Pictures, Working Title Films, and Gramercy Pictures.

The company has been hindered of late by weak pop music sales, a lack of big-screen hits, and the delayed delivery of several major albums. Philips Electronics owns 75% of the firm.

WHEN

PolyGram began as a classical music company in 1962 in a joint venture between German uberconglomerate Siemens AG and Philips Electronics. Siemens contributed its Deutsche Grammophon label (founded in 1898) and Philips its self-titled classical label. The venture quickly became noted for its classical music selection. However, it needed to boost revenues to support an international distribution network, so in 1972 it rushed into the US market, purchasing MGM Records, Verve Records, and the United Artists distribution network. That year the subsidiaries were reorganized as PolyGram.

With its headquarters in Europe and its background in classical music, PolyGram was ill-suited for the era of "Disco Inferno." In 1976 it bought 50% of disco label RSO, whose *Saturday Night Fever* soundtrack became one of the biggest-selling albums ever. The company also set up an American branch of Polydor, its European pop label. The firm planned to introduce the US to non-English-speaking European stars, including such legends as 13-year-old Dutch artist Hein Tje, who played to sellout crowds on the Continent. The US audiences were not impressed, and PolyGram's fortunes began to crumble. Adding to the company's woes in the late 1970s was its short-lived, money-losing film unit, PolyGram Pictures (closed in 1983) which made such films as *An American Werewolf in London*.

After purchasing Casablanca Records, home to musical heavyweights KISS and the Village People, PolyGram discovered that while these acts sold millions of records, the costs of promoting them were extraordinary, resulting in huge losses. By 1980 the soul train came to a halt, and with it the popularity of many of the company's biggest 1970s artists. The firm would not see a profit again until 1985, after losing $220 million in the US. It cut 170 acts from the roster, shut warehouses around the US, and reduced its myriad of sales offices.

In the 1980s Philips introduced its new CD format through PolyGram. With PolyGram's extensive selection of classical titles, the CD became a cash cow, generating profits far in excess of vinyl records due to higer prices and lower production costs. At the same time, hard rock became the soup du jour, and groups such as Bon Jovi, Def Leppard, Rush, and the Scorpions generated huge profits for the company. By 1987 Philips had purchased Siemens's 50% interest in PolyGram, which went public in 1989.

After restructuring its US operations in 1989, PolyGram set out to conquer the US music market once again. That year it bought Island Records and in 1990, A&M Records, adding artists such as U2 and Janet Jackson to its roster and boosting its share of the world music market from 15% to 18%. Also that year Alain Levy became president and CEO.

In the 1990s PolyGram strengthened its international portfolio, adding such companies as Sonet Media AB, a Finnish concern, and Japanese labels Nippon Phonogram and Polydor KK. The firm also started acquiring small independent film operations such as A&M Films and Propaganda Films.

PolyGram joined with MTV Networks in 1995 to launch 2 MTV channels in Asia and acquired Rodven Records, the leading independent record company in Latin America.

PolyGram entered a joint venture in 1996 with Polish company Atomic Entertainment and British TV producer Planet 24 to form Atomic TV, a Warsaw-based channel featuring local and international music videos. New musical releases in 1996 included Lionel Richie, Sting, and Soundgarden.

President and CEO: Alain Levy
EVP and CFO: Jan Cook
EVP; President, PolyGram Filmed Entertainment:
Michael Kuhn
Chairman and CEO, A&M Records, USA: Al Cafaro
Chairman and CEO, PolyGram UK: Roger Ames
President, PolyGram Far East: Norman Cheng
President, Continental Europe: Rick Dobbis
President, PolyGram Classics and Jazz:
Christopher Roberts
President and COO, PolyGram Holding, Inc., USA:
Eric Kronfeld
SVP International Manufacturing and Logistics:
Peter Bouwens
SVP Human Resources: Gareth Jones
VP Treasury: Jan Bolger
General Counsel: Richard Constant
Auditors: KPMG Peat Marwick LLP

WHERE

HQ: Gerrit van der Veenlaan 4, 3743 DN, Baarn,
The Netherlands
Phone: +31-(0)2154-19911
Fax: +31-(0)2154-16400
US HQ: PolyGram Holding Inc., Worldwide Plaza, 825
Eigth Ave., New York, NY 10019
US Phone: 212-333-8000
US Fax: 212-333-8203
Web site: http://www.polygramnv.com

PolyGram operates 117 film and music subsidiaries in 42
countries.

	1995 Sales	
	$ mil.	% of total
Europe	2,866	52
US & Canada	1,283	24
Asia	1,008	18
Other regions	342	6
Total	**5,499**	**100**

HOW MUCH

WHAT

	1995 Sales	
	$ mil.	% of total
Music	4,727	86
Filmed entertainment	772	14
Total	**5,499**	**100**

Selected Artists	Selected Subsidiaries
Blues Traveler	A&M Records, Inc. (US)
Bon Jovi	A&M Records Ltd. (UK)
Boyz II Men	Decca Record Company
The Cranberries	Ltd. (UK)
Sheryl Crow	Def Jam Records, Inc. (US)
The Cure	Gramercy Pictures (US)
Def Leppard	Island Entertainment
Al DiMeola	Group, Inc. (US)
Gianluca Grignani	ITC Entertainment Group
Herbie Hancock	Ltd. (UK)
Joe Henderson	Mercury Records B.V.
Janet Jackson	MTV Asia LDC (50%,
Elton John	Singapore)
LL Cool J	PolyGram do Brasil, Ltda.
Metallica	PolyGram GmbH
Willie Nelson	(Germany)
PJ Harvey	PolyGram India Ltd. (51%)
Pulp	PolyGram Leisure Ltd.
Andre Rieu	(New Zealand)
Soundgarden	PolyGram Merchandising,
Sting	Inc. (US)
Shania Twain	PolyGram Records, Inc.
U2	(US)

KEY COMPETITORS

All American Communications	Samuel Goldwyn
Bertelsmann	Savoy Pictures
DreamWorks SKG	Sony
LIVE Entertainment	THORN EMI
MCA	Time Warner
MGM	Walt Disney
Rush Communications	

NYSE symbol: PLG (ADR) FYE: December 31	Annual Growth	1986	1987	1988	1989	1990	1991	1992	1993	1994	1995
Sales ($ mil.)	15.9%	—	—	—	2,274	2,942	3,544	3,676	4,097	4,837	5,499
Net income ($ mil.)	16.6%	—	—	—	184	200	250	281	339	415	463
Income as % of sales	—	—	—	—	8.1%	6.8%	7.1%	7.6%	8.3%	8.6%	8.4%
Earnings per share ($)	14.3%	—	—	—	1.15	1.18	1.47	1.66	1.97	2.31	2.57
Stock price – high ($)	—	—	—	—	18.13	20.50	24.50	30.88	40.13	46.88	66.50
Stock price – low ($)	—	—	—	—	16.25	15.25	15.50	21.88	23.25	37.38	45.88
Stock price – close ($)	19.8%	—	—	—	17.75	17.88	24.50	24.25	39.38	46.13	52.38
P/E – high	—	—	—	—	16	17	17	19	20	20	26
P/E – low	—	—	—	—	14	13	11	13	12	16	18
Dividends per share ($)	21.7%	—	—	—	—	—	0.21	0.27	0.31	0.34	0.46
Book value per share ($)	22.8%	—	—	—	3.05	3.59	3.59	4.09	7.70	9.01	10.48
Employees	6.9%	—	—	—	—	8,600	10,600	11,162	11,223	11,475	12,002

1995 YEAR-END

Debt ratio: 15%
Return on equity: 26.9%
Cash (mil.): $379
Current ratio: 1.38
Long-term debt (mil.): $199
No. of shares (mil.): 180
Dividends
  Yield: 0.9%
  Payout: 17.9%
Market value (mil.): $9,428

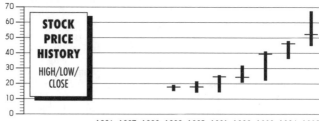

STOCK PRICE HISTORY HIGH/LOW/ CLOSE

PUBLICIS SA

OVERVIEW

When it comes to advertising, Publicis has its bases covered and then some. With offices in 19 countries, more than 100 subsidiaries, and an international client portfolio that includes Perrier, Nestlé, Colgate-Palmolive, and L'Oréal, the Paris-based advertising, media, and communications company's reach extends far beyond the Champs-Elysées.

In addition to creating advertising campaigns, through subsidiaries the company conducts research and develops strategy (Intelligences, Publicis Consultants), handles press and public relations (Idées Dialogue Conseil), and manages direct-marketing campaigns (Publicis Direct). Yet another subsidiary, Procis, handles marketing promotion, and other Publicis units develop employment advertising and internal employee communication (Média System), financial communications (Média Finance), and print and electronic publishing (Mundocom). The marketing and management of media space in newspapers, on radio, in cinemas, and via billboard is the responsibility of subsidiary Régies et Médias.

In the US, Publicis operates through its New York- and Dallas-based Publicis/Bloom subsidiary, whose clients include Anheuser-Busch, Bacardi, Cellular One, and T.G.I. Friday's.

Publicis also operates a retail chain called Le Drugstore. Something of a Parisian phenomenon, the shops are open 24 hours and offer food and entertainment (such as movies and video games) in addition to pharmaceuticals, tobacco, and gift items.

WHEN

When 19-year-old Marcel Bleustein, a grade-school dropout and the son of a Russian Jewish immigrant, founded Publicis in Paris in 1926 (the name was a takeoff on "publicity" and "six"), he established France's first advertising agency. It took Bleustein a year before he captured his first account, but two years later the youth came up with the idea that would bring him success: radio advertising. By year's end, Bleustein had become the exclusive agent for all 18 of France's government-run radio stations. In 1934, the government banned advertising on state-run stations. Bleustein bounced back by creating his own radio station, Radio Cité, the next year. Radio Cité was the first to broadcast from 6 a.m. to midnight and include contests, commercial jingles, and news reporting along with music from such stars as Edith Piaf and Charles Trenet. By 1939 Bleustein had expanded into film distribution and theaters.

When the Nazis invaded, Bleustein (an intelligence agent under General de Gaulle) fled to Spain and adopted the name Bleustein-Blanchet. When he returned to France following the liberation, his radio station had been destroyed, so he relaunched his advertising business. He pioneered market research in addition to capturing international accounts and developing an advertising network across Europe.

In 1958 Bleustein-Blanchet bought the former Hotel Astoria on the Champs-Elysées and opened the first Le Drugstore.

An acquisition campaign started in the 1970s. In 1972 the company acquired the Dutch Intermedia network (with operations in 10 countries). In 1991 it acquired holdings in Germany, the Netherlands, and the UK.

Since Publicis had no presence in North America, in 1988 it reached a global alliance with Chicago-based Foote, Cone & Belding Communications (FCB), whereby Publicis would represent clients in Europe, Africa, and the Middle East and FCB would handle North and South America, South Africa, and the Asia/Pacific region. Each firm agreed to work through its partner on any business outside of its core region, allowing them to offer global representation. The two firms swapped stock and set up a European joint venture, Publicis/FCB (51% controlled by Publicis, 49% by FCB) to coordinate their activities.

Although the deal allowed it some entry into the North American market, Publicis wanted more. In 1993 Publicis acquired France's Groupe FCA, owner of the US-based Bloom FCAL agency. FCB held that the acquisition of this competing agency was a breach of their agreement. When Publicis refused to cancel the deal, FCB established True North Communications, a new holding company, that was seen as a declaration that it would work worldwide without its partner. Publicis countered by threatening to dissolve the agreement. When this public squabbling began to scare off clients, the two side agreed to discuss their differences more privately. The alliance was finally terminated in 1996, although Publicis/FCB continued to operate.

Bleustein-Blanchet died in April 1996 at age 89. His daughter Elisabeth Badinter assumed control of the company.

WHO

President, Supervisory Board: Elisabeth Badinter
President, Management Board: Maurice Lévy
Supervisory Board Member: Michèle Bleustein-Blanchet
Supervisory Board Member: Michel David-Weill
Supervisory Board Member: Jean-Yves Haberer
Supervisory Board Member: Claude Marcus
Supervisory Board Member: Edmond de Rothschild
Supervisory Board Member: Henri-Calixte Suaudeau
Management Board Member: Bruno Desbarats
Management Board Member: Gérard Pedraglio
General Secretary: Jean-Paul Morin
Chairman and CEO, Publicis/Bloom New York:
Bob Bloom
Chairman and CEO, Publicis/Bloom Dallas: Bob Kantor
Auditors: Pierre Loeper, Cabinet Robert Mazars

WHERE

HQ: 133, avenue des Champs-Elysées, 75008,
Paris, France
Phone: +33-1-47-20-78-00
Fax: +33-1-47-20-28-55
US HQ: Publicis/Bloom, 304 E. 45th St.,
New York, NY 10017
US Phone: 212-370-1313
US Fax: 212-984-1695

Publicis's network includes operations in Austria,
Belgium, Denmark, Finland, France, Germany, Greece,
Hungary, Italy, the Netherlands, Norway, Poland,
Portugal, Russia, Spain, Switzerland, Turkey, the UK,
and the US.

	Sales
	% of total
France	43
Other Europe	51
US	6
Total	**100**

WHAT

Principal Activities	Principle Clients
Advertising	Air France
Advertising space sales	Anheuser-Busch
management	AT&T
Direct marketing	Bacardi
Employment advertising	Cellular One Network
Financial communica-	Club Med
tions	Colgate-Palmolive
Internal employee com-	Duracell
munication	Lancome
Marketing promotion	L'Oréal
Marketing research	Nestlé
Press relations	Perrier
Public relations	Renault
Publishing	Shell
Retail drugstores	Whirlpool
Television brand	
sponsorship	

KEY COMPETITORS

Bozell, Jacobs
Cordiant
Creative Artists
D'Arcy Masius
Dentsu
Grey Advertising
Havas
Interpublic Group
Leo Burnett
Omnicom Group
True North
WPP Group
Young & Rubicam

HOW MUCH

Principal exchange: Paris FYE: December 31	Annual Growth	1986	1987	1988	1989	1990	1991	1992	1993	1994	1995
Sales (FF mil.)	13.2%	—	—	8,607	14,733	16,277	19,891	20,002	18,236	20,002	20,540
Net income (FF mil.)	3.2%	—	—	123	142	226	150	149	127	151	153
Income as % of sales	—	—	—	1.4%	1.0%	1.4%	0.8%	0.7%	0.7%	0.8%	0.7%
Earnings per share (FF)	(3.2%)	—	—	23.93	18.35	29.21	19.41	19.24	16.04	18.71	19.10
Stock price – high (FF)	—	—	—	253.47	484.72	466.67	366.67	325.00	491.25	489.58	383.33
Stock price – low (FF)	—	—	—	125.00	261.53	213.75	201.33	198.75	211.25	320.00	261.00
Stock price – close (FF)	2.5%	—	—	243.06	466.67	274.58	238.33	215.83	477.08	366.67	289.00
P/E – high	—	—	—	11	26	16	19	17	31	26	20
P/E – low	—	—	—	5	14	7	10	10	13	17	14
Dividends per share (FF)	(28.0%)	—	—	40.00	34.00	8.00	8.00	8.00	8.00	4.00	4.00
Book value per share (FF)	—	—	—	314.99	125.00	149.49	164.33	179.57	163.62	165.38	175.31
Employees	3.7%	—	—	—	—	5,000	5,763	5,500	4,690	5,540	6,000

1995 YEAR-END

Debt ratio: 24.9%
Return on equity: 7.4%
Cash (mil.): FF1,168
Long-term debt (mil.): FF131
No. of shares (mil.): 8
Dividends
  Yield: 1.4%
  Payout: 20.9%
Market value (mil.): $477
Sales (mil.): $4,184

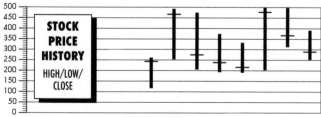

STOCK PRICE HISTORY HIGH/LOW/CLOSE

1986 1987 1988 1989 1990 1991 1992 1993 1994 1995

Note: $ = FF4.9 (December 31, 1995)

QUAD/GRAPHICS, INC.

OVERVIEW

"Ink is in our veins," says Quad/Graphics founder and president Harry V. Quadracci. While other printing companies are scrambling into multimedia, Pewaukee, Wisconsin-based business is reaffirming its commitment to putting ink on paper. The largest private printing company in North America, it provides design and prepress services, binding, and distribution from 10 US printing plants for clients worldwide. The company also formulates and produces inks and designs and manufactures hi-tech printing machinery. Clients include *Time*, *Newsweek*, and *Playboy*.

Quad/Graphics is one of the most employee-oriented companies in the industry. The company is not unionized because Quadracci rejects the adversarial relationship that is often characteristic of union shops. Instead it promotes a flexible, egalitarian culture (employees

at all levels wear the same dark blue uniform) and promotes from within. It also provides free medical care, health clubs, and subsidized childcare (and is investigating providing housing developments for workers at one of its rural plants). Despite these benefits, however, printing union leaders have criticized Quad/Graphics for its pay levels (entry level pay hovers at the lower end of union pay scales.)

Quad/Graphics has grown by anticipating customers' needs and staying on the cutting edge of technology (it replaces its equipment approximately every 5 years). The company avoids planning and budgeting so it can recognize and respond to new opportunities.

Employees own 80% of the company; Quadracci owns a controlling share.

WHEN

Ink certainly is in Harry V. Quadracci's blood. His father, Harry R., founded his own printing business, Standard Printing Co., in Racine, Wisconsin, in 1930, when he was just 16. Four years later, however, Quadracci sold out to William A. Krueger. Though he worked to build Krueger into a major regional printer, the elder Quadracci had little equity in the company.

In the 1960s son Harry V. joined Krueger as a company lawyer. Within a few years he had worked his way up to a position as plant manager. Krueger was a union shop, and in those days unions dictated the work rules and often salary levels as well. In 1970 there was a 3-1/2 month strike. At odds with new management and reportedly dissatisfied with the way Krueger caved in to union demands, as well as with the generally adversarial relationship between company and union, Quadracci left (not voluntarily, it is said).

After 18 months of unemployment, in 1971 Quadracci formed a limited partnership with 12 others to get a loan to buy a press, which was installed in a building in Pewaukee. The next year his father joined the company as chairman. Within 2 years the partners had recouped their initial investment, but the business's future remained in question until about 1976. One of its most innovative moves was to make its delivery fleet drivers into entrepreneurs by requiring them to find cargo to haul on their return trips after making their deliveries.

Working on a shoestring, Quadracci hired inexperienced workers and trained them, moving them up as the company grew. The need to

improvise fostered a flexibility that Quadracci institutionalized by keeping management layers flat and remaining accessible to his employees. Beginning in 1974, Quadracci rewarded his workers with equity in the company.

In the 1980s Quad/Graphics rode its commitment to technology, offering better service than many of its competitors could. It was also immune to the mergers and acquisition fever of the time. Free of acquisition debt, the company had excellent credit and was able to finance equipment upgrades with bank loans. Quad/Graphics expanded by opening a plant in Saratoga Springs, New York (1985), and buying a plant in Thomaston, Georgia (1989).

But there were missteps, such as its 1985 attempt to break into the newspaper coupon insert business dominated by Treasure Chest Advertising. Quad/Graphics sold the operation in 1988. At the same time, the company could not avoid the national downturn that began about then, which forced it to lay off employees in the late 1980s and early 1990s, and prompted it to restructure weekend overtime pay (from double time to time-and-a-half). The company was also hit when a major customer consolidated its printing outside the Midwest. In response, Quad/Graphics increased its capacity in other regions of the US during the 1990s.

In 1996 the company bought 40% of an Argentinean printer, Anselmo L. Morvillo S.A.; it will build a new printing plant for the company, which will be its first printing facility outside the US.

Chairman: Harry R. Quadracci
President: Harry V. Quadracci
SVP Sales and Administration: Carl L. Bennett
VP Finance and CFO: John C. Fowler
VP Finishing Operations: Frank M. Arndorfer
VP Manufacturing and Technology; President,
  Quad/Tech: Thomas A. Quadracci
VP Employee Services: Emily M. Labode
Auditors: Andersen Worldwide

WHERE

HQ: W.224 N.3322 Duplainville Rd., Pewaukee, WI 53072
Phone: 414-246-9200
Fax: 414-246-4322
Web site: http://www.qg.com

Manufacturing Sites
Hartford, WI
Lomira, WI
New Berlin, WI
Pewaukee, WI
Saratoga Springs, NY
Sussex, WI
The Rock, GA
Thomaston, GA
West Allis, WI

Quad/Imaging Facilities
Anaheim, CA
Boston
Minneapolis
New York

WHAT

	1995 Sales
	% of total
Catalogs	45
Publications	40
Other	15
Total	**100**

Prior-to-Press Services
Quad/Creative
Quad/Imaging
Quad/Photo

Printing Services
Gravure Press
Quad/Custom Web
Sheetfed Printing Services
Web Offset Press

Post-Press Services
Duplainville Transport
Finishing
Mailing & Distribution Services
Quad/Direct
Quad/List Management

Research & Development
Quad/Tech

Selected Subsidiaries
Duplainville Transport (trucking and distribution)
Quad/Tech International (printing equipment)

KEY COMPETITORS

Arandell
Banta
Big Flower Press
Cadmus Communications
Continental Graphics
Courier
Dai Nippon Printing
Devon Group
Duplex Products
Graphic Industries
Meehan-Tooker
Merrill Corp.
Quebecor
Queens Group
R. R. Donnelley
Taylor Corp.

HOW MUCH

Private company FYE: December 31	Annual Growth	1986	1987	1988	1989	1990	1991	1992	1993	1994	1995
Sales ($ mil.)	23.1%	154	226	306	376	454	509	582	703	801	1,002
Employees	16.6%	2,122	3,114	3,532	4,550	5,077	5,369	6,425	6,807	7,662	8,444

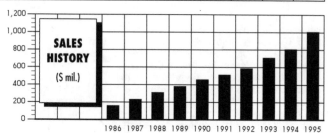

SALES
HISTORY
($ mil.)

QUEBECOR INC.

OVERVIEW

As Quebecor's 70-year-old bespectacled coxswain, Pierre Péladeau, calls out "print ... print ... print," the sound answering from the woods is "chop ... chop ... chop." Headquartered in Montreal, Quebecor is North America's #2 commercial printer, outpaced only by R. R. Donnelley. Its Quebecor Printing subsidiary makes advertising inserts, books, checks, phone books, and passports. It also prints catalogs for national retailers Bloomingdale's, L.L. Bean, Radio Shack, and Sears, as well as editions of *People*, *Sports Illustrated*, *Time*, and *TV Guide* magazines. Subsidiary Donahue Inc. is one of North America's largest producers of newsprint, with an annual capacity of 1.5 million tons.

The company's Quebecor Group publishes *Le Journal de Montréal*, the city's #1 paper (with some 1.2 million readers), and *Le Journal de Québec*. The unit also publishes approximately 50 regional weekly papers throughout Quebec. Quebecor Group also has a majority stake in Trans-Canada Archambault (formed by the 1995 merger of Quebecor's Trans-Canada distribution arm and retailer Ed. Archambault), which distributes musical recordings and operates book and record stores. Quebecor Multimedia provides new media publishing services and is moving several of Quebecor Group's publications onto the Internet.

The company positioned itself to take advantage of prospects for strong growth in Europe by acquiring leading French printer Groupe Jean Didier and a 2nd French printing concern, Groupe Jacques Lopes.

WHEN

In 1950 Pierre Péladeau borrowed $1,500 from his mother so he could buy a small Montreal newspaper called *Le Journal de Rosemont*. This became the base for Péladeau's publishing empire, and within a few years he had established 5 other weekly newspapers and his first printing firm.

In 1964 Péladeau seized the opportunity presented to him by a strike at the major Montreal paper *La Presse*. He assembled a team from his various weeklies and, according to company legend, had the tabloid *Le Journal*, which would become Quebecor's flagship, on the streets within 3 days.

Quebecor went public in 1972. By the late 1970s Péladeau had expanded beyond Quebec and bought printing plants in Ontario. He also branched out into a variety of communications activities, including music publishing and pay TV, but by the late 1980s had refocused the company on its core printing businesses.

In 1985 Quebecor got a foothold in the US with the purchase of printing plants in New Jersey and Michigan. Péladeau teamed up with Robert Maxwell in 1987 to form Mircor Inc. to buy a stake in forestry concern Donohue Inc. The company took a major step into the international arena when it purchased the printing group BCE PubliTech in 1988 for $161 million. The purchase catapulted the company to become the #1 commercial printer in Canada.

In 1990 Maxwell sold his US printing plants for $510 million to Péladeau, who formed Quebecor Printing (USA) around the new assets. In addition to the printing plants, Quebecor had access to a customer base that was bringing in $744 million a year and to Maxwell's state-of-the-art printing presses. Maxwell subsequently bought a 25.8% stake in the new company for $100 million.

When the mysterious death of Robert Maxwell in 1991 was followed by revelations of deceptive finances and shady business dealings by the Maxwell empire, Péladeau was able to buy back all of Maxwell's shares in Quebecor at bargain basement prices.

Anticipating new opportunities with the passage of NAFTA, Quebecor expanded into Mexico with the 1991 purchase of Gráficas Monte Albán SA de CV, a specialist in book binding and publishing for the Mexican and South American markets. Quebecor acquired US-based printer Arcata in 1994.

In 1995 Quebecor acquired Group Jean Didier, the largest commercial printer in France. That year Quebecor Printing went public, reducing the parent company's interest to less than 50%. Quebecor also set up its multimedia unit in 1995 and expanded it by acquiring 50% of multimedia products producer Sierra Creative Communications (1995) and 25% of multimedia software publisher Micro-Intel (1996).

The company strengthened its Dohahue subsidiary in 1996 with the purchase of North American lumber producer QUNO for $1.1 billion. Also that year Quebecor Printing and Minnesota-based printer and distributor Merrill Corp. combined their Canadian financial printing units to form a joint venture, Quebecor Merrill Canada Inc.

WHO

Chairman, President, and CEO: Pierre Péladeau, age 70, C$925,000 pay
EVP: Raymond Lemay
Chairman and CEO, Quebecor Printing Inc.: Jean Neveu, C$736,305 pay
Chairman and CEO, Quebecor Multimedia Inc.: Erik Péladeau
President and COO, Quebecor Printing Inc.: Charles G. Cavell, C$728,680 pay
Managing Director, Quebecor Printing Europe: Pierre K. Péladeau, C$2,130,880 pay
President and CEO, Quebecor Printing (USA): James A. Dawson
VP; Chairman, Donohue Inc.: Charles-Albert Poissant, C$610,000 pay
VP Legal Services and Secretary: Louis Saint-Arnaud
VP Finance and Treasurer: François R. Roy
VP Human Resources, Quebecor Group: Yves Dubuc
Auditors: KPMG Peat Marwick LLP

WHERE

HQ: 612 Saint-Jacques St., Montreal, PQ, H3C 4M8, Canada
Phone: 514-877-9777
Fax: 514-877-9757
US HQ: Quebecor Printing (USA) Corp., 125 High St., Boston, MA 02110
US Phone: 617-346-7300
US Fax: 617-346-7361

	1995 Sales		1995 Operating Income	
	$ mil.	% of total	$ mil.	% of total
Canada	1,868	46	361	66
US	1,646	40	143	26
Europe & other	553	14	40	8
Adjustments	—	—	(84)	—
Total	**4,067**	**100**	**460**	**100**

WHAT

	1995 Sales		1995 Operating Income	
	$ mil.	% of total	$ mil.	% of total
Printing	3,021	74	252	47
Forest products	823	20	274	50
Other operations	276	6	18	3
Adjustments	(53)	—	(84)	—
Total	**4,067**	**100**	**460**	**100**

Selected Operations
Donohue Inc. (newsprint, lumber, pulp, and paper production)
Quebecor Group Inc. (newspaper publishing, retail distribution)
Quebecor Multimedia Inc. (online publishing, CD-ROM production)
Quebecor Printing Inc. (48%, commercial printing)

Selected Publications
Clin d'Oeil
Femme Plus
Le Journal de Montréal
Le Journal de Québec
L'Essentiel
The Winnipeg Sun

KEY COMPETITORS

Banta
Big Flower Press
Boise Cascade
Bowater
Canadian Pacific
Courier
Georgia-Pacific
Graphic Industries
Hollinger Inc.
International Paper
James River
Kimberly-Clark
Lagardère
Mead
Pearson
Quad/Graphics
R. R. Donnelley
Southam
Sullivan
Communications
Thomson Corp.
Torstar
Treasure Chest Advertising
Valassis
Communications
Wallace Computer
Webcraft
World Color Press

HOW MUCH

AMEX symbol: PQB FYE: December 31	Annual Growth	1986	1987	1988	1989	1990	1991	1992	1993	1994	1995
Sales ($ mil.)	32.6%	321	521	1,057	1,516	2,098	2,052	1,994	2,336	2,834	4,067
Net income ($ mil.)	31.1%	12	18	27	16	67	16	69	56	63	137
Income as % of sales	—	3.6%	3.4%	2.6%	1.1%	3.2%	0.8%	3.4%	2.4%	2.2%	3.4%
Earnings per share ($)	20.7%	0.38	0.48	0.67	0.34	1.32	0.30	1.05	0.83	0.93	2.07
Stock price – high ($)	—	7.19	8.38	8.69	9.13	6.81	9.50	13.50	16.13	15.88	16.00
Stock price – low ($)	—	4.31	4.25	5.00	6.19	4.75	6.56	8.88	13.25	11.63	11.88
Stock price – close ($)	11.4%	5.75	4.88	8.38	6.50	6.81	8.88	13.38	13.50	12.38	15.25
P/E – high	—	19	18	13	27	5	32	13	19	17	8
P/E – low	—	11	9	8	18	4	22	9	16	13	6
Dividends per share ($)	22.0%	0.04	0.08	0.10	0.12	0.11	0.11	0.12	0.15	0.17	0.24
Book value per share ($)	20.2%	2.07	3.10	3.87	4.98	6.23	11.58	7.87	8.44	8.94	10.87
Employees	15.2%	—	—	—	—	—	16,400	16,500	20,600	25,900	28,900

1995 YEAR-END

Debt ratio: 59.2%
Return on equity: 20.9%
Cash (mil.): $113
Current ratio: 1.52
Long-term debt (mil.): $955
No. of shares (mil.): 66
Dividends
  Yield: 1.6%
  Payout: 11.7%
Market value (mil.): $1,007

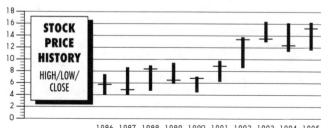

STOCK PRICE HISTORY HIGH/LOW/CLOSE 1986 1987 1988 1989 1990 1991 1992 1993 1994 1995

THE READER'S DIGEST ASSOCIATION

OVERVIEW

The Reader's Digest Association has a lot on its plate as the publisher of the world's most widely read magazine prepares for the 21st century. *Reader's Digest* magazine offers middle-brow inspirational and informational articles (originals and reprints) to almost 100 million readers of 47 editions in 18 languages. The Pleasantville, New York-based company also produces condensed best-selling and how-to books, music, videos, CD-ROMS, and special-interest magazines. Reader's Digest markets its products via direct mailings based on its proprietary database. But the company is still searching for new outlets (it recently launched a pilot sales program with Avon).

Reader's Digest is restructuring itself to meet the challenges of an interactive age. It is reducing its print editorial personnel (through early retirement and layoffs) and beefing up its electronic staff, adding new editors to take charge of its CD-ROM and online businesses. In 1996 the worldwide editor-in-chief, Kenneth Tomlinson, took an early retirement and was replaced by Christopher Willcox.

The DeWitt Wallace-Reader's Digest Fund and the Lila Wallace-Reader's Digest Fund, named for the founders, together control the company through ownership of 71% of a special class of voting stock.

WHEN

DeWitt "Wally" Wallace started in the publishing business before WWI, with a 128-page book on farming that included his distillation of information from agricultural bulletins. After serving in the war, he assembled a collection of "digested" articles, which he used while trying to find a job as an editor in New York. When this failed, in 1921 he and his wife, Lila Acheson, sold subscriptions to their then nonexistent digest by direct mail. In 1922 they produced the first pocket-sized issue of the *Reader's Digest*. It was an immediate success, which allowed the Wallaces to move from New York City to Pleasantville, New York. At first fearful that magazines would take action against them for using the articles, the Wallaces did not expand into newsstand sales until 1929. Circulation had reached one million by 1935. In 1939 the company moved to Chappaqua, New York, but kept Pleasantville as a mailing address.

In the 1940s the *Digest* expanded internationally (the first overseas edition started in England in 1938), opening company offices on 5 continents and providing foreign-language translations. During that decade Wally began to write his own articles (partly because some magazines had indeed stopped allowing him reprint rights), imparting to the *Digest* its conservative, optimistic style.

The first Reader's Digest Condensed Book was published in 1950. Five years later the *Digest* accepted its first advertising but did not carry liquor ads until 1978 and never carried cigarette ads. The company added the Recorded Music Division in 1959 and General Books in 1963. Reader's Digest was the first publisher to use direct-mail advertising with "personalized" letters to promote its products.

It also used its huge mailing list for promotions like the Reader's Digest Sweepstakes.

The Wallaces continued to manage the company until 1973. Wally died in 1981; Lila, 3 years later. Their voting stock passed to 2 trust funds; other stock endowments were made to 10 organizations, including Lincoln Center, the Metropolitan Museum of Art, and the New York Zoological Society.

George Grune took over as chairman and CEO in 1984. He cut staff by 20% and disposed of unprofitable international subsidiaries, ushering in an era of increased profitability for the company. He also diversified by adding a line of specialty magazines, including *Travel Holiday* (sold to Hachette in 1996), *Family Handyman*, *New Choices*, *American Health*, and *Moneywise*. The company bought 50% of British publisher Dorling Kindersley in 1987. It went public in 1990.

James Schadt succeeded Grune as CEO in 1994 and as chairman the following year. In 1995 the company launched a Polish edition of *Reader's Digest*, and the next year it started a Thai edition. As part of its effort to diversify into new areas, the firm concluded an agreement in 1995 with Meredith Corp. (publisher of *Better Homes & Gardens* magazine) that gives Reader's Digest access to Meredith's marketing database and certain rights to some of Meredith's popular home-oriented books and magazines.

In 1996 Reader's Digest joined with Microsoft to release a series of Home Improvement CD-ROMs. Later that year Kenneth Gordon, the company's president and COO, retired after 35 years with Reader's Digest. Profits fell to $81 million that year on sales of nearly $3.1 billion.

WHO

Chairman and CEO: James P. Schadt, age 57, $975,866 pay (prior to promotion)
EVP and CFO: Stephen R. Wilson, age 48
SVP; Editor-in-Chief, Books and Home Entertainment: Barbara J. Morgan, age 50
SVP, General Counsel, and Corporate Secretary: Paul A. Soden, age 51
SVP Global Direct Marketing: Peter J. C. Davenport
SVP Human Resources: Glenda K. Burkhardt, age 45
Editor-in-Chief, *Reader's Digest* Magazine: Christopher Willcox, age 49
VP; President, US Magazine Publishing: Thomas M. Kenney, $571,038 pay
VP; President, Reader's Digest Pacific: Martin J. Pearson, age 48, $457,346 pay
VP; President, Reader's Digest Europe: Heikki K. Helenius, age 53
VP; President, Special Markets Group: William H. Willis, age 44
VP Global Operations: Bruce G. Koe
VP and Senior Counsellor: Melvin R. Laird, age 73
Auditors: KPMG Peat Marwick LLP

WHERE

HQ: The Reader's Digest Association, Inc., Reader's Digest Rd., Pleasantville, NY 10570-7000
Phone: 914-238-1000
Fax: 914-238-4559

	1995 Sales		1995 Operating Income	
	$ mil.	% of total	$ mil.	% of total
Europe	1,456	47	225	50
US	1,197	39	152	34
Other regions	425	14	71	16
Adjustments	(9)	—	(56)	—
Total	**3,069**	**100**	**392**	**100**

WHAT

	1995 Sales		1995 Operating Income	
	$ mil.	% of total	$ mil.	% of total
Books, CDs, cassettes & videos	2,100	68	339	76
Reader's Digest	733	24	78	17
Special-interest magazines	96	3	—	—
Other	144	5	31	7
Adjustments	(4)	—	(56)	—
Total	**3,069**	**100**	**392**	**100**

Books and Home Entertainment Products
General-interest books and CDs (how-to and reference books, cookbooks, and songbooks; 12 languages)
Reader's Digest Condensed Books (popular fiction; 15 editions in 12 languages)
Recorded music (original and licensed recordings)
Series books (multiple volumes; 9 languages)
Videocassettes and original video productions

Magazines
American Health
The Family Handyman
Moneywise (UK)
New Choices: Living Even Better After 50
Reader's Digest (47 editions in 18 languages)

Other Businesses
Fund-raising products and services for school and youth groups (QSP, Inc.)
Sweepstakes direct-mail promotion
Other direct marketing (language courses, globes)

KEY COMPETITORS

AARP	Hearst	Sony
Advance Publications	K-III	Time Warner
Bertelsmann	Lagardère	Viacom
Cox Enterprises	New York Times	Virgin Group
	News Corp.	

HOW MUCH

NYSE symbol: RDA FYE: June 30	Annual Growth	1986	1987	1988	1989	1990	1991	1992	1993	1994	1995
Sales ($ mil.)	10.4%	1,255	1,420	1,712	1,832	2,009	2,345	2,614	2,868	2,806	3,069
Net income ($ mil.)	15.4%	73	95	141	152	176	209	234	258	272	264
Income as % of sales	—	5.8%	7.6%	8.2%	8.3%	8.8%	8.9%	9.0%	9.0%	9.7%	8.6%
Earnings per share ($)	16.6%	0.59	0.78	1.18	1.28	1.48	1.74	1.95	2.16	2.34	2.35
Stock price – high ($)	—	—	—	—	—	29.50	49.00	56.38	55.88	49.38	52.00
Stock price – low ($)	—	—	—	—	—	21.00	26.13	43.00	36.13	39.88	38.25
Stock price – close ($)	11.7%	—	—	—	—	29.50	48.38	54.00	45.00	49.13	51.25
P/E – high	—	—	—	—	—	20	28	29	26	21	22
P/E – low	—	—	—	—	—	14	15	22	17	17	16
Dividends per share ($)	—	—	—	0.00	0.00	0.12	0.57	0.80	1.15	1.35	1.55
Book value per share ($)	11.8%	—	—	2.68	3.57	5.06	6.12	7.79	6.72	6.95	5.84
Employees	(2.9%)	—	—	—	7,400	7,400	7,400	7,400	7,300	6,700	6,200

1995 YEAR-END

Debt ratio: 0.0%
Return on equity: 36.9%
Cash (mil.): $215
Current ratio: 1.13
Long-term debt (mil.): $0
No. of shares (mil.): 110
Dividends
  Yield: 3.0%
  Payout: 66.0%
Long-term debt (mil.): $5,627

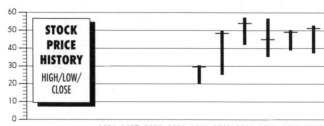

STOCK PRICE HISTORY HIGH/LOW/CLOSE 1986 1987 1988 1989 1990 1991 1992 1993 1994 1995

REED ELSEVIER PLC

OVERVIEW

With money jangling in its pocket, London-based Reed Elsevier is looking to buy its way into the future. The joint venture juggernaut (holding companies Reed International P.L.C., of London, and Elsevier NV, of Amsterdam, each own 50%) publishes more than 1,200 scientific journals, as well as business, consumer, and professional magazines primarily in the US and Europe. Reed Elsevier also owns Lexis-Nexis, the world's largest provider of full-text online information. (Altogether, electronic publishing, including CD-ROMs, accounts for about 16% of Reed Elsevier's sales.) Its business segment publishes travel and business directories and organizes exhibitions around the world. The consumer segment publishes mag-

azines such as *Marie Claire* and *Yachting World*, and Reed Consumer Books enjoys rights to characters such as Winnie-the-Pooh.

Cochairmen Ian Irvine and Herman Bruggink have shed many of the company's consumer publishing businesses to escape a relatively volatile market. (The firm has held onto its prestigious Reed Consumer Books for want of a buyer.) Reed Elsevier has honed its focus to the publication of "must have" information for the business, legal, and scientific markets. It expects printed material to yield the greater proportion of sales for years. However, flush with cash, the firm may expand its electronic publishing (including CD versions of many of its products) significantly.

WHEN

Named after the man who founded it as a newsprint manufacturing company in 1894, Albert E. Reed & Co. went public in 1903. For the next 50 years, Reed grew by buying UK pulp and paper mills. In the 1930s Reed began making packaging materials and in 1954 added building products. Reed expanded into New Zealand (1955), Canada and Australia (1960), and Norway (1962).

Chairman Sir Don Ryder radically altered the company in the 1960s and 1970s, leading Reed into other paper-related products and into the wallpaper, paint, and interior-decorating and do-it-yourself markets. In 1970 Reed bought International Publishing Corp., Mirror Group Newspapers, and 29% of Cahners Publishing; it bought the rest of Cahners in 1977.

By 1978 Ryder's strategy proved flawed. Reed had difficulty coordinating its many companies and their independent business cycles. Strapped for cash, Reed dumped most of its Australian businesses.

The company sold the Mirror Group to Robert Maxwell in 1984. Under CEO Peter Davis, a former grocery executive, Reed sold off the remainder of its nonpaper and nonpublishing companies by 1987 and focused on publishing. It bought Octopus Publishing, the UK's 2nd largest book publisher (1987), the UK's *TV Times* (1989), News Corporation's Travel Information Group (electronic and printed guides, 1989), and Martindale-Hubbell (1990).

Davis, who had become chairman in 1990, announced in September 1992 that Reed would merge with Elsevier, the world's leading scholarly journal publisher, with which Reed had considered merging in 1987. Elsevier had been founded by 5 booksellers and publishers

in Rotterdam in 1880 and had taken its name from a famous Dutch family publishing company, which had operated from the late 16th century to the early 18th century. Early successes for the company, which moved to Amsterdam in 1887, included Dutch versions of Jules Verne novels.

Elsevier entered the scientific publishing market in the 1930s, and following WWII it diversified into trade journals and consumer manuals and also continued to build its scientific publishing business. In 1979 the company merged with newspaper publisher Nederlandse Dagbladunie. That year it made its first US acquisition when it acquired the Congressional Information Service.

In 1988 the company fended off a takeover bid by Maxwell by planning to merge with UK publisher Pearson; Maxwell was thwarted, the merger ultimately failed, and Elsevier later sold its Pearson stock. In 1991 Elsevier bought Maxwell's Pergamon Press.

In an effort to increase US ownership, Reed International and Elsevier were both listed on the NYSE in 1994. The company also built its US presence that year with its $1.5 billion purchase of Mead's Lexis-Nexis online service. Reed's Davis stepped down as cochairman when the Dutch contingent pushed for (and won) management by a 4-person executive committee.

Reed Elsevier sold Bonaventura's consumer magazines, Cahners Consumer Magazines, Dagbladunie (Dutch newspapers), and Reed Regional Newspapers (UK) in 1995. The next year it launched an online version of *Estates Gazette*, a more than 100-year-old estate agent publication.

WHO

Cochairman; Chairman, Elsevier NV: Herman Bruggink, age 49
Cochairman; Chairman, Reed International: Ian A. N. Irvine, age 59
Executive Committee Member: John Mellon, age 55
Executive Committee Member: Paul Vlek, age 51
CFO: Nigel J. Stapleton, age 49
CEO, Lexis-Nexis (US): Ira Siegel
CEO, Cahners Publishing Co. (US): Robert L. Krakoff, age 60
President, Elsevier Science (US): Russell White
Auditors: Deloitte & Touche LLP

WHERE

HQ: Reed House, 6 Chesterfield Gardens, London, W1A 1EJ, UK
Phone: +44-171-499-4020
Fax: +44-171-491-8212
US HQ: Reed Elsevier Inc., MetLife Building, 200 Park Ave., New York, NY 10166
US Phone: 212-309-8136
US Fax: 212-309-7818
Web site: http://www.r-e.com

	1995 Sales		1995 Operating Income	
	£ mil.	% of total	£ mil.	% of total
North America	1,376	38	313	38
UK	1,002	28	231	28
The Netherlands	362	10	119	14
Rest of Europe	270	7	69	8
Asia/Pacific	195	5	29	4
Adjustments	444	12	67	8
Total	**3,649**	**100**	**828**	**100**

WHAT

	1995 Sales		1995 Operating Income	
	£ mil.	% of total	£ mil.	% of total
Business	1,183	32	246	30
Professional	937	26	226	27
Scientific	557	15	212	26
Consumer	528	14	77	9
Adjustments	444	13	67	8
Total	**3,649**	**100**	**828**	**100**

Selected Operations

Business
Cahners Publishing Company (*Variety, Publishers Weekly*; US)
Reed Business Publishing (*Estates Gazette*, UK)
Reed Exhibition Companies (trade shows)
Reed Travel Group (travel information and services)

Consumer
IPC Magazines (*Marie Claire, Yachting World*; UK)
Reed Consumer Books (UK)

Professional
Butterworths (legal and tax publishing, UK)
Congressional Information Service (US)
Lexis-Nexis (online databases, US)
Reed Educational & Professional Publishing (UK)
Reed Reference Publishing (US)

Scientific
Elsevier Science (scientific journals, the Netherlands)

KEY COMPETITORS

Advance Publications	International Data Group	Thomson Corp.
Bertelsmann	Knight-Ridder	Time Warner
Carlson	Lagardère	Times Mirror
Dial	McGraw-Hill	Viacom
Dow Jones	News Corp.	VNU
Havas	Pearson	Wolters Kluwer

HOW MUCH

NYSE symbols: RUK, ENL FYE: December 31	Annual Growth	1986	1987	1988	1989	1990	1991	1992	1993	1994	1995
Sales (£ mil.)	17.0%	—	—	—	—	—	2,262	2,461	2,796	3,035	3,649
Net income (£ mil.)	(5.2%)	—	—	—	—	—	251	309	380	452	552
Income as % of sales	—	—	—	—	—	—	11.1%	12.6%	13.6%	14.9%	15.1%
Earnings per share (p)	11.2%	20	27	33	35	28	24	31	36	43	52
Stock price – high (p)[1]	—	308	633	471	471	475	529	655	912	960	1,045
Stock price – low (p)[1]	—	163	299	332	345	328	345	447	618	722	714
Stock price – close (p)[1]	14.0%	303	394	370	444	378	529	641	896	798	982
P/E – high[1]	—	12	19	14	12	17	22	21	25	23	20
P/E – low[1]	—	6	9	10	9	12	14	15	17	17	14
Dividends per share (p)[1]	17.8%	5.6	8.0	10.0	14.0	15.0	15.8	16.8	18.8	21.5	24.5
Book value per share (p)[1]	1.1%	—	—	180	266	245	236	245	161	133	194
Employees	(1.4%)	34,600	31,300	22,100	17,700	19,000	18,000	18,100	25,700	26,900	30,400

1995 YEAR-END

Debt ratio: 60.6%
Return on equity: 26.6%
Cash (mil.): L843
Long-term debt (mil.): L1,089
No. of shares (mil.): 632
Dividends
  Yield: 2.5%
  Payout: 47.4%
Market value (mil.): $8,600
Sales (mil.): $5,654

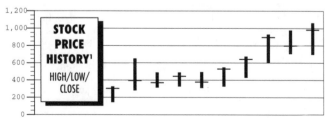

STOCK PRICE HISTORY[1]
HIGH/LOW/CLOSE

[1] Stock information is for Reed only. Note: £ = $1.55 (December 31, 1995)

REUTERS HOLDINGS PLC

OVERVIEW

Reuters has good writers. But the London-based media group's cutting edge is in transmitting financial data, news photos, and text to media outlets and the world's financial capitals faster than its competitors. Reuters has progressed a long way since it transmitted data via carrier pigeon. In 1995 the company relayed news and financial information to 327,000 computer terminals in 154 nations. It provides data feeds to financial markets and software to analyze bonds, currencies, futures, options, and stocks. Its Teknekron trading room software and Triarch datafeed links let customers manage their own information.

Through its Instinet unit, Reuters offers traders a way to deal in foreign exchange, futures and options, and securities and other markets from their personal computers. Reuters also operates GLOBEX, an international after-hours futures exchange developed with the Chicago Mercantile Exchange and the Marché à Terme International de France bourses. As a news agency, the company delivers graphics, sound, still pictures, television images, and text, to broadcasters and newspaper publishers around the world.

Although Reuters went public in 1984, it is controlled by the Reuters Founders Share Co., Ltd., set up by the companies that bought into Reuters as a trust in the 1940s. This organization was designed to preserve Reuters's "independence, integrity, and freedom from bias."

WHEN

In 1850, as the Paris-Berlin telegraph line crept toward completion, Paul Julius Reuter, a former bookseller and sometime news correspondent, saw a chance to scoop his competitors. He first used carrier pigeons to bridge the telegraph gap between Aachen, Germany, and Brussels, Belgium. When the gap narrowed, he used gallopers on horseback. Reuter's business was briefly successful.

Moving to London in 1851, just as the first English Channel cable was laid, Reuter began telegraphing stock quotes between Paris and London and selling them to financial institutions. Coverage expanded to agricultural information and then general news, and the company grew with the British Empire. In 1865 Reuter's Telegram Co. was organized as a limited company in order to capitalize a proprietary North Sea cable to Germany. The Duke of Saxe-Coburg-Gotha (Germany; a relative of the British royal family) dubbed Reuter a baron in 1871.

Reuter ceded management to his son Herbert in 1878 and died in 1899. Herbert made the disastrous decision to establish Reuter's Bank (1913). In 1915, under pressure of anti-German feeling due to WWI, as well as the death of his wife and estrangement from his son, Herbert committed suicide.

Under successor Roderick Jones the company changed its name to Reuters Ltd. (1916) and sold the bank (1917). Following its founder's lead in exploiting new technology, Reuters started using radios and teleprinters in the 1920s. But the company suffered in the Depression, and its efforts to keep on top of the deteriorating international scene as WWII approached were insupportably expensive. After a managerial crisis that led Jones to resign, the UK government persuaded a British newspaper group to buy Reuters in 1941.

In the 1950s Reuters experienced problems as the empire broke up and it had to contend with the sometimes restrictive press rules of the new governments. It needed a new twist to remain profitable.

Reuters gained non-US rights to Ultronic Systems Corporation's electronic stock reporting system, Stockmaster, in 1964. The company's return to financial reporting had begun. In 1973, after currency exchange rates began to float, Reuters launched its Monitor electronic marketplace, which kept track of the foreign exchange market. Monitor Dealing, introduced in 1981, enabled dealers to trade currencies online.

With computer-based businesses dominating its general news services, Reuters went public in 1984 as Reuters Holdings PLC. Since then the company has acquired numerous online related services and gone into multimedia.

In this effort it has been so successful that in 1993 it unloaded some of its cash in a stock repurchase program and went on a buying spree that included leading bank Citicorp's real-time news and stock quote vendor, Quotron. Reuters formed an agricultural information service with US co-op Farmland Industries in 1994.

In 1995 Reuters teamed up with satellite TV programmer British Sky Broadcasting (BSkyB) to increase the news quality of BSkyB's Sky News Channel. In 1996 the company launched Business Briefing for Macintosh, a business information service for users of Apple computers.

Chairman: Sir Christopher A. Hogg, age 59, £75,000 pay
CEO: Peter J. D. Job, age 54, £650,000 pay
Finance Director: Robert O. Rob Rowley, age 46, £408,000 pay
Editor-in-Chief: Mark W. Wood, age 43, £343,000 pay
Director, Marketing and Technical Policy: David G. Ure, age 48, £440,000 pay
Director of Personnel and Quality Programmes: Patrick A. V. Mannix, age 53
Company Secretary: Simon A. Yeancken
President, Reuters America: Andre Villeneuve, age 51
Auditors: Price Waterhouse LLP

WHERE

HQ: 85 Fleet St., London, EC4P 4AJ, UK
Phone: +44-171-250-1122
Fax: +44-171-510-5896
US HQ: Reuters America Inc., 1700 Broadway, New York, NY 10019
US Phone: 212-603-3300
US Fax: 212-247-0346
Web site: http://www.reutersnm.com

	1995 Sales	
	$ mil.	% of total
Europe, Middle East & Africa	2,285	55
Asia/Pacific	761	18
Americas	646	15
Worldwide (Instinet)	377	9
Worldwide (Teknekron)	119	3
Total	**4,188**	**100**

WHAT

	1995 Sales	
	$ mil.	% of total
Information products	2,911	70
Transaction products	1,040	25
Media products	237	5
Total	**4,188**	**100**

Selected Products

Information
2000 Series (data feeds to financial markets and software tools to analyze data)
Teknekron (data management software for subscribers)
Triarch (data management software for subscribers)

Transaction
Dealing 2000-1 (transaction service)
GLOBEX (after-hours future exchange)
Instinet (electronic brokering service)

Media
Graphics
Online services
Television
Textual information

KEY COMPETITORS

ADP	Electronic	NYSE
Agence France-	Broking	New York Times
Presse	Service	News Corp.
AMEX	Global Financial	Quick Corp.
Associated Press	Information	Telekurs A.G.
Bloomberg	Knight-Ridder	Times Mirror
Bowne	McGraw-Hill	Tribune
Citicorp	Minex	UPI
CSK	Misys	
Dow Jones	NASD	

HOW MUCH

Nasdaq symbol: RTRSY (ADR) FYE: December 31	Annual Growth	1986	1987	1988	1989	1990	1991	1992	1993	1994	1995
Sales ($ mil.)	18.3%	921	1,409	1,815	1,948	2,642	2,742	2,374	2,773	3,614	4,188
Net income ($ mil.)	20.6%	119	177	241	296	400	429	395	442	543	642
Income as % of sales	—	12.9%	12.6%	13.3%	15.2%	15.1%	15.7%	16.6%	16.0%	15.0%	15.3%
Earnings per share ($)	20.7%	0.44	0.21	0.88	1.19	1.44	1.54	1.41	1.38	1.02	2.39
Stock price – high ($)	—	12.72	22.72	15.31	26.13	35.56	29.06	34.56	42.56	48.38	58.88
Stock price – low ($)	—	7.56	10.44	11.56	14.13	16.06	17.88	27.19	27.69	38.94	36.38
Stock price – close ($)	18.0%	12.47	13.84	14.19	24.81	20.25	28.88	31.88	39.50	43.88	55.13
P/E – high	—	29	108	17	22	25	19	25	27	47	25
P/E – low	—	17	50	13	12	11	12	19	17	38	15
Dividends per share ($)	31.0%	0.10	0.35	0.24	0.28	0.41	0.45	0.54	0.61	0.66	1.14
Book value per share ($)	21.0%	0.96	1.26	1.76	2.39	3.68	4.63	4.49	3.47	14.72	5.33
Employees	8.6%	6,852	9,586	10,064	10,071	10,731	10,450	10,393	11,306	12,718	14,348

1995 YEAR-END

Debt ratio: 21.2%
Return on equity: 50.4%
Cash (mil.): $820
Current ratio: 1.39
Long-term debt (mil.): $209
No. of shares (mil.): 280
Dividends
 Yield: 2.1%
 Payout: 47.6%
Market value (mil.): $15,407

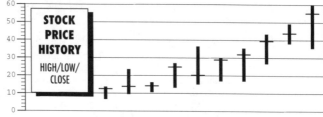

STOCK PRICE HISTORY HIGH/LOW/CLOSE

1986 1987 1988 1989 1990 1991 1992 1993 1994 1995

R. R. DONNELLEY & SONS COMPANY

OVERVIEW

Is print dying? Has the proliferation of electronic products made books, magazines, and even mail-order catalogs obsolete? Chicago-based R. R. Donnelley & Sons is betting that it's not; but it's also hedging that bet with investments in electronic goods and services. As the world's largest printer, Donnelley prints the *National Enquirer* and *Star* tabloids and 15 million copies of the *Reader's Digest* US edition each month. At the same time it is one of the largest reproducers and distributors of software (its Stream International affiliate handled the launch of Microsoft's Windows 95). Donnelley believes that print and electronic media are complementary and that each creates demand for the other.

The company is meeting those demands by restructuring itself along 4 product lines: commercial printing (its traditional business), global commercial printing (its traditional business, practiced outside the US), information management (book and directory publishing, financial printing, and information management consulting), and Stream International. This reorganization entails both plant openings and closings, but the new plants are more automated and these shifts will entail a net loss of jobs.

The restructuring, which began in 1995, also included the creation of new products like WebDirect, an Internet database publishing system. The firm also formed a new subsidiary, Donnelley Enterprise Solutions, to provide integrated information management services. Descendants of founder R. R. Donnelley own 17.5% of the company.

WHEN

In 1864 Richard Robert Donnelley, a Canadian printer, joined Chicago publishers Edward Goodman and Leroy Church. Their partnership became the Lakeside Publishing and Printing Co. in 1870. Lakeside produced a variety of periodicals and some of the first inexpensive paperback books. The Lakeside Building was destroyed in the 1871 Chicago fire, but by 1873 it had reopened.

By 1877 Lakeside no longer existed, but its paperback subsidiary survived as Donnelley, Loyd & Co. Donnelley bought out his partners in 1879 and separated the printing component (reorganized as R. R. Donnelley & Sons in 1882) from publishing (Chicago Directory Co.). Chicago Directory became the Reuben H. Donnelley Corp. (1916), named for a Donnelley son. In 1961 Dun & Bradstreet bought Reuben H. Donnelley Corp.

By 1900 Donnelley was printing telephone books and the Montgomery Ward catalog. It began printing the *Encyclopaedia Britannica* in 1910. In 1927 it won the contract to print *Time*. The company's innovation in high-speed printing was a major factor in Henry Luce's 1936 decision to begin *Life*.

For most of Donnelley's history, family members have served as chairman and president. An in-law, Charles Haffner (chairman, 1952-64), took the company public in 1956. The first outsider to become chairman was Charles Lake (1975).

During the 1980s Donnelley developed the Selectronic process, which tailors magazines and catalogs to small target audiences. In 1987 it bought Metromail, the largest US mailing-list business. In the past 2 decades the company has moved into international markets, acquiring printing companies in France, Japan, Ireland, Mexico, Singapore, and the UK. It also increased the range of products available in some countries. Amid all the expansion, there were closures as well — the Southside Chicago plant, its oldest, was shuttered in 1993 when Sears discontinued its general-merchandise catalogs.

In 1995, to further expand capacity, Donnelley merged its software operations with Corporate Software to form Stream International, a mail-order software services company. This business handled the duplication and distribution of disks for the worldwide launch of Microsoft's Windows 95 operating system and also provided the customer services that fielded buyers' inquiries about the system's intricacies.

The company's international expansion also continued that year, when Donnelley began placing special emphasis on global regions where there are few giant competitors. These efforts included expansion of its capacity in Chile and Poland (through joint ventures), the opening of a printing plant in China, and the acquisition of a 25% interest in the printing operations of India's industrial giant, Tata.

In 1996 Donnelley announced that it would take its Metromail subsidiary public, partly to pay down debt. That unit came under fire in 1996 when it was charged that its database contained confidential information derived from voter registration lists.

Chairman and CEO: John R. Walter, age 49,
$1,455,000 pay
VC: James R. Donnelley, age 60
EVP; Sector President, Commercial Print: Jonathan P.
Ward, age 41, $564,444 pay
EVP; Sector President, Information Management:
W. Ed Tyler, age 43, $493,889 pay
EVP; CEO, Stream International Holdings, Inc.: Rory J.
Cowan, age 43, $473,241 pay
EVP; Sector President, Global Commercial Print:
Steven J. Baumgartner, age 44, $458,611 pay
EVP and CFO: Cheryl A. Francis, age 42
SVP and General Counsel: T. J. Quarles, age 46
SVP Human Resources: Ann Weiser, age 38
Auditors: Andersen Worldwide

WHERE

HQ: 77 W. Wacker Dr., Chicago, IL 60601-1696
Phone: 312-326-8000
Fax: 312-326-8543
Web site: http://www.rrdonnelley.com

	1995 Sales	
	$ mil.	% of total
US	5,503	84
Other countries	1,018	16
Adjustments	(9)	—
Total	**6,512**	**100**

WHAT

	1995 Sales	
	$ mil.	% of total
Global software services	1,433	22
Catalogs	1,337	21
Magazines	1,235	19
Books	783	12
Directories	631	10
International commercial	345	5
Financial printing	334	5
Other	414	6
Total	**6,512**	**100**

Operations

Commercial Printing
Catalogs and other promotional materials
Magazines
Telephone and other directories

Information Resources
Design services
Digital printing
Mailing list and database development and management
Online services

Global Commercial Printing
Books
Financial documents (offerings and related discounts)
Stream International (80%, software manufacture and
marketing)

KEY COMPETITORS

ADVO	Graphic	Sullivan
Banta	Industries	Communications
Bertelsmann	Merrill Corp.	Taylor Corp.
Big Flower Press	Moore	U S WEST Media
Bowne	NYNEX	Valassis
Cadmus	Quad/Graphics	Communications
Communications	Quebecor	Volt Information
Courier	Ringier	World Color Press
Dun & Bradstreet		

HOW MUCH

NYSE symbol: DNY FYE: December 31	Annual Growth	1986	1987	1988	1989	1990	1991	1992	1993	1994	1995
Sales ($ mil.)	12.6%	2,233	2,482	2,878	3,122	3,497	3,914	4,193	4,387	4,888	6,512
Net income ($ mil.)	7.3%	158	218	205	222	226	205	235	179	269	299
Income as % of sales	—	7.1%	8.8%	7.1%	7.1%	6.5%	5.2%	5.6%	4.1%	5.5%	4.6%
Earnings per share ($)	7.5%	1.02	1.40	1.32	1.43	1.46	1.32	1.51	1.16	1.75	1.95
Stock price – high ($)	—	20.00	22.69	19.38	25.63	26.31	25.56	33.75	32.75	32.50	41.25
Stock price – low ($)	—	14.72	12.75	14.94	17.13	17.06	19.44	23.75	26.13	26.88	28.88
Stock price – close ($)	11.0%	15.38	16.31	17.31	25.63	19.88	25.00	32.75	31.13	29.50	39.38
P/E – high	—	20	16	15	18	18	19	22	28	19	21
P/E – low	—	14	9	11	12	12	15	16	23	15	15
Dividends per share ($)	8.7%	0.32	0.35	0.39	0.44	0.48	0.50	0.51	0.54	0.60	0.68
Book value per share ($)	8.7%	6.45	7.45	8.17	9.28	10.30	11.14	11.93	11.96	12.47	13.70
Employees	7.9%	20,600	22,000	24,500	26,100	27,500	29,100	30,400	32,100	39,000	41,000

1995 YEAR-END

Debt ratio: 42.6%
Return on equity: 14.4%
Cash (mil.): $33
Current ratio: 1.69
Long-term debt (mil.): $1,561
No. of shares (mil.): 159
Dividends
  Yield: 1.7%
  Payout: 34.9%
Long-term debt (mil.): $6,246

STOCK PRICE HISTORY HIGH/LOW/CLOSE

1986 1987 1988 1989 1990 1991 1992 1993 1994 1995

SONY CORPORATION

OVERVIEW

For all of Sony's vaunted technical know-how, the company has suffered some embarrassing setbacks in recent years. Echoing a similar situation from 2 decades earlier (when Tokyo-based Sony's superior Betamax VCR tape technology was outmarketed by electronics rival Godzilla Matsushita's VHS system), Sony has lost out in a compact-disc format war to another competitor, Toshiba. Several product launches have also fizzled in the 1990s (such as the Sony Data Discman, a portable CD player that displays text and audio from reference books). Worse, expansion into the entertainment market has cost the company a fortune. Part of Sony's $3.3 billion loss in 1995 was its $2.7 billion write-off from its 1989 acquisition of Columbia Pictures.

Sony's electronic products, which include audio and video equipment, semiconductors, and televisions, account for nearly 60% of its sales. Its entertainment assets include Columbia Pictures and Tri-Star Pictures film studios and Columbia and Epic records.

Company veteran Noboyuki Idei was appointed president in 1995 and forced the resignation of 21-year veteran Michael Schulhof, president of Sony Corp. of America. Undeterred by setbacks, Sony is expanding its product development. Idei is pushing Sony into the communications and computer fields with moves including the introduction of a line of PCs. Among other high-tech products under development have been multimedia eyeglasses (wireless projection of TV images and data on eyeglasses), net-ready televisions (TV screens that double as computer monitors), online stereo systems, Web appliances (stripped-down PCs and handheld personal assistants that access the World Wide Web), and digital cellular telephones (in collaboration with telecommunications equipment maker Qualcomm).

WHEN

Akio Morita, Masaru Ibuka, and Tamon Maeda, Ibuka's father-in-law, established Tokyo Telecommunications Engineering in 1946 with funding from Morita's father's sake business. Determined to innovate and create new markets, the company produced the first Japanese tape recorder (1950).

In 1953 Morita paid Western Electric (US) $25,000 for transistor technology licenses - a move that sparked a consumer electronics revolution in Japan. His company launched one of the first transistor radios in 1955, followed by the first Sony-trademarked product, a pocket-sized radio, in 1957. The company changed its name to Sony in 1958, taking it from "sonus," the Latin word for "sound." It introduced the first transistor TV (1959) and the first solid-state videotape recorder (1961). Sony preempted the competition, becoming a leader in these newly emerging markets.

Morita moved to New York in 1960 to oversee US expansion. Sony launched the first home video recorder (1964), solid-state condenser microphone (1965), and integrated circuit-based radio (1966). Sony's 1968 introduction of the Trinitron color TV tube began another decade of explosive growth. However, its Betamax VCR (1976) fell prey to products employing rival Matsushita's VHS technology. The Walkman (1979), in all its forms, was another Sony success.

By 1980 Sony faced an appreciating yen and intense price and quality competition, especially from developing Far Eastern countries. The company used its technology to diversify outside consumer electronics, and it began to move production to other countries to reduce the effects of currency fluctuations. In the 1980s Sony introduced Japan's first 32-bit workstation and became a major producer of computer chips and floppy disk drives. It also developed compact disc technology in partnership with Dutch electronics innovator Philips.

Sony acquired CBS Records from CBS for $2 billion in 1988 and Columbia Pictures from Coca-Cola in 1989 for $4.9 billion. The purchases made Sony a major force in the rapidly growing entertainment industry.

Sony manufactures Apple's wildly successful PowerBook and the portable CD-player Data Discman, a hit in Japan in 1991 that failed to take off in the US. In 1992 Sony allied with SEGA to develop CD video games and with Microsoft to make electronic audio/video/textbooks. Morita suffered a brain hemorrhage in 1993 but recovered after surgery; he resigned in 1994.

The company made plans in 1995 to enter the crowded computer market. It teamed up with software maker Intel to develop a line of PC desktop systems that went on sale in 1996. Sony is also developing a new software operating system — combining computers with audio, video, and networking capabilities. For its fiscal 1996 it reported earnings of $513 million on revenue of $43.5 billion.

Honorary Chairman: Akio Morita
Chairman and CEO: Norio Ohga, age 65
VC: Tsunao Hashimoto
President and COO: Nobuyuki Idei, age 58
Executive Deputy President and Chief Technology Officer: Minoru Morio
Executive Deputy President: Kozo Ohsone
Executive Deputy President: Yoshiyuki Kaneda
Executive Deputy President: Tamotsu Iba
CEO, Sony Corp. of America: Ted Kawai
CFO, Sony Corp. of America: S. Kober
Director Human Resources, Sony Corp. of America: Michael Mimnaugh
President, Sony Electronics, Inc. (US): Carl Yankowski
Auditors: Price Waterhouse LLP

WHERE

HQ: 7-35 Kitashinagawa 6-chome, Shinagawa-ku, Tokyo, 141, Japan
Phone: +81(03)5448-2111
Fax: +81(03)5448-2244
US HQ: Sony Corp. of America, 550 Madison Ave., 33rd Fl., New York, NY 10022-3211
US Phone: 212-833-6849
US Fax: 212-833-6938
Web site: http://www.sony.co.jp

	1995 Sales	
	$ mil.	% of total
US	12,945	29
Japan	12,342	28
Europe	10,173	22
Other regions	9,298	21
Total	**44,758**	**100**

WHAT

	1995 Sales	
	$ mil.	% of total
Audio equipment	10,096	23
Televisions	7,962	18
Video equipment	7,765	17
Music Group	5,561	12
Pictures Group	3,165	7
Other products	10,209	23
Total	**44,758**	**100**

Selected Products

Audio Equipment	Entertainment
Audio systems	Movies
Audiotapes	Recorded music
Car navigation systems	TV shows
Televisions	**Other Products**
Color TVs	Cathode ray tubes
Hi-Vision TVs	Computers and peripherals
Monitors	Electronic components
	Home video game software
Video Equipment	Semiconductors
VCRs	Telephone and telecommunications equipment
Videotapes	

KEY COMPETITORS

Apple Computer	Hitachi	Packard Bell
AT&T Corp.	IBM	Philips
BASF	LG Group	Pioneer
Bertelsmann	Matsushita	Polygram
Blaupunkt	3M	Rank
Bose	MCA	Samsung
Canon	Motorola	Sanyo
Compaq	NEC	Sharp
Dell	News Corp.	Thomson SA
Fuji Photo	Nintendo	THORN EMI
Fujitsu	Nokia	Time Warner
Gateway 2000	Oki	Toshiba
Hewlett-Packard	Olivetti	Viacom

HOW MUCH

NYSE symbol: SNE FYE: March 31	Annual Growth	1986	1987	1988	1989	1990	1991	1992	1993	1994	1995
Sales ($ mil.)	23.3%	6,805	8,246	11,655	16,677	18,616	26,248	29,494	34,766	36,249	44,758
Net income ($ mil.)	—	345	257	268	549	650	832	905	316	149	(3,296)
Income as % of sales	—	5.1%	3.1%	2.3%	3.3%	3.5%	3.2%	3.1%	0.9%	0.4%	—
Earnings per share ($)	—	1.25	0.95	1.05	1.65	1.76	1.85	2.21	0.80	0.41	(7.83)
Stock price – high ($)[1]	—	—	21.36	36.59	53.18	59.77	55.90	49.88	38.00	50.63	63.25
Stock price – low ($)[1]	—	—	16.48	16.59	32.16	45.22	36.59	31.38	28.25	32.00	49.38
Stock price – close ($)[1]	14.8%	—	18.63	34.31	52.61	54.99	39.09	34.63	34.13	49.88	56.13
P/E – high	—	—	23	35	32	34	30	23	48	124	—
P/E – low	—	—	17	16	20	26	20	14	35	78	—
Dividends per share ($)	13.3%	0.14	0.19	0.25	0.27	0.25	0.27	0.29	0.34	0.39	0.43
Book value per share ($)	11.8%	11.14	14.60	19.28	21.25	27.44	28.11	30.97	32.99	34.54	30.28
Employees	13.3%	44,900	48,700	60,500	78,900	95,600	112,900	119,000	126,000	130,000	138,000

1995 YEAR-END

Debt ratio: 57.8%
Return on equity: —
Cash (mil.): $5,343
Current ratio: 1.33
Long-term debt (mil.): $10,185
No. of shares (mil.): 374
Dividends
  Yield: 0.8%
  Payout: —
Market value (mil.): $20,986

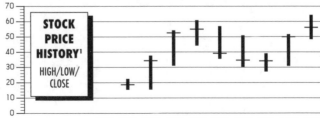

STOCK PRICE HISTORY[1] HIGH/LOW/CLOSE

1986 1987 1988 1989 1990 1991 1992 1993 1994 1995

[1]Stock Prices are for the prior calendar year

TCI COMMUNICATIONS, INC.

OVERVIEW

John Malone is no ordinary cable guy. Under his leadership, Tele-Communications, Inc. (TCI) and its subsidiaries have become the largest cable company in the US, serving about 12.5 million customers, and rapidly moving into other media. The passage of the Telecom Act in 1996 initiated a no-holds-barred battle royal between cable, Internet, telephone, digital TV, and satellite companies. Englewood, Colorado-based TCI is a holding company run by Malone that controls several other companies including TCIC Communications (domestic cable) and Tele-Communications International (overseas operations), which are separately traded companies.

The company is positioning itself to be an all-purpose information provider, from the Internet to *I Love Lucy*. It boosted its cable rates in 1995 to pay for system upgrades such as implementing fiber-optic cables and preparing for the switch to digital for clearer picture and sound. Many of these promised advancements have been slow in coming because of the costs of their implementation. Denver is one of the few cities where the firm is already laying fiber-optic lines to carry digital programming.

The company is also preparing to advance into wireless and wireline telephone services. Through a joint venture with fellow cable giants Comcast and Cox Communications and long-distance provider Sprint, the company planned to offer phone service in certain areas of the country in 1996.

WHEN

Tele-Communications, Inc., began in 1956 when rancher Bob Magness sold some cattle to build his first cable TV system in the Texas Panhandle. In 1965 he moved the company to Denver to serve small Rocky Mountain towns.

TCI went public in 1970 just as the capital-intensive cable TV industry was taking off. Magness hired 32-year-old John Malone in 1973. The deal-making Malone stabilized the company and extended its reach. His first battle was with the city of Vail, Colorado, over services and rates. For one weekend Malone showed nothing on the cable system but the names and phone numbers of city officials. The city backed down.

In 1977 Malone restructured TCI's debt. He then sat out the bidding for big-city franchises and bought them later at hefty discounts after bigger competitors stumbled.

After deregulation in 1984, TCI bought more than 150 cable companies in the late 1980s. In 1986 it won control of movie theater operator United Artists Communications (later UAE). TCI purchased Heritage Communications in 1987.

Cable programmers kept prices low to curry favor with the giant TCI. Malone, recognizing that his systems needed a variety of programming, financed nascent channels in exchange for stock. He helped save debt-plagued Turner Broadcasting in 1987; TCI came away with substantial Turner stock. TCI also invested in Black Entertainment Television (1979), Discovery Channel (1986), and American Movie Classics (1987).

In a complex 1991 transaction, TCI spun off its interests in QVC Network (shopping), other networks, and various cable systems as Liberty Media, with Malone as chairman and principal shareholder. That same year TCI, Baby Bell U S WEST, and AT&T began testing video on demand in Denver.

Also in 1991 UAE became a wholly owned subsidiary of TCI, which sold the UAE theater division in 1992 and kept the cable division. TCI acquired 49.9% of Teleport Communications Group, a specialized telecommunications services company and competitor of regional telephone companies, in 1992.

Despite much-publicized merger preparations with Bell Atlantic in late 1993 and early 1994, TCI went its own way. In 1994 TCI and Comcast Corp. bought the 65% of QVC that they didn't already own.

The company entered the telephony market in a big way when the FCC auctioned the next generation of telephone services in 1995 (30-MHz licenses for personal communications service). TCI's partnership gained licenses for 29 of the 51 major trading areas auctioned. That same year TCI restructured into 4 separate business units: domestic cable (TCIC), programming (Liberty Media), new technology (TCI Technology Ventures), and overseas operations (Tele-Communications International).

In 1995 TCIC potentially added another 1.2 million cable subscribers to its ranks when it agreed to purchase broadcasting peer Viacom's cable systems.

TCIC planned to introduce @Home in 1996, a service that uses cable modems as a conduit for high-speed Internet access as well as other online services.

WHO

Chairman: Bob Magness, age 72, $850,000 pay
President and CEO: John C. Malone, age 55, $853,758 pay
EVP; Chairman and CEO, Tele-Communications International, Inc.: Fred A. Víerra, age 64, $653,207 pay
EVP; President and CEO, TCI Communications, Inc.: Brendan R. Clouston, age 43, $553,181 pay
EVP; President, TCI Technology Ventures, Inc.: Larry Romrell, age 57
EVP, General Counsel, and Secretary: Stephen M. Brett, age 56
SVP Finance and Treasurer, TCI Communications, Inc.: Brendan W. Schotters, age 51
SVP: Camille K. Jayne, age 44
Auditors: KPMG Peat Marwick LLP

WHERE

HQ: 5619 DTC Pkwy., Englewood, CO 80111-3000
Phone: 303-267-5500
Fax: 303-779-1228
Web site: http://www.tcinc.com

	1995 Cable Subscribers No. (mil.)
Great Lakes division	4.2
West division	2.7
Central division	2.5
Southeast division	2.5
Other holdings	0.6
Total	**12.5**

Regional Operating Divisions and Markets Served

Great Lakes (Connecticut, Illinois, Indiana, Kentucky, Maine, Massachusetts, Michigan, Minnesota, New Hampshire, New Jersey, New York, Ohio, Pennsylvania, Rhode Island, Vermont, West Virginia, and Wisconsin)

West (Arizona, California, Idaho, Nevada, Montana, Oregon, Utah, and Washington)

Central (Colorado, Kansas, Nebraska, New Mexico, North Dakota, Oklahoma, South Dakota, Texas, and Wyoming)

Southeast (Alabama, Arkansas, Delaware, District of Columbia, Florida, Georgia, Iowa, Louisiana, Maryland, Mississippi, Missouri, North Carolina, South Carolina, Tennessee, and Virginia)

WHAT

Types of Service Offered

Basic service (local broadcast signals and public, educational, and governmental access channels)
Expanded service (specialized programming services in such areas as health, family entertainment, religion, news, weather, public affairs, education, shopping, sports, and music)
Premium service (pay-per-view feature films and live and taped sports events and concerts

KEY COMPETITORS

Adelphia Communications	Comcast Cox Communications	SBC Communications
Advance Publications	DIRECTV	Sprint TCA Cable
Ameritech	GTE	Teledesic
AT&T Corp.	Marcus Cable	Time Warner
Bell Atlantic	MCI	United States Satellite
BellSouth	NYNEX	Broadcasting
Cablevision Systems	Pacific Telesis Rogers	U S WEST Communications
Century Communications	Communications	U S WEST Media

HOW MUCH

Nasdaq symbol: TCOMA FYE: December 31	Annual Growth	1986	1987	1988	1989	1990	1991	1992	1993	1994	1995
Sales ($ mil.)	20.3%	973	3,016	4,284	3,026	3,625	3,827	3,574	4,153	4,936	5,118
Net income ($ mil.)	—	95	6	56	(257)	(287)	(102)	(34)	(7)	55	(120)
Income as % of sales	—	9.7%	0.2%	1.3%	—	—	—	—	—	1.1%	—
Earnings per share ($)	—	0.31	0.02	0.16	(0.73)	(0.81)	(0.28)	(0.12)	(0.02)	0.09	—
Stock price – high ($)	—	9.72	14.81	13.88	21.38	18.50	17.50	22.00	33.25	30.25	26.25
Stock price – low ($)	—	5.88	8.09	10.31	12.81	8.38	11.63	15.38	17.50	18.25	16.63
Stock price – close ($)	11.2%	7.63	11.81	13.06	17.88	13.25	17.00	21.25	30.25	21.75	19.88
P/E – high	—	20	—	87	—	—	—	—	—	336	—
P/E – low	—	19	—	64	—	—	—	—	—	203	—
Dividends per share ($)	—	0.00	0.00	0.00	0.00	0.00	0.00	0.00	0.00	0.00	0.00
Book value per share ($)	(2.7%)	2.44	2.40	3.41	2.54	1.74	3.44	3.46	4.70	0.78	1.91
Employees	9.1%	14,800	22,000	28,300	34,000	33,000	33,000	22,000	24,000	32,000	32,500

1995 YEAR-END

Debt ratio: 88%
Return on equity: —
Cash (mil.): $0
Current ratio: 0.24
Long-term debt (mil.): $12,635
No. of shares (mil.): 906
Dividends
  Yield: —
  Payout: —
Long-term debt (mil.): $18,009

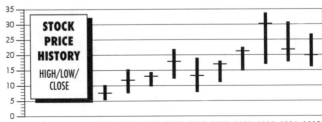

STOCK PRICE HISTORY HIGH/LOW/CLOSE 1986 1987 1988 1989 1990 1991 1992 1993 1994 1995

GRUPO TELEVISA, S.A.

OVERVIEW

Billionaire Emilio Azcárraga Milmo might well be shouting "¡Viva Televisa!" As chairman of Grupo Televisa, the Spanish-speaking world's largest media enterprise, Azcárraga oversees the Mexico City-based company's interests in television and radio production and broadcasting, magazine publishing, music recording, movie production, and other communications services.

Televisa is the world's largest producer of Spanish-language programs and, with its 4 TV networks (broadcasting to about 300 stations including 240 wholly owned by the company), it controls a whopping 80% of the broadcast TV audience share in Mexico. The company also has an interest in Univision, a US Spanish-language media firm whose television network reaches 90% of US Spanish-speaking households. Through a partnership with the US's #1

cable TV provider, Tele-Communications Inc. (TCI), Televisa will run a satellite TV service.

The company is also the world's largest publisher of Spanish-language magazines (including Spanish-language versions of *Cosmopolitan* and *Good Housekeeping*), with more than 50 titles. The firm's 3 record labels comprise one of Mexico's top 5 recording companies.

With its home turf (about 80% of its sales are in Mexico) still reeling from the peso's mid-1990s plunge, Televisa plans to extend its television operations throughout the world, by increasing international sales and forming joint ventures in new markets. To improve its focus on creating entertainment programming, Televisa is divesting some of its lesser operations, reflected in the 1995 sale of 49% of its cable TV businesses to telephone giant Teléfonos de México (Telmex).

WHEN

In 1930 Emilio Azcárraga Vidaurreta (father of the current chairman Emilio Azcárraga Milmo) founded one of the first radio stations in Mexico. During the 1950s Azcárraga was granted a license to operate a television channel in Mexico City and other TV stations throughout the country. At the time, Rómulo O'Farrill Sr. also won a license to operate a TV station in the capital. Their respective companies grew during the 1960s, and in 1973 they joined (with investor Miguel Alemán) to form Televisa.

The new company operated the TV stations as well as provided programming and advertising sales. During its initial year the company became the first Western television broadcaster to transmit live from China. In 1978 Televisa started producing feature films for markets in Mexico and abroad and made international broadcasts covering the Pope's 1979 visit to Mexico City. In addition to producing programming and operating its own stations, Televisa managed its founders' cable TV and music recording businesses. The company also managed a regional TV network, which it bought in 1982.

Televisa started Video Visa in 1985 to distribute and sell prerecorded videocassettes; the business was sold as part of a company reorganization in 1991. Under that restructuring, Televisa became a holding company for the founders' private businesses, which they sold to the broadcaster in exchange for stock. In addition, that year Televisa acquired a stake in Chile's #3 TV network Red Televisa Megavisión. Televisa went public in 1991.

The next year Televisa purchased a 50% interest in the PanAmSat global satellite communications network and launched its Skytel Mexico-wide paging service with US-based Mobile Telecommunications Technologies. Also in 1992 Televisa bought a minority stake in Univision. The Mexican government privatized the Televisión Azteca network in 1993, giving Televisa its first taste of competition for the country's TV broadcast market.

An economic crisis rocked Mexico in 1994, devaluating the national currency, increasing inflation, raising interest rates, elevating unemployment, and decreasing consumer purchasing power — all of which hurt company performance. That year Televisa sold its 76% interest in Compañía Peruana de Radiodifusión (Peruvian TV stations) but also got the legal go-ahead to develop 67 TV stations in Mexico City and elsewhere.

In 1995 Televisa started operating 2 English-language TV stations on the Mexico-Texas border. That year the company's satellite telecommunications provider, PanAmSat, went public, though Televisa kept a 40% interest. During an 18-month period ending at the close of 1995, Televisa pared its staff by 12% (nearly 3,000 positions) and took a charge of $30 million for the restructuring.

A rocket carrying a satellite for Televisa's satellite TV system exploded in 1996, postponing the start of its direct-to-home service in Mexico. That year the company named Emilio Azcárraga Jean (the chairman's son) COO.

Chairman and President: Emilio Azcárraga Milmo
VC: Alejandro Burillo Azcárraga
EVP and COO: Emilio Azcárraga Jean
EVP and CFO: Guillermo Cañedo White
General Counsel: Francisco Javier Mondragón Alarcón
President of Information, International Relations, and Events: Emilio Diez Barroso Azcárraga
President of Music Recording: Guillermo R. Santizo
President of Newscasts: Jacobo Zabludovsky Kraves
President of Publishing: Laura Diez Barroso de Laviada
President of Radio: Ricardo Rocha Reynaga
President, Telesistema Mexicano: Felix Araujo Ramírez
Chairman and CEO, Univisa: Jaime Dávila
President, Univisa: Lawrence W. Dam
VP and Chief Accounting Officer: Raúl López Martínez
VP Corporate Communications: Miguel Alemán Magnani
VP Official, Legal, and International Affairs: Guillermo Cañedo de la Bárcena
VP Sales: Rafael de Haro Lebrija
VP Strategic Planning: Alejandro Reynoso del Valle
VP Television Stations: José Alberto Ciurana Macías
VP Human Resources: Alejandro Gayou Almada
Auditors: Coopers & Lybrand L.L.P.

WHERE

HQ: Av. Chapultepec 28, México, D.F. 06724, Mexico
Phone: +52-5-709-3333
Fax: +52-5-709-0448

Televisa licenses its TV programming in more than 75 countries.

WHAT

	1995 Sales	1995 Operating Income
	% of total	% of total
Television	55	48
Publishing	20	22
Audio	9	10
Cable television	5	14
Other	11	6
Total	**100**	**100**

Selected Operations
Cablevision (cable TV system)
Dubbing (translations of dialogs and scripts)
Film production
Magazine publishing (*Eres, Somos, Vanidades*)
Music recording (Discos y Cintas Melody, Fonovisa, and Musivisa)
PanAmSat (40.5%, satellite telecommunications)
Radio stations
Skytel (51%, paging service)
Soccer (2 professional teams)
Univision (minority interest, US-based Spanish-language TV)
Vendor, S.A. (37%, billboards)

Television Networks — Mexico City
Channel 2 (the Channel of the Stars, world's largest Spanish-language TV network)
Channel 4 (movies, sports, and other programming)
Channel 5 (cartoons, movies, and children's programming)
Channel 9 (news, comedies, variety shows, sports, and other programming)

KEY COMPETITORS

BMG	Televisión Azteca
Multivision	Time Warner
NBC	Viacom
Sprint	Westinghouse/CBS

HOW MUCH

NYSE symbol: TV (ADR) FYE: December 31	Annual Growth	1986	1987	1988	1989	1990	1991	1992	1993	1994	1995
Sales ($ mil.)	12.3%	—	—	—	571	750	923	1,355	1,670	760	1,148
Net income ($ mil.)	—	—	—	—	(25)	(163)	106	608	26	(54)	64
Income as % of sales	—	—	—	—	—	—	11.5%	44.9%	1.6%	—	5.6%
Earnings per share ($)	(19.1%)	—	—	—	—	—	0.14	0.66	0.03	(0.30)	0.06
Stock price – high ($)	—	—	—	—	—	—	—	—	72.00	73.75	33.38
Stock price – low ($)	—	—	—	—	—	—	—	—	63.50	31.75	12.13
Stock price – close ($)	(43.3%)	—	—	—	—	—	—	—	70.00	42.75	22.50
P/E – high	—	—	—	—	—	—	—	—	—	—	—
P/E – low	—	—	—	—	—	—	—	—	—	—	—
Dividends per share ($)	—	—	—	—	—	—	—	—	—	—	—
Book value per share ($)	(6.5%)	—	—	—	—	—	—	—	0.95	0.75	0.83
Employees	2.9%	—	—	—	17,487	17,366	17,500	21,200	23,600	21,600	20,700

1995 YEAR-END

Debt ratio: 47.3%
Return on equity: 8.7%
Cash (mil.): $359
Current ratio: 2.50
Long-term debt (mil.): $752
No. of shares (mil.): 48
Dividends
  Yield: 0.3%
  Payout: 23.3%
Market value (mil.): $1,090

STOCK PRICE HISTORY HIGH/LOW/CLOSE
1986 1987 1988 1989 1990 1991 1992 1993 1994 1995

THE THOMSON CORPORATION

OVERVIEW

At work and play, the Thomson Corporation can serve your needs. One of the world's largest publishers of reference and trade materials, the Toronto-based company provides specialized information services (online, CD-ROM, newsletter, and reference materials) for a variety of businesses, including finance, law, health care, and auto repair. When its UK customers need some R&R, its travel group can whisk them off to faraway lands on its own airline or find them a cottage to rent at home.

Once a major publisher of local and regional newspapers throughout North America, the company has been shifting its media focus to electronic publishing. It has invested heavily in technology to remain competitive in the fast-growing electronic information field, and it has realigned its North American newspapers to boost circulation and, it hopes, advertising revenues. Thomson has announced plans to sell its regional UK papers and many of its Canadian dailies.

In 1996 Thomson Corp. bought law and textbook publisher West Publishing. West's annotation system for case citations is the standard, and West even claims copyrights over the decisions themselves. But some courts have begun publishing decisions over the Internet; if this becomes standard, West might lose its market position, which would impair its value. Chairman Kenneth Thomson controls 72% of the company's stock.

WHEN

After failing at farming and auto parts distribution, Roy Thomson left Toronto for the hinterlands of Ontario and started a radio station in 1930. Four years later he purchased the *Timmons Press*, a newspaper serving a gold-mining town. Frugal and bottom-line oriented, Thomson bought other small-town newspapers, venturing outside Ontario in 1949 and into the US in 1952. The Thomson Newspaper empire grew rapidly during the 1950s.

In 1953 Thomson moved to Great Britain, where he bought the *Scotsman*, an Edinburgh-based paper. When commercial TV broadcasting began in the UK, Thomson started Scottish Television Ltd. (1957) and merged it with the UK's Kemsley Newspapers, publisher of rural newspapers and the *Sunday Times*, to create International Thomson Organization in 1959.

International Thomson bought the *Times* of London (1967) and entered the travel business. Queen Elizabeth II conferred the title of Lord Thomson of Fleet upon Thomson in 1970. J. Paul Getty invited International Thomson into a North Sea oil drilling venture in 1971. The consortium struck oil in 1973, just as the OPEC oil embargo took hold. Oil accounted for the bulk of International Thomson's profits by 1976, when Lord Thomson died. His son, Kenneth, took over.

The company used its oil earnings to expand and diversify its publishing interests. It sold the *Times* to Rupert Murdoch's News Corporation in 1981, and it began shopping for specialty publishers with subscription-based (rather than advertising-based) revenues, which would be less vulnerable to recession. Purchases included American Banker and

Bond Buyer (financial publications, 1983), Gale Research (library reference materials, 1985), Associated Book Publishers (legal information, textbooks; 1987), Lawyers Cooperative Publishing (1989), and several online information providers. The company completed the sale of its oil and gas holdings a year later.

Thomson Newspapers and International Thomson merged to become the Thomson Corporation in 1989 and in 1991 bought Maxwell's Macmillan Professional and Business Reference Publishing. It then acquired JPT Publishing (databases, including the Institute for Scientific Information — the world's #1 commercial scientific research database). The spree continued in 1994 with the purchase of Information Access Company (a reference database service) from Ziff Communications as well as a developer of medical information databases.

Thomson Corp. said it would regroup its newspapers into regional clusters, and by the end of 1995 it had sold 19 Canadian newspapers to Hollinger Inc. and 12 daily newspapers in the US to American Publishing. That year the company's travel operations were hammered by a slowdown in UK vacation business attributable in part to the unusually warm weather, which prompted many people to summer at home. Also in 1995 the company closed its Thomson Learning unit (which targeted the school and library markets) because of the cancellation of a distribution contract by Wolters Kluwer.

In 1996 Thomson Corp. announced plans to sell 12 of its Canadian dailies for about $48 million.

Chairman and CEO: Kenneth R. Thomson,
$1,074,204 pay
President: W. Michael Brown, $2,440,000 pay
**EVP; President and CEO, Thomson Financial and
Professional Publishing Group:** Andrew G. Mills,
$3,307,500 pay
EVP; CEO, Thomson Corp. Publishing International: J.
Gordon Paul, $2,296,450 pay
EVP and CFO: Nigel R. Harrison, $1,528,881 pay
EVP; President and CEO, Thomson Newspapers:
Richard J. Harrington
EVP; Chairman and CEO, Thomson Travel Group: Paul
Brett
**SVP Human Resources, Thomson Corp. Publishing
International:** Bruce A. Hubler
Auditors: Price Waterhouse LLP

WHERE

HQ: Toronto Dominion Bank Tower, Ste. 2706. PO Box
24, Toronto Dominion Centre, Toronto, ON, M5K 1A1,
Canada
Phone: 416-360-8700
Fax: 416-360-8812
US HQ: The Metro Center, One Station Place, 6th Fl.,
Stamford, CT 06902
US Phone: 203-328-9400
US Fax: 203-328-9408
Web site: http://www.thomson.com

	1995 Sales		1995 Operating Income	
	$ mil.	% of total	$ mil.	% of total
UK	3,145	43	221	28
US	3,336	46	511	63
Canada	483	7	50	6
Other countries	261	4	27	3
Adjustments	—	—	(19)	—
Total	**7,225**	**100**	**790**	**100**

WHAT

	1995 Sales		1995 Operating Income	
	$ mil.	% of total	$ mil.	% of total
Info./publishing	3,600	50	524	65
Travel	2,375	33	98	12
Newspapers	1,250	17	187	23
Adjustments	—	—	(19)	—
Total	**7,225**	**100**	**790**	**100**

Selected Business Units

Thomson Information/Publishing Group
International Thomson Publishing (educational, vocational, technical publishing)
Thomson Business Information (database and reference
services)
Thomson Financial & Professional Publishing Group
(books, directories, online and CD-ROM publications
for law, tax, accounting, and financial professionals)

Thomson Travel Group (UK)
Britannia Airways
Holiday Cottages Group
Lunn Poly (travel agencies)
Thomson Tour Operations

Thomson Newspapers (daily and weekly papers throughout North America)

KEY COMPETITORS

Accor	Gannett	Pearson
American	HCIA	Rank
Business	Hearst	Reed Elsevier
Information	Hollinger Inc.	Thomas Cook
American Express	John Wiley	Times Mirror
Bloomberg	K-III	Tribune
Carlson	Knight-Ridder	United News &
Cox Enterprises	Lufthansa	Media
Dow Jones	Matsushita	Viacom
Dun & Bradstreet	McGraw-Hill	Wolters Kluwer
E.W. Scripps	News Corp.	W.W. Norton

HOW MUCH

Principal exchange: Toronto FYE: December 31	Annual Growth	1986[1]	1987[1]	1988[1]	1989	1990	1991	1992	1993	1994	1995
Sales ($ mil.)	7.0%	3,946	3,940	4,726	5,112	5,364	5,980	5,980	5,849	6,354	7,225
Net income ($ mil.)	13.2%	258	304	380	420	385	166	166	277	427	789
Income as % of sales	—	6.5%	7.7%	8.0%	8.2%	7.2%	2.8%	2.8%	4.7%	6.7%	10.9%
Earnings per share ($)	10.9%	0.53	0.66	0.80	0.78	0.70	0.53	0.30	0.48	0.74	1.34
Stock price – high ($)[2]	—	19.31	20.81	17.96	17.27	14.66	15.79	13.86	12.75	13.55	14.29
Stock price – low ($)[2]	—	13.17	13.55	15.12	13.60	11.21	12.12	9.54	10.39	10.52	12.00
Stock price – close ($)[2]	(2.8%)	18.04	16.54	16.43	14.36	14.66	13.85	11.21	12.28	12.21	13.92
P/E – high	—	—	—	—	22	21	30	46	27	18	11
P/E – low	—	—	—	—	17	16	23	32	22	14	9
Dividends per share ($)	15.9%	—	—	—	0.21	0.44	0.45	0.45	0.45	0.46	0.51
Book value per share ($)	—	—	—	—	—	—	—	—	—	—	—
Employees	1.7%	—	—	—	44,000	44,800	45,800	46,000	46,400	48,600	48,600

1995 YEAR-END

Debt ratio: 4.9%
Return on equity: 22.0%
Cash (mil.): $391
Current ratio: 1.18
Long-term debt (mil.): $3
No. of shares (mil.): 595
Dividends
  Yield: 3.7%
  Payout: 38.2%
Market value (mil.): $11,747

**STOCK PRICE HISTORY[2]
HIGH/LOW/CLOSE**

1986 1987 1988 1989 1990 1991 1992 1993 1994 1995

[1] Pro forma. [2] Adjusted prices of Thomson Newspapers, Ltd., common stock prior to 1989.

THORN EMI PLC

OVERVIEW

What recently split music and rental conglomerate was a thorn in the side of music business rivals Warner (owned by Time Warner), Polygram (Philips) and Sony? London-based THORN EMI, which operated 3 major businesses: EMI Music (recording and music publishing, 50% of total revenues), THORN (consumer goods rental stores), and HMV Group (music stores).

In 1996 the company separated into 2 publicly listed companies — EMI Group PLC (music businesses) and THORN PLC (other lines, including its rental and rent-to-purchase businesses). With a roster that includes Garth Brooks and the Rolling Stones, EMI remains a pain to its rivals.

Prior to the split, THORN EMI sold off nonentertainment subsidiaries (security and automation equipment concerns, UK electrical retailing, defense electronics, and sensor businesses) to focus on its 3 core businesses.

In 1994 THORN EMI expanded its share in a music recording and publishing venture with Toshiba. By 1995 EMI Music was operating 65 record labels (including Virgin and Capitol Records) and 23 music companies in 37 countries. The company opened 22 HMV stores that year, bringing the total of stores worldwide to 201. About 50% of HMV sales come from outside the UK.

WHEN

Jules Thorn founded the Electrical Lamp Service Company in London in 1928 to sell lamps he had imported from other parts of Europe. He acquired several radio and lamp companies and combined these into Thorn Electrical Industries in 1936.

After WWII Thorn diversified into appliances, electronics, and TV manufacturing. By the 1960s the company was the UK's largest radio and TV maker. It became the largest global TV rental company when it acquired Robinson Radio Rentals in the late 1960s.

Diversification continued in the 1970s as Thorn picked up a host of small companies. In 1979 it swallowed its biggest fish, struggling electronics and entertainment concern Electric & Musical Industries (EMI), for L165 million, becoming THORN EMI the following year.

EMI, established in 1931 as a successor to a 19th-century gramophone producer, had gradually expanded its operations to produce everything from radar systems during WWII to the first television system for the BBC. In 1954 the company acquired Capitol Records in the US and became a major force in the entertainment industry, signing such artists as the Beatles in the 1960s and Pink Floyd in the 1970s. In 1972 EMI released its new scanning X ray, which won global market leadership until it lost its technological edge and competitors' models made it obsolete.

For the next several years after the EMI purchase, each constituent company operated in isolation from the others. Colin Southgate became CEO in 1985 and refocused operations on 4 business sectors (music, technology, rental and retail, and lighting), selling everything that did not fit.

THORN EMI purchased US-based Rent-A-Center for $594 million in 1987. It acquired 50% of Chrysalis Records, whose artists included Pat Benatar and Jethro Tull, in 1989. In 1990 THORN EMI added Filmtrax music publishing (UK) and the 50% it did not own of SBK Record Productions, whose artists included Vanilla Ice and Wilson Phillips. That year the HMV stores unit opened the US's largest music store, in New York City.

In 1991 the company sold its European lightbulb operations to General Electric for $138 million and received approval from the British government to buy control of UK broadcasting company Thames Television.

The following year THORN EMI acquired Virgin Records, whose artists include Mick Jagger and Phil Collins, for $960 million, placing itself with Warner, Polygram, and Sony as one of the world's top music companies. It also purchased Sparrow, the US's largest Christian music company; Denmark's Medley Records; and the remaining 50% of Chrysalis.

The company sold its stake in Thames Television and its lighting division (upon which the company was founded) in 1993. During the next year THORN EMI's Central Research Laboratory subsidiary announced a "suspended image system" that projects a 3D-like image beyond a computer screen.

In 1995 the company acquired UK bookstore business Dillons, and in 1996 THORN EMI's Virgin label beat out several competitors when it signed singer Janet Jackson to an exclusive contract valued at $60-90 million. That year the company enjoyed blockbuster sales of the *Beatles Anthology* albums, and sales climbed above L5 billion.

Chairman: Sir Colin Southgate, age 56, £711,000 pay
President and CEO, EMI Music: James G. Fifield,
age 53, £6,661,000 pay
CEO, THORN: Michael E. Metcalf, age 43, £313,000 pay
Chairman and CEO, HMV Group: Stuart McAllister
Group Finance Director: Simon P. Duffy, age 45,
£293,000 pay
Director Human Resources: John Rayman
Auditors: Ernst & Young LLP

WHERE

HQ: 4 Tenterden St., Hanover Square, London,
W1A 2AY, UK
Phone: +44-171-355-4848
Fax: +44-171-355-1308
US HQ: THORN EMI Inc., 2751 Centerville Rd., Ste. 205,
Wilmington, DE 19808
US Phone: 302-994-4100
US Fax: 302-994-4299

	1995 Sales		1995 Operating Income	
	£ mil.	% of total	£ mil.	% of total
UK	1,371	30	109	24
North America	1,293	29	118	26
Other Europe	1,207	27	162	36
Asia/Pacific	525	12	56	12
Other regions	111	2	10	2
Total	**4,507**	**100**	**455**	**100**

	1995 Sales		1995 Operating Income	
	£ mil.	% of total	£ mil.	% of total
EMI Music	2,189	50	295	64
THORN	1,589	37	152	33
HMV	503	12	14	3
Other	47	1	(3)	—
Adjustments	178	—	(3)	—
Total	**4,507**	**100**	**455**	**100**

Selected Subsidiaries
EMI Music Group
Capitol Records Inc. (US)
Capitol-EMI Music Inc. (US)
Chrysalis Records Ltd.
Dillons
EMI Entertainment World Inc. (US)
EMI Music Publishing Ltd
EMI Records Ltd
HMV (music retailer)
Toshiba-EMI Ltd (55%, Japan)
Virgin Records Ltd

THORN
Consumer Electronics Insurance Company Ltd
Remco America Inc. (US)
THORN Americas Inc. (US)
Visea THORN EMI S.A. (France)

KEY COMPETITORS

Aaron Rents	Musicland	Viacom
Bertelsmann	PolyGram	Virgin Group
Best Buy	Sony	W H Smith
Camelot Music	Time Warner	Wherehouse
Hastings Books	Trans World	Entertainment
MCA	Music	
MTS		

HOW MUCH

OTC symbol: THE FYE: March 31	Annual Growth	1986	1987	1988	1989	1990	1991	1992	1993	1994	1995
Sales (£ mil.)	3.5%	3,317	3,203	3,054	3,291	3,716	3,571	3,660	4,452	4,292	4,507
Net income (£ mil.)	6.4%	61	100	138	182	204	230	85	205	223	107
Income as % of sales	—	1.9%	3.1%	4.5%	5.5%	5.5%	4.5%	4.0%	4.6%	5.2%	2.4%
Earnings per share (p)	10.6%	25	42	51	62	68	54	48	51	53	62
Stock price – high (p)[1]	—	464	506	796	646	859	790	793	888	1,017	1,617
Stock price – low (p)[1]	—	288	362	418	511	599	547	585	633	809	995
Stock price – close (p)[1]	16.5%	385	450	511	599	745	649	712	881	990	1,517
P/E – high	—	19	12	16	10	13	15	16	17	19	26
P/E – low	—	12	9	8	8	9	10	12	12	15	16
Dividends per share (p)	9.0%	17	18	21	26	29	29	30	32	34	37
Book value per share (p)	(4.4%)	231	249	201	182	205	189	160	111	172	154
Employees	(9.9%)	85,700	74,321	66,630	65,444	61,124	57,932	53,757	47,000	41,000	33,547

1995 YEAR-END

Debt ratio: 49.9%
Return on equity: 15.3%
Cash (mil.): £292
Long-term debt (mil.): £407
No. of shares (mil.): 428
Dividends
  Yield: 2.4%
  Payout: 59.0%
Market value (mil.): $10,051
Sales (mil.): $6,984

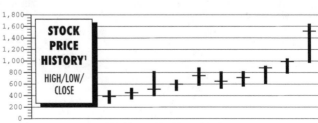

STOCK PRICE HISTORY[1]
HIGH/LOW/CLOSE

[1] Stock prices are for the prior calendar year. Note: £ = $1.60 (December 31, 1995)

TIME WARNER INC.

OVERVIEW

"Media through every medium" could be Time Warner's slogan. The New York City–based company operates in virtually every segment of the media industry (except newspapers), and it is the 2nd largest entertainment and information business in the world, after Walt Disney. Subsidiary Time Inc. operates the hulk's news and information division, which markets books, magazines (*FORTUNE, People, Sports Illustrated, Time*), music, and videos. Time Warner's Pathfinder Internet service delivers news and information via an "electronic newsstand" on the Internet.

Time Warner Entertainment (TWE) conducts the company's recording, movie, and TV production businesses. TWE also operates the Home Box Office (HBO) cable movie channel, consumer product licensing, computer game development, Internet programming, movie theater, pay television, and theme park businesses. Time Warner Cable leads the company's telecommunications operations, with about 11.7 million cable television subscribers in the US, making it the #2 multiple system operator in the nation (after TCI).

In 1996 Time Warner received government approval of its $6.5 billion purchase of Turner Broadcasting (CNN and other cable networks), allowing it to surpass Disney in size.

Other interests include a 50% stake in publisher DC Comics, 33% of the Courtroom Television Network, and 14% of toy maker Hasbro. In 1995 TWE sold 51% of its theme park operator, Six Flags Entertainment Corp. Also that year Time Warner sold its half of the Interscope Records "gangsta rap" music label following a highly emotional political debate about the distribution of music containing violent and sexually degrading lyrics. This and other problems led to turmoil in the Music Group, which culminated in the firing of division chairman Michael Fuchs.

WHEN

Time Warner came to life in 1989 when Time Inc. merged with Warner Communications Inc. Henry Luce had founded Time Inc. with Briton Hadden in 1922. Their first magazine, *Time*, summarized a week's worth of news. In the 1930s they added *FORTUNE, Life*, and other magazines. Luce, a controversial business manager, stepped down as editor-in-chief in 1964; he died in 1967.

During the 1970s and 1980s, Time Inc. explored new ventures. It entered the cable TV market with HBO (1972) and bought Book-of-the-Month Club (1977). In magazines, *Money* (1972) was a moderate success and *People* (1974) was a hit, but *TV-Cable Week* lasted only 5 months.

Warner Brothers, founded by Harry, Albert (Abe), Jack, and Sam Warner, was one of Hollywood's largest movie studios. It made such film classics as *Little Caesar* (1930), *Casablanca* (1942), and *Rebel Without a Cause* (1955). Sam died in 1927, Harry and Abe retired in 1951, and Jack remained until 1967, when Seven Arts Ltd. bought the studio. Steven Ross's Kinney National Services, owner of National Periodical Publications (*Superman* and *Batman* comics and *Mad* magazine), bought the studio in 1969.

Kinney sold the pre-1948 movies to United Artists and shared the studios with Columbia. The company changed its name to Warner Communications Inc. in 1972. During the late 1970s and early 1980s, video game subsidiary Atari (purchased in 1976) was the main revenue generator.

Under threat of a possible takeover, Time agreed to merge with Warner at a cost of $14 billion, most of it in debt. During the 1990s the new conglomerate launched magazines *Entertainment Weekly, Martha Stewart Living, In Style*, and *Vibe*. In 1992 the company created Time Warner Entertainment, a limited partnership for its film, music, and TV production businesses.

In 1993, shortly after Ross's death, Gerald Levin, former Time Inc. VC and one of the architects of the merger, became chairman. The Warner Books unit of Time Warner bought a stake in Hoover's, Inc., creator of this profile, in 1994. In 1995 Canadian spirits maker Seagram, the company's largest shareholder (14.5%), bought rival studio MCA. Also that year Time Warner launched the WB Network.

The company added 3 million cable subscribers in 1995 and 1996 through aquisitions. Congress's easing of telecommunications restrictions in 1996 led the company to seek further expansion of its cable TV and related operations. For approval of its purchase of Turner Broadcasting, Time Warner agreed to carry news channel MSNBC on half of its cable systems, in competition with CNN. It was a harsh blow to News Corp.'s start-up news channel.

Chairman and CEO: Gerald M. Levin, age 56, $5,050,000 pay
President: Richard D. Parsons, age 47, $2,825,000 pay
EVP, General Counsel, and Secretary: Peter R. Haje, age 61, $1,675,000 pay
SVP and CFO: Richard J. Bressler, age 38, $1,200,000 pay
SVP Communications and Public Affairs: Tod R. Hullin, age 52, $1,075,000 pay
SVP: Philip R. Lochner Jr., age 53
SVP: Timothy A. Boggs, age 45
President and CEO, Time Inc.: Don Logan
Editor-In-Chief, Time Warner Inc.: Norman Pearlstine
Chairman, President, and CEO, Home Box Office: Jeffrey L. Bewkes
Chairman and Co-CEO, Warner Bros. and Warner Music Group: Robert A. Daly
Chairman and Co-CEO, Warner Bros. and Warner Music Group: Terry S. Semel
Chairman and CEO, Time Warner Cable: Joseph J. Collins
VP Administration (HR): Carolyn McCandless
Auditors: Ernst & Young LLP

WHERE

HQ: 75 Rockefeller Plaza, New York, NY 10019
Phone: 212-484-8000
Fax: 212-956-2847
Web site: http://www.pathfinder.com/Corp

	1995 Sales		1995 Operating Income	
	$ mil.	% of total	$ mil.	% of total
Time Warner				
US	5,447	68	457	66
Europe	1,552	19	158	23
Pacific Rim	775	10	57	8
Other regions	293	3	25	3
Total	**8,067**	**100**	**697**	**100**

WHAT

	1995 Sales		1995 Operating Income	
	$ mil.	% of total	$ mil.	% of total
Time Warner				
Music	4,196	52	321	46
Publishing	3,722	46	381	54
Cable	172	2	(5)	—
Adjustments	(23)	—	—	—
Subtotal	**8,067**	**100**	**697**	**100**
Entertainment Group	9,629	100	992	100
Total	**17,696**	**—**	**1,689**	**—**

Selected Operations

Cable	*Sports Illustrated*
Time Warner Cable	*Time*
	Warner Books
Film	
Warner Bros.	**Other Interests**
WB Television (*ER*, *Friends*)	Courtroom Television Network (33%)
Music	DC Comics (50%)
Atlantic Recording Corp.	Six Flags Entertainment (49%)
Warner Bros. Records	
Publishing	Time Warner Entertainment Japan (37%)
Book-of-the-Month Club	
FORTUNE	Turner Broadcasting
People	

KEY COMPETITORS

Advance Publications	Gannett	News Corp.
Bertelsmann	Harcourt General	Polygram
Cablevision Systems	Hearst	Sony
Comcast	Marvel Entertainment	TCI
Cox Enterprises	MCA	Times Mirror
EMI	McGraw-Hill	Viacom
Forbes	MGM	Walt Disney
	NBC	Westinghouse/CBS

HOW MUCH

NYSE symbol: TWX FYE: December 31	Annual Growth	1986	1987	1988	1989	1990	1991	1992	1993[1]	1994	1995
Sales ($ mil.)	8.8%	3,762	4,193	4,507	7,642	11,517	12,021	13,070	6,581	7,396	8,067
Net income ($ mil.)	—	376	250	289	(256)	(227)	(99)	86	(164)	(91)	(124)
Income as % of sales	—	10.0%	6.0%	6.4%	—	—	—	0.7%	—	—	—
Earnings per share ($)	—	1.49	1.05	1.25	(1.09)	(3.42)	(2.40)	(1.46)	(0.75)	(0.27)	(0.46)
Stock price – high ($)	—	22.84	29.22	30.63	45.69	31.16	31.25	29.75	46.88	44.25	45.63
Stock price – low ($)	—	14.38	16.44	19.69	25.91	16.53	19.44	21.63	28.75	31.50	33.63
Stock price – close ($)	8.9%	17.50	20.56	26.75	30.16	21.44	21.88	29.25	44.25	35.13	37.75
P/E – high	—	15	28	25	—	—	—	—	—	—	—
P/E – low	—	10	16	16	—	—	—	—	—	—	—
Dividends per share ($)	4.1%	0.25	0.25	0.25	0.25	0.25	0.26	0.27	0.31	0.35	0.36
Book value per share ($)	6.3%	5.40	5.98	5.99	29.40	26.94	22.61	21.61	3.62	3.02	9.38
Employees	13.2%	21,500	20,000	21,000	34,700	41,000	41,700	44,000	50,000	53,300	65,500

1995 YEAR-END

Debt ratio: 74.8%
Return on equity: —
Cash (mil.): $628
Current ratio: 1.23
Long-term debt (mil.): $10,856
No. of shares (mil.): 388
Dividends
  Yield: 1.0%
  Payout: —
Market value (mil.): $14,686

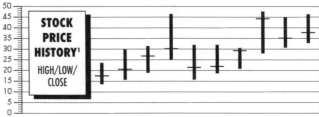

STOCK PRICE HISTORY[1]
HIGH/LOW/CLOSE

1986 1987 1988 1989 1990 1991 1992 1993 1994 1995

[1] The company stopped consolidating Time Warner Entertainment Group results in 1993.

THE TIMES MIRROR COMPANY

OVERVIEW

After gilding its frame, media company Times Mirror has taken a hard look at itself and wiped off some operations to improve its image — and its performance. The company has sold its cable TV operations to empire-builder Cox Communications and, in an effort to cut costs, launched a company-wide slash-and-burn operation that included folding 2 papers (the [Baltimore] *Evening Sun* and *New York Newsday*), cutting staff, and terminating its consumer multimedia business.

The Los Angeles-based media company publishes 7 newspapers, including the *Los Angeles Times* (4th in circulation, after *USA Today*, the *Wall Street Journal*, and the *New York Times*), and the *Baltimore Sun*. Its subsidiary Times Mirror Magazines publishes periodicals such as *Field & Stream*, *Popular Science*, and *Ski*

Magazine. Other subsidiaries produce reference books and other materials for the aviation, higher education, legal, medical, and scientific communities. Times Mirror Training offers various business training courses throughout the world.

CEO Mark Willes (whose cost-cutting efforts as VC at General Mills earned him the nickname "cereal killer") is largely eschewing acquisitions and hoping for internal growth within the company's leading segments. The company is slowly expanding its online services in the search for a wider audience, as well as continuing to experiment with new special interest magazines, such as *Snowboard Life* (launched in 1995).

Times Mirror is effectively controlled by descendants of cofounder Harry Chandler.

WHEN

Union Army general Harrison Gray Otis moved to California after the Civil War and became rich from the 1880s land boom. He acquired the *Los Angeles Times* (started 1881) and his son-in-law Harry Chandler set out to destroy rivals by controlling circulation routes. In 1884 Otis and Chandler formed Times Mirror to own the *Los Angeles Times*. Chandler took over after Otis's death in 1917, and by the 1930s he had amassed a fortune in shipping, road building, oil, and land.

The *Los Angeles Times* had a reputation for serving Otis's and Chandler's political and economic interests. The paper successfully prevented unionization long after unions had become strong in the East. The paper faked photos in its campaign against 1935 gubernatorial candidate Upton Sinclair and for years was known for its right-wing slant.

In 1960 Otis Chandler, grandson of Harry, was named *Times* publisher and began to give the paper a more balanced character. He hired better journalists and transformed the paper into one of the nation's finest. During his tenure the paper was awarded 7 Pulitzer Prizes.

The 1960s also marked the beginning of diversification under president and CEO Norman Chandler, Harry's son and Otis's father. Times Mirror acquired Jeppesen Sanderson (publisher of pilot information, 1961); Matthew Bender & Company (legal publisher, 1963); C.V. Mosby (medical publisher, 1967); Long Island Cablevision (1970); KDFW-TV, Dallas-Fort Worth (1970); and *Newsday* (1970). Times Mirror entered the magazine field by buying *Popular Science* (1967), *Outdoor Life* (1967),

Golf Magazine (1972), and *Ski Magazine* (1972).

In the 1980s the company experimented with an online service that failed to generate consumer interest. Times Mirror sold the New American Library (1984), the *Dallas Times Herald* (1986), and the *Denver Post* (1987).

In the late 1980s Times Mirror spent $1.5 billion on acquisitions of TV stations, cable TV systems, newspapers (the *Baltimore Sun*, 1986), magazines (*Yachting, Skiing, Field & Stream, Home Mechanix*; 1987), and publishers (CRC Press, 1986; Richard D. Irwin, 1988). New divisions included training systems Zenger-Miller and Kaset (1989). In 1990 the company bought 50% of *La Opinion*, the #1 US Spanish-language newspaper, and in 1991 it sold *Broadcasting* magazine at a loss.

In the early 1990s the company sold its TV stations. In 1994 the beginnings of an economic recovery in Southern California helped improve the company's bottom line.

The following year Times Mirror sold its cable TV interests to Cox Communications and took a $554 million charge for a sweeping restructuring intended to slash annual operating expenses. It also firmly ensconced itself online when the *Los Angeles Times* created its own World Wide Web page and moved its online service from Prodigy to the Internet.

In 1996 the company engaged in a complicated deal that swapped its Higher Education Group publishing subsidiaries for McGraw-Hill's Shepard's legal citation unit. The company then sold Shepard's to a new joint venture it set up with Reed Elsevier.

WHO

Chairman, President, and CEO: Mark H. Willes, age 54, $934,616 pay
EVP; Publisher and CEO, Los Angeles Times: Richard T. Schlosberg III, age 51, $923,077 pay
SVP and CFO: Thomas Unterman, age 51, $663,019 pay
SVP: Donald F. Wright, age 61, $554,230 pay
SVP: Edward E. Johnson, age 52, $524,038 pay
SVP Human Resources: James R. Simpson, age 55
VP and General Counsel: Kathleen G. McGuinness, age 47
Auditors: Ernst & Young LLP

WHERE

HQ: Times Mirror Square, Los Angeles, CA 90053
Phone: 213-237-3700
Fax: 213-237-3800
Web site: http://www.latimes.com

WHAT

	1995 Sales		1995 Operating Income	
	$ mil.	% of total	$ mil.	% of total
Newspaper publishing	2,057	60	(109)	—
Professional information	1,091	32	(131)	—
Consumer media	301	8	(76)	—
Adjustments	(1)	—	(139)	—
Total	**3,448**	**100**	**(455)**	**—**

Selected Newspapers and News Organizations
The Advocate (Stamford, CT; 28,840 daily circulation)
Greenwich Time (CT; 12,797 daily circulation)
The Hartford Courant (CT; 214,751 daily circulation)
Los Angeles Times (1,026,697 daily circulation)
Los Angeles Times Syndicate
Los Angeles Times-Washington Post News Service (50%)

The Morning Call (Allentown, PA; 131,628 daily circulation)
Newsday (Long Island, NY)
La Opinion (Southern California, 50% interest)
The Baltimore Sun (283,660 daily circulation)

Selected Magazines
Field & Stream
Golf Magazine
Government Executive
Home Mechanix
National Journal
Outdoor Life
Popular Science
Salt Water Sportsman
Ski Magazine
Skiing Trade News
Snowboard Life
The Sporting News
TransWorld SNOWboarding
Yachting

Book Publishing
Jeppesen Sanderson (aeronautical)
Matthew Bender & Co. (legal)

Professional Training
Kaset International
Learning International
Times Mirror Training
Zenger-Miller

KEY COMPETITORS

Advance Publications	Dun & Bradstreet	Reed Elsevier
Associated Press	E.W. Scripps	Thomson Corp.
Bertelsmann	Gannett	Time Warner
Capital Cities/ABC	Hearst	Tribune
Copley Press	Knight-Ridder	Viacom
Cox Enterprises	McGraw-Hill	Washington Post
Dow Jones	NBC	Wolters Kluwer
	New York Times	
	News Corp.	

HOW MUCH

NYSE symbol: TMC FYE: December 31	Annual Growth	1986	1987	1988	1989	1990	1991	1992	1993	1994	1995
Sales ($ mil.)	1.9%	2,920	3,079	3,259	3,475	3,620	3,614	3,702	3,714	3,357	3,448
Net income ($ mil.)	13.1%	408	267	332	298	181	82	57	317	185	1,240
Income as % of sales	—	14.0%	8.7%	10.2%	8.6%	5.0%	2.3%	1.5%	8.5%	5.5%	35.9%
Earnings per share ($)	13.8%	3.16	2.06	2.58	2.30	1.40	0.64	0.44	2.46	1.44	10.13
Stock price – high ($)	—	26.60	38.12	28.98	32.40	28.35	23.49	27.63	25.38	26.73	35.25
Stock price – low ($)	—	18.05	21.74	20.88	23.31	15.30	18.36	20.52	19.71	20.70	17.25
Stock price – close ($)	4.5%	22.86	25.83	23.67	25.74	19.26	22.32	22.50	24.03	22.59	33.88
P/E – high	—	8	19	11	14	20	37	63	10	19	4
P/E – low	—	6	11	8	10	11	29	47	8	14	2
Dividends per share ($)	(5.5%)	0.75	0.82	0.92	1.00	1.08	1.08	1.08	1.08	1.08	0.45
Book value per share ($)	1.7%	10.09	11.31	13.17	14.61	15.08	14.81	13.23	14.81	15.22	11.78
Employees	(2.7%)	27,941	27,915	27,963	29,066	29,121	27,732	28,313	26,936	26,902	21,877

1995 YEAR-END

Debt ratio: 12.1%
Return on equity: 61.2%
Cash (mil.): $183
Current ratio: 1.21
Long-term debt (mil.): $248
No. of shares (mil.): 104
Dividends
  Yield: 1.3%
  Payout: 4.4%
Market value (mil.): $3,535

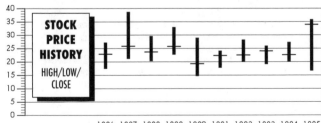

STOCK PRICE HISTORY
HIGH/LOW/CLOSE

1986 1987 1988 1989 1990 1991 1992 1993 1994 1995

TRIBUNE COMPANY

OVERVIEW

This media conglomerate is buying more than just air. Aside from adding KHTV (Houston) and KTTY (San Diego) to its coterie of 8 television stations, Chicago-based Tribune spent a hefty chunk of change ($282 million) in early 1996 to buy 2 education media companies, Educational Publishing and NTC Publishing Group. The company has also established footholds in cyberspace to widen the potential audience for its flagship *Chicago Tribune* (7th in daily US circulation) and other publications.

Tribune Company sports a wide variety of operations. Its Broadcasting and Entertainment business segment includes the Chicago Cubs baseball team, 10 TV stations (7 in the top 11 US markets, including WGN in Chicago), 5 radio stations, the Tribune Entertainment Company (which produces TV programming

such as *Geraldo*), and joint ventures such as the Warner Bros. Television Network (11.25%). The planned acquisition of Renaissance Communications (6 UHF TV stations) would give it the broadest reach of any US TV station group. The company's Publishing segment comprises the *Tribune* and 3 other daily papers, Tribune Media Services (syndication), and various online information services. Tribune's Education businesses serve national and international markets.

President John Madigan succeeded 38-year company veteran Charles Brumback as CEO in 1995 and as chairman in early 1996. Madigan is continuing a winning strategy: expand local news and entertainment, develop brand-name recognition, build value for advertisers by linking them with specific market segments, and take advantage of emerging technologies.

WHEN

Tribune Company had its beginnings as the *Chicago Tribune*, which produced 400 copies on its first day in 1847. Joseph Medill, a promoter who, some say, gave the Republican party its name, became part owner and editor in 1855. He spent the next 44 years building the *Tribune* into a conservative newspaper.

Medill reportedly warned that Chicago was a fire hazard just a month before the Great Fire of 1871. He rallied his employees to publish the paper despite being burned out of their building. Medill died in 1899 and was succeeded by son-in-law Robert Patterson and grandson Medill McCormick. In 1914 his other 2 grandsons, Robert McCormick and Joseph Patterson, took over the newspaper.

McCormick, great-nephew of the inventor of the harvest machine, built the *Tribune* into the self-proclaimed "World's Greatest Newspaper," whose acronym, WGN, became part of the company's subsequent radio and TV station call letters. Patterson left for New York in 1919 to found the *News* (later the *Daily News*).

In 1924 the company branched into radio by starting WGN, which became the first radio station to broadcast the World Series, Indianapolis 500, and Kentucky Derby. WGN moved into TV broadcasting in 1948, the same year the paper prematurely published its "Dewey Defeats Truman" headline.

McCormick took over the *Daily News* when Patterson died in 1946 and ran both papers from Chicago. He remained at that post until his death in 1955.

Tribune expanded its radio and TV broadcasting outside of Chicago. It founded WPIX-

TV in New York (1948) and bought TV stations in Denver (1965), New Orleans (1983), Atlanta (1984), Los Angeles (1985), Philadelphia (1992), and Boston (1994). The company also bought newspapers in Florida (Ft. Lauderdale, 1963; Orlando, 1965), California (Los Angeles, 1973, sold 1985; Escondido, 1977; Palo Alto, 1978, closed 1993), and Virginia (Newport News, 1986).

Tribune diversified with news and entertainment programming, beginning Independent Network News in 1980 (shut down, 1990) and the Tribune Broadcasting Co. in 1981. That year it bought the Chicago Cubs baseball team from chewing gum maker Wm. Wrigley. Tribune went public in 1983.

A protracted strike at the *Daily News* prompted the company to sell the newspaper in 1991. Also that year Tribune began to invest in online technology companies, buying a stake in America Online, with which it launched the local Chicago Online.

The company bought Compton's Multimedia Publishing Group and print-based Contemporary Books in 1993.

In 1995 Tribune sold Compton's to educational software developer SoftKey for $123.5 million; Tribune also invested $150 million in SoftKey. In 1996 the company said it would pay about $1.1 billion for broadcaster Renaissance Communications (majority-owned by investment firm Warburg, Pincus, Capital Co.).

Chairman, President, and CEO: John W. Madigan, age 58, $1,186,139 pay (prior to promotion)
EVP Media Operations: James C. Dowdle , age 62, $858,808 pay
EVP Tribune Broadcasting Co.: Dennis J. FitzSimons, age 45, $662,270 pay
EVP Tribune Publishing Co.: Joseph D. Cantrell, age 51, $504,904 pay
EVP and General Manager, Tribune Education Co.: Robert D. Bosau, age 49
SVP Development: David D. Hiller, age 42, $484,000 pay
SVP and CFO: Donald C. Grenesko, age 47
SVP Information Systems: John S. Kazik, age 53
SVP Administration (HR): John T. Sloan, age 44
President and CEO, Tribune Entertainment Co.: Dick Askin
VP and Chief Legal Counsel: Crane H. Kenney, age 33
Auditors: Price Waterhouse LLP

WHERE

HQ: 435 N. Michigan Ave., Chicago, IL 60611
Phone: 312-222-9100
Fax: 312-222-9205
Web site: http://www.tribune.com

WHAT

	1995 Sales		1995 Operating Income	
	$ mil.	% of total	$ mil.	% of total
Publishing	1,313	58	270	62
Broadcasting & Entertainment	829	37	161	37
Education	103	5	4	1
Adjustments	—	—	(30)	—
Total	**2,245**	**100**	**405**	**100**

Selected Publishing Operations
America Online (5%, electronic publishing)
Chicago Online (electronic publishing)
Chicago Tribune (683,000 daily circulation)
Knight-Ridder/Tribune Information Services (50%)
The Orlando Sentinel (268,000 daily circulation)
Orlando Sentinel Online (electronic publishing)
Peapod, LP (17%, online grocery shopping and delivery)
Sun-Sentinel (Ft. Lauderdale; 262,000 daily circulation)
Tribune Media Services (syndicator)

Selected Broadcasting and Entertainment Operations
Chicago National League Ball Club, Inc. (Chicago Cubs)
CLTV News (24-hour local cable TV news)
Orlando Baseball Club, Inc. (minor league baseball)
Qwest Broadcasting LLC (33%; acquires and operates radio and TV stations)
Tribune Entertainment Co. (TV programming)
TV Food Network (31%)

Education Operations
Educational Publishing Corp. (curriculum programs)
NTC/Contemporary Publishing Co.
The Wright Group (educational materials)

Radio and Television Stations

KEZW (AM), Denver	WGN-TV, Chicago
KHTV-TV, Houston	WGNO-TV, New Orleans
KOSI (FM), Denver	WGNX-TV, Atlanta
KTLA-TV, Los Angeles	WLVI-TV, Boston
KTTY-TV, San Diego	WPHL-TV, Philadelphia
KVOD (FM), Denver	WPIX-TV, New York
KWGN-TV, Denver	WQCD (FM), New York
WGN (AM), Chicago	

KEY COMPETITORS

Advance Publications	Gannett	News Corp.
Associated Press	Hearst	Reuters
Capital Cities/ABC	Hollinger Inc.	Sony
Chicago White Sox	King World	Time Warner
Chris-Craft	Lagardère	Times Mirror
Cox Enterprises	McGraw-Hill	Viacom
Dow Jones	Media General	Washington Post
	Microsoft	Westinghouse/
	NBC	CBS
	New York Times	

HOW MUCH

NYSE symbol: TRB FYE: December 31	Annual Growth	1986	1987	1988	1989	1990	1991	1992	1993	1994	1995
Sales ($ mil.)	1.1%	2,029	2,160	2,334	2,454	2,353	2,034	2,108	1,952	2,154	2,245
Net income ($ mil.)	(0.6%)	293	142	210	242	(64)	142	137	189	242	278
Income as % of sales	—	14.4%	6.6%	9.0%	9.9%	—	7.0%	6.5%	9.7%	11.2%	12.4%
Earnings per share ($)	0.2%	3.63	1.80	2.78	3.00	(1.22)	1.83	1.70	2.36	3.07	3.68
Stock price – high ($)	—	39.00	49.75	43.00	63.13	48.25	48.38	50.75	61.25	64.50	68.88
Stock price – low ($)	—	24.75	28.63	33.75	36.38	31.25	33.13	38.75	48.00	48.88	50.75
Stock price – close ($)	8.8%	28.50	41.00	38.88	47.38	35.25	41.00	48.00	60.13	54.75	61.13
P/E – high	—	11	28	16	21	—	26	30	26	21	19
P/E – low	—	7	16	12	12	—	18	23	20	16	14
Dividends per share ($)	9.4%	0.50	0.60	1.00	0.88	0.96	0.96	0.96	0.96	1.04	1.12
Book value per share ($)	2.2%	13.91	14.35	15.88	10.63	6.49	7.84	8.72	11.35	15.05	16.90
Employees	(5.4%)	17,300	16,800	16,800	17,100	16,100	12,900	12,400	9,900	10,500	10,500

1995 YEAR-END

Debt ratio: 36.3%
Return on equity: 19.0%
Cash (mil.): $23
Current ratio: 0.98
Long-term debt (mil.): $757
No. of shares (mil.): 63
Dividends
  Yield: 1.8%
  Payout: 30.4%
Market value (mil.): $3,823

STOCK PRICE HISTORY HIGH/LOW/CLOSE

1986 1987 1988 1989 1990 1991 1992 1993 1994 1995

TURNER BROADCASTING SYSTEM, INC.

OVERVIEW

Turner Broadcasting can't beat 'em, so it's joining 'em. The purchase of the strong-willed Ted Turner's Atlanta-based company by news and entertainment colossus Time Warner was approved by the government in 1996, allowing Turner Broadcasting to become part of the world's #1 media operation. Turner Broadcasting owns 8 cable TV entertainment networks, including Turner Network Television, TBS Superstation, and the Cartoon Network. It also owns news programming pioneer CNN, with 4 networks covering national, international, and financial news.

Turner Broadcasting produces TV shows and movies and maintains an extensive library of movies, shorts, cartoons, TV episodes, and specials. The company owns Major League baseball team Atlanta Braves and the professional basketball team Atlanta Hawks. It has minority interests in cable network SportSouth and German news network n-tv. Other operations include CNN Airport Network (news broadcasting in airports) and World Championship Wrestling (wrestling programming and events management).

Ted Turner's consent to Time Warner's $6.5 billion purchase of his company followed Turner's various attempts to acquire other media powerhouses, including unsuccessful bids for NBC (1994) and programming distributor King World (1995). The deal called for Ted Turner to become owner of 10% of Time Warner's voting stock, the conglomerate's VC, and head of movie channel HBO.

WHEN

In 1970 Turner, using profits from his billboard advertising business, bought Rice Broadcasting, a small Atlanta TV station, and formed Turner Communications Corp. In its first year the station lost $689,000, but its prospects were considered good enough to justify keeping it on the air. The following year WTSG (which stood for "watch this station grow," according to staffers) was the #1 independent TV station in the South. Turner spun the billboard business off in 1975.

Discovering he could reach cable systems around the country by satellite, in 1979 Turner turned WTSG into "superstation" WTBS and broadcast older TV shows, movies, and Atlanta Braves and Hawks games (teams Turner had bought in 1976 and 1977, respectively). In 1979 the station reached 5.8 million homes.

Turner launched the first serious challenge to broadcast network TV news — the 24-hour Cable News Network (CNN), in 1980. CNN frequently "scooped" the competition, reporting first on the 1981 attempt to assassinate President Reagan and broadcasting live the space shuttle explosion in 1986. CNN2 (later Headline News) was introduced in 1982. CNN began European distribution in 1985 and added Headline News in Spanish in 1988.

In 1986, after failing to take over the CBS broadcast network, power-hungry Turner bought movie studio MGM/UA. The $1.4 billion price nearly caused Turner to founder, but cable operators who saw Turner's importance to their systems bailed the company out. Turner formed Turner Network Television (TNT) in 1988 to air its MGM/UA film library, many in colorized versions criticized by purists.

In 1990 a subsidiary of the company bought a stake in SportSouth, a regional sports network serving the Southeast. Turner and an investment company bought the Hanna-Barbera cartoon library in 1991; in 1993 Turner acquired 100%. The Cartoon Network, launched in 1992 (US) and 1993 (Latin America), quickly equaled and then surpassed CNN's ratings.

TNT started Latin American operations in 1991. The following year Turner furthered his global reach by beginning to broadcast in Russia. In 1993 Turner bought film producer Castle Rock Entertainment and a stake in n-tv. In 1994 Turner bought independent movie distributor New Line Cinema and launched its 4th US entertainment network, Turner Classic Movies.

Ted Turner and his wife, actress Jane Fonda, were among the celebrants when the Atlanta Braves won the World Series in 1995. More importantly, that year the company agreed to be purchased by Time Warner. Along with the deal, Turner will sell its interest in SportSouth to venture partner LMC Southeast Sports.

In 1996 the company purchased the rights to 25 motion pictures (including *A River Runs Through It* and *Sleepless in Seattle*) from the films' distributor, Columbia TriStar Television Distribution. Also that year, Turner announced discussions with Sony, MCA, and other entertainment industry giants about selling Castle Rock, which has lost money and produced a string of box-office disappointments.

Chairman and President: Robert E. Ted Turner III, age 57, $1,693,776 pay
EVP: Terence F. McGuirk, age 44, $1,593,776 pay
Chairman and CEO, New Line Cinema Corp.: Robert Shaye, age 56, $3,661,999 pay
VP, Turner Entertainment Group: Scott M. Sassa, age 37, $1,541,084 pay
VP News: W. Thomas Johnson, age 54, $1,115,131 pay
VP Marketing and Communications: Julia W. Sprunt, age 42
VP Finance and CFO: Wayne H. Pace, age 49
VP Sports Programming: Harvey W. Schiller, age 56
VP, Controller, and Chief Accounting Officer: William S. Ghegan, age 47
VP, General Counsel, and Secretary: Steven W. Korn, age 42
VP and Treasurer: Christian L. Becken, age 42
VP and Chief Information Officer: Elahe Hessamfar, age 42
VP Worldwide Distribution: William H. Grumbles, age 46
VP Advertising Sales and Marketing: Steven J. Heyer, age 43
VP Administration (HR): William M. Shaw, age 51
Auditors: Price Waterhouse LLP

WHERE

HQ: One CNN Ctr., 100 International Blvd., Atlanta, GA 30303
Phone: 404-827-1700
Fax: 404-827-2437
Web site: http://www.turner.com

Turner Broadcasting operates worldwide, but most of its activities are centered in Atlanta. CNN maintains news bureaus in 9 US and 21 foreign locations.

WHAT

	1995 Sales	
	$ mil.	% of total
Entertainment	2,504	73
News	765	22
Other	207	5
Total	**3,437**	**100**

Entertainment Division

Selected Networks
Cartoon Network (animation programming)
TBS SuperStation (Atlanta TV station on cable systems)
TNT (Turner Network Television)
Turner Classic Movies (TCM)

Production and Distribution
Castle Rock Entertainment (film production)
Hanna-Barbera, Inc. (new animation products)
New Line Cinema (film production)

News Division

Cable News Network (CNN, US newscasts)
CNN Financial News (CNNFn)
CNN Headline News (30-minute newscasts)
CNN International (news for a worldwide audience)
n-tv (33.1% interest; Germany)

Selected Other Interests
Atlanta Hawks L.P. (96% NBA basketball team)
Atlanta National League Baseball Club, Inc. (Braves)
World Championship Wrestling

KEY COMPETITORS

Cox Enterprises
DreamWorks SKG
International Family
  Entertainment
King World
LucasFilm
MCA
Metromedia International
MGM
Microsoft
NBC
News Corp.
Rank
Samuel Goldwyn
Savoy Pictures
Sony
TCI
Tribune
Viacom
Walt Disney
Westinghouse/CBS

HOW MUCH

Subsidiary FYE: December 31	Annual Growth	1986	1987	1988	1989	1990	1991	1992	1993	1994	1995
Sales ($ mil.)	22.4%	557	652	807	1,065	1,394	1,480	1,770	1,922	2,809	3,437
Net Income ($ mil.)	—	(187)	(131)	(95)	28	(16)	43	34	72	46	103
Income as % of sales	—	—	—	—	2.6%	—	2.9%	1.9%	3.8%	1.6%	3.0%
Employees	17.8%	1,600	2,774	3,187	3,466	3,802	4,370	5,239	5,317	6,000	7,000

1995 YEAR-END

Debt ratio: 85%
Return on equity: 78.8%
Cash (mil.): $85
Current ratio: 1.66
Long-term debt (mil.): $2,480

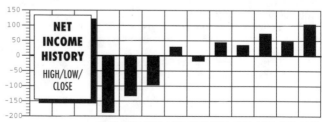

NET INCOME HISTORY HIGH/LOW/CLOSE

UNITED NEWS & MEDIA PLC

OVERVIEW

In a laudably bipartisan move, Conservative Party supporter Lord Stevens has merged his newspaper and TV company, United News & Media, with Labour Party champion Lord Hollick's TV and financial group, MAI. The expanded London-based company, which has sales of more than $2.8 billion and retains the United News & Media name, is 51%-owned by United shareholders and 49% by MAI shareholders. The enterprise's many media offerings include the national newspapers *Daily Express*, *Daily Star*, and *Sunday Express*; regional newspapers; and stakes in the UK commercial TV broadcasters Anglia TV, Meridian Broadcasting (76%), and Yorkshire-Tyne Tees TV (14%). It also holds a 29% stake in Channel 5 Broadcasting, the UK's 5th TV broadcasting channel, scheduled to be launched in 1997. The

company owns Miller Freeman (advertising and trade periodicals), the PR Newswire services in the US, and a number of brokerage, financial services, and market research companies.

The 1996 merger is part of United's strategy to broaden its media activities beyond its traditional newspaper businesses. (The company changed its name from United Newspapers to United News & Media in 1995.) At the same time the firm is hoping to revive the fortunes of its flagship *Daily Express* and of *Sunday Express*, which have been losing circulation to rival newspapers *Daily Mail* and *Mail on Sunday*.

Following the merger, United put noncore assets up for sale, such as Wagon Finance and Tolley Publishing (legal and business publishers).

WHEN

United Newspapers was formed in 1918 when Prime Minister David Lloyd George, stung by criticism of his war strategy in the *Daily Chronicle* newspaper, persuaded a group of Liberal Party supporters to buy out the newspaper company. In addition to the *Daily Chronicle*, United Newspapers Ltd. acquired *Lloyd's Weekly News*, which had been founded in 1842 and had been the first newspaper with a circulation of one million. The company published a northern edition of the *Daily Chronicle* to challenge Conservative Lord Northcliffe's *Daily Mail*. United went public in 1925. The company was subsequently acquired by the Daily Chronicle Investment Group, a joint venture of Liberal Party politicians and supporters. Yorkshireman William Harrison acquired United in 1928.

When Northcliffe expanded his newspaper empire in the 1930s and threatened to open an evening paper in every city where United Newspapers published a daily, Harrison sold its stake in the *News Chronicle* (a successor of the *Daily News and Chronicle*, which had changed its name from the *Daily Chronicle* in the early 1930s) to stay profitable. With its printing activities located for the most part outside London, United Newspapers fared better during WWII than its rivals based in the heavily bombed capital.

Harold Drayton bought 1/3 of the company in 1946 and became chairman in 1948. During the 1960s the company accelerated its acquisition of regional newspapers such as the northern England publications *Nelson Leader* and the *Colne Times* (both bought in 1963). United

Newspapers acquired a group of weekly papers in London in 1969 and later moved into periodicals.

After a period of consolidation in the 1970s, in 1981 David Stevens (later Lord Stevens) took over the leadership of the company and led it on an expansion drive. In 1983 it acquired Gralla, a US publisher and promoter of trade shows; Miller Freeman, a US medical and computer magazine publisher; and PR Newswire, a corporate and financial news agency.

In 1985 the company acquired Fleet Holdings, owner of the *Daily Express*, the *Star*, and the *Sunday Express*. United Newspapers purchased Extel, a UK-based financial information company, in 1987 (sold to media titan Pearson in 1993).

In 1994 the company acquired the Hong Kong International Trade Fair Group as a beachhead for trade fairs in China, and Visual Communications Group (photo library).

United News & Media merged with MAI in 1996. MAI was founded as the J.H. Vavasseur Group Ltd. in 1974. Lord Hollick, a former Hambros Bank director, was appointed to head the struggling financial services company that year. He turned its fortunes around, changing Vavasseur's name to Mills & Allen in 1977 before taking it public in 1981. It was renamed MAI in 1985. Its NOP Research Group is a leading market research company in the UK, while its Mediamark Research is a leading US market research firm. MAI's media activities include 2 UK TV stations and TV programming and online services.

WHO

Chairman: Lord Stevens, age 59, $814,421 pay
Deputy Chairman: James McKinnon, age 66
Chief Executive: Lord Hollick, age 50, $891,857 pay
Finance Director: Charles R. Stern, age 45, $332,398 pay
Director Broking and Information: Charles Gregson, age 48, $591,912 pay
Director Broadcasting and Entertainment: Roger Laughton
Chief Executive, Newspaper Division: Stephen Grabiner, age 37
Chairman and CEO, Miller Freeman, Inc.: Marshall Freeman, age 63, $474,530 pay
Chairman and CEO, United Advertising Publications: Nigel Donaldson, age 51, $367,925 pay
Chairman, Link House Publications: Michael Toulmin, age 52, $327,563 pay
Secretary: John Burns
Auditors: Binder Hamlyn

WHERE

HQ: Ludgate House, 245 Blackfriars Rd., London, SE1 9UY, UK
Phone: +44-(0)71-921-5000
Fax: +44-(0)71-928-2717
Web site: http://www.unm.com

WHAT

	1995 Sales		1995 Operating Income	
	$ mil.	% of total	$ mil.	% of total
Magazines & exhibitions	574	34	78	34
National newspapers	463	27	29	12
Regional newspapers	294	17	46	20
Advertising periodicals	285	17	60	26
Other	95	5	20	8
Total	**1,711**	**100**	**233**	**100**

Selected United Publications

Express Newspapers Plc
Daily Express
Daily Star
Sunday Express

Link House Publications
Dalton Weekly
Euro Trader

Miller Freeman Asia
Asian Computer Weekly
Travel Trade Gazette Asia

Miller Freeman Inc. (US)
3-D Design
Bass Player
Impressions Magazine

Other Operations
Gavin
MBI
Miller Freeman Exhibitions Ltd.

Interplan
Kitchen & Bath Business
LAN Magazine
Microsoft Systems Journal
National Jeweler

Tolley Publishing

United Advertising Periodicals(US)
Advertising Periodical Publishers
Apartments for Rent
Photo Shopper On-Line

United Provincial Newspapers plc

Miller Freeman Information Services
PR Newswire

Selected MAI Subsidiaries

Butler Asset Finance
Graban Securities Inc.
Information
Garbin Information Systems
Mediamark Research

NOP Research Group
Media
Anglia TV
Meridian Broadcasting (76%)

KEY COMPETITORS

BBC	Granada Group	Mirror Group
BSkyB	IBC	News Corp.
Business Wire	International Data	Pearson
Capital Cities/ABC	Group	Reed Elsevier
Carlton	International	Reuters
Dun & Bradstreet	Holdings	Telegraph PLC
EMAP PLC	Johnston Press	Times Mirror
Euromoney	M/A/R/C	VNU
Publications	Maritz	WPP Group

HOW MUCH

Nasdaq symbol: UNEWY FYE: December 31	Annual Growth	1986	1987	1988	1989	1990	1991	1992	1993	1994	1995
Sales ($ mil.)	4.9%	1,109	1,281	1,347	1,433	1,482	1,526	1,260	1,294	1,589	1,711
Net income ($ mil.)	1.0%	101	171	193	195	150	40	121	148	120	110
Income as % of sales	—	9.1%	13.3%	14.3%	13.6%	10.1%	2.6%	9.6%	11.4%	7.5%	6.4%
Earnings per share ($)	(0.1%)	0.90	1.29	1.34	1.36	1.13	0.40	1.18	1.33	1.24	0.89
Stock price – high ($)	—	—	22.50	16.88	16.88	15.13	14.50	16.50	19.75	21.63	17.75
Stock price – low ($)	—	—	12.63	12.75	12.50	9.88	10.75	12.00	14.63	15.38	14.75
Stock price – close ($)	1.2%	—	15.50	13.25	15.00	11.50	11.75	16.25	19.50	15.50	17.00
P/E – high	—	—	17	13	12	13	37	14	15	17	20
P/E – low	—	—	10	10	9	9	27	10	11	12	17
Dividends per share ($)	0.0%	—	0.73	0.79	0.81	0.81	0.76	0.63	0.65	0.72	0.73
Book value per share ($)	(2.2%)	—	3.48	3.13	4.83	5.79	5.38	2.53	5.06	3.93	2.91
Employees	0.1%	13,420	13,500	14,030	13,100	12,550	12,020	11,860	11,850	13,333	13,573

1995 YEAR-END

Debt ratio: 48.0%
Return on equity: 26.1%
Cash (mil.): $28
Current ratio: 0.97
Long-term debt (mil.): $310
No. of shares (mil.): 123
Dividends
  Yield: 4.3%
  Payout: 81.1%
Market value (mil.): $2,089

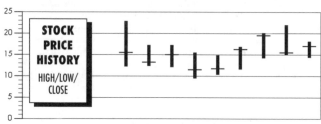

STOCK PRICE HISTORY HIGH/LOW/CLOSE

1986 1987 1988 1989 1990 1991 1992 1993 1994 1995

U S WEST MEDIA GROUP

OVERVIEW

In the future people will be able to talk, send pictures, conduct transactions, and receive information and entertainment through a single system — no separate phone, television, and computer lines, and maybe even no lines at all. Englewood, Colorado-based U S WEST Media Group is preparing for this future by assembling a collection of cable, wireless telecommunications, and directory services companies in the US and abroad.

A grandchild of the AT&T breakup in 1984, the company is part of Baby Bell U S WEST, Inc. In 1995, however, it began trading on its own, separate from U S WEST Communications Group.

U S WEST Media Group encompasses domestic and international cable services, with access to more than 40 million homes. The company intends to upgrade these existing networks so that they can carry multiple services, including cable TV, Internet access, and telephone communications.

In addition, U S WEST Media Group offers cellular phone services in the US, Europe, and Asia. Because many of its markets (such as Poland and Russia) are developing and have a very low penetration of standard wired service, it is expected that these will leapfrog straight to wireless communications, providing a potentially lucrative field for the company.

U S WEST Marketing Resources includes over 300 *Yellow Pages* directories in 14 western and northwestern states, as well as databases that allow targeted marketing.

WHEN

In the beginning there was AT&T — Ma Bell — the nationwide monopoly that worked as long as communications meant phones connected by wires. By the 1980s, however, new methods, including computer networks and cellular phones, had the Bell monopoly on the run. In 1982, after prolonged antitrust litigation, the monopoly was ordered to dismember itself. AT&T kept its long-distance telephone business and launched its local telephone operations as 7 independent regional public companies in 1984. U S WEST was created by packaging the Mountain Bell, Northwestern Bell, and Pacific Northwest Bell units (serving customers in 14 states) along with an interest in Bell's R&D arm (Bellcore) and a young cellular phone operation (NewVector).

The CEO of Northwestern Bell, Jack MacAllister, became CEO of U S WEST. Noting that the local phone service business was growing only 3-5% annually, U S WEST hoped to expand into new areas such as cable and was the first Bell company to seek changes in the divestiture agreement that would allow it to do so. It also revamped the directory services, shuffling the *Yellow Pages* operations into Landmark Communication, now part of U S WEST Marketing Resources, which has added about 20 smaller directory publishers. In 1988 U S WEST moved into the international arena with an investment in a French cable TV business. Other foreign ventures followed in Czechoslovakia, France, Hungary, Russia, and the UK. It also moved into cable TV in the US.

The company increased its interest in NewVector, and MacAllister retired and was succeeded by Richard McCormick in 1990. The next year U S WEST and cable player TCI agreed to combine their European cable TV and telephone operations in a 50/50 joint venture.

In 1993 the company paid $2.5 billion for a 25.5% stake in Time Warner Entertainment (the company's film, TV, and cable operations) and 12.75% of Time Warner Entertainment Japan.

Meanwhile, U S WEST was expanding its directory capacities overseas with the purchase of Thomson Directories (in the UK) from publishers Thomson Corporation and Dun & Bradstreet in 1994. That year U S WEST formed a cellular joint venture with AirTouch Communications (the former cellular division of Baby Bell Pacific Telesis Group).

Because U S WEST's 2 main operations were so different, in 1995 the company offered its stockholders a clear choice of investment vehicles. Although it remained the parent company, U S WEST, Inc., divided its stock into 2 classes: U S WEST Communications Group (local phone operations) and faster-growing U S WEST Media Group (cellular, cable, and directory services).

Time Warner's 1995 agreement to buy Turner Broadcasting soured its relationship with U S WEST, which — fearing that a Time Warner-Turner union could compromise its own ventures with Time Warner — unsuccessfully sued to block the deal.

In 1996 U S WEST Media Group agreed to buy Continental Cablevision (the US's 3rd largest cable company, after TCI and Time Warner) for $5.3 billion in cash and stock and the assumption of $5.5 billion in debt.

Chairman, U S WEST, Inc.: Richard D. McCormick, age 55, $1,210,000 pay
EVP, U S WEST, Inc.; President and CEO: Charles M. Lillis, age 54, $865,000 pay
President and CEO, U S WEST International: A. Gary Ames
President and CEO, U S WEST Marketing and Resources Group, Inc.: Stephen D. Boyd
VP Group Operations and Strategy: Roger K. Christensen
VP and CFO: Douglas D. Holmes
VP Public Relations: Judith A. Servoss
VP Human Resources: Patty A. Klinge
Auditors: Coopers & Lybrand L.L.P.

WHERE

HQ: 7800 E. Orchard Rd., Ste. 290, Englewood, CO 80111
Phone: 303-793-6500
Fax: 303-793-6309
Web site: http://www.uswest.com

U S WEST Media Group operates in Argentina, Australia, Brazil, the Czech Republic, France, Hungary, India, Indonesia, Japan, Lithuania, Malaysia, the Netherlands, Norway, Poland, Russia, Singapore, Slovakia, Sweden, the UK, and the US.

	1995 Sales
	% of total
US	89
Other countries	11
Total	**100**

WHAT

	1995 Sales	
	$ mil.	% of total
Directory & info. services	1,180	50
Wireless communications	941	40
Cable & telecommunications	215	9
Other	38	1
Total	**2,374**	**100**

Selected Subsidiaries

Cable and Telecommunications
A2000 (50%, Netherlands)
ARIAWEST (35%, Indonesia)
Binariang Communications Sdn Bhd (20%, Malaysia)
Kabel Plus (29%, Czech Republic)
MediaOne
TeleWest (UK)

Wireless Communications
EuroTel (25%, Czech Republic and Slovakia)
U S WEST NewVector (92%)

Directory and Information Services
Listel (50%, Brazil)
Thomson Directories (UK)
U S WEST Marketing Resources Group
U S WEST Polska (Poland)

KEY COMPETITORS

ALLTEL	Jones Intercable
Ameritech	Knight-Ridder
AT&T Corp.	MCI
Carrefour	Metromedia International
Comcast	NTT
Cox Communications	Rogers Communications
E.W. Scripps	Sprint
GTE	TCI
Hearst	

HOW MUCH

AMEX symbol: UMG FYE: December 31	Annual Growth	1986	1987	1988	1989	1990	1991	1992	1993	1994	1995
Sales ($ mil.)	17.1%	—	—	—	—	—	1,261	1,384	1,549	1,908	2,374
Net income ($ mil.)	18.9%	—	—	—	—	—	69	146	85	276	138
Income as % of sales	—	—	—	—	—	—	5.5%	10.5%	5.5%	14.5%	5.8%
Earnings per share ($)	(52.5%)	—	—	—	—	—	—	—	—	0.61	0.29
Stock price – high ($)	—	—	—	—	—	—	—	—	—	—	20.00
Stock price – low ($)	—	—	—	—	—	—	—	—	—	—	17.38
Stock price – close ($)	—	—	—	—	—	—	—	—	—	—	19.00
P/E – high	—	—	—	—	—	—	—	—	—	—	69
P/E – low	—	—	—	—	—	—	—	—	—	—	60
Dividends per share ($)	—	—	—	—	—	—	—	—	—	—	0.00
Book value per share ($)	—	—	—	—	—	—	—	—	—	—	6.02
Employees	55.7%	—	—	—	—	—	—	—	—	10,279	16,000

1995 YEAR-END

Debt ratio: 37.4%
Return on equity: 3.2%
Cash (mil.): $20
Current ratio: 0.47
Long-term debt (mil.): $1,265
No. of shares (mil.): 742
Dividends
  Yield: —
  Payout: —
Market Value (mil): $14,104

STOCK PRICE HISTORY
HIGH/LOW/CLOSE

NV VERENIGD BEZIT VNU

OVERVIEW

VNU, one of the largest publishers in Europe, is fast becoming a multimedia group. The Haarlem, Netherlands-based company is a leading publisher of regional newspapers and mass-circulation magazines in its country. It also produces educational publications, business and professional magazines, and databases and holds stakes in 2 television stations (one Dutch and one Belgian.)

The company is expanding its publishing activities in the Netherlands and Belgium as well as growing its business information services internationally. Its Business Information US division (directories, marketing and media information services, newsletters, professional magazines, seminars, and trade shows) accounts for about 21% of its total revenues. VNU's well-known US publications include such magazines as *Adweek*, *Billboard*, and the *Hollywood Reporter*. To stay competitive, VNU plans to expand its commercial broadcasting and multimedia activities.

WHEN

VNU (United Dutch Publishing Companies) was formed through the 1964 merger of 2 of the Netherlands's largest mass-market consumer publishing companies: Cebema, based in 'sHertogenbosch, and De Spaarnestad, headquartered in Haarlem. The new company added to its empire through a series of acquisitions during the late 1960s.

In 1967 it bought regional newspaper publisher Het Nieuwsblad van het Zuiden and book publisher Het Spectrum. Founded as a Roman Catholic printing house, Het Spectrum shifted its emphasis to nonreligious books following its acquisition and began to publish Dutch translations of authors such as J. R. R. Tolkien, Somerset Maugham, Dorothy Sayers, and Ellery Queen. In 1968 VNU acquired magazine publisher NRM and Smeets, one of the largest offset printers in Europe.

The company's buying spree pumped up its sales and profits but also created an unwieldy organization. During the early 1970s VNU hired US management consultant McKinsey and Company to help it streamline its operations.

VNU continued to add more companies to the fold, including trade journal publisher Intermediair (1973), Belgian bookbinder Reliure Industrielle de Barchon (1974), and trade journal publisher Diligentia (1975). In the late 1970s the company began a move into professional publishing, and in 1980 VNU acquired the publishing portions of Computing Publications and of Business and Career Publications.

During the 1980s VNU began to focus on expanding its US business. In 1985 it acquired Disclosure, a provider of financial information on publicly owned companies, and used it as a vehicle to build its business information operations in the US. VNU acquired New Jersey-based Hayden Publishing the following year, but the acquisition proved to be a major debacle. Hayden's publications, whose titles included computer and electronics magazines *Electronic Design*, *Computer Decisions*, and *Personal Computing*, were hit by a decline in the computer business during the late 1980s, and the publishers also suffered high turnover in middle management. In 1989 VNU began selling off Hayden's assets.

Although its prospects were not particularly rosy in the US, VNU continued to expand its operations elsewhere. Its 1988 acquisition of Audet made it the #1 publisher of regional newspapers in the Netherlands. The next year the company made its first foray into television when it bought an 11% stake in VTM, a new commercial Belgian TV station. That same year it acquired a 19% interest in Dutch TV station RTL 4.

The company entered the Eastern European market in 1990, launching *Moscow Magazine*. In 1992 VNU increased its stake in RTL 4 to 38%, acquired 50% of Spectra Marketing Systems (US), and entered a joint venture with Arbitron (US).

As part of a plan to focus on its publishing operations, in 1993 VNU sold its printing operations to Koninklijke De Boer Boekhoven, creating a new company, Roto Smeets De Boer, in which VNU holds a 27% interest.

VNU acquired US-based BPI Communications, publisher of *Billboard* and the *Hollywood Reporter*, for $220 million in 1994. The next year it sold Disclosure to information provider Primark for $200 million and used a portion of the proceeds to buy SRDS, a business information provider, as part of its strategy to increase its US market share of business information services. SRDS produces over 20 advertising directories.

VNU announced plans to acquire a 33% stake in IFMS Data & Services, a German marketing information firm, in 1996.

WHO

Chairman: J. L. Brentjens
Chairman and CEO, VNU USA inc.: G. S. Hobbs
CFO, VNU USA inc.: Rosalee Lovett
Director, Financial and Economic Affairs:
J. J. van der Rest
Director, Business Development and Analysis:
R. J. Goedkoop
Director, Business Development and Analysis:
E.E.C. Hupkens van der Elst
Director, Business Development and Analysis: R. J. Kat
Director, Human Resources: G. Abendanon
Auditors: Ernst & Young LLP

WHERE

HQ: Ceylonpoort 5-25, NL-2037 AA, Haarlem,
The Netherlands
Phone: +31-23-5-463-463
Fax: +31-23-5-463-938
US HQ: VNU USA Inc., 11 W. 42nd St., New York, NY
10036-8088
US Phone: 212-789-3680
US Fax: 212-789-3650
Web site: http://www.vnu.com

VNU has operations in Belgium, the Czech Republic,
France, Germany, Hungary, Italy, Luxembourg, the
Netherlands, Spain, the UK, and the US.

	1995 Sales
	% of total
The Netherlands	55
US	23
Belgium	11
UK	7
Other countries	4
Total	**100**

WHAT

	1995 Sales	
	Fl mil.	% of total
Consumer magazines	1,213	36
Business Information USA	711	21
Newspapers	644	19
Business Information Europe	395	12
Commercial broadcasting	323	9
Educational publishing	89	3
Adjustments	(323)	—
Total	**3,052**	**100**

Selected Operations

Consumer Magazines
General interest
Special interest
Women's
Youth

Bus. Information USA
Directories
Marketing and media information services
Newsletters
Professional magazines
Seminars
Trade shows

Newspapers

Bus. Information Europe
Career planning
Computer information
Electronics
Engineering
Finance
Textile industry

Commercial Television

Educational Publishing

KEY COMPETITORS

Advance
Publications
Axel Springer
Bertelsmann
Bonnierforetagen
CMP Publications
Cowles Media
Crain
Communications
De Telegraaf

Dun & Bradstreet
Euromonitor
International
Data Group
Knight-Ridder
Lagardère
Market Guide
McGraw-Hill
News Corp.
Pearson

Reader's Digest
Reed Elsevier
SOFTBANK
Thomson Corp.
Time Warner
United News &
Media
Viacom
Wolters Kluwer

HOW MUCH

OTC symbol: VNUNY (ADR) FYE: December 31	Annual Growth	1986	1987	1988	1989	1990	1991	1992	1993	1994	1995
Sales (Fl mil.)	6.5%	1,735	1,972	2,504	2,612	2,718	2,735	2,737	2,310	2,776	3,052
Net income (Fl mil.)	21.4%	75	92	134	158	146	117	48	145	206	430
Income as % of sales	—	4.3%	4.7%	5.4%	6.0%	5.4%	4.3%	1.8%	6.3%	7.4%	14.1%
Earnings per share (Fl)	9.4%	0.64	0.79	0.94	0.11	0.10	0.82	0.31	0.94	1.21	1.44
Stock price – high (Fl)	—	8.91	9.75	9.59	11.65	11.50	9.97	9.20	17.70	20.30	23.90
Stock price – low (Fl)	—	6.76	4.53	5.78	8.65	7.37	6.82	6.87	8.77	16.45	16.29
Stock price – close (Fl)	10.8%	8.75	5.60	9.48	10.87	8.23	6.95	8.77	17.37	18.02	22.03
P/E – high	—	14	12	10	105	112	12	30	19	17	17
P/E – low	—	11	6	6	78	72	8	22	9	14	11
Dividends per share (Fl)	8.5%	0.23	0.28	0.32	0.36	0.36	0.36	0.36	0.36	0.40	0.48
Book value per share (Fl)	9.3%	2.13	2.52	2.58	4.58	4.78	5.23	4.20	3.94	3.46	4.74
Employees	1.9%	8,713	9,479	11,979	11,864	11,594	11,448	10,971	8,367	9,919	10,306

1995 YEAR-END

Debt ratio: 39.4%
Return on equity: 33.4%
Cash (mil.): Fl279
Long-term debt (mil.): Fl407
No. of shares (mil.): 189
Dividends
  Yield: 2.2%
  Payout: 33.1%
Market value (mil.): $2,608
Sales (mil.): $1,735

Note: $ = Fl1.6 (December 31, 1995)

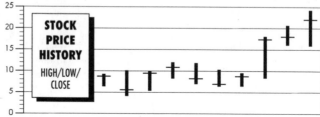

STOCK PRICE HISTORY
HIGH/LOW/CLOSE

1986 1987 1988 1989 1990 1991 1992 1993 1994 1995

VIACOM INC.

OVERVIEW

Of paramount importance to Viacom is finding the best way to compete with the biggest players in the media business. The New York City-based company offers diverse entertainment and publishing products. It has carved out a major slice of the US television market through its cable channels (MTV, VH1, Nickelodeon/Nick at Nite and its 50% ownership of USA Network, Comedy Central, the Sci-Fi Channel, and the All News Channel). Viacom owns pay movie channels Showtime, the Movie Channel, and Flix as well as 12 broadcast TV stations and 12 radio stations. It also produces movies and produces and syndicates TV shows through its Spelling Entertainment (*Melrose Place* and *Beverly Hills 90210*) and Paramount subsidiaries.

Other business lines include the world's #1 video and music retailer (Blockbuster Video and Blockbuster Music), a book publisher (Simon & Schuster), theme parks, and movie theaters in the US and Europe.

Chairman Sumner Redstone owns 61% of Viacom's common stock through his privately held company, National Amusements.

To pay down debt arising from the $9.9 billion Paramount and the $8.4 billion Blockbuster purchases in 1994, Redstone sold off his Madison Square Garden sporting assets in 1995.

Paramount's 1996 movie release *Mission: Impossible*, starring Tom Cruise, became a record-breaking smash that had Paramount executives talking sequels within days of its release.

WHEN

CBS formed Viacom in 1970 after the FCC ruled that TV networks could not own cable systems and TV stations in the same market. Viacom took over CBS's program syndication division. In 1978 it formed Showtime, a subscription TV service, with media firm Teleprompter, becoming full owner in 1982.

Paramount was started in 1912 by Adolph Zukor, becoming Paramount Pictures after merging with Famous Players-Lasky, a studio formed by Jesse Lasky, Samuel Goldwyn, and Cecil B. DeMille. In the 1940s the government forced Paramount to divest its theater holdings. Movie attendance slipped as TV grew, and in 1966 Gulf + Western bought the struggling Paramount Pictures.

Gulf + Western began in 1956 when Charles Bluhdorn bought Michigan Plating and Stamping (Studebaker rear bumpers). Two years later he merged his company with Beard & Stone Electric and in 1959 adopted the name Gulf + Western Industries. The company acquired many diverse firms. When Bluhdorn died in 1983, successor Martin Davis sold off everything but Paramount Pictures, Associates Investment (auto loans, sold in 1989), Simon & Schuster (acquired in 1975), and Madison Square Garden (acquired in 1977). Gulf + Western became Paramount Communications in 1989, the same year it made an unsuccessful $200-per-share bid for publisher Time.

In the late 1970s and early 1980s, Viacom purchased TV and radio stations in 5 states. The company and media joint venture Warner/Amex combined Showtime with the Movie Channel to form Showtime Networks in 1983. American Express left the Warner/Amex

venture in 1986, and Viacom bought Warner's share of Showtime Networks and MTV Networks. It also began producing for network TV shows and bought a St. Louis TV station.

Sumner Redstone's National Amusements, a movie theater chain, bought 83% of Viacom for $3.4 billion in 1987 after a bidding war against corporate high-flier Carl Icahn and a Viacom management group. The next year Viacom tried unsuccessfully to buy the Orion Pictures production company.

In the early 1990s Paramount bought TV station operator TVX, King's Entertainment (theme parks), and a Detroit TV station. Viacom bought ICOM Simulations (CD-ROM and video game software) in 1993.

Whether it was fate or destiny no one knows, but the 1994 acquisition of Paramount brought Viacom a windfall from the surprising box office success of *Forrest Gump*. In 1995 Viacom launched a new TV network (United Paramount Network) with New York-based Chris-Craft. Congress's repeal of an FCC tax credit program for minorities killed Viacom's planned 1995 sale of its cable system to Mirgo, a partnership between Frank Washington, a black entrepreneur, and major institutional investors. In 1996 the company agreed to sell Viacom Cable Television, the 12th largest cable TV system in the world, to TCI for more than $2 billion.

Turmoil hit Viacom's upper management ranks in 1996. Redstone fired president and CEO Frank Biondi — his long-time business associate — and assumed the CEO mantle himself. Two months later Steven Berrard, president and CEO of the Blockbuster Entertainment Group, resigned.

WHO

Chairman and CEO: Sumner M. Redstone, age 72
Deputy Chairman, EVP, General Counsel, Chief Administrative Officer, and Secretary: Philippe P. Dauman, age 42, $3,060,000 pay
Deputy Chairman, EVP Finance, Corporate Development, and Communications: Thomas E. Dooley, age 39, $3,060,000 pay
SVP Technology; Chairman and CEO, Viacom Interactive Media: Edward D. Horowitz, age 48, $1,075,000 pay
SVP Government Affairs: Mark M. Weinstein, age 53, $1,045,000 pay
SVP and CFO: George S. Smith Jr., age 47
SVP Human Resources and Administration: William A. Roskin, age 53

WHERE

HQ: 1515 Broadway, New York, NY 10036
Phone: 212-258-6000
Fax: 212-258-6354
Web site: http://www.viacom.com

WHAT

	1995 Sales		1995 Operating Income	
	$ mil.	% of total	$ mil.	% of total
Entertainment	3,650	31	307	19
Video/music/parks	3,333	28	502	30
Publishing	2,171	19	186	11
Networks & broadcasting	2,137	18	561	34
Cable TV	444	4	101	6
Adjustments	(46)	—	(164)	—
Total	**11,689**	**100**	**1,493**	**100**

Selected Operations

Entertainment
Movie Theaters
Famous Players (Canada)
Cinamerica (50%; US)
Paramount Pictures
Paramount Television
Spelling Entertainment Group (78%)
  Republic Pictures
  Spelling Television
  Virgin Interactive Entertainment
  Worldvision Enterprises
Viacom Interactive Media

Video/Music/Theme Parks
Blockbuster Music
Blockbuster Video
Discovery Zone, Inc. (49%)
Paramount Parks (5 theme parks in the US and Canada)

Publishing
Simon & Schuster
  Allyn & Bacon

Educational Management Group
MacMillan Publishing USA
Pocket Books
Prentice Hall
Scribner

Networks and Broadcasting
All News Channel (50%)
Comedy Central (50%)
MTV Networks
  MTV: Music Television
  Nickelodeon/Nick at Nite
  VH1 Music First
Showtime Networks
  Flix
  The Movie Channel
  Showtime
USA Networks (50%)
  Sci-Fi Channel
  USA Network
Radio stations (12)
TV stations

KEY COMPETITORS

Advance Publications	Heritage Media	Pearson
Anheuser-Busch	K-III	Reed Elsevier
Bertelsmann	King World	Sony
Camelot Music	MCA	TCI
Comcast	McGraw-Hill	Thomson Corp.
DreamWorks SKG	Metromedia International	THORN EMI Time Warner
Gannett	MTS	Tribune
Harcourt General	Musicland	Walt Disney
Hearst	NBC	Westinghouse/
	News Corp.	CBS

HOW MUCH

AMEX symbol: VIA FYE: December 31	Annual Growth	1986	1987	1988	1989	1990	1991	1992	1993	1994	1995
Sales ($ mil.)	32.7%	919	1,011	1,259	1,436	1,600	1,712	1,865	2,005	7,363	11,689
Net income ($ mil.)	—	(10)	(124)	(123)	131	(90)	(50)	49	158	15	163
Income as % of sales	—	—	—	—	9.1%	—	—	2.6%	7.9%	0.2%	1.4%
Earnings per share ($)	—	(0.13)	(1.64)	(1.77)	1.07	(0.84)	(0.44)	0.41	1.23	0.07	0.43
Stock price – high ($)	—	—	14.25	15.69	32.62	29.56	35.38	44.00	67.50	49.75	54.13
Stock price – low ($)	—	—	5.00	8.87	15.25	15.63	23.50	28.13	37.13	24.50	41.00
Stock price – close ($)	22.6%	—	9.06	15.56	28.75	26.25	34.25	44.00	48.88	41.63	46.25
P/E – high	—	—	—	—	31	—	—	104	55	—	126
P/E – low	—	—	—	—	14	—	—	69	30	—	95
Dividends per share ($)	—	—	0.00	0.00	0.00	0.00	0.00	0.00	0.00	0.00	0.00
Book value per share ($)	24.9%	—	4.98	3.21	4.27	3.43	5.82	6.28	7.60	29.45	29.47
Employees	37.3%	4,700	4,800	4,400	4,900	5,000	4,900	5,000	17,500	70,000	81,700

1995 YEAR-END

Debt ratio: 47%
Return on equity: 1.4%
Cash (mil.): $464
Current ratio: 1.27
Long-term debt (mil.): $10,712
No. of shares (mil.): 370
Dividends
  Yield: —
  Payout: —
Market value (mil.): $17,099

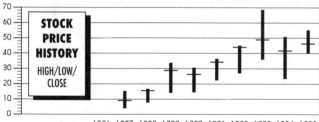

STOCK PRICE HISTORY
HIGH/LOW/CLOSE
1986 1987 1988 1989 1990 1991 1992 1993 1994 1995

THE WALT DISNEY COMPANY

OVERVIEW

Jiminy Cricket is whistling a happy tune after Disney's Dumbo-sized acquisition of media lion king Capital Cities/ABC left its competitors looking goofy. More than a Mickey Mouse operation, Burbank, California-based Disney is an entertainment fantasia that possesses the world's strongest media brand. With the $19 billion purchase in 1996, Disney picked up greater national and international exposure through the US's #1 TV network, several TV and radio stations, 3 cable channels (including top sports channel ESPN), and extensive holdings in publishing. With revenues of some $16.5 billion, the combined company began life as the world's biggest entertainment company.

Even before the acquisition, Disney boasted a huge stable of TV and movie production assets (including Buena Vista Television, the Disney Channel, Miramax Film Corp., and Touchstone Pictures), theme parks (including Disneyland, Disneyland Paris, and Epcot), publication companies (Disney Hachette Presse, Disney Press, Hyperion Press, and Mouse Works), and professional sports franchises (the

Mighty Ducks of Anaheim hockey team and a part of the California Angels baseball franchise).

However, Disney has not been without its disappointments. Disneyland Paris, formerly EuroDisney, has been Red Inkland since it opened in 1992. Also, Disney scuttled controversial plans for a US history theme park near a Civil War battlefield in Virginia.

Undeterred, CEO Michael Eisner is building on the Disney brand. He has assembled a new management team and is looking for new ways to extend the company's reach, such as the continuing release on video of Disney classics and the Broadway production of the *Beauty and the Beast* musical (originally released as an animated film).

Disney followed its 1994 blockbuster movie *The Lion King* with the release of *Pocahontas* and *Toy Story* the next year. *Pocahontas* brought in $140 million and was the #3 grossing film of 1995. But Disney doesn't cater just to kids. Miramax's *Pulp Fiction,* a very adult crime drama, was a smash hit, too.

WHEN

After his first animated film business failed, artist Walt Disney and his brother Roy started a film studio in 1923 in Hollywood. Walt directed the first Mickey Mouse cartoon, *Plane Crazy*, in 1928 (the 3rd, *Steamboat Willie*, was the first cartoon with a soundtrack). Disney's studio created short cartoons such as *The Three Little Pigs*.

The studio produced its first animated feature film, *Snow White*, in 1937 and *Fantasia* and *Pinocchio* in the 1940s. Disney produced *The Mickey Mouse Club* (1955-59) and a weekly television series (under a number of titles) that ran for 29 straight years. Disneyland opened in 1955 in Anaheim, California.

Walt Disney died in 1966 of lung cancer, and Roy became chairman. Disney World opened in Florida in 1971, and Roy died the same year. His son Roy E., then animation VP, became the company's principal individual shareholder. Without Walt's and Roy's leadership, Disney films went from over 50% of company revenues in 1971 to only 20% in 1979.

Walt's son-in-law Ron Miller became president in 1980. Two years later Epcot opened in Florida. Miller started Touchstone Pictures in order to produce films like *Splash* (1984), Disney's first hit since *The Love Bug* (1969). Texas's Bass family, in alliance with Roy E. Disney, bought a controlling interest in the

company in 1984. New CEO Michael Eisner (from film maker Paramount) and president Frank Wells (from movie producer Warner Bros.) ushered in a new era of innovation, prosperity, and high executive salaries.

The company started the Disney Channel (cable TV) and opened retail stores in the 1980s. Disney opened Tokyo Disneyland in 1984 and Disney-MGM Studios Theme Park in Florida in 1989.

Disney established Hollywood Records, a mainstream label, in 1990. Euro Disney opened near Paris in 1992 amid French concern over the park's possible effects on the nation's culture. The next year Disney bought Miramax Film Corp.

In 1994 Eisner underwent heart bypass surgery and president Frank Wells died in a helicopter crash, raising concerns about the company's future leadership. These worries were compounded by the resignation of Jeffrey Katzenberg (chairman of Disney's film unit) but apparently resolved with the naming of Creative Artists Agency chairman Michael Ovitz as the new Disney president in 1995.

That year Disney teamed up with 3 Baby Bells to develop, market, and deliver video programming. In 1996 Walt Disney Television signed a multimedia deal with production company Colossal Pictures.

WHO

Chairman and CEO: Michael D. Eisner, age 53, $8,774,707 pay
VC; Chairman, Walt Disney Feature Animation: Roy E. Disney, age 65, $900,000 pay
President: Michael Ovitz, age 48
SEVP and Chief of Corporate Operations: Sanford M. Litvack, age 59, $2,247,115 pay
SEVP and CFO: Richard D. Nanula
EVP Corporate Affairs: John F. Cooke, age 53, $1,119,616 pay
EVP Strategic Planning and Development: Lawrence P. Murphy, age 43, $1,025,769 pay
Chairman, Walt Disney Attractions: Richard A. Nunis, age 63
Chairman, Walt Disney Studios: Joseph E. Roth, age 47
President, Disney Consumer Products: Barton K. Boyd
President, Walt Disney Imagineering: Martin A. Sklar
SVP Human Resources: William J. Wilkinson, age 46
Auditors: Price Waterhouse LLP

WHERE

HQ: 500 S. Buena Vista St., Burbank, CA 91521
Phone: 818-560-1000
Fax: 818-560-1930
Web site: http://www.disney.com

WHAT

	1995 Sales		1995 Operating Income	
	$ mil.	% of total	$ mil.	% of total
Films	6,000	50	1,070	44
Theme parks	3,960	32	861	35
Consumer prods.	2,152	18	511	21
Total	**12,112**	**100**	**2,442**	**100**

Walt Disney

Filmed Entertainment
Buena Vista Television
Caravan Pictures
The Disney Channel
Hollywood Pictures
Hollywood Records
KCAL-TV, Los Angeles
Miramax Film Corp.
Touchstone Pictures
Touchstone Television
Walt Disney Pictures
Walt Disney Television
Walt Disney Theatrical Productions

Theme Parks and Resorts
Disney Vacation Club
Disneyland Paris (39%, France)
Disneyland Park (California)
Disney-MGM Studios Theme Park (Florida)
Disney's Fort Wilderness (camping and recreational areas)
Epcot (Florida)
Magic Kingdom (Florida)

Tokyo Disneyland (royalty earnings, Japan)
Walt Disney World (Florida)

Consumer Products
Disney Adventures magazine
Disney Hachette Presse
Disney Press
The Disney Stores
FamilyFun magazine
FamilyPC magazine
Hyperion Books For Children
Hyperion Press

Other
Capital Cities/ABC (ABC television network, cable TV channels, newspapers)
Disney Development Company
Disney Interactive (entertainment and educational software)
Disney Sports Enterprises
Walt Disney Imagineering

KEY COMPETITORS

Advance Publications	Hearst	Rank
Anheuser-Busch	King World	Samuel Goldwyn
Bertelsmann	Knight-Ridder	Savoy Pictures
Carsey-Werner	Lagardère	Scholastic
Cox Enterprises	LucasFilm	Sony
Dow Jones	MCA	Thomson Corp.
DreamWorks SKG	MGM	Time Warner
Gannett	Microsoft	Viacom
Golden Books	NBC	Virgin Group
	News Corp.	Washington Post
	Pearson	Westinghouse

HOW MUCH

NYSE symbol: DIS FYE: September 30	Annual Growth	1986	1987	1988	1989	1990	1991	1992	1993	1994	1995
Sales ($ mil.)	19.3%	2,470	2,925	3,497	4,594	5,843	6,182	7,504	8,529	10,055	12,112
Net income ($ mil.)	21.1%	247	445	522	703	824	637	817	671	1,110	1,380
Income as % of sales	—	10.0%	15.2%	14.9%	15.3%	14.1%	10.3%	10.9%	7.9%	11.0%	11.4%
Earnings per share ($)	21.2%	0.46	0.81	0.95	1.28	1.50	1.20	1.52	1.23	2.04	2.60
Stock price – high ($)	—	13.72	20.63	17.09	34.06	34.13	32.44	45.25	47.88	48.63	64.25
Stock price – low ($)	—	7.02	7.94	13.50	16.22	21.50	23.41	28.47	36.00	37.75	45.00
Stock price – close ($)	20.8%	10.78	14.81	16.44	28.00	25.38	28.63	43.00	42.63	46.00	58.88
P/E – high	—	30	26	18	27	23	27	30	39	24	25
P/E – low	—	15	10	14	13	14	20	19	29	19	17
Dividends per share ($)	17.1%	0.08	0.08	0.09	0.11	0.13	0.16	0.19	0.23	0.28	0.33
Book value per share ($)	18.7%	2.71	3.50	4.43	5.62	6.62	7.43	8.97	9.39	10.51	12.68
Employees	9.3%	32,000	30,000	39,000	47,000	52,000	58,000	58,000	62,000	65,000	71,000

1995 YEAR-END

Debt ratio: 31.0%
Return on equity: 22.7%
Cash (mil.): $1,077
Current ratio: 2.19
Long-term debt (mil.): $2,984
No. of shares (mil.): 524
Dividends
  Yield: 0.6%
  Payout: 12.7%
Market value (mil.): $30,877

STOCK PRICE HISTORY
HIGH/LOW/CLOSE

THE WASHINGTON POST COMPANY

OVERVIEW

The Washington Post Company posted record revenues in 1995 despite rising newsprint costs and a weak economy in the District of Columbia that hurt its core newspaper business. The Washington, DC-based media company is also engaged in magazine publishing, TV broadcasting, and cable TV. Its flagship publications are the *Washington Post* newspaper (whose publication of the Unabomber's manifesto in 1995 helped lead to the arrest of suspect Ted Kaczynski) and *Newsweek* magazine, the #2 weekly international news magazine (after *Time*). Its other publishing interests include Gazette Newspapers, which publishes 16 Maryland community newspapers; the Daily Herald Co., publisher of the *Herald* newspaper in Everett, Washington; and 50% of the English-language *International Herald Tribune* (Paris), which is distributed worldwide.

The company is looking to its nonprint media to boost profits. It owns 6 network-affiliated TV stations in Detroit; Hartford, Connecticut; Houston; Jacksonville, Florida; Miami; and San Antonio. Most are #1 or #2 in their markets. The firm also owns cable TV systems in 16 western, midwestern, and southern states. The Graham family controls the company.

In the search for a place in new media, the Post Company has made some mammoth errors. In 1995 the firm admitted it had made a "lousy decision," and wrote off the $28 million it had invested in Mammoth Micro Products, a CD-ROM maker it had purchased a year earlier, before it realized that the CD-ROM market was already overcrowded. Blaming costs and delays, the company sold its 80% stake (acquired in 1990) in American Personal Communications (wireless telephone systems).

WHEN

Stilson Hutchins, journalist and politician, published the first edition of the *Washington Post* in 1877. Strong reporting made the *Post* successful. Hutchins retired in 1889 and sold the *Post* to banker/politician Beriah Wilkins and journalist Frank Hatton. Hatton died in 1894, and the *Post* took on Wilkins's conservative leanings. In 1905 John McLean, an Ohio Democratic politician and inheritor of the *Cincinnati Enquirer*, bought the *Post*.

McLean focused on society columns and added color comics and sensational headlines. Hard news coverage took a back page to crime and scandal. By McLean's death (1916), the *Post* had resorted to the yellow journalism pioneered by William Randolph Hearst.

McLean's son Ned took over the *Post* and the *Enquirer*. Ned ruined the *Post*'s integrity by lying to a Senate committee (1924) about his involvement in the Teapot Dome oil scandal. He yielded *Post* management in 1932.

Wealthy, conservative banker Eugene Meyer bought the bankrupt *Post* for $825,000 in 1933. Meyer spent the next 12 years building a first-class news staff. By 1946, when Meyer's son-in-law Philip Graham took over as publisher, the *Post* was in the black again. In 1948 Meyer transferred his stock to Philip and his daughter Katharine.

Graham bought radio and TV stations and established overseas bureaus. In 1961 he bought *Newsweek* magazine and started a news service with the *Los Angeles Times*. In

1963 Philip Graham lost a struggle with manic depression and killed himself.

An editor since 1939, Katharine Graham became publisher after her husband's death. In 1971 the *Post* went public, though the Graham family retained control of the company. In 1972 young reporters Bob Woodward and Carl Bernstein broke the Pulitzer Prize-winning Watergate story, which led to President Richard Nixon's resignation. In the 1970s and 1980s, Graham bought TV and radio stations, databases, cable TV companies, newspapers, newsprint mills, and Stanley H. Kaplan Educational Centers.

In 1991 Katharine Graham's son Donald became CEO, and longtime executive editor Ben Bradlee retired. Also that year the *Post* and the *New York Times* bought out Whitcom's 1/3 interest in the *International Herald Tribune*. In 1992 the *Post* bought 84% of Gaithersburg Gazette (community newspapers, upped to 100% in 1993).

Donald Graham became chairman when his mother stepped down in 1993. Also that year the company created Digital Ink to explore interactive electronic publishing.

In 1994 the Post Company bought TV stations in Houston and San Antonio. In 1996 the company acquired Columbus Television Cable Corp., in Mississippi, for $23 million. Also in 1996, Newsweek columnist Joe Klein resigned after it was revealed that he was the anonymous author of *Primary Colors*, a thinly-veiled satire of the Clinton White House.

WHO

Chairman of the Executive Committee: Katharine Graham, age 78
Chairman and CEO; Publisher, *The Washington Post*: Donald E. Graham, age 50, $399,996 pay
President and COO: Alan G. Spoon, age 44, $830,279 pay
VP Planning and Development: Ross F. Hamachek
VP Technology: Ralph S. Terkowitz
VP, General Counsel, and Secretary: Diana M. Daniels, age 46
VP Finance, CFO, and Chief Accounting Officer: John B. Morse Jr., age 49, $447,247 pay
VP Human Resources: Beverly R. Keil, age 49, $376,836 pay
Controller: Hal S. Jones
Auditors: Price Waterhouse LLP

WHERE

HQ: 1150 15th St. NW, Washington, DC 20071
Phone: 202-334-6000
Fax: 202-334-1031
Web site: http://www.washingtonpost.com

WHAT

	1995 Sales		1995 Operating Income	
	$ mil.	% total	$ mil.	% total
Newspaper	729	42	110	37
Magazine	353	21	15	5
Broadcasting	306	18	132	44
Cable	194	11	41	14
Other	137	8	(27)	—
Total	**1,719**	**100**	**271**	**100**

News Publications and Organizations
Cowles Media Co. (28%, Minneapolis-St. Paul *Star Tribune*)
The Daily Herald Co. (*The Herald*; Everett, WA)
The Gazette Newspapers, Inc. (one newspaper and 15 weekly community papers in Maryland)
Hankuk Pan (Korean-language edition of *Newsweek*)
International Herald Tribune (50%, New York Times Co.)
Los Angeles Times-Washington Post News Service (50%)
Newsweek, *Newsweek Business Plus*, and *Newsweek Woman*
Newsweek InterActive (online magazine and CD-ROM)
Newsweek International (3 English-language editions)
Nihon Ban (Japanese-language edition of *Newsweek*)
The Washington Post (807,818 daily circulation)
The Washington Post National Weekly Edition

Television
PASS Sports (regional sports cable network, Detroit)
Post-Newsweek Cable (systems in 16 states)
Post-Newsweek Stations (KPRC-TV, Houston; KSAT-TV, San Antonio; WDIV-TV, Detroit; WFSB-TV, Hartford, CT; WJXT-TV, Jacksonville, FL; WPLG-TV, Miami)

Selected Other Businesses and Holdings
Bear Island Paper Co. (35%, newsprint)
Kaplan Educational Centers
LEGI-SLATE, Inc. (online database and legal publishing)
Moffett, Larson & Johnson (71%, telecommunications)

KEY COMPETITORS

Advance Publications	Knight-Ridder	Time Warner
Bloomberg	McGraw-Hill	Times Mirror
Capital Cities/ABC	NBC	Tribune
Cox Enterprises	New York Times	U.S. News & World Report
Dow Jones	News Corp.	Washington Times
E.W. Scripps	Pearson	Westinghouse/CBS
Gannett	Reed Elsevier	
Hearst	Reuters	
	TCI	
	Thomson Corp.	

HOW MUCH

NYSE symbol: WPO FYE: December 31	Annual Growth	1986	1987	1988	1989	1990	1991	1992	1993	1994	1995
Sales ($ mil.)	3.9%	1,215	1,315	1,367	1,444	1,438	1,380	1,450	1,498	1,614	1,719
Net income ($ mil.)	7.4%	100	187	269	198	175	119	128	154	170	190
Income as % of sales	—	8.2%	14.2%	19.7%	13.7%	12.1%	8.6%	8.8%	10.3%	10.5%	11.1%
Earnings per share ($)	9.1%	7.80	14.52	20.91	15.50	14.45	10.00	10.80	13.10	14.65	17.15
Stock price – high ($)	—	184.50	269.00	229.00	311.00	295.50	251.00	246.00	256.50	284.00	315.00
Stock price – low ($)	—	115.00	150.00	186.50	204.00	167.00	169.00	191.50	212.00	221.75	237.50
Stock price – close ($)	6.8%	156.00	187.00	210.75	281.50	198.00	194.50	229.75	254.75	242.50	282.00
P/E – high	—	24	19	11	20	20	25	23	20	19	18
P/E – low	—	15	10	9	13	12	17	18	16	15	14
Dividends per share ($)	16.4%	1.12	1.28	1.56	1.84	4.00	4.20	4.20	4.20	4.20	4.40
Book value per share ($)	13.6%	34.04	47.80	67.49	75.40	76.31	77.84	84.17	92.84	101.08	107.61
Employees	1.0%	6,400	6,400	6,300	6,200	6,200	6,100	6,400	6,600	6,800	7,010

1995 YEAR-END

Debt ratio: 4.1%
Return on equity: 16.5%
Cash (mil.): $160
Current ratio: 1.32
Long-term debt (mil.): $0
No. of shares (mil.): 11
Dividends
  Yield: 1.6%
  Payout: 25.7%
Market value (mil.): $3,104

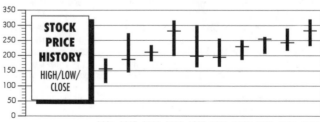

STOCK PRICE HISTORY HIGH/LOW/CLOSE 1986 1987 1988 1989 1990 1991 1992 1993 1994 1995

WESTINGHOUSE/CBS GROUP

OVERVIEW

Lagging behind other networks in the ratings war, "the Tiffany network" is trying to bring back some luster with a shake-up of its prime-time shows. New York City-based CBS, the world's 2nd oldest broadcasting network and the centerpiece of the Westinghouse/CBS Group under new owner Westinghouse, produces and distributes news, public affairs, entertainment, sports, and other programs. Top rated TV programs include *Cybill, Dr. Quinn, Medicine Woman*, and *60 Minutes*. It owns 15 TV stations and 39 radio stations and has 206 TV and 1,200 radio affiliates.

Group W Satellite Communications is Westinghouse/CBS Group's cable TV programming, satellite distribution, and new media division. It distributes the Nashville Network (TNN) to 65 million US homes.

CBS has been plagued by the losses of top executives, key station affiliates, and NFL broadcast rights. Plus, a ratings slump has placed it 3rd among the major networks and 4th behind Fox with younger viewers. To boost ratings it is shifting several programs' time slots and adding new shows starring Ted Danson and Bill Cosby.

Engineering powerhouse Westinghouse, through its Group W broadcasting unit, had already teamed up with CBS in the joint ownership of several TV stations before acquiring the network in 1995 as part of a plan to broaden its media operations.

WHEN

William Paley was plugging his father's Philadelphia-based La Palina cigars in radio advertisements. Sensing an opportunity, he bought control of the year-old Columbia Broadcasting System radio network in 1928, which had 16 affiliates but no stations of its own.

Paley changed the face of broadcasting, set industry standards, and gave the company its reputation as a first-class network. He promoted daytime dramas; raided stars from NBC such as George Burns, Gracie Allen, and Jack Benny; and built a strong news organization. Edward R. Murrow, who was at CBS from 1930 to 1960, broke new ground in news broadcasting. Local affiliates grew from 22 in 1928 to 97 in 1935.

In 1938 CBS bought American Recording (renamed CBS Records). CBS had hired scientist Peter Carl Goldmark in 1936; he invented the long-playing record in 1948. Goldmark worked on a color TV system, but the FCC approved RCA/NBC's color system in 1953.

CBS was #1 in entertainment ratings from 1955 to 1968. But it lost ratings and revenues in the early 1970s because its programs were not geared toward younger viewers. CBS bought cable companies in the 1960s, but the FCC soon prohibited network ownership of cable systems. Today's media behemoth Viacom was formed by CBS in a forced divestiture in 1970.

From the 1960s to the 1980s, CBS bought and sold the New York Yankees, Fender guitars, Steinway pianos, and other famous US corporate names in its attempts to diversify. In 1982 CBS and Twentieth Century Fox-Video formed CBS/Fox to distribute videocassettes, and in

1983 CBS, cable channel HBO, and CPI Film Holdings formed Tri-Star Pictures (sold, 1985).

Paley's inability to pick a successor left CBS leaderless between 1971 and 1986. During the mid-1980s it was also hurt financially by takeover attempts and a tumble in ratings after trusted news anchor Walter Cronkite retired. Cablemeister Ted Turner's attempt to bag the company in 1985 was blocked by CBS, which instead allowed conglomerate Loews Corp., led by Laurence Tisch, to buy almost 25% of CBS stock (later reduced to 18%). Tisch joined the CBS board, and in 1987 he became CEO.

Tisch sold CBS Records (to Sony) and the remaining book and magazine businesses in 1988. When Paley died in 1990, Tisch became chairman. Despite a jump to #1 in the ratings in 1991, the company was still losing money.

The broadcasting company was stunned in 1994 when it lost rights to National Football Conference games (after 38 years) to the Fox network and when key affiliates owned by New World Communications Group switched from CBS to Fox.

One of CBS's 2 top institutional investors gave Tisch a no-confidence vote in 1995. Taking the hint, Tisch struck a deal to sell CBS to Westinghouse for $5.4 billion. After the acquisition, Westinghouse's broadcast operations (Group W, including 5 TV and 18 radio stations) became part of the parent company's new Westinghouse/CBS Group.

In 1996 CBS took a step into Spanish-language broadcasting when Westinghouse bought Telenoticias, a 24-hour news channel seen in 22 countries, from Telemundo Group.

WHO

President and CEO, CBS Inc.: Peter A. Lund, age 54, $898,458 pay (prior to promotion)
EVP and CFO, Westinghouse: Fredric G. Reynolds
EVP, General Counsel, and Secretary: Ellen Oran Kaden, age 43
EVP; President, CBS Station Group: Bill Korn
President, CBS Entertainment Division: Leslie Moonves, age 45
President, CBS News Division: Andrew Heyward
President, CBS Television Network: Jame A. Warner
President, CBS Television Station Group: Jonathan Klein
President, CBS Sports Division: David Kenin, age 53
President, CBS Radio Station Group: Dan R. Mason
President, Group W Satellite Communications: Donald H. Mitzner
SVP Human Resources: Joan Showalter
Auditors: Price Waterhouse LLP

WHERE

HQ: 51 W. 52nd St., New York, NY 10019-6188
Phone: 212-975-4321
Fax: 212-975-8714
Web site: http://www.cbs.com

WHAT

Selected CBS TV Programs

Daytime
The Bold and the Beautiful
The Price Is Right
The Young and the Restless

Prime Time
60 Minutes
Cosby
Cybill
Dr. Quinn, Medicine Woman
The Nanny

Operating Business Groups:
CBS Entertainment, News and Sports
CBS Production and Syndication
CBS Radio Stations and Networks
CBS Television Network
CBS Television Stations
Group W Satellite Communications

Selected Holdings

CBS Radio Stations
KCBS (AM)/KRQR (FM), San Francisco
KCBS (FM)/KNX (AM), Los Angeles
KKRW (FM), Houston-Galveston
KLOU (FM)/KMOX (AM), St. Louis
KRRW (FM)/KTXQ (FM), Dallas-Fort Worth
WARW (FM), Washington, DC
WBBM (AM/FM), Chicago
WCBS (AM/FM), New York
WCCO (AM)/WLTE (FM), Minneapolis-St. Paul
WODS (FM), Boston
WOGL (FM)/WGMP (AM), Philadelphia
WYST (FM)/WWJ (AM), Detroit

CBS Television Stations
KCBS-TV, Los Angeles
WBBM-TV, Chicago
WCBS-TV, New York
WCCO-TV, Minneapolis-St. Paul
WFRV-TV, Green Bay-Appleton, WI
WGPR-TV, Detroit

Other
CBS Americas (Spanish-language radio news service)
CBS Broadcast International (overseas TV program sales)
CBS Enterprises (program distributor)
CBS Entertainment (TV programming)
CBS Video (50%, videocassette distributorship)
Radford Studio Center Inc. (production studio)
Station Partners (50%, Westinghouse TV stations)
Telenoticias (Spanish-language television broadcasting)

KEY COMPETITORS

BET	General Electric	News Corp.
A&E Networks	Hearst	Sony
Capital Cities/ABC	International	TCI
Chris-Craft	Family	Time Warner
Clear Channel	Entertainment	Tribune
Cox Enterprises	King World	Viacom
Gannett	New World	Westwood One
Gaylord	Communications	
Entertainment	NBC	

HOW MUCH

Private Company FYE: December 31	Annual Growth	1986	1987	1988	1989	1990	1991	1992	1993	1994	1995
Sales ($ mil.)	(3.6%)	4,646	2,762	2,778	2,962	3,261	3,035	3,503	3,510	3,712	3,333
Net income ($ mil.)	9.6%	389	453	283	297	112	(86)	163	326	282	—
Income as % of sales	—	8.4	16.4	10.2	10.0	3.4	—	4.6	9.3	7.6	—
Employees	(7.5%)	18,300	7,025	6,500	6,750	6,650	6,160	6,500	6,500	6,400	9,000

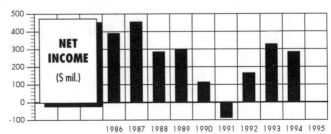

NET INCOME ($ mil.)

W H SMITH GROUP PLC

OVERVIEW

Based in London, W H Smith is the largest music, book, newspaper, and magazine retailer in the UK. The company operates 4 retail chains: W H Smith (newspapers and magazines, popular books, stationery, CDs, tapes, and videos), Waterstone's (bookstores), the Virgin Our Price entertainment megastore group, and a chain of home improvement centers. The growth of supermarket and specialist chains in the UK has contributed to W H Smith Group's first decline in retail sales in nearly 20 years.

The company also distributes newspapers and periodicals via W H Smith News and Heathcote Books. Its 2nd largest unit, W H Smith News serves 3 primary customers: newspaper publishers, magazine publishers,

and newsstands. The division began restructuring in 1995, introducing separate operational networks for its newspaper and magazine distribution and an integrated service for its retail customers. Heathcote sales increased in 1995 as a result of growing distribution to retail chains Boots and Virgin Retail.

In the US W H Smith operates 3 retail chains: W H Smith (news and gifts), The Wall (music), and Waterstone's (books) that have defied the normally flat performance of UK retailers in the US. The company is one of the leading book retailers in the Northeast US, with stores in airports and resort hotels. Though Waterstone's is still at an experimental stage in the US, 7 new stores were opened in airports around the US in 1995.

WHEN

When Henry Walton Smith died in 1792, his wife was left to run the family store. Their sons, Henry Edward and William Henry, took over the business in 1816 and made newspaper distribution outside London a top priority. The brothers opened a branch office in 1820 and the business was renamed W H Smith (after William Henry) in 1829.

The first trains were introduced into England in the mid-1800s, and with them came a new type of consumer — travelers. By 1851 W H Smith operated 35 bookstalls in train stations around England, selling not only newspapers, but rugs, foot warmers, and games. In 1857 William Henry Smith retired, leaving the business to his son, William Henry II.

The company operated 1,240 train station bookstalls by 1901. But rent disputes forced W H Smith to vacate these premises, relocating on the main roads on the way into the railway stations. Grasping the potential for bookshops in town centers, the company opened 144 shops in a few months. To meet the increased demand for newspapers outside London, the company also built provincial warehouses, which supplied local newsstands.

By 1920 the wholesale businesses established 2 decades earlier expanded to meet more diverse needs, selling anything from sweets to china dolls. W H Smith & Son Ltd became a publicly held company in 1949, after acquiring bookseller Sherrat & Hughes in 1946. It bought book retailer Bowes & Bowes in 1953.

The company continued to expand throughout the 1950s. Rock-n-roll was shaking the collective British booty and by the early 1960s the retailer had expanded its music sections.

W H Smith sought diversification, and the home improvement market beckoned in the 1970s. It acquired a home center chain in 1979, renaming it W H Smith Do It All.

W H Smith increased its book retail holdings in 1985, acquiring the Websters chain and changing its name to Sherrat & Hughes. The company entered the US market via airport and hotel shops for travelers that same year, acquiring Elson Holdings and renaming the company W H Smith Inc.

To meet the challenge posed by the growth of specialty retail chains in the 1980s, it acquired the 100-store Our Price Music chain in 1986 and 74 stores from Virgin Retail in 1988. The W H Smith Group (as the parent company became known) also expanded into video in the late 1980s, introducing the first Our Price Video shop in 1989. In the US the 19-store Wee Three music chain was bought the same year and through acquisitions the company expanded its music stores in this country to more than 100 locations. When the Sherrat & Hughes chain merged with Waterstone's that same year, W H Smith became majority shareholder.

In 1991 a Waterstone's bookstore was opened in Boston. The next year the company formed a joint venture with Virgin Retail to develop megastores in select UK markets.

In 1996 W H Business Supplies was sold to Guilbert of France to reduce company debt. It also planned to open 50 new W H Smith stores. Waterstone's Booksellers unit closed a Chicago store in 1996 but the company planned to open as many as 10 Waterstone's stores in the US throughout the year.

WHO

Chairman: Jeremy Hardie, age 57, £178,000 pay
Group CEO: Bill Cockburn
Director Group Finance: John Napier, age 58,
£210,000 pay
Managing Director, Distribution and Support Services:
David Roberts, age 52, £172,000 pay
CEO, W H Smith Group (USA) Inc.: John Hancock
Auditors: Deloitte & Touche LLP

WHERE

HQ: Strand House, 7 Holbein Place, London,
SW1W 8NR, UK
Phone: +44-(0)71-730-1200
Fax: +44-(0)71-259-0195
US HQ: 3200 Windy Hill Rd., Ste. 1500, Atlanta, GA
30339-770
US Phone: 770-952-0705
US Fax: 770-951-1352

	1995 Sales	
	£ mil.	% of total
Europe	2,449	91
US	240	9
Total	**2,689**	**100**

WHAT

	1995 Sales	
	£ mil.	% of total
Retailing — UK and Europe		
W H Smith Retail	916	34
Virgin Our Price	414	15
Waterstone's	148	6
Retailing — USA		
W H Smith Inc	127	5
The Wall Inc	106	4
Waterstone's Inc	7	—
Distribution — UK and Europe		
W H Smith News and Books	806	30
W H Smtih Business Supplies	165	6
Total	**2,689**	**100**

KEY COMPETITORS

Barnes & Noble
Best Buy
Borders
Camelot Music
Crown Books
Dayton Hudson
Hollywood Entertainment
Host Marriott
Kmart
Ladbroke
Lauriat's
Marks & Spencer
MTS
Musicland
Thorn EMI
Trans World Entertainment
Venture Stores
Wal-Mart
The Wiz

HOW MUCH

Principal exchange: London FYE: May 31	Annual Growth	1986	1987	1988	1989	1990	1991	1992	1993	1994	1995
Sales (£ mil.)	8.6%	1,281	1,543	1,745	1,941	2,209	2,171	2,128	2,312	2,442	2,689
Net income (£ mil.)	9.3%	30	—	—	98	85	46	81	84	55	67
Income as % of sales	—	2.3%	—	—	5.1%	3.8%	2.1%	3.8%	3.6%	2.3%	2.5%
Earnings per share (p)	—	0	0	0	47	40	28	32	30	20	24
Stock price – high (p)	—	351	404	327	348	382	494	528	528	550	483
Stock price – low (p)	—	212	254	185	208	258	302	356	428	425	247
Stock price – close (p)	5.5%	262	297	218	328	363	450	498	510	479	424
P/E – high	—	—	—	—	7	10	18	17	18	28	20
P/E – low	—	—	—	—	4	6	11	11	14	21	10
Dividends per share (p)	13.8%	5	8	9	10	11	12	13	14	15	16
Book value per share (p)	4.1%	—	—	—	137	144	122	170	179	170	174
Employees	3.0%	25,710	28,423	30,780	34,530	35,131	30,136	30,517	30,088	30,512	33,625

1995 YEAR-END:

Debt ratio: 58.5%
Return on equity: 13.9%
Cash (mil.): £70
Current ratio: —
Long-term debt (mil.): £190
No. of shares (mil.): 280
Dividends
    Yield: 3.8%
    Payout: 66.9%
Market value (mil.): $1,837
Sales (mil.): $4,617

Note: £=$1.55 (May 31, 1995)

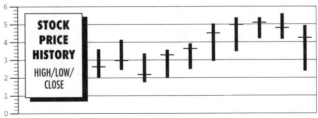

STOCK PRICE HISTORY HIGH/LOW/CLOSE

1986 1987 1988 1989 1990 1991 1992 1993 1994 1995

WOLTERS KLUWER NV

OVERVIEW

Amsterdam-based Wolters Kluwer plans to be a world leader in the professional publishing market. To that end, it has acquired leading US law and tax publisher Commerce Clearing House (CCH) for $1.9 billion. The Dutch publisher produces information in print and electronic formats for professionals in the US and 16 European countries. Its publications cover business, education, legal and tax affairs, medical and scientific information, trade publishing, and other markets. It also offers training and educational services through its Swiss-based Krauthammer International.

The company's earlier strategy of acquiring medium-sized companies, primarily in Europe, took a major turn with the 1995 acquisition of CCH. Before the purchase only 10% of Wolters Kluwer's employees were based in the US; now, approximately 35% are. The acquisition also boosted the company's tax and legal publishing activities from 28% of sales to about 45%. More importantly, the purchase gave Wolters Kluwer a beachhead in the rapidly growing US electronic publishing market (1/3 of CCH's products are online).

Facing a rapidly consolidating market, the company had to pay a hefty price to outbid Anglo-Dutch rival Reed Elsevier (owner of the Lexis-Nexis electronic information system) for the US firm.

WHEN

Wolters Kluwer was formed in 1987 when venerable Dutch publisher Wolters Samson merged with its fellow publisher Kluwer.

Wolters, Samson, and Kluwer were all pioneers in the Dutch publishing industry in the 19th century. J. B. Wolters founded a publishing house in 1836 to provide instructional material for the growing number of educational establishments in the Netherlands. The company later merged with educational publisher Noordhoff, founded in 1858. J. B. Wolters had no children and his family business went to his brother-in-law E. B. ter Horst in 1860.

Dutch academic Anthony Schepman took over the management of Wolters-Noordhoff in 1917 and led it on a major expansion drive. (In 1920 the company opened an office in the Dutch colony of Indonesia.)

Wolters-Noordhoff and Information and Communication Union (ICU) merged in 1972. ICU had been formed by the 1970 merger of Samson (founded by Nicholaas Samson in 1883 to print government publications) and publisher A. W. Sijthoff. After the Wolters-Noordhoff-ICU merger, the resulting company initially took the ICU name but in 1983 changed it to the Wolters Samson Group to greater reflect the company's heritage. That year Wolters Samson began exploring a merger with Kluwer.

Abele Kluwer, a former assistant schoolteacher, became a publisher in 1889. His publishing house specialized in educational publications and children's books, including *De Sollicitant (The Applicant)*, an advertising paper for schoolteachers, and *The Thinker*, an arithmetic book for secondary schools. The company expanded its range of publications in the 1920s to provide readers with up-to-date information regarding new laws, regulations, court decisions, and scholarly texts, in a growing number of loose-leaf publications. Kluwer hired its first nonfamily managing director, J. M. Gorter, in 1957 and went public in 1967.

Reed Elsevier, 50%-owned by publishing titans Reed International (UK) and Elsevier (the Netherlands), made a bid to acquire Kluwer in 1987, buying 30% of Kluwer's shares. The Anglo-Dutch concern was rebuffed by the subsequent merger of Wolters Samson with Kluwer, however, and was left with about 1/3 of the shares in the new company.

Despite Reed Elsevier's repeated advances to work closely with Wolters Kluwer, the new company pursued an independent growth strategy. In 1990 it acquired J.B. Lippincott, a US health care publisher. That year Reed Elsevier sold its 33% stake in the company.

As part of its strategy of acquiring European medium-sized companies, in 1992 Wolters Kluwer purchased Spanish legal publisher Actualidad. The next year it bought Liber, Sweden's #2 publisher. The company acquired Groupe Lamarre, a Paris-based publisher of medical periodicals, in 1994.

In 1995 Wolters Kluwer acquired CCH from the Thorne family. CCH had been founded in 1892 as Commerce Clearing House to publish import/export and income tax guides. The Thorne family bought into the company in 1907. By the 1980s CCH was so well versed in tax law that its largest customer was the US Internal Revenue Service. In the years leading up to its purchase by Wolters Kluwer, CCH had been delving deeper into electronic publishing.

WHO

Chairman: Cor J. Brakel
Executive Director; Chairman, Wolters Kluwer UK; Chairman, Wolters Kluwer US: P. W. van Wel
Executive Director, Central and Eastern Europe: C. H. van Kempen
Executive Director: R. Pieterse
Director and CFO: J. E. M. van Dinter
Director, Accounting & Control, Real Estate: P. C. Kooijmans
Director, Business Development: A. S. F. Kuipers
Director, Personnel & Organization: M. H. Sanders
Secretary to the Executive Board: H. van Zaaijen
Auditors: KPMG Peat Marwick LLP

WHERE

HQ: Stadhouderskade 1, Postbus 818, NL-1000 AV Amsterdam, The Netherlands
Phone: +31-20-607-0450
Fax: +31-20-607-0490
US HQ: Wolters Kluwer US, 2700 Lake Cook Rd., Riverwoods, IL 60015-3888
US Phone: 847-267-7000
US Fax: 847-267-2674
Web site: http://www.kluwer.nl

	1995 Sales % of total
The Netherlands	33
Sweden/Norway/Denmark	10
US	10
Belgium	9
France	7
UK	7
Germany	6
Italy	5
Other countries	13
Total	**100**

WHAT

	1995 Sales		1995 Operating Income	
	Fl mil.	% of total	Fl mil.	% of total
Business publishing	911	31	191	31
Legal & tax publishing	834	28	204	34
Educational publishing & professional training	627	21	103	17
Medical/scientific publishing	460	16	94	15
Trade publishing & other	112	4	17	3
Total	**2,944**	**100**	**609**	**100**

Selected Publishers
Actualidad (legal publishing, Spain)
CCH (law and tax publishing, US)
Croner Publications (business and educational publishing, UK)
Educatieve Partners Nederland (educational publications)
Groupe Lamarre (medical periodicals, France)
Krauthammer International (professional training, Switzerland)
Lamy Juristes (electronic legal database, France)
Liber (educational publishing, Sweden)
Lippincott-Raven Publishers (medical publications, US)
Teleroute International (European electronic road transport information system, Belgium)

KEY COMPETITORS

Bureau of National Affairs	John Wiley McGraw-Hill	Thomson Corp. Times Mirror
CDB Infotek	Pearson	Tribune
Equifax	Plenum	VNU
Hearst	Publishing	Waverly
Houghton Mifflin	Reed Elsevier	W.W. Norton

HOW MUCH

OTC symbol: WTKWY (ADR) FYE: December 31	Annual Growth	1986	1987	1988	1989	1990	1991	1992	1993	1994	1995
Sales (Fl mil.)	7.5%	—	1,651	1,739	1,883	2,036	2,381	2,355	2,616	2,736	2,944
Net income (Fl mil.)	22.5%	—	89	112	140	173	214	258	318	382	452
Income as % of sales	—	—	5.4%	6.4%	7.4%	8.5%	9.0%	11.0%	12.2%	14.0%	15.4%
Earnings per share (Fl)	17.1%	—	1.91	2.36	2.88	3.19	3.67	4.28	4.90	5.79	6.75
Stock price – high (Fl)	—	—	35.00	40.15	53.30	57.20	63.80	86.00	129.00	133.50	151.90
Stock price – low (Fl)	—	—	22.25	27.40	36.20	42.20	44.80	61.50	81.00	101.20	117.80
Stock price – close (Fl)	23.3%	—	28.40	36.30	44.90	48.10	60.70	81.50	122.70	128.40	151.80
P/E – high	—	—	18	17	19	18	17	20	26	23	23
P/E – low	—	—	12	12	13	13	12	14	17	17	17
Dividends per share (Fl)	16.2%	—	0.65	0.78	0.88	1.00	1.16	1.32	1.52	1.80	2.16
Book value per share (Fl)	42.3%	—	11.58	12.95	12.85	8.38	7.45	10.72	8.57	9.19	10.94
Employees	1.6%	—	7,937	8,037	8,234	7,842	8,732	8,089	8,052	8,693	8,993

1995 YEAR-END:

Debt ratio: 7.8%
Return on equity: 67.5%
Cash (mil.): Fl317
Current ratio: 0.97
Long-term debt (mil.): Fl62
No. of shares (mil.): 67
Dividends
  Yield: 1.4%
  Payout: 32.0%
Market value (mil.): $6,326
Sales (mil.): $1,830

Note: $=Fl1.6 (December 31, 1995)

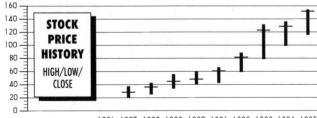

STOCK PRICE HISTORY HIGH/LOW/CLOSE 1986 1987 1988 1989 1990 1991 1992 1993 1994 1995

WORLD COLOR PRESS, INC.

OVERVIEW

World Color has made a strong impression on several leading US magazine publishers. Hearst, Forbes, K-III Communications, and the New York Times Sports & Leisure Group are among those that use its printing services. Magazines printed by the company include *Cosmopolitan*, *Good Housekeeping*, *Newsweek*, *Rolling Stone*, and *Vogue*. The New York City-based enterprise is also a leading US producer of catalogs (for companies such as Spiegel and Victoria's Secret). It produces commercial material (such as annual reports and travel brochures), directories (primarily for Pacific Bell), and direct mail; and it offers binding and finishing services. Through its New Media division, it also converts cus-

tomers' printed materials for use on electronic media, such as on video, CD-ROMs, and the World Wide Web. The company runs a network of 24 production and distribution facilities and an extensive sales network across the US.

World Color is diversifying its markets, moving away from a dependence on publications. In 1991 publications accounted for more than 60% of revenues, but by 1995 they made up only 31%. The company has also expanded by acquiring other printers. Between 1993 and 1995 it acquired 9 companies for more than $400 million.

Prior to its IPO in 1996, World Color was wholly owned by investment marauders KKR. KKR currently owns 50% of the company.

WHEN

Like the Eiffel Tower, the World Color Press was set up as a short-term project in connection with an international exposition, but it lasted far beyond it. The company was formed as World's Fair Color Printing in 1903 by the owners of the St. Louis *Star* newspaper with the object of providing the color printing for the World's Fair in St. Louis in 1904. After the fair the company continued operating as a commercial printer, under the name World Color Printing, to produce the newspaper's color cartoon section.

Star employees Robert Grable and Roswell Messing acquired the company in 1922. Under their leadership the company, renamed World Color Press, made its first major acquisition, St. Louis-based printer Commercial Color Press, in 1928. The business moved into producing comic books. Though at first the comics were compilations of the Sunday "funnies," by 1936 World Color was printing comic books with original material. The company was the country's leading producer of comic books in the 1940s and 1950s. It introduced one of the industry's first web-offset presses in its Sparta, Illinois, plant.

In 1968 World Color was acquired by City Investing, a New York City-based diversified company. The firm boosted its standing as a printing house with the acquisition in 1974 of Fawcett Printing (Louisville, Kentucky), a printing company with rotogravure presses (advance color presses used in magazine printing). The firm built another rotogravure plant a year later.

World Color diversified into the catalog, retail insert, commercial, and directory markets

in the 1980s. During that decade it built several plants, each offering sophisticated prepress, customized binding, and inkjet labeling services, and the printing industry's most advanced shipping and mailing systems. Under the ownership of KKR, which took over the company in 1984, World Color acquired high-end commercial printers Bradley Printing Co. (1985) and Midwest Litho Arts (1987). In 1989 it opened Network Color Technology. A new management team, led by CEO Robert Burton (a former VP with media juggernaut Capital Cities/ABC), took over running the company in 1991.

In 1993 the firm acquired the Alden Press Co., the #1 printer and distributor of specialty consumer catalogs and direct mail advertising, and George Rice & Sons, a leading commercial printer. World Color accelerated its acquisition drive in 1994 and 1995, purchasing 7 more companies. In 1994 it bought Web Inserts (catalog inserts) and Universal Graphics (digital prepress operations). The following year it absorbed the Lanman Cos. (prepress and commercial production), Northeast Graphics (commercial printing), Wessel Co. (direct mail printing), Image Technologies (multimedia), and Digital Pre-Press.

In 1996 the company went public. That year World Color agreed to acquire Shea Communications, a closely held commercial printer with plants in Oklahoma and Kentucky. Shea had 1995 revenues of $85 million.

WHO

Chairman, President, and CEO: Robert G. Burton, age 57, $1,587,500 pay
EVP, COO, CFO, and Treasurer: Marc L. Reisch, age 40, $730,833 pay
EVP, Chief Legal and Administrative Officer, and Secretary (HR): Jennifer L. Adams, age 36, $550,833 pay
President, Publication and Directory Sales: Martin K. Jacobus, age 44, $427,500 pay
President, Manufacturing: Michael W. Harris, age 41, $356,000 pay
President, Catalog Sales: Dennis R. Hiser, age 55
Group President, Publication and Catalog: John E. Van Horn, age 55
SVP Purchasing and Logistics: Jerome V. Brofft, age 51
SVP and Controller: Raymond B. Zerrusen, age 35
SVP Sales: Rick Johnson
Auditors: Deloitte & Touche LLP

WHERE

HQ: 101 Park Ave., 19th Fl., New York, NY 10178
Phone: 212-986-2440
Fax: 212-455-9266

WHAT

	1995 Sales
	% of total
Magazines	31
Commercial	30
Catalogs	23
Direct mail	9
Directories	7
Total	**100**

Selected Products

Advertising inserts
Annual reports
Bind-in envelopes
Brochures
Catalogs
Directories
Interactive multimedia (CD-ROMS and Web sites)
Magazines
Order forms
Posters
Product labels
Retail inserts

Selected Services

Conventional and digital prepress operations; direct-to-plate capability; all-digital printing
Customized binding and inkjet imaging
Distribution and mailing services
Perfect and saddlestitch binding
Sheetfed, web offset, rotogravure, and flexographic printing for short and long runs

KEY COMPETITORS

Banta
Big Flower Press
Cadmus Communications
Champion Industries
Continental Graphics
Courier
Dai Nippon Printing
Graphic Industries
Merrill Corp.
Moore
Quad/Graphics
Quebecor
Ringier
R. R. Donnelley
Taylor Corp.
Treasure Chest Advertising

HOW MUCH

NYSE symbol: WRC FYE: December 31	Annual Growth	1986	1987	1988	1989	1990	1991	1992	1993	1994	1995
Sales ($ mil.)	17.4%	—	—	—	—	—	681	661	826	972	1,295
Net income ($ mil.)	0.0%	—	—	—	—	—	(59)	(6)	(121)	24	10
Income as % of sales	—	—	—	—	—	—	—	—	2.4%	0.8%
Employees	9.7%	—	—	—	—	—	—	6,219	6,450	7,300	8,200

1995 YEAR-END:

Debt ratio: 55.6%
Cash (mil.): $9
Current ratio: 1.68
Long-term debt (mil.): $450

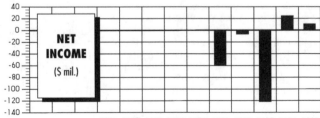

NET INCOME ($ mil.)

WPP GROUP PLC

OVERVIEW

WPP has the worldwide advertising market all wired up. Headquartered in London, it is the world's largest advertising holding company, maintaining more than 780 offices in 84 countries around the globe and provides services to more than 300 of the *FORTUNE* 500 companies. Its advertising operations are led by J. Walter Thompson Company and Ogilvy & Mather Worldwide.

WPP's Millward Brown International and Research International units perform marketing research and track the effectiveness of clients' advertising campaigns. The holding company's specialized communications services include direct marketing, sales promotion, design, and special-market advertising. Its Hill and Knowlton and Ogilvy Adams & Rinehart subsidiaries make up WPP's public relations businesses. Finally, subsidiary Wire and Plastic Products continues the company's original business — the manufacture of commercial, industrial, and consumer products — though it brings in a minute percentage of WPP's sales.

North America accounts for about 40% of the company's sales, but it is growing throughout the world. Increased market share in Continental Europe and in emerging markets, such as Asia/Pacific and Latin America, have buoyed its revenues.

WHEN

The company was founded in 1971 in the UK and operated until 1985 as Wire and Plastic Products, a maker of grocery baskets and other goods. A group of investors led by a former Saatchi & Saatchi advertising executive, Martin Sorrell, bought the company in 1986 and shortened its name to WPP. He used the company to buy several small marketing firms specializing in graphics and design, incentives and motivation, promotions, and electronic communications. The company began purchasing US marketing firms in 1987. Late that year it bought its first traditional advertising firm when Sorrell used revenues from the acquired businesses and a sizable loan to purchase J. Walter Thompson, a US advertising warhorse (and owner of Hill & Knowlton) founded in 1878. WPP established Conquest advertising in 1988 to serve multinational clients in Europe.

The company (and its debt) grew again in 1989 when WPP bought the Ogilvy Group, Inc., which was founded in 1948 and owned Ogilvy & Mather advertising. The purchase made WPP the world's largest advertising agency passing Sorrell's former employer, Saatchi & Saatchi. However, it also set up the company for a big fall in 1991 when the depressed economies of the US and the UK put the brakes on its clients' advertising expenditures. WPP suspended its dividend (restored in 1993) and renegotiated its debts.

Though some analysts predicted the slump would lead WPP to break up and sell off its assets, the company survived when markets in the US, Asia/Pacific, and South America rebounded in 1992. That year WPP started its CommonHealth unit to provide specialized health care marketing services around the world.

WPP learned from its previous overextension and entered a period of controlled growth (no major acquisitions) in 1993. The company expanded throughout the world in 1994, opening new offices in Amsterdam, Brazil, Chile, Bulgaria, Colombia, Cyprus, Estonia, Germany, Italy, Tokyo, Turkey, and Vietnam.

Winning the estimated $500 million international advertising contract for computer giant IBM in 1994 reflected WPP's recovery from its skid in the early 1990s. Unfortunately for the company, however, the addition of IBM to its client roster led to the departure of key rivals, including telephone service and equipment maker AT&T, computer maker Compaq's European division, and software maker Microsoft.

Pressure from shareholders over Sorrell's salary in 1995 led the WPP board to modify the CEO's compensation package, which could have netted him $39 million for the year. The new plan, which placed tougher standards on Sorrell's bonus, lessened his maximum salary to a paltry $35 million.

Sorrell focused the company in 1996 on such fast-growing markets as Asia and Latin America. That year WPP formed the Enterprise Identity Group, which combined units in New York, Hong Kong, London, San Francisco, and Taiwan, allowing the company to more easily offer its international corporate identity consulting services to clients around the globe.

Also in 1996 WPP purchased a 5% stake in the HotWired Internet-based service of Wired Ventures. The move symbolized its ambition to stay at the forefront of technology and explore how advertising will be used on the Internet.

Chairman: Gordon K. G. Stevens, age 69
Group CEO: Martin S. Sorrell, age 50
Group Finance Director: Robert E. Lerwill, age 43
Chairman and CEO, Ogilvy & Mather Worldwide:
Charlotte Beers
Chairman and CEO, J. Walter Thompson Co.:
Burt Manning
CEO, Kantar Group: Philip Barnard
Director Human Resources: Brian J. Brooks, age 39
Auditors: Andersen Worldwide

WHERE

HQ: 27 Farm St., London, W1X 6RD, UK
Phone: +44-71-408-2204
Fax: +44-71-493-6819
US HQ: 309 W. 49th St., New York, NY 10019-7399
US Phone: 212-632-2200
US Fax: 212-632-2222

	1995 Sales	1995 Operating Profits
	% of total	% of total
North America	42	39
Continental Europe	20	26
UK	19	16
Other regions	19	19
Total	**100**	**100**

WHAT

	1995 Sales	1995 Operating Profits
	% of total	% of total
Media advertising	56	71
Specialist communications	22	18
Market research	16	13
Public relations	6	(2)
Total	**100**	**100**

Selected Operations

Media Advertising
J. Walter Thompson Co.
Ogilvy & Mather
Worldwide

Market Research
BMRB
Millward Brown
Research International

Public Relations
Hill and Knowlton
Ogilvy Adams & Rinehart

Specialist Communications
Anspach Grossman
Portugal
Brouillard
Communications
Einson FreemanFerguson
Communications
Mendoza Dillon &
Asociados
Oakley Young
Promotional Campaigns
RTC Direct
Scott Stern

KEY COMPETITORS

Bozell, Jacobs
Catalina
Marketing
CKS
Cordiant
Creative Artists
D'Arcy Masius
Dentsu
Edelman Public
Relations
Grey Advertising
Havas
Heritage Media
Interpublic
Group
Leo Burnett
M/A/R/C
New Saatchi
Agency
Omnicom Group
Publicis
TMP Worldwide
True North
Young &
Rubicam

HOW MUCH

Principal exchange: London FYE: December 31	Annual Growth	1986	1987	1988	1989	1990	1991	1992	1993	1994	1995
Sales (£ mil.)	59.0%	24	284	547	1,005	1,264	1,204	1,273	1,431	1,427	1,555
Net income (£ mil.)	60.1%	1	7	21	38	51	31	(12)	23	47	69
Income as % of sales	—	4.2%	2.5%	3.8%	3.8%	4.0%	2.6%	—	1.6%	3.3%	4.4%
Earnings per share (p)	(4.0%)	13	32	54	73	67	24	(8)	3	7	9
Stock price – high (p)	—	—	—	—	—	579	196	96	105	129	164
Stock price – low (p)	—	—	—	—	—	38	27	26	44	90	101
Stock price – close (p)	24.0%	—	—	—	—	56	42	40	89	110	164
P/E – high	—	—	—	—	—	9	8	—	31	20	18
P/E – low	—	—	—	—	—	1	1	—	13	14	11
Dividends per share (p)	(20.5%)	—	—	5	24	13	0	0	1	1	1
Book value per share (p)	—	—	—	1.28	(7.55)	(5.23)	(4.51)	(0.95)	(0.33)	(0.15)	(0.08)
Employees	52.6%	426	5,366	10,443	17,568	22,590	21,218	20,717	20,416	19,198	19,138

1995 YEAR-END:

Debt ratio: 125.5%
Return on equity: —
Cash (mil.): £376
Current ratio: 0.89
Long-term debt (mil.): £233
No. of shares (mil.): 737
Dividends
  Yield: 0.8%
  Payout: 14.4%
Market value (mil.): $1,873
Sales (mil.): $2,410

Note: £=$1.55 December 31, 1995

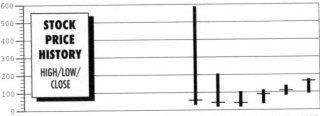

STOCK PRICE HISTORY
HIGH/LOW/CLOSE

1986 1987 1988 1989 1990 1991 1992 1993 1994 1995

YOUNG & RUBICAM INC.

OVERVIEW

How many tubes of toothpaste does a company have to sell to pay for $650 million in advertising billings? Young & Rubicam (Y&R) is going to find out. In 1995 Colgate-Palmolive consolidated its worldwide brand advertising with Young & Rubicam Advertising (the New York City-based company's flagship business), pulling an estimated $200 million in billings from True North Communications, parent of Foote, Cone & Belding. This puts the advertising agency at the forefront of 2 industry trends — account consolidation and "cost-and-performance" compensation. As more multibrand manufacturers award their accounts to fewer agencies, competition will become more intense. And performance-based payment will bring increasing profit pressure.

For now, employee-owned Y&R is well placed to handle these developments. It is the US's 3rd largest advertising agency, after Omnicom and Interpublic. The company operates in 5 primary areas: advertising, public relations, sales promotion/direct marketing, corporate and product identity consulting, and health care communications. And it has the international strength to provide all the services a multinational company requires, with more than 300 offices worldwide.

WHEN

In 1923 Raymond Rubicam and John Orr Young founded their Philadelphia advertising agency literally on a shoestring — their first client was Presto Quick Tip Shoelaces. Y&R got its first major client, General Foods, when it asked for and received the account for the company's least-successful product, Postum. Its success in increasing sales of that beverage led to more business with General Foods and to a 1926 move to New York at that client's request. With its informal atmosphere and tolerance for eccentric behavior, the agency soon became a haven for leading creative people.

In 1931 the firm opened an office in Chicago. In the early 1930s Rubicam, who by then dominated the firm, recruited George Gallup to create advertising's first research department. In 1934 Young was forced out; the firm, despite its unconventional working environment, had become a hard-driving place.

The Depression put many agencies out of business, but Y&R's billings grew from $6 million in 1927 to $22 million in 1937. It became the 2nd largest agency, after J. Walter Thompson. WWII brought surprising prosperity to the advertising industry. By 1945 Y&R's billings reached $53 million. Rubicam had retired to Arizona in 1944 at age 52.

The agency prospered during the 1950s: billings reached $212 million in 1960. During the next decade Y&R produced the first color television commercials and a series of notable campaigns. The company's emphasis on creativity, teamwork, and group management worked less effectively, as growth slowed and expenses and staff ballooned.

Edward Ney became CEO in 1970. He cut staff and installed Alex Kroll as creative director. Kroll required that creativity be controlled and disciplined and that it produce sales results. Ney expanded the agency through acquisitions, which included Wunderman Worldwide (direct marketing, 1973), Cato Johnson (sales promotion, 1976), and Burson-Marsteller (public relations, 1979).

By 1975, when Kroll became president of US operations, billings of $477 million had made Y&R the #1 US agency. Since 1979 it has been the largest independent agency in the US. The advertising industry underwent considerable consolidation during the 1980s, forcing Y&R to compete with increasingly large and deep-pocketed advertising holding companies (like Omnicom and Interpublic). During this period the company became increasingly bureaucratic, known more for good strategy than for creativity.

The company's problems grew in the 1990s. Early in the decade Y&R pleaded guilty to bribery charges in connection with a Jamaican tourism account, and HDM Worldwide, a partnership with Dentsu (Japan) and Eurocom (France), fell apart when the latter withdrew. Y&R and Dentsu, partners for 30 years, regrouped as Dentsu, Young & Rubicam Partnerships.

In 1994 the company was shaken when one of its top executives, Thomas Mosser, was killed by a bomb attributed to the Unabomber. Restructuring continued that year and the next, as the company separated its administrative operations from its creative side. This allowed Young & Rubicam Advertising to concentrate on its core business. As part of the effort, the company cut staff and even closed some small operations. It paid off in 1995 as Y&R Advertising began rebuilding its reputation for creativity.

WHO

Chairman and CEO: Peter A. Georgescu
VC; Worldwide Creative Director, Young & Rubicam Advertising: Ted Bell
President: John P. McGarry Jr.
Chairman and CEO, Young & Rubicam Advertising: Ed Vick
President and CEO, Burson-Marsteller: Tom Bell
EVP and CFO: Dave Greene
EVP; CEO, Young & Rubicam Advertising Europe: Fernan Montero
EVP; COO, Young & Rubicam Advertising: Alan Sheldon
EVP and General Counsel: Stephanie Abramson
EVP and Worldwide Director Client Services: Tim Pollak
EVP and Director People Services Worldwide: Robert Wells
Auditors: Price Waterhouse LLP

WHERE

HQ: 285 Madison Ave., New York, NY 10017-6486
Phone: 212-210-3000
Fax: 212-370-3796

Young & Rubicam's subsidiaries have more than 300 offices in 64 countries.

WHAT

Selected Divisions
Burson-Marsteller (image management)
  Black, Kelly, Scruggs and Healey (lobbying and public affairs)
  BM Campaigns (grassroots communications)
  The Burson Production Group (industrial films)
  Cohn & Wolfe (public relations)
  Prima (public policy research and consulting, UK)
  Robinson Linton Associates (government relations, Belgium)
Dentsu, Young & Rubicam Partnerships (joint venture)
Special Communications Group
  Bravo Group (Hispanic communications)
  Chapman Direct Advertising (direct marketing)
  Landor Associates (identity and design)
  Sudler & Hennessey (health care communications)
Wunderman Cato Johnson (sales promotion)
Young & Rubicam Advertising

Representative Clients
American Express
American Home Products
AT&T
Cadbury/Dr Pepper Beverages
Clorox
Colgate-Palmolive
Danone
DEC
DuPont
Ford
MetLife
Miller Brewing
PepsiCo
Philip Morris
Sears
US Army
US Postal Service
Viacom
Xerox

KEY COMPETITORS

Bozell, Jacobs	Heritage Media
Carlson	Interpublic Group
Cordiant	Leo Burnett
Creative Artists	Maritz
D'Arcy Masius	Omnicom Group
Edelman Public Relations	WPP Group
Grey Advertising	

HOW MUCH

Private company FYE: December 31	Annual Growth	1986	1987	1988	1989	1990	1991	1992	1993	1994	1995
Sales ($ mil.)	6.7%	628	736	758	865	1,074	1,057	1,059	1,009	1,060	1,122
Employees	(0.5%)	10,844	11,634	12,311	10,473	11,133	11,133	10,122	9,846	9,932	10,404

Young&Rubicam Inc.

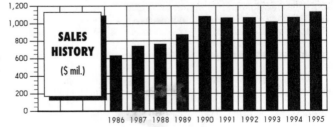

SALES HISTORY ($ mil.)

ZIFF-DAVIS PUBLISHING COMPANY

Ziff-Davis has a big byte of the computer magazine market. The New York City-based company publishes such top computer magazines as *PC Magazine*, *FamilyPC*, and *MacUser*. Its magazines have an estimated global circulation of nearly 6 million. Other units publish newsletters (the Cobb Group), conduct market research (Computer Intelligence Infocorp), perform Benchmark testing (Ziff-Davis Benchmark Operation), produce training products (Logical Operations), and provide online services (ZDNet).

In early 1996 the company was acquired by SOFTBANK, Japan's top publisher of computer magazines and books. SOFTBANK paid $2.1 billion to investment firm Forstmann Little, which purchased Ziff-Davis in 1994 and turned an estimated profit of $700 million on the deal.

Ziff-Davis has been busy since its acquisition by SOFTBANK. It announced the creation of ZDTV, an independent unit that will produce television and Internet programming. It also formed a new Internet advertising representative group with Interactive Marketing Inc. (initial clients include the National Football League and Playboy) and started USWeb, a Web site development and consulting service.

SOFTBANK is Japan's largest distributor of computer software and peripherals. Its founder and 61% owner is 39-year-old Masayoshi Son, who has been called "Japan's Bill Gates." The Ziff-Davis purchase moves Son closer to his goal of building SOFTBANK into the leading global provider of computer infrastructure services, such as distributing and trade shows.

William Ziff (a famed WWI flyer, author, and lecturer) and Bernard Davis founded Ziff-Davis Publishing in 1927 with the publication of *Popular Aviation* (now *Flying*). The pair concentrated on hobby- and leisure-related publications. When Ziff died of a heart attack in 1953, Ziff-Davis was publishing *Modern Bride*, *Popular Electronics*, and *Popular Photography*, among others.

Ziff's 24-year-old son Bill Jr. gave up a promising career in academia to take over the company. In 1956 he bought out Davis and began an unprecedented buying spree, seeking out niche markets in which a continuous supply of new products and services would keep readers interested.

In 1973 Ziff acquired the publishing arm of paper products company Boise Cascade, inheriting, among other titles, *Psychology Today*. By the mid-1980s his enterprise published about 35 magazines, including *Car & Driver*, *Yachting*, and *Travel Weekly*, and owned 6 television stations.

During the 1980s, Ziff's battle with prostate cancer hampered the company's growth and most of its holdings were sold. The television stations were sold for $100 million in 1983. In 1985, 12 trade magazines went to Rupert Murdoch for $350 million, and 12 consumer magazines were sold to CBS for $363 million. Ziff also passed ownership of the company to his 3 sons and 3 nephews.

The firm did keep its computer magazines, which were already among the strongest in the industry. In 1988, having beaten cancer, Ziff resumed chairmanship of the renamed Ziff

Communications; by the early 1990s the company was the US's #1 publisher of computer magazines. In 1993 it began expanding into trade shows, newsletters, and electronic services. That year Bill Ziff retired at age 63.

In 1994 Ziff's successors decided the market had peaked and put Ziff Communications up for sale. The surprise winner of the bidding for Ziff-Davis Magazines was Forstmann Little, which beat out SOFTBANK and media companies Time Warner and Bertelsmann. In November 1995 that company accepted SOFTBANK's offer to buy Ziff-Davis.

SOFTBANK was founded in 1981 by Son, who, as a teenager, made his first million exporting video games from Japan to the US. SOFTBANK is Japan's largest distributor of computer software, peripherals, and systems and its leading publisher of high-tech magazines. Its publishing division, created just 6 months after SOFTBANK was founded, issues Japanese versions of leading computer magazines. Despite losing its bid for Ziff-Davis in 1994, SOFTBANK did pick up the company's trade show business, ZD Expos.

In 1996 Ziff-Davis joined with Yahoo!, the online search service, and converted *ZD Internet Life* magazine into *Yahoo! Internet Life*. That year Ziff-Davis created 3 new US divisions: US Publications (consisting of Business Media, Consumer Media, and Magazine Networks), Interactive Media and Development (ZDNet and a newly created Internet Publishing Group), and Training and Support Publishing (Logical Operations and the Cobb Group).

WHO

Chairman and CEO: Eric Hippeau
CFO: Timothy O'Brien
President, US Publications: Ronni Sonnenberg
President, Interactive Media and Development:
Jeff Ballowe
President, Training and Support Publishing; President,
Logical Operations Group: William Rosenthal
President, Business Media: Claude Sheer
President, Consumer Media: J. Scott Briggs
President, Computer Intelligence/Infocorp: Bob Brown
President, International Media Group: J. B. Holston III
VP Human Resources: Rajna Brown

WHERE

HQ: One Park Ave., New York, NY 10016-5801
Phone: 212-503-3500
Fax: 212-503-4599
Web site: http://www.zd.com

Ziff-Davis publishes 12 magazines in the US and 10 in
foreign countries. The company licenses or syndicates its
editorial content to 56 other publications.

WHAT

US Publications
Computer Gaming World
Computer Life
Computer Shopper
FamilyPC (with the Walt
Disney Co.)
Inter@ctive Week (with
Inter@ctive Enterprises)
MacUser
MacWEEK
PC Computing
PC Magazine
PC WEEK
Windows Sources
Yahoo! Internet Life

Foreign Publications
China
PC Magazine (with
Richina Media)
France
PC Direct
PC Expert
Germany
PC Direkt
PC Professional
PI@net
Mexico
*PC Computing en
Espanol* (with Editorial
Televisa)
United Kingdom

Computer Life
PC Direct
PC Magazine

Other Operations
The Cobb Group newslet-
ters
Inside NetWare
Inside OS/2
Inside the Internet
Inside Visual Basic
Computer Intelligence
Infocorp (market re-
search)
Logical Operations (man-
agement training)
USWeb (World Wide Web
site development and
consulting service)
ZD Europe (European
magazine operations)
ZD Deutschland
ZD France
ZD UK
ZDNet (online informa-
tion)
ZDTV (production of televi-
sion and Internet pro-
gramming)
Ziff-Davis Benchmark
Operation (Benchmark
testing)

KEY COMPETITORS

Bronner Slosberg
CMP Publications
C/NET
Cowles Media
HyperMedia
International Data Group
International Post
McGraw-Hill

Mecklermedia
Modem Media
New York Times
Pittway
Reed Elsevier
Sendai Media Group
Times Mirror
Wired

HOW MUCH

Subsidiary FYE: December 31	Annual Growth	1986	1987	1988	1989	1990	1991	1992	1993	1994	1995
Estimated sales ($ mil.)	20.7%	175	145	200	240	—	436	620	718	852	950
Employees	2.3%	2,200	—	—	—	—	3,100	4,100	4,300	2,800	2,700

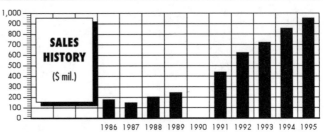

SALES
HISTORY
($ mil.)

Selected Media Companies

A&E TELEVISION NETWORKS

OVERVIEW

With Nostradamus, Grace Kelly, Adolph Hitler, the *Titanic*, and the *Hindenburg* in its lineup, cable TV programmer A&E Television Networks has aced it. The New York City-based company's A&E Network, led by its flagship *Biography* series, has won more CableACE awards than any other cable network. A&E Network also features mysteries and specials.

A&E is a joint venture of communication giants Hearst (37.5%), Walt Disney's Capital Cities/ABC (37.5%), and General Electric's NBC (25%). The company's programs reach more than 69 million homes across the US and Canada. A&E's operations also consist of *A&E Monthly* (a special interest magazine); A&E New Media (audio, video, CD-ROM, laser disc, books, and online products); History Television Network Productions (H-TV; original programming); and the History Channel (historical documentaries, movies, and miniseries).

In 1984 fledgling cable companies Alpha Repertory Television Series (ARTS, owned by Hearst and ABC) and the Entertainment Channel (controlled by RCA, the owner of NBC before being bought by GE in 1986, and the Rockefeller Center investment group) merged to become the Arts & Entertainment Network (A&E). Most of its early programming was acquired from the UK, Canada, the Public Broadcasting Service and other cable networks. By 1990 A&E's original programming accounted for 35-40% of the total program content. The company launched A&E Home Video the next year to market videotaped versions of its programs.

In 1994, the year the enterprise adopted its present name, *Biography* went from a weekly series to being shown 5 nights a week, which helped boost the network's ratings to record levels. In 1995 A&E launched the History Channel as a separate network with a million subscribers; the new channel finished the year with 7.8 million US subscribers, 50% ahead of the firm's projections. In 1996 the History Channel bowed to criticism and cancelled plans to air a series on jumbo corporations such as General Motors and AT&T that would have been sponsored by the subjects themselves.

WHO

President and CEO: Nickolas Davatzes
EVP, CFO, and Chief Administrative Officer: Seymour H. Lesser
EVP Sales and Marketing: Whitney Goit II
SVP and General Manager, The History Channel: Daniel E. Davids
SVP Programming and Production: Brooke Bailey Johnson
SVP Affiliate Sales and Marketing: Eric Kronen
SVP Advertising Sales: Ronald M. Schneier
SVP Production: Abbe Raven
VP and General Counsel: Anne Atkinson
VP Corporate Business Development: Joseph Warren
VP Human Resources: Rosalind C. Carter

WHERE

HQ: 235 E. 45th St., New York, NY 10017
Phone: 212-661-4500
Fax: 212-983-4370
Web site: http://www.aetv.com

WHAT

Media Products
Audio
Books
CD-ROM
Laser discs
Magazines
Online
TV programming

Operating Units
A&E Home Video
A&E Monthly (magazine)
A&E Network
A&E New Media
The History Channel
History Television Network Productions (H-TV)

KEY COMPETITORS

Advance Publications
BET
BMG
Corporation for Public Broadcasting
Discovery Communications
International Family Entertainment
Gaylord Entertainment

King World
Learningsmith
MCA
News Corp.
Sony
Time Warner
Viacom
Westinghouse/CBS

HOW MUCH

Joint Venture FYE: December 31	Annual Growth	1990	1991	1992	1993	1994	1995
Sales ($ mil.)	22.9%	93.8	115.3	141.7	174.2	214.1	263.1
Employees	21.0%	—	—	—	215	260	315

ADVANCED MARKETING SERVICES, INC.

OVERVIEW

Warehouse clubs just aren't where most people think of buying books, but San Diego-based Advanced Marketing Services (AMS) has made it its business to place business guides, bestsellers, children's books, and coffee table tomes alongside the clubs' mammoth jars of condiments, cleaning products, and pickles. AMS's customers offer books to consumers at prices 30-45% lower than the suggested retail rate.

The company packages, distributes, and promotes its titles (both English- and Spanish-language books) for sale in over 600 warehouse clubs (including Sam's and Price/Costco) in Canada, Mexico, South Korea, the UK, and the US. AMS also sells to more than 850 office product superstores in Canada, Mexico, and the US and owns and operates 12 Publisher's Outlet retail stores in 9 states. In 1995 AMS began marketing books on the Home Shopping Network on Prodigy, the Internet, and America Online.

AMS was founded in 1982 expressly to sell books to membership warehouse clubs. Two of the company's 3 founders, Charles Tillinghast and Loren Paulsen, together own 34.8% of AMS stock. In 1987 the company began serving the burgeoning office product superstore industry. A 1991 loss, caused largely by the overbuying of nonreturnable titles, changed the company's growth strategy to include ordering a select number of titles with high-volume potential, bundling titles, and shipping titles to customers weekly. AMS is also trying to wean itself away from dependence on wholesale clubs. It opened distribution units in Mexico and the UK and increased its US factory outlet stores, adding 2 new units in 1993. Plans for the future include the addition of CD-ROM titles and further growth in the Spanish-language market.

WHO

Chairman and CEO: Charles C. Tillinghast III, age 58, $218,008 pay
President and COO: Michael M. Nicita, age 42, $104,436 pay
EVP Operations: Loren C. Paulsen, age 45, $196,006 pay
EVP Finance and CFO: Jonathan S. Fish, age 50, $186,006 pay
VP Merchandising: Kevan M. Lyon, age 50, $135,755 pay
VP Management Information Systems: Kenneth C. Hayes, age 49
VP Operations: Ronald E. Osborne, age 38
VP Marketing: Adam R. Zoldan, age 42
VP Human Resources: Alisa R. Judge, age 39
Auditors: Andersen Worldwide

WHERE

HQ: 5880 Oberlin Dr., Ste. 400, San Diego, CA 92121-9653
Phone: 619-457-2500
Fax: 619-452-2237

WHAT

	1995 Sales
	% of total
Membership warehouse clubs	93
Office superstores, mass merchandisers, computer superstores & other retail outlets	7
Total	**100**

	1995 Sales
	% of total
Price/Costco	46
Sam's Club (Wal-Mart)	39
Other companies	15
Total	**100**

KEY COMPETITORS

Baker & Taylor	Golden Lee	Ludington News
Bookazine	Handleman	Pacific Pipeline
Brodart	Ingram	Welk Group
Chas. Levy	Koen	
East Texas Distributing	Distributers	

HOW MUCH

Nasdaq symbol: ADMS FYE: March 31	Annual Growth	1990	1991	1992	1993	1994	1995
Sales ($ mil.)	7.9%	207.2	176.2	218.1	258.4	264.5	303.7
Net income ($ mil.)	8.1%	2.3	(1.2)	1.8	3.0	0.2	3.4
Income as % of sales	—	1.1%	—	0.8%	1.2%	0.1%	1.1%
Earnings per share ($)	9.0%	0.39	(0.21)	0.34	0.53	0.03	0.60
Stock price – high ($)[1]	—	17.50	13.75	4.63	6.75	9.75	7.00
Stock price – low ($)[1]	—	10.00	1.00	1.50	4.25	4.38	4.00
Stock price – close ($)[1]	(15.9%)	14.25	2.13	4.25	6.25	4.88	6.00
P/E – high	—	45	—	14	13	—	12
P/E – low	—	26	—	4	8	146	7
Dividends per share ($)	—	0.00	0.00	0.00	0.00	0.00	0.00
Book value per share ($)	4.6%	6.55	6.76	7.11	7.65	7.66	8.21
Employees	8.5%	271	265	301	312	334	407

[1] Stock prices are for the prior calendar year.

1995 YEAR-END
Debt ratio: 0.0%
Return on equity: 7.8%
Cash (mil.): $18.2
Current ratio: 1.46
Long-term debt (mil.): $0.0
No. of shares (mil.): 5.4
Dividends
    Yield: —
    Payout: —
Market value (mil.): $32.4

ADVO, INC.

OVERVIEW

If your mailbox is full of junk mail, chances are good that ADVO is responsible. The Windsor, Connecticut-based company is the US's #1 full-service direct mailer and the US Postal Service's biggest private customer. ADVO sends more than 25 billion pieces of mail annually. Shared mail, which bundles ads from several advertisers in a single envelope, is its biggest seller, reaching more than 61 million households a week. ADVO also offers solo mail for individual customers and rents mailing lists. The company has printing services as well, and in some areas it provides its own delivery services. (Investment banker Warburg Pincus owns almost 24% of the company.)

ADVO was founded in 1929 as a hand-delivery company. In 1946 it entered the solo direct-mail market. It joined the relatively new shared-mail business in 1980. ADVO grew along with direct mail's reputation as a better way to target customers. In 1988 Robert "Kam" Kamerschen joined the company as CEO (he owns about 7% of ADVO stock) and took steps to curb costs.

ADVO's huge mailing list (including more than 111 million US households) is one of the company's strongest assets. But attempts to capitalize on the database by including demographic and individual buying preference data proved costly, and in 1995 the company sold its 50% of the joint venture to partner Acxiom.

In the 1990s the company has been hit by increases in paper and postal costs and by pressure for quarter-by-quarter growth. It has dealt with the postal costs by cutting deals with the US Postal Service. ADVO has also jettisoned operations that do not show instant profits, such as the company's in-store marketing unit, Marketing Force (bought in 1993, sold in 1995). President and CEO Joseph Durrett resigned in 1996 after CEO Kamerschen's contract was extended for five years.

WHO

Chairman and CEO: Robert "Kam" Kamerschen, age 59, $855,748 pay
SEVP and Chief Administrative and Process Development Officer: Larry G. Morris, age 57, $351,253 pay
EVP and CFO: Lowell W. Robinson, age 46, $244,642 pay
SVP Special Accounts: Peter A. Corrao, age 41, $214,077 pay
SVP Legal and Public Affairs, General Counsel, and Secretary: David M. Stigler
SVP and Chief Marketing Officer: Rick Kurz , age 55
SVP Operations: Frederick Leick , age 51
SVP Sales: Myron L. Lubin, age 55
SVP Human Resources: J. Thomas Van Berkem
Auditors: Ernst & Young LLP

WHERE

HQ: One Univac Ln., PO Box 755, Windsor, CT 06095-0755
Phone: 860-285-6100
Fax: 860-285-6393

WHAT

	1995 Sales		1995 Pretax Income	
	$ mil.	% of total	$ mil.	% of total
Direct mail	954.2	94	50.6	100
In-store marketing	57.7	6	(5.4)	—
Total	**1,011.9**	**100**	**45.2**	**100**

Direct Mail Products and Services
Commercial printing
Mailing list rental
Promotional publication production
Shared mail
Solo mail
Transportation

Selected Subsidiaries
ADVOLink, Inc. (promotional materials)
ADVO Target Communications, Inc. (promotional materials)
MidCoast Press (printing)
Trans ADVO, Inc. (transportatation)

KEY COMPETITORS

Banta
CKS
Consolidated Graphics
Cox Enterprises
Graphic Industries
Harte Hanks Comm.
Heritage Media
Meldrum & Fewsmith Communications
R. R. Donnelley
Valassis Communications

HOW MUCH

NYSE symbol: AD FYE: September 30	Annual Growth	1990	1991	1992	1993	1994	1995
Sales ($ mil.)	9.1%	655.0	697.4	787.6	910.8	975.5	1,011.9
Net income ($ mil.)	10.0%	16.4	19.3	20.5	5.4	25.2	26.4
Income as % of sales	—	2.5%	2.8%	2.6%	0.6%	2.6%	2.6%
Earnings per share ($)	8.4%	0.76	0.85	0.88	0.21	1.05	1.14
Stock price – high ($)	—	10.00	18.90	22.30	24.75	20.00	27.50
Stock price – low ($)	—	6.80	9.00	12.40	14.25	15.00	16.50
Stock price – close ($)	22.3%	9.50	18.60	21.00	18.00	17.25	26.00
P/E – high	—	13	22	25	118	19	24
P/E – low	—	9	11	14	68	14	15
Dividends per share ($)	—	0.00	0.00	0.00	0.06	0.09	0.10
Book value per share ($)	11.5%	3.64	4.87	5.79	5.32	5.17	6.26
Employees	2.5%	4,600	4,800	4,800	5,700	5,300	5,200

1995 YEAR-END
Debt ratio: 0.0%
Return on equity: 22.1%
Cash (mil.): $54.5
Current ratio: 1.61
Long-term debt (mil.): $1.0
No. of shares (mil.): 20.8
Dividends
  Yield: 0.4%
  Payout: 8.8%
Market value (mil.): $541.4

AGENCE FRANCE-PRESSE

OVERVIEW

Agence France-Presse (AFP) never stops. Twenty-four hours a day, the press cooperative transmits words, photos, and graphics from its 150 photographers, more than 900 correspondents, and 2,000 freelancers in 165 countries. In addition to its general news service, AFP covers financial markets through its AFX-News and AFX-Asia wires and manages an archive of some 7 million photos. The world's oldest international news agency, AFP has some 12,500 clients, including newspapers, periodicals, TV and radio broadcasters, and business and government interests. AFP's largest client, the French government, provides more than 40% of its revenue, which has led to criticism of the agency with regard to impartiality.

The news operations of French media house Agence Havas were begun in 1835 by agency founder Charles-Louis Havas. The news distributor used mail coaches, couriers, carrier pigeons, and the telegraph to spread information throughout Europe. In 1940, during WW II, the news operation was split off from Havas's advertising arm to form the government-subsidized French Information Office. Agence France-Presse was established in 1944 when members of the French Resistance took control of the organization. The agency remained dependent on French government subsidies, however.

In 1957 AFP head Jean Marin secured the agency's political and editorial independence with a Parliamentary decree, and by the end of the 1950s, the agency counted clients in 140 countries. In 1975 the French president insisted Marin step down. Despite his protests that AFP was independent, he left after discovering that AFP subscribers on the governing board were prepared to vote against him.

In 1996, after the agency's coverage of the 1995 housing scandal involving Prime Minister Alain Juppé and the antigovernment strikes by public employees, the government's influential role at AFP was again highlighted. Agency director Lionel Fleury was denied reelection after government representatives on AFP's board voted against him despite overwhelming support from the board's press representatives. Jean Miot, from the conservative daily *Le Figaro*, replaced Fleury.

WHO

President and General Director: Jean Miot, age 56
Directeur Délégué à Présidence: Philippe Gustin
Director, Information: Yvan Chemla
Director, Finance: Michel Tourmen
Director, North and South: Pierre Lesourd
Director, Asia and Pacific: Denis Brulet
Interim Director, Middle East: Jacques Abelous

WHERE

HQ: 13, Place de la Bourse, Paris, 75002, France
Phone: +33-1-40-41-4646
US HQ: 1612 K Street NW, Washington, DC 20036-202
US Phone: 202-861-8535
US Fax: 202-861-4245
Fax: +33-1-40-41-4632
Web site: http://www.afp.com

AFP has 27 bureaus in France, 49 bureaus in Africa, 30 in Asia and the Pacific, 37 in Europe, 22 in the Middle East, and 42 in North and South America.

WHAT

Principal Products and Services
Financial news services (coverage of European and Asia/Pacific financial markets)
General news wires (politics, economics, finance, sports, cultural affairs, science, fashion, and general interest stories in English, French, German, Arabic, Spanish, and Portuguese)
Graphics services (graphics produced in English, French, Spanish, and German)
News profiles (news tailored to customer specifications and delivered by e-mail, fax, or conventional mail)
Photo services (general news and magazine photos, photos on demand, and photo archives)
Sports services (major sports, Olympics)
Text services (available on several databases, including DataTimes, Dialog, Infomart, Innovative Telematics, Newsnet, and Lexis-Nexis)

Subsidiaries and Joint Ventures
AFP-EXTEL (English economic service; joint venture with Financial Times Group)
European Pressphoto Agency (participation with 9 other European press agencies)Intermonde-Presse (full-page layouts; subsidiary)
PolyCom (satellite transmission; joint venture with France Télécom)
SPDV (video and teletext production; subsidiary)

KEY COMPETITORS

Associated Press	Dow Jones	Reuters
Bloomberg	Gamma	Sipa
Corbis	Knight-Ridder	Sygma
Crain	Magnum	Times Mirror
Communications	New York Times	UPI

HOW MUCH

Cooperative FYE: December 31	Annual Growth	1990	1991	1992	1993	1994	1995
Sales ($ mil.)	10.7%	—	—	184.5	185.8	231.0	250.0
Employees	0.0%	—	—	—	—	3,100	3,100

A. H. BELO CORPORATION

OVERVIEW

Based in Dallas, A. H. Belo Corporation operates more than a dozen newspapers and television stations in Texas and other markets throughout the US. Its flagship, the *Dallas Morning News*, has the nation's 7th largest Sunday circulation (over 800,000). Three of its 7 TV stations, WFAA (ABC), KHOU (CBS), and KIRO (UPN), are network affiliates in top-12 markets: Dallas/Fort Worth, Houston, and Seattle/Tacoma, respectively. The company also publishes the biannual *Texas Almanac*, begun in 1857. The Dealey family, which includes chairman Robert Decherd, owns about 23% of the company.

The oldest continuously operated Texas business started in 1842 when Samuel Bangs and George French published the *Daily News* in Galveston. Alfred Horatio Belo joined the paper in 1865 and became the owner in 1876. The company first published the *Dallas Morning News* in 1885. Belo died in 1901. In 1922 the firm started the state's first network radio station, Dallas's WFAA, and 4 years later took its present name. The *Daily News* was sold in 1932 in order to focus on the thriving Dallas paper. Belo entered the television business in 1950 when it purchased Dallas station WFAA. In 1963 it acquired 7 community newspapers from Dallas/Fort Worth Suburban Newspapers. The firm went public in 1981. Belo purchased its Dallas newspaper competitor, the *Times-Herald*, in 1991 and shut it down, making the *Dallas Morning News* the only major paper in the city.

The company purchased TV stations in New Orleans (1994) and Seattle/Tacoma (1995.) In 1996 Belo decided to start its 2nd major paper in the Dallas/Fort Worth metroplex, the *Arlington Morning News*, to compete with the *Fort Worth Star-Telegram*, owned by Capital Cities/ABC. Also, it agreed to buy Providence Journal Co. for $1.5 billion

WHO

Chairman, President, and CEO: Robert W. Decherd, age 44, $705,994 pay
VC; President, Broadcast Division: Ward L. Huey Jr., age 57, $547,175 pay
Publisher and Editor, The Dallas Morning News, Inc.: Burl Osborne, age 58, $520,489 pay
SVP, General Counsel, and Secretary: Michael J. McCarthy, age 51, $297,684 pay
SVP and CFO: Michael D. Perry, age 49, $294,069 pay
Director Human Resources: Jeff Lamb
Auditors: Ernst & Young LLP

WHERE

HQ: 400 S. Record St., Dallas, TX 75202
Phone: 214-977-6606
Fax: 214-977-6603
Web site: http://www.pic.net/tdmn

WHAT

Selected Newspapers and Other Publications
Arlington News (Texas)
Bryan-College Station Eagle (Texas)
The Dallas Morning News
Garland News (Texas)
Irving News (Texas)
Owensboro Messenger-Inquirer (Kentucky)
Richardson News (Texas)
The Texas Almanac

Television Stations
KHOU-TV (CBS), Houston
KIRO-TV (UPN), Seattle/Tacoma
KOTV (CBS), Tulsa, OK
KXTV (ABC), Sacramento, CA
WFAA-TV (ABC), Dallas/Fort Worth
WVEC-TV (ABC), Hampton/Norfolk, VA
WWL-TV (CBS), New Orleans

KEY COMPETITORS

Advance Publications
Capital Cities/ABC
Gannett
Gaylord Entertainment
Harte Hanks
  Communications
LIN Television
New Times
Tribune
Washington Post
Westinghouse

HOW MUCH

NYSE symbol: BLC FYE: December 31	Annual Growth	1990	1991	1992	1993	1994	1995
Sales ($ mil.)	10.9%	439.1	431.6	515.9	544.8	628.1	735.3
Net income ($ mil.)	17.6%	29.6	12.4	37.2	44.5	68.9	66.6
Income as % of sales	—	6.7%	2.9%	7.2%	8.2%	11.0%	9.1%
Earnings per share ($)	16.6%	0.78	0.33	0.95	1.10	1.71	1.68
Stock price – high ($)	—	19.31	16.88	23.44	26.50	28.63	36.75
Stock price – low ($)	—	14.13	12.13	15.31	19.38	21.56	27.81
Stock price – close ($)	16.8%	16.00	15.75	21.00	26.50	28.25	34.75
P/E – high	—	25	51	25	24	17	22
P/E – low	—	18	37	16	18	13	17
Dividends per share ($)	5.9%	0.24	0.26	0.27	0.28	0.30	0.32
Book value per share ($)	11.1%	5.99	6.11	7.18	8.56	9.63	10.16
Employees	6.0%	2,602	2,627	2,788	2,863	3,082	3,489

1995 YEAR-END
Debt ratio: 58.9%
Return on equity: 17.3%
Cash (mil.): $12.8
Current ratio: 2.02
Long-term debt (mil.): $557.4
No. of shares (mil.): 38.2
Dividends
  Yield: 0.9%
  Payout: 19.0%
Market value (mil.): $1,327.5

ALL AMERICAN COMMUNICATIONS, INC.

OVERVIEW

Life's a beach party for All American Communications. The Santa Monica, California-based producer and distributor of TV programs makes *Baywatch*, the world's most popular TV show (seen in more than 110 countries). The company has holdings in more than 50 TV series and over 135 motion pictures, children's programs, and game shows, including *The Price is Right*, *Let's Make a Deal*, and *The Dating Game*. It is also an independent record producer. (Its recording artists include James Brown and "Weird Al" Yankovic.)

In 1974 brothers and former college football stars Anthony and Ben Scotti formed Ben Scotti Promotions, a music marketing company. In 1979 the 2 moved into TV production with *America's Top Ten with Casey Kasem*. The Scottis formed All American in 1991 (named after Ben's All American status as a football player) and picked up the *Baywatch* series shortly after it had been canceled by broadcaster NBC. The international popularity of the series lifted All American's revenues from $32.9 million in 1991 to $114.9 million in 1994. The Scottis own 68% of All American.

The company acquired Fremantle International from the Interpublic Group in 1994. Renamed All American Fremantle International, it produces more than 90 TV series in 28 countries and is the #1 producer and distributor of TV game shows (including *The Newlywed Game* and *Supermarket Sweep*) outside the US.

In 1995 the firm acquired the David Gerber Company, a production business whose namesake had revitalized Columbia Pictures Television and MGM Television. That year All American and Interpublic Group jointly acquired Mark Goodson Productions L.P. (TV game shows); it purchased Interpublic's 50% interest the following year.

WHO

Chairman and CEO: Anthony J. Scotti, age 55, $689,000 pay
President and COO: Myron I. Roth, age 62, $487,000 pay
SEVP; EVP, Records Group: Benjamin J. Scotti
SEVP, CFO, and Treasurer: Thomas Bradshaw, age 53, $441,000 pay
SEVP; President, All American TV Entertainment Group: Sydney D. Vinnedge, age 51, $384,000 pay
CEO and President, All American Fremantle Television Group: Lawrence E. Lamattina, age 50, $458,000 pay
President, All American Television Production, Inc: David Gerber
SVP Administration (HR): Frederick J. Scotti
Auditors: Ernst & Young LLP

WHERE

HQ: 808 Wilshire Blvd., Santa Monica, CA 90401-1810
Phone: 310-656-1100
Fax: 310-656-7410
Web site: http://165.121.1.145

WHAT

	1995 Sales	
	$ mil.	% of total
Television	206.8	90
Recorded music	22.0	10
Total	**228.8**	**100**

Selected Subsidiaries
All American Goodson, Inc.
All American Fremantle International, Inc.
All American Music Group, Inc.
All American Television, Inc.
All American Television Production, Inc.
Scotti Brothers Entertainment Industries, Inc.

KEY COMPETITORS

Bertelsmann	International	Sony
Carsey-Werner	Family	Spelling
dick clark productions	Entertainment	Entertainment
DreamWorks SKG	King World	THORN EMI
GoodTimes	MCA	Time Warner
Entertainment	News Corp.	Viacom
	PolyGram	Walt Disney

HOW MUCH

Nasdaq symbol: AACI FYE: December 31	Annual Growth	1990[1]	1991	1992	1993	1994	1995
Sales ($ mil.)	91.9%	8.8	35.2	57.9	70.6	114.9	228.8
Net income ($ mil.)	135.2%	0.1	(1.9)	1.0	0.4	0.5	7.2
Income as % of sales	—	1.1%	—	1.7%	0.6%	0.4%	3.1%
Earnings per share ($)	28.8%	0.20	(0.80)	(0.38)	0.78	0.07	0.71
Stock price – high ($)	—	17.50	15.00	10.50	11.00	10.50	14.00
Stock price – low ($)	—	8.00	2.25	7.00	6.50	5.25	6.25
Stock price – close ($)	(1.0%)	10.50	8.00	7.63	9.25	6.25	10.00
P/E – high	—	88	—	—	14	150	20
P/E – low	—	40	—	—	8	75	9
Dividends per share ($)	—	—	—	0.00	0.00	0.00	0.00
Book value per share ($)	(13.6%)	12.47	1.36	0.45	1.56	3.54	6.02
Employees	40.0%	—	—	—	125	207	245

[1] 10-month fiscal year

1995 YEAR-END
Debt ratio: 66.4%
Return on equity: 14.9%
Cash (mil.): $20.1
Current ratio: 0.92
Long-term debt (mil.): $135.0
No. of shares (mil.): 11.4
Dividends
  Yield: —
  Payout: —
Market value (mil.): $113.5

ALLEGRO NEW MEDIA, INC.

OVERVIEW

Allegro is upping the tempo of small office and home CD-ROM software. The Fairfield, New Jersey-based company publishes about 2 dozen titles, including Berlitz Executive Travel Guide, Cooking With Dom DeLuise, Guide to Raising Money, and Small Business Encyclopedia. Allegro sells its programs under its own brand, Learn To Do, as well as under licensed names including Berlitz, Betty Crocker, and *Entrepreneur Magazine*. Chairman Barry Cinnamon owns nearly 30% of the company.

Allegro was founded in 1992 by Cinnamon, Lori Kramer (now husband and wife, both formerly with the Bureau of Electronic Publishing, a CD-ROM publishing pioneer), and Cinnamon's cousin, Richard Bergman. Cinnamon, an innovator in the CD-ROM industry, was named Entrepreneur of the Year by the Optical Publishing Association in 1992. As the demand for CD-ROMs exploded in the early 1990s, the enterprise developed products for the nonentertainment market, avoiding direct competition with more established game and children's software designers. Initial offerings included artwork, interactive books, and how-to software. By 1994 the company had 14 titles.

In 1995 Allegro benefited from the increased prevalence of CD-ROM drives and greater use of business software by small- and home-office workers. That year the company introduced 11 new titles, including Learn To Do Windows 95 with John C. Dvorak and Multimedia Business 500. Also that year the company went public as it moved away from consumer titles to business titles.

In 1996 Allegro acquired SERIF, a desktop publishing and graphics software maker with 1995 sales of about $10 million. SERIF's UK unit will provide Allegro with a European base of operations.

WHO

Chairman, President, and CEO: Barry A. Cinnamon, age 38, $73,814 pay
VP Marketing and Secretary: Lori Kramer Cinnamon, age 36
VP Sales: James Tsonas, age 48
VP Finance, CFO, and Treasurer: Mark E. Leininger, age 45
VP Business Development: Anne M. Zink
Auditors: Ernst & Young LLP

WHERE

HQ: 16 Passaic Ave., Unit 6, Fairfield, NJ 07004
Phone: 201-808-1992
Fax: 201-808-2645
Web site: http://www.allegronm.com

WHAT

Selected Titles
25 Hottest Businesses for the 90's
Berlitz Executive Travel Guide
Best Part-Time Businesses for the 90's
Cooking with Dom DeLuise
Guide to Raising Money
Learn To Do Windows 95 with John C. Dvorak
Multimedia Business 500
Top Low-Investment Businesses for the 90's

Selected Retailers
Best Buy
CompUSA
Computer City
Egghead Software
Micro Center
OfficeMax
Wal-Mart

KEY COMPETITORS

Adams Media
Broderbund
Expert Software
Gametek
Graphix Zone
IVI Publishing

Legacy Software
Microsoft
Sierra On-Line
SoftKey
StarPress

HOW MUCH

Nasdaq symbol: ANMI FYE: December 31	Annual Growth	1990	1991	1992	1993	1994	1995
Sales ($ mil.)	67.3%	—	—	—	0.5	1.0	1.4
Net income ($ mil.)	144.9%	—	—	—	(0.2)	(0.8)	(1.2)
Income as % of sales	—	—	—	—	—	—	—
Earnings per share ($)	—	—	—	—	—	—	(0.78)
Stock price – high ($)	—	—	—	—	—	—	7.63
Stock price – low ($)	—	—	—	—	—	—	6.25
Stock price – close ($)	—	—	—	—	—	—	6.75
P/E – high	—	—	—	—	—	—	—
P/E – low	—	—	—	—	—	—	—
Dividends per share ($)	—	—	—	—	—	—	0.00
Book value per share ($)	—	—	—	—	—	—	0.90
Employees	34.2%	—	—	—	20	30	36

1995 YEAR-END
Debt ratio: 0.0%
Return on equity: —
Cash (mil.): $2.9
Current ratio: 5.14
Long-term debt (mil.): $0.0
No. of shares (mil.): 3.4
Dividends
 Yield: —
 Payout: —
Market value (mil.): $22.9

AMERICAN BOOKSELLERS ASSOCIATION

OVERVIEW

What do Newt Gingrich, the Duke of Windsor, Eleanor Roosevelt, Kurt Vonnegut, Rod McKuen, and Martin Luther King Jr. have in common? They have all addressed American Booksellers Association (ABA) conventions. Tarrytown, New York–based ABA is a member-owned trade organization dedicated to protecting book retailers' interests on national and international issues. Its more than 7,200 members include independent bookstores and chains, college and university stores, and franchise and specialty shops. For a yearly fee of $50–100, ABA provides its members with an annual trade conference and exhibition; free print, disk, and online publications; group and discount book-buying; and other services.

Inspired by a similar British association, ABA was formed by 6 booksellers in 1900. The association's purpose was to stabilize prices by establishing a "fair" net price for books (and prevent sellers being undersold by pirated or counterfeit copies). Henry Coates, of the bookseller Porter & Coates, was the first president. In 1924 ABA hired its first full-time staff member. The ABA convention introduced a "Buyers' Book Browse" in 1947, which was a forerunner of its major event in later decades, the ABA Trade Exhibit. By 1966 ABA's bookstore membership passed 2,000.

ABA became financially independent in 1993 when it sold a 49% stake in its annual convention to Reed Publishing for $17 million. Over the past few years ABA has focused on creating programs to let small and midsize bookstores benefit from group buying power. The organization has arranged a special freight program with carrier Roadway Parcel Service. It also offers ABA-sponsored property and casualty insurance for its members.

In 1994 ABA sued publishers Houghton Mifflin, Hugh Lauter Levin Associates, Penguin USA, Rutledge Hill Press, and St. Martins, alleging they broke antitrust laws by offering illegal promotional and pricing policies to national bookstore chains and warehouse clubs. These publishers came to an agreement with ABA in 1995. The next year ABA filed a similar suit against Random House, which led to that publisher's boycott of the 1996 Trade Exhibit.

WHO

President: Barbara B. Thomas
Executive Director: Bernard E. Rath
Treasurer: Ned Densmore
Secretary: Linda Brummett
Director Finance: Eleanor Chang
Director Human Resources: Deirdre Fitzsimmons
Auditors: KPMG Peat Marwick LLP

WHERE

HQ: American Booksellers Association, Inc., 828 S. Broadway, Tarrytown, NY 10591
Phone: 914-591-2665
Fax: 914-591-2720
Web site: http://www.bookweb.org

WHAT

	1995 Sales	
	$ mil.	% of total
ABA Convention	3.0	38
Publications	1.9	24
Dues	1.3	16
Products & services	1.0	12
Investments	0.5	6
Education	0.2	3
Other	0.1	1
Total	**8.0**	**100**

	1995 ABA Membership	
	No.	% of total
Bookstores	4,109	57
Associates (publishers & wholesalers)	1,807	25
Other	1,317	18
Total	**7,233**	**100**

Selected Services
Advocacy and legal representation
Booksellers Order Service (discount book-buying)
Conventions and exhibitions
Freight services (with Roadway Parcel Service)
Property and casualty insurance arrangements
Publications
  American Bookseller (monthly)
  Bookselling This Week
  Quarterlies and annuals in print, disk, and online

Subsidiary
Booksellers Publishing, Inc. (book publisher)

HOW MUCH

Trade association FYE: September 30	Annual Growth	1990	1991	1992	1993	1994	1995
Sales ($ mil.)	7.0%	5.7	8.0	9.2	26.9	6.9	8.0
Employees	0.0%	—	—	—	55	55	55

1995 YEAR-END
Assets (mil.): $21.3
Cash (mil.): $1.2

AMERICAN BUSINESS INFORMATION

OVERVIEW

American Business Information (ABI) gives the term "phone book" a whole new meaning. The Omaha, Nebraska-based company's latest coup is the Ultimate Phone Book, a CD-ROM with 14 million business telephone listings. ABI packages and sells basic information — names, phone numbers, addresses, type of business — and also creates sales leads and provides market research. Cofounder and CEO Vinod Gupta owns 44% of the company.

ABI was founded in 1972 by Gupta and Glen Humphrey, who spent nights compiling a complete list of US mobile home dealers from the *Yellow Pages*. The company expanded the original list to include other businesses, then began packaging the information, releasing state business directories, a manufacturers directory, and a listing of companies by Standard Industrial Classification (SIC) code. ABI had all the US *Yellow Pages* in its database by 1986. The company went public in 1992. That year it formed a joint venture with conglomerate TRW to provide customers with marketing and credit information. ABI began acquiring related companies in 1993 to expand its products and distribution channels. The company's use of telephone book listings, challenged by a BellSouth subsidiary, was upheld by the US Supreme Court in 1994.

ABI made its database available on Bloomberg financial terminals and accessible via America Online and the Microsoft Network in 1995. The next year ABI and Disclosure (a provider of financial business information) debuted the Big Business Database, listing 100,000 companies, on Disclosure's home page. Also in 1996 ABI founded its own Web site:, which boasts 3 free information services, including one that lets users find companies by *Yellow Page* heading — anywhere in the US.

WHO

Chairman and CEO: Vinod Gupta, age 49, $120,000 pay
VC: Jon D. Hoffmaster, age 47, $222,167 pay
SVP: Fred Vakili, age 42, $230,120 pay
SVP: Edward C. Mallin, age 46
SVP: Monica Messer, age 33
SVP: Jack Betts, age 45
SVP: William Chasse, age 37
SVP: William Kerrey, age 48
CFO: Jon H. Wellman, age 44
Manager Human Resources: Jeff Bauman
Auditors: Coopers & Lybrand L.L.P.

WHERE

HQ: American Business Information, Inc.,
5711 S. 86th Circle, Omaha, NE 68127
Phone: 402-593-4500
Fax: 402-331-1505
Web site: http://www.abii.com

WHAT

Selected Products and Services

Business Directories
American Manufacturers Directory
Big Business Directory
Credit Reference Directory
SIC Business Directories
State Business Directories

CD-ROM products
575,000 Physicians & Surgeons on CD-ROM
1.1 Million Female Business Owners Executives and Professionals on CD-ROM
1.1 Million Professionals on CD-ROM
3.7 Million Small Business Owners on CD-ROM

KEY COMPETITORS

Acxiom	GTE	SBC
Ameritech	Harris InfoSource	Communications
AT&T Corp.	Manufacturers'	Thomas
Bell Atlantic	News	Publishing
BellSouth	Microlytics	Thomson Corp.
Big Book	NYNEX	U S WEST Media
Database America	Omnigraphics	Volt Information
Dun & Bradstreet	Pacific Telesis	
Equifax	R. L. Polk	

HOW MUCH

Nasdaq symbol: ABII FYE: December 31	Annual Growth	1990	1991	1992	1993	1994	1995
Sales ($ mil.)	22.8%	31.1	41.5	48.5	58.9	76.3	86.8
Net income ($ mil.)	33.5%	3.4	2.3	9.9	10.8	12.8	14.4
Income as % of sales	—	10.9%	5.5%	20.4%	18.3%	16.8%	16.6%
Earnings per share ($)	41.9%	0.12	0.13	0.45	0.52	0.62	0.69
Stock price – high ($)	—	—	—	12.17	12.34	12.75	21.50
Stock price – low ($)	—	—	—	6.84	7.00	8.34	10.84
Stock price – close ($)	16.8%	—	—	12.17	9.67	12.34	19.38
P/E – high	—	—	—	27	24	21	31
P/E – low	—	—	—	15	14	14	16
Dividends per share ($)	—	—	0.00	0.00	0.00	0.00	0.00
Book value per share ($)	61.8%	—	0.55	1.92	2.45	3.06	3.77
Employees	19.8%	—	422	512	621	632	870

1995 YEAR-END
Debt ratio: 2.5%
Return on equity: 20.2%
Cash (mil.): $35.3
Current ratio: 6.01
Long-term debt (mil.): $1.1
No. of shares (mil.): 20.8
Dividends
    Yield: —
    Payout: —
Market value: $402.6

AMERICAN MEDIA, INC.

OVERVIEW

Bizarre stories, creative facts, and celebrity news have made American Media's *National Enquirer* and *Star* the US's 2nd and 3rd largest weekly periodicals, trailing only *TV Guide*. The company's stable also includes *Weekly World News* (#9), *Soap Opera Weekly* (#12), and *Country Weekly* (#13). About 85% of its revenues are from circulation, mainly single-copy sales at supermarkets and other retail outlets. The company also owns Distribution Services, Inc. (DSI), which places its periodicals in about 175,000 locations in the US and Canada; it also provides marketing services to magazine publishers. Boston Ventures and Macfadden Holdings jointly control about 76% of the company's voting stock.

Generoso Pope Jr. bought the weekly *New York Evening Enquirer* in 1952, changed it into a tabloid, added unusual news items, and gave it a more national focus. It was renamed *National Enquirer* in 1957. Pope died in 1988, and Macfadden Holdings (publisher of such magazines as *True Confessions*) and Boston Ventures bought the company the next year. In 1990 they formed American Media and bought the *Star* from Rupert Murdoch; one year later it went public. To lower the debt assumed for these purchases, the company reduced staff, cut TV advertising, reduced page counts, and raised its newsstand prices.

In 1994 Macfadden Holdings and Boston Ventures were rebuffed by a few key shareholders in a $315 million LBO that would have taken the company private again; they later withdrew the bid but declared a $7.00 taxable special cash dividend. Price hikes, advertising cuts, and increased competition from TV and other magazines have caused circulation to slide, and paper price increases have cut into profits. In 1996 the company announced plans to raise prices on several of its publications.

WHO

Chairman, President, and CEO: Peter J. Callahan, age 54, $350,000 pay
VC Finance, Administration, and Legal Affairs and Secretary: Maynard Rabinowitz, age 54, $350,000 pay
VC Publishing Operations: Michael J. Boylan, age 49, $300,000 pay
EVP Publishing Operations; President, National Enquirer, Inc., and Country Weekly, Inc., and Editor-in-Chief, *National Enquirer*: Iain Calder, age 57, $506,539 pay
SVP and Publisher, *National Enquirer* and *Star*: Anthony S. Hoyt, age 57, $442,308 pay
SVP and CFO: Richard W. Pickert, age 55
VP Human Resources: Susan Napolitano, age 42
Auditors: AndersenWorldwide

WHERE

HQ: 600 S. East Coast Ave., Lantana, FL 33462
Phone: 561-540-1000
Fax: 561-540-1018

WHAT

	1996 Sales	
	$ mil.	% of total
Circulation	257.4	87
Advertising	23.3	8
Other	14.4	5
Total	**295.1**	**100**

Publications
Country Weekly
National Enquirer
Soap Opera Magazine
Star
Weekly World News

Subsidiary
Distribution Services, Inc. (provides marketing services for magazine publishers)

KEY COMPETITORS

Globe Communications
Hearst
K-III
Meredith
News Corp.
Time Warner
Wenner Media

HOW MUCH

NYSE symbol: ENQ FYE: March 31	Annual Growth	1991	1992	1993	1994	1995	1996
Sales ($ mil.)	4.1%	240.9	283.4	275.4	300.0	315.3	295.1
Net income ($ mil.)	—	(24.7)	(3.2)	19.4	27.8	11.8	(1.0)
Income as % of sales	—	—	—	7.1%	9.3%	3.7%	—
Earnings per share ($)	—	(1.75)	(0.09)	0.47	0.67	0.28	(0.02)
Stock price – high ($)[1]	—	—	21.25	21.88	19.75	19.25	16.13
Stock price – low ($)[1]	—	—	13.50	14.50	14.63	13.13	4.00
Stock price – close ($)[1]	(26.5%)	—	21.00	18.13	19.00	16.25	4.50
P/E - high	—	—	—	47	29	69	—
P/E - low	—	—	—	31	22	47	—
Dividends per share ($)	—	—	0.08	0.19	0.20	7.10	0.00
Book value per share ($)	(40.7%)	—	6.94	7.23	7.70	0.89	0.86
Employees	6.6%	1,250	1,330	1,330	1,650	1,575	1,720

[1]Stock prices are for the prior calendar year.

1996 YEAR-END
Debt ratio: 94.0%
Return on equity: —
Cash (mil.): $4.6
Current ratio: 0.24
Long-term debt (mil.): $524.2
No. of shares (mil.): 41.8
Dividends
  Yield: —
  Payout: —
Market value (mil.): $188.0

ASCAP

OVERVIEW

That jangle of music in the air translates into a jingle of change in the pockets of members of the American Society of Composers, Authors and Publishers (ASCAP). The New York City–based organization is the US's largest performance rights society, with more than 68,000 members, among them composers, songwriters, lyricists, and music publishers. ASCAP licenses its members' copyrighted musical works and collects and distributes the royalties generated when the music is played in public. According to US copyright laws, public places include radio and TV stations, concert halls, restaurants, clubs, shopping centers, airlines, and yes, even the dentist's office. In 1995 ASCAP distributed $356.7 million in licensing revenues (it only withholds for operating expenses) to its members (50% each to a song's composer and publisher) and foreign affiliates.

In 1913 composer Raymond Hubbell, publisher George Maxwell, and attorney Nathan Burkan teamed with musician Victor Herbert to form ASCAP to ensure that music artists were paid for the performance of their works. The group charged writers $10 and publishers $50 (the same fees as today) to join the association. ASCAP sold its first license, in 1914, to Rectors restaurant, in New York. The popularization of radio in the 1920s gave ASCAP a new market for selling its licenses.

The next big boost for ASCAP came in 1941 when it licensed its first TV station. Rock 'n' roll's explosion onto the music scene in the 1950s brought a renewed interest in radio and more royalties for ASCAP members. Bob Dylan, Jimi Hendrix, and John Denver became members in the 1960s, followed by such artists as Neil Diamond, Stevie Wonder, and Bruce Springsteen in the 1970s.

During the 1980s cable TV became more prevalent and ASCAP quickly licensed music to movie channel HBO and music video channel MTV. In 1995 ASCAP found a way to make money on the Internet, issuing its first license for computer transmission of music. In 1996 ASCAP drew criticism when it demanded royalties from such nonprofit groups as the Girl Scouts of America. It later issued an apology and reimbursed several groups that had paid for the rights to sing campfire songs.

WHO

Chairman and President: Marilyn Bergman
VC: Cy Coleman
VC: Jay Morgenstern
EVP and COO: John LoFrumento
SVP and Director Membership: Todd Brabec
SVP and Director Operations and Systems: Al Wallace
VP and Director Communications: Karen Sherry
VP and Chief Economist: Peter Boyle
VP and CFO: Jim Collins
VP and Director Licensing: Vincent Candilora
Director Human Resources: Sally McKinney
Auditors: Andersen Worldwide

WHERE

HQ: American Society of Composers, Authors and Publishers, One Lincoln Plaza, New York, NY 10023
Phone: 212-621-6000
Fax: 212-724-9064
Web site: http://www.ascap.com

WHAT

Selected Past and Present Artists

The Artist Formerly Known As Prince	Cole Porter
	Lionel Richie
Fred Astaire	Smokey Robinson
Irving Berlin	Jimmie Rodgers
Johnny Cash	Carl Sandburg
John Denver	Carly Simon
Neil Diamond	John Philip Sousa
Bob Dylan	Bruce Springsteen
Duke Ellington	Igor Stravinsky
George Gershwin	Barbra Streisand
Jimi Hendrix	Bob Wills
Madonna	Stevie Wonder
Henry Mancini	Neil Young

	Selected Annual Licensing Fees
75-seat cafe with free, live instrumentalist on weekends only	$386
100-seat bar with music on one big-screen TV	$505
300-seat nightclub with karaoke machine and disc jockey	$1,248
600-seat hall with live bands (fee charged)	$4,064

KEY COMPETITORS

BMI
JASRAC (Japan)

HOW MUCH

Not-for-profit organization FYE: December 31	Annual Growth	1990	1991	1992	1993	1994	1995
Sales ($ mil.)	4.1%	358.1	375.9	380.0	386.2	422.7	436.8
Employees	(11.3%)	910	935	907	814	688	500

THE ASSOCIATED PRESS

OVERVIEW

The Associated Press (AP) is the ultimate gatekeeper when it comes to deciding what's news. Headquartered in New York City, the world's largest news-gathering organization has some 235 bureaus around the globe. AP provides news, photos, graphics, and audiovisual services to more than 1,700 newspapers and 5,500 television and radio stations, reaching more than one billion people per day. It also runs the All News Radio network and the APTV video news-gathering service.

AP was formed in 1848 when 6 New York City newspapers (some of which had been co-operating since the late 1820s) joined to share news that arrived by telegraph wire. Two years later AP began selling its wire reports to other papers. As the service grew, AP kept costs low by transmitting news to one location within a geographical area, which led to the creation of regional AP associations. The group's reporters at times went to great lengths for their stories; Mark Kellogg's cable, "I go with Custer and will be at the death," was his last report.

Until 1915 AP members were prohibited from buying news stories from competitors such as United Press (formed in 1907) or International News Service (begun in 1909). In the 1920s AP began covering sports, financial, and public interest stories. It started a news photo service in 1927 and 2 years later opened news bureaus in the UK, France, and Germany. AP began selling news reports to radio stations in the 1940s. During WWII AP began using transatlantic cable and radio-teletype circuits.

AP and media conglomerate Dow Jones introduced services in the late 1960s to improve business and financial news reporting. AP began transmitting news by satellite and offering color photographs to newspapers in the 1980s.

AP correspondent Terry Anderson was freed in 1991 after being held nearly 7 years in Lebanon as a hostage of Muslim extremists. In 1994 AP launched its APTV international video news service and the All News Radio network, and the next year it began providing news reports for the World Wide Web. In 1996 it used electronic cameras to cover Super Bowl XXX without using film. AP announced it would increase the use of exit polls to report voting results more quickly in 1996.

WHO

Chairman: Frank Daniels Jr.
VC: Ruth S. Holmberg
President and CEO: Louis D. Boccardi
President, Associated Press Managing Editors: Robert G. McGruder
SVP Business and Finance and CFO: Patrick T. O'Brien
VP and Executive Editor: William E. Ahearn
VP and Executive Photo Editor: Vincent Alabiso
VP and Director World Services: Claude E. Erbsen
VP and Director Communications and Technology: John Reid
VP and Special Columnist: Walter R. Mears
VP and Director Newspaper Membership: Wick Temple
VP and Director Broadcast Services: James R. Williams III
VP, Secretary, and Director Human Resources: James M. Donna

WHERE

HQ: The Associated Press Bldg., 50 Rockefeller Plaza, New York, NY 10020
Phone: 212-621-1500
Fax: 212-621-5447

AP has more than 235 news bureaus in 68 countries worldwide.

WHAT

Selected Products and Services
AdSEND (digital transmission of advertisements)
All News Radio (commercial-free news network)
AP wire service (provides text, graphics, pictures, and audiovisual news and information)
APTV (international television news service)
Associated Press Stylebook and Libel Manual (guide to journalistic writing style and ethics)
Grand Central Stocks service (customized stock tables)
Multimedia Services (news content for the Internet)
NewsCenter (television newsroom software system)

KEY COMPETITORS

Agence France-Presse
Bloomberg
Corbis
Crain Communications
Dow Jones
E.W. Scripps
Gannett
Knight-Ridder
New York Times
Reuters
Times Mirror
Tribune
UPI
Washington Post

HOW MUCH

Not-for-profit organization FYE: December 31	Annual Growth	1990	1991	1992	1993	1994	1995
Sales ($ mil.)	4.9%	335.0	348.0	364.8	382.0	406.0	426.0
Employees	0.6%	3,050	3,100	3,100	3,150	3,150	3,150

 **Associated Press**

AVID TECHNOLOGY, INC.

OVERVIEW

George Lucas is an avid fan of Avid Technology; his Lucasfilm Ltd. chose systems developed by the company to edit the 4th *Star Wars* movie. Avid's all-digital, disk-based systems (which combine the company's software with other manufacturers' hardware) have revolutionized the way audio, film, and video are edited. The Tewksbury, Massachusetts-based firm's customers include leading film studios, television networks, and recording studios. Average annual revenue growth has exceeded 100% since 1989. Investment firms Capital Group and FMR Corp. hold about 16% and 8% of the company's shares, respectively.

Avid was founded in 1987 by William Warner, an MIT graduate who quit his job at Apollo Computers (now part of Hewlett-Packard) to develop a prototype digital editor based on Apollo workstation hardware. After switching to Macintosh hardware in 1989, Avid produced its first digital video editing system. In 1991 Warner left the firm to start Wildfire Communications. Avid went public in 1993. The following year it acquired SofTECH Systems (newsroom automation) and the newsroom systems division of Basys Automation Systems.

The CamCutter, unveiled by Avid in 1995, was the first disk-based recording and editing system, allowing broadcasters to edit video on a PC without tape. That year the company acquired Digidesign (digital audio production software and related hardware), the Parallax Software (digital effects and animation software), and Elastic Reality (warping and morphing technology). In 1996 Avid and Hewlett-Packard teamed up to provide open standard computer products for the broadcast industry.

WHO

Chairman: William J. Miller
President: Daniel A. Keshian, age 39, $160,000 pay
VP Broadcast Engineering Paul B. Madden, $160,000 pay
VP Technology and Chief Technology Officer: Eric C. Peters, age 44, $140,000 pay
VP Manufacturing: Robert W. Puffer, age 55, $140,000 pay
VP and CFO: Jonathan H. Cook, age 49
VP Human Resources: Judith M. Oppenheim, age 54
Auditors: Coopers & Lybrand L.L.P.

WHERE

HQ: One Park West, Tewksbury, MA 01876
Phone: 508-640-6789
Fax: 508-640-1366
Web site: http://www.avid.com

	1995 Sales	
	$ mil.	% of total
North America	283.5	65
Europe	131.0	30
Asia/Pacific & Latin America	23.4	5
Adjustments	(31.2)	—
Total	**406.7**	**100**

WHAT

Selected Products

Audio	Image Manipulation
AudioVision	Elastic Reality
Pro Tools	Jester
Session for Windows '95	Matador

Editing
Avid Media Fusion
Avid Media Spectrum
MCXpress for Macintosh
MCXpress for Windows NT
Media Composer
NewsCutter

Network and Server Systems

Newsroom Automation Systems
Avid NetStation
Avid NewsView

KEY COMPETITORS

Adobe	Fast Multimedia	Scitex
Ampex	Matsushita	Silicon Graphics
Data Translation	Radius	Sony
Discreet Logic	RasterOps	

HOW MUCH

Nasdaq symbol: AVID FYE: December 31	Annual Growth	1990	1991	1992	1993	1994	1995
Sales ($ mil.)	122.8%	7.4	20.1	51.9	112.9	203.7	406.7
Net income ($ mil.)	—	(2.8)	(0.9)	2.3	3.7	13.0	15.4
Income as % of sales	—	—	—	4.4%	3.3%	6.4%	3.8%
Earnings per share ($)	—	(0.84)	(0.27)	0.29	0.38	1.10	0.77
Stock price – high ($)	—	—	—	—	27.50	43.75	49.25
Stock price – low ($)	—	—	—	—	16.00	20.50	16.75
Stock price – close ($)	(5.7%)	—	—	—	21.38	32.13	19.00
P/E – high	—	—	—	—	72	40	64
P/E – low	—	—	—	—	42	19	22
Dividends per share ($)	—	—	—	0.00	0.00	0.00	0.00
Book value per share ($)	55.4%	—	—	3.16	7.90	9.09	11.85
Employees	57.0%	—	243	243	408	776	1,476

1995 YEAR-END
Debt ratio: 1.9%
Return on equity: 8.9%
Cash (mil.): $50.4
Current ratio: 3.01
Long-term debt (mil.): $2.9
No. of shares (mil.): 20.9
Dividends
  Yield: —
  Payout: —
Market value (mil.): $397.8
R&D as % of sales: 13.2%

BAKER & TAYLOR, INC.

OVERVIEW

Charlotte, North Carolina-based Baker & Taylor (B&T) has cooked up a powerful combination of information and entertainment products. Through its B&T Books division, the privately owned wholesaler supplies books, spoken-word audio, calendars, and related information services to more than 100,000 bookstores, schools, libraries, and government agencies around the world. The B&T Entertainment division supplies audiocassettes, CD-ROMs, compact discs, peripherals, videocassettes, games, and other software to over 25,000 libraries and retailers in the US.

B&T traces its roots back to a bindery founded by David Robinson and B. B. Barber in Hartford, Connecticut, in 1828. After changing hands (and names) several times, the enterprise became Baker & Taylor Co. in 1885 when James Baker and Nelson Taylor took over. After Taylor died in 1912, the company shifted its focus. It discontinued publishing, selling most of its book titles, and concentrated on wholesaling. Parents' Institute, Inc., publisher of *Parents Magazine*, bought the company in 1958 and then sold it to diversified behemoth W. R. Grace in 1969.

In 1991 Grace began selling nonstrategic assets in order to specialize in the chemical and health care industries. Grace sold B&T Books, B&T Video, and Softkat (later renamed B&T Software) to the investment firm Carlyle Group and to B&T managers and employees in 1992. B&T's new owners combined the 3 companies into a single unit and named Gerald Garbacz, who had headed B&T's book division, CEO. In 1993 B&T Video and B&T Software were combined to form B&T Entertainment.

Following an abortive attempt to sell the company to college bookstore leader Follett in 1994, Garbacz resigned. Patrick Gross (former CEO of management consulting firm Amer-ican Management Systems) and company veteran Joseph Wright were appointed cochairmen, and Craig Richards (a former managing director of investment firm Bear Stearns & Co.) was named CEO.

In 1995 B&T completed the first phase of an overhaul of its 20-year-old fulfillment and distribution systems, introducing bar code technology and radio frequency scanners to its 4 service centers.

WHO

Cochairman: Patrick Gross
Cochairman: Joseph Wright
CEO: Craig M. Richards
EVP: President, B&T Books: James S. Ulsamer
EVP: President, B&T Entertainment: Frank A. Wolbert
SVP Sales: Martin Keeley
SVP, Treasurer, and CFO: Edward H. Gross
SVP, Secretary, and General Counsel: Susan E. Backstrom
VP Marketing: Mary Shapiro
VP Human Resources: Chuck Mankoff
Auditors: Andersen Worldwide

WHERE

HQ: 2709 Water Ridge Pkwy., Charlotte, NC 28217
Phone: 704-357-3500
Fax: 704-329-9105
Web site: http://www.baker-taylor.com

Baker & Taylor has offices and service centers across the US and in Australia and Japan.

WHAT

Baker & Taylor Books

Products	Selected Services
Bargain books	B&T Consulting Group
Calendars	(technical services, li-
Children's and young	brary development, and
adults' books	training)
Hardcover books	B&T Link (title search and
Mass-market paperbacks	ordering system for
Spoken-word audio	bookstores and libraries)
Trade paperbacks	Libris 2020 (library au-
	tomation system)

Baker & Taylor Entertainment

Products	
Audiocassettes	Video games
CD-ROMs	Videocassettes
Educational software	
Entertainment software	**Selected Services**
Home/office productivity	Independent's Days (incen-
software	tive program featuring
Laser discs	products from indepen-
Music CDs	dent producers)
Video and audio accessories	TalkMedia (24-hour touch-
	tone ordering and infor-
	mation service)

KEY COMPETITORS

ABCO	Chas. Levy	Koen
Distributors	CompuCom	Ludington News
Advanced	East Texas	Merisel
Marketing	Distributing	Software
Blackwell's	Follett	Spectrum
Bookazine	Handleman	Tech Data
Brodart	Ingram	Wal-Mart

HOW MUCH

Private company FYE: Last Friday in June	Annual Growth	1990	1991	1992	1993	1994	1995
Sales ($ mil.)	0.0%	784.0	780.0	838.0	872.0	800.0	785.0
Employees	(6.2%)	—	—	—	2,500	2,480	2,200

✦ BAKER & TAYLOR

BET HOLDINGS, INC.

OVERVIEW

African-Americans ante up to BET for its black-oriented media. The Washington, DC-based holding company's core business is the Black Entertainment Television (BET) Cable Network, which broadcasts music videos and originally produced and syndicated programming 24 hours a day to about 44.3 million households. The BET Action Pay-Per-View service offers movies to more than 7 million households. The enterprise also publishes *Young Sisters & Brothers* (*YSB*) lifestyle magazine (100,000 subscribers) and *Emerge*, an upscale general interest magazine. In addition, BET makes films through 3 joint-venture production companies: United Image Entertainment (with Butch Lewis Productions and actor Tim Reid), BET Film Productions (with Encore Media and LIVE Entertainment), and BET Pictures (with Blockbuster Entertainment). Chairman Robert Johnson owns about 55% of the company.

Johnson formed Black Entertainment Television in 1979; it debuted on cable in 1980 with 2 hours of weekly music programming. BET went public in 1991, becoming the first black-controlled company on the NYSE. That year it acquired a controlling stake in *Emerge*. Also in 1991 BET formed 2 subsidiaries: Paige Publications to publish *YSB* and United Image Entertainment. It started a direct marketing firm (BET Direct) in 1993 and formed BET International to distribute its programs overseas. It formed joint ventures BET Film Productions and BET Pictures in 1994.

BET repurchased nearly $60 million (about 18%) of its stock from initial investor Time Warner in 1995. In 1996 the company launched a cable jazz channel, BET on Jazz. Also that year it announced a joint venture with Microsoft to develop interactive TV, Internet entertainment software, and CD-ROMs.

WHO

Chairman, President, and CEO: Robert L. Johnson, age 49, $869,873 pay
President and COO : Debra L. Lee, age 41, $331,193 pay prior to promotion
EVP Media Sales: James A. Ebron, age 41, $387,044 pay
EVP Network Operations and Programming: Jefferi K. Lee, age 38, $328,736 pay
EVP Direct Marketing and Advertising Services: Janis P. Thomas, age 40, $326,550 pay
EVP Finance, CFO, and Treasurer: William T. Gordon III, age 42
EVP Affiliate Sales and Marketing: Curtis Symonds, age 40
VP Human Resources: Curtis Scott
Auditors: Price Waterhouse LLP

WHERE

HQ: 1900 West Place NE, Washington, DC 20018-1211
Phone: 202-608-2000
Fax: 202-608-2595
Web site: http://www.betnetworks.com

WHAT

Selected Operations
Avalon Pictures (BET Action Pay-Per-View)
BET Cable Network (television network)BET Direct (markets merchandise to viewers)
BET Film Productions (joint venture with Encore Media Corp. and LIVE Entertainment, Inc.)
BET on Jazz: The Cable Jazz Network
BET Pictures (joint venture with Blockbuster Entertainment Corp.)
Magazine Division (*Young Sisters & Brothers* and *Emerge*)

KEY COMPETITORS

A&E Networks	News Corp.
BHC Communications	Qwest
Discovery Communications	Spelling Entertainment
Essence Communications	Time Warner
Harpo Entertainment	Viacom
Home Shopping Network	Video Jukebox
Johnson Publishing	Walt Disney
Lifetime Television	Westinghouse/CBS
NBC	

HOW MUCH

NYSE symbol: BTV FYE: July 31	Annual Growth	1990	1991	1992	1993	1994	1995
Sales ($ mil.)	26.3%	35.8	50.8	61.7	74.2	97.5	115.2
Net income ($ mil.)	26.7%	6.1	9.3	11.7	12.6	14.8	19.9
Income as % of sales	—	17.0%	18.3%	19.0%	17.0%	15.2%	17.3%
Earnings per share ($)	24.8%	0.33	0.50	0.58	0.61	0.72	1.00
Stock price – high ($)	—	—	26.38	23.88	20.13	21.25	23.75
Stock price – low ($)	—	—	15.13	12.00	13.63	13.25	14.75
Stock price – close ($)	1.1%	—	21.88	13.63	19.75	15.13	22.88
P/E – high	—	—	53	41	33	30	24
P/E – low	—	—	30	21	22	18	15
Dividends per share ($)	—	0.00	0.00	0.00	0.00	0.00	0.00
Book value per share ($)	57.2%	0.51	1.01	3.12	3.75	4.07	4.90
Employees	15.9%	—	249	313	399	435	450

1995 YEAR-END
Debt ratio: 27.1%
Return on equity: 22.3%
Cash (mil.): $28.6
Current ratio: 2.98
Long-term debt (mil.): $34.0
No. of shares (mil.): 19.7
Dividends
  Yield: —
  Payout: —
Market value (mil.): $451.1

BIG ENTERTAINMENT, INC.

OVERVIEW

Big Entertainment has no illusions about the attraction of comic books. Based in Boca Raton, Florida, the publisher owns the rights to original characters and concepts created by such media luminaries as Tom Clancy, Mickey Spillane, Gene Roddenberry, Arthur C. Clarke, and Isaac Asimov. Using its comic books and illustrated novels (7 of which are published monthly) as a gauge, the company tests the market potential of its characters and concepts to cross over into movies, TV programs, books, online formats, and toys and other merchandise. Those that catch on are licensed to other entertainment companies. The firm also operates a book licensing and packaging division and Entertainment Super*Kiosk retail stores, which sell its own products as well as trading cards, video games, and related merchandise. CEO Mitchell Rubenstein and VC Laurie Silvers together own about 35% of the company. Asbury Park Press owns 15%.

Big Entertainment was founded in 1993 by Rubenstein and Silvers, who also cofounded the Sci-Fi Channel (selling it to the USA Network in 1992). Based on the potential of products created by Mickey Spillane and others, the company went public in its first year. By 1994 Big Entertainment had published its first comic books under the Tekno-Comix imprint and opened 7 retail outlets in Florida and Virginia malls. The company's first comics were a huge success, in part because of international distribution in the UK, Canada, and Australia. Also in 1994 the company established Tekno Books, a publishing and book packaging division.

Big Entertainment formed TeknoToys in 1995 to make action figures based on its comic book characters. In addition, it signed an agreement with Microsoft to launch comics online.

WHO

Chairman and CEO: Mitchell Rubenstein, age 42, $232,000 pay
VC, President, and Publisher: Laurie S. Silvers, age 44, $232,000 pay
CEO, Tekno Books: Martin H. Greenberg, age 55
CFO: Michael La Belle
Director Human Resources: Beth Krumper
Auditors: Arthur Andersen & Co, SC

WHERE

HQ: 2255 Glades Rd., Ste. 237 W., Boca Raton, FL 33431-7383
Phone: 561-998-8000
Fax: 561-998-2974
Web site: http://www.scifi.com/pulp/teknation/tnation.htm

	1995 Stores
	No.
Florida	6
Texas	5
Georgia	2
Minnesota	2
Maryland	1
New Jersey	1
Virginia	1
Total	**18**

WHAT

Retail Operations	Selected Properties
Entertainment Super*Kiosks	Gene Roddenberry's
	Xander in Lost Universe
Selected Publishing	Isaac Asimov's I-Bots
Operations	L. Ron Hubbard's The
NetCo Partners	Crossroads
New Media Division	Leonard Nimoy's
Tekno Books (51%)	Primortals
Tekno-Comix	Neil Gaiman's Lady Justice

KEY COMPETITORS

Acclaim Entertainment	Marvel
Classics International	Time Warner
Golden Books	Topps
Harvey Entertainment	Wizards of the Coast
Image Comics	

HOW MUCH

Nasdaq symbol: BIGE FYE: December 31	Annual Growth	1990	1991	1992	1993	1994	1995
Sales ($ mil.)	693.7%	—	—	—	0.1	1.5	6.3
Net income ($ mil.)	205.5%	—	—	—	(0.9)	(5.9)	(8.4)
Income as % of sales	—	—	—	—	—	—	—
Earnings per share ($)	132.7%	—	—	—	(0.36)	(1.49)	(1.95)
Stock price – high ($)	—	—	—	—	8.88	9.75	9.63
Stock price – low ($)	—	—	—	—	4.50	3.88	5.63
Stock price – close ($)	24.6%	—	—	—	4.75	7.63	7.38
P/E – high	—	—	—	—	—	—	—
P/E – low	—	—	—	—	—	—	—
Dividends per share ($)	—	—	—	—	0.00	0.00	0.00
Book value per share ($)	(66.9%)	—	—	—	2.55	1.38	0.28
Employees	85.2%	—	—	—	—	81	150

1995 YEAR-END
Debt ratio: 10.4%
Return on equity: —
Cash (mil.): $0.6
Current ratio: 0.81
Long-term debt (mil.): $0.2
No. of shares (mil.): 4.7
Dividends
  Yield: —
  Payout: —
Market value (mil.): $34.8

BLOOMBERG L.P.

OVERVIEW

If information is power, Bloomberg is Superman. Headquartered in New York City, the financial news and data company publishes magazines and operates national TV, radio, and newspaper wire services. Its 400 journalists work out of 62 bureaus, gathering news and information. BLOOMBERG computer terminals provide institutional investors and other users up-to-the-minute financial data, analyses, news, sports, advertising, and access to Hoover's company profiles around the clock. (There are 60,000 terminals in use, at a price of around $1,100 per month.) The firm also publishes weekly newsletters for the energy industry, including *Bloomberg Oil Buyers' Guide*, and *Bloomberg Asphalt Report*. Founder and CEO Michael Bloomberg owns 70% of the company; brokerage firm Merrill Lynch owns the other 30%.

Educated in engineering as well as business, Bloomberg was a partner at Salomon Brothers investment bank, where he was chief of equity trading and sales and later chief of systems. Fired in 1981 for criticizing management, Bloomberg founded Innovative Marketing Systems and designed the prototype of his computer terminal. He then pitched it to former colleagues and clients; in exchange for a 30% stake, Merrill Lynch helped bankroll its development and bought the first 20 terminals, installed in 1983.

The company built a news operation from scratch, hiring reporters from the *Wall Street Journal*, *Forbes*, *Business Week*, and the like. The firm adopted its present name in 1986. It bought a New York radio station in 1992 and converted it to an all-news format. The next year the company built an in-house TV studio and created a business news show for PBS. It debuted a satellite TV station in 1994. The firm teamed up with Salomon in 1995 to launch an online bond trading service in Europe. Also that year it launched a Web site.

Lexis-Nexis agreed in 1996 to distribute Bloomberg's Business News and Daily Market Summaries through its online service. Bloomberg also began publishing personal finance and business reference books, including *Swap Literacy: A Comprehensive Guide* and *A Common Sense Guide to Mutual Funds*.

WHO

President and CEO: Michael R. Bloomberg
COO: Susan Friedlaender
CFO: Wolf Boehm
Editor-in-Chief, Bloomberg Business News: Matthew Winkler
VP Marketing: Elisabeth DeMarse
VP Development: Tom Secunda
Bloomberg Information Radio: Bob Leverone
Manager Personnel: Geri Ingram
Auditors: Arthur Andersen & Co, SC

WHERE

HQ: 499 Park Ave., New York, NY 10022
Phone: 212-318-2000
Fax: 212-980-4585
Web site: http://www.bloomberg.com

	1995 Sales
	% of total
US	57
Europe	33
Other regions	10
Total	**100**

WHAT

Selected Products and Services
Bloomberg (monthly business magazine, also published in Japanese; 100,000 circulation)
Bloomberg Business News (radio and TV program broadcast to 35 radio and 188 TV stations)
Bloomberg Business News Service (financial and market information and analysis, general news, sports, and advertising)
Bloomberg Direct TV (24-hour video cable channel)
Bloomberg Forum (interviews with leading business executives; on USA Network and Bloomberg terminals)
Bloomberg Information Radio (WBBR-AM, New York City, also syndicated and carried by satellite to Bloomberg Information Television subscribers)
Bloomberg Personal (monthly magazine on personal finance)
Bloomberg Personal Online (World Wide Web site of personal financial information)
THE BLOOMBERG terminal (financial information and analysis relayed to 60,000 dedicated terminals)

KEY COMPETITORS

ADP	FMR	NBC
Agence France-	Forbes	New York Times
Presse	Global	News Corp.
Associated Press	Knowledge	Primark
Bowne	Knight-Ridder	Reuters
Data Broadcasting	McGraw-Hill	Time Warner
Dow Jones	Media General	Thomson Corp.
Dun & Bradstreet	Morningstar, Inc.	

HOW MUCH

Private company FYE: December 31	Annual Growth	1990	1991	1992	1993	1994	1995
Estimated sales ($ mil.)	35.9%	140.0	192.0	290.0	370.0	550.0	650.0
Employees	23.9%	—	850	1,100	1,800	2,000	2,000

Bloomberg
FINANCIAL MARKETS
COMMODITIES
NEWS

BOOKS-A-MILLION, INC.

OVERVIEW

Books-A-Million has its customers whistling Dixie. Headquartered in Birmingham, Alabama, the company is the 4th largest book chain in the US and a dominant book retailer in the Southeast. It operates about 129 bookstores in 17 states, including 66 superstores (average size: 25,000 square feet). Most of the 32 traditional stores (3,500 square feet) are located in regional malls and operate under the Bookland name. There are also 31 larger "combination" Bookland stores, which offer greeting cards and gifts in addition to a wide range of books. In addition, Books-A-Million is a wholesaler of bargain books to bookstore chains and of a range of books to independent bookstores and mass merchandisers. Though the company's sales have been rising, its profits have been hurt by fierce industry competition, particularly in malls.

The business has been run by the Anderson family for 3 generations. In 1917, 14-year-old Clyde W. Anderson started a street corner newsstand in Florence, Alabama, as a way to support his family after the sudden death of his father. The company moved into the retail book business (under the leadership of the founder's son, current chairman Charles Anderson), establishing Bookland stores throughout the South from the 1950s through the 1970s. Clyde B. took over the reins of Books-A-Million in 1992. That year the company also went public. The Anderson family owns 42% of the stock.

Books-A-Million has earned a reputation for knowing its readers by focusing on regional tastes and offering deep discounts on best-sellers and a wide selection of bargain books.

During 1995 the company merged its Book$mart wholesale subsidiary into its other business unit, American Wholesale, and opened 21 new superstores.

WHO

Chairman: Charles C. Anderson, age 61
CEO and President: Clyde B. Anderson, age 35
EVP and COO: R. Lew Burdette, age 37
EVP and CFO: Sandra B. Cochran, age 37
VP Merchandising: Terrance G. Finley, age 42
Director Human Resources: Christine Sanders
Auditors: Auditors: Andersen Worldwide

WHERE

HQ: 402 Industrial Ln., Birmingham, AL 35211
Phone: 205-942-3737
Fax: 205-945-1772

WHAT

	1996 Stores
	No.
Superstores	66
Traditional	32
Combination	31
Total	**129**

Operating Units
American Wholesale Book Co., Inc. (hardcover, paperback, and bargain book wholesaling)
Bookland (traditional mall-based bookstores and combination book and greeting card stores)
Books-A-Million (superstores)

KEY COMPETITORS

Barnes & Noble
Borders
Crown Books
Hallmark
Hastings Books
MTS
Oxford Books
Wal-Mart

HOW MUCH

Nasdaq symbol: BAMM FYE: January 31	Annual Growth	1991	1992	1993	1994	1995	1996
Sales ($ mil.)	28.9%	64.5	72.8	95.1	123.3	172.4	229.8
Net income ($ mil.)	44.3%	1.2	1.9	3.3	5.6	8.1	7.5
Income as % of sales	—	1.8%	2.6%	3.5%	4.5%	4.7%	3.3%
Earnings per share ($)	27.0%	0.13	0.21	0.32	0.37	0.47	0.43
Stock price – high ($)[1]	—	—	—	9.13	12.88	17.75	18.63
Stock price – low ($)[1]	—	—	—	7.00	5.88	9.25	12.38
Stock price – close ($)[1]	14.9%	—	—	8.50	10.88	16.88	12.88
P/E – high	—	—	—	29	35	38	43
P/E – low	—	—	—	22	16	20	29
Dividends per share ($)	—	—	0.00	0.00	0.00	0.00	0.00
Book value per share ($)	56.0%	—	0.88	2.61	4.29	4.75	5.21
Employees	25.7%	—	—	1,450	1,596	1,703	2,883

[1] Stock prices are for the prior calendar year.

1996 YEAR-END
Debt ratio: 13.5%
Return on equity: 8.7%
Cash (mil.): $1.9
Current ratio: 1.64
Long-term debt (mil.): $14.1
No. of shares (mil.): 17.4
Dividends
  Yield: —
  Payout: —
Market value (mil.): $223.9

BOWNE & CO., INC.

OVERVIEW

Bowne & Co. is the US's largest financial and corporate printer and one of a handful of companies that have been operating continuously since the 18th century. The New York City-based company prints prospectuses, offering circulars, 10-Ks, stock certificates, and legal documents. Bowne also prints custom business forms and promotional materials for clients in the US and throughout the world. Investor Thomas Stanley owns about 10% of the company.

Robert Bowne established himself as a general merchant in New York in 1775; among his wares were cloth, paper, and cutlery. The business, which later specialized in stationery, printing, and binding, remained under family management until 1898, when Bowne's grandson, Robert, retired. Bowne & Co. incorporated in 1909 and gradually abandoned the stationery business in the early 20th century. The company's printing operations received a major boost in the 1930s, when the newly created SEC began requiring stock issue prospectuses and instituted annual reporting requirements for corporations. Bowne went public in 1968.

The financial printing business is dependent on the economic cycles that influence stock issues and mergers and acquisitions. The computer age has also changed the business. In response, Bowne has expanded into electronic media. The company has particularly targeted the reformatting of documents for online viewing and has created an online business database called Baseline Financial Services (in which this and other Hoover's company profiles appear).

The globalization of high finance has opened up new markets overseas, and in 1995 Bowne opened offices in Buenos Aires, Frankfurt, Jakarta, and Singapore.

WHO

Chairman: Richard H. Koontz, age 55, $569,000 pay
VC and CEO: Robert M. Johnson, age 50
EVP and COO: James P. O'Neil, age 51, $345,000 pay
VP: Brendan Keating, age 41, $200,000 pay
VP Human Resources and Administration: Allen D. Marold, age 55, $195,000 pay
VP Technical Services: John O. Penhollow, age 60, $180,000 pay
VP Marketing: Thomas J. Vos, age 48
Corporate Secretary and Counsel: Douglas F. Bauer, age 53
Auditors: Ernst & Young LLP

WHERE

HQ: 345 Hudson St., New York, NY 10014
Phone: 212-924-5500
Fax: 212-229-3420
Web site: http://www.bowne.com

Bowne has offices in Atlanta, Boston, Chicago, Cleveland, Dallas, Los Angeles, New York, and Phoenix as well as in Canada, France, Germany, Hong Kong, Indonesia, Mexico, Singapore, and the UK.

	1995 Sales	
	$ mil.	% of total
US printing	336.5	85
Canadian printing	56.2	14
Other	3.7	1
Total	**396.4**	**100**

WHAT

	1995 Sales
	% of total
Financial & corporate printing	81
Commercial & legal printing	19
Total	**100**

KEY COMPETITORS

Bloomberg
Consolidated Graphics
FactSet
Graphic Industries
Mail-Well, Inc.
Merrill Corp.
R. R. Donnelley
StockVale
World Color Press

HOW MUCH

AMEX symbol: BNE FYE: October 31	Annual Growth	1990	1991	1992	1993	1994	1995
Sales ($ mil.)	14.3%	205.1	240.1	286.0	337.6	385.9	396.4
Net income ($ mil.)	22.6%	8.4	14.3	28.3	35.3	31.2	23.3
Income as % of sales	—	4.1%	6.0%	9.9%	10.5%	8.1%	5.9%
Earnings per share ($)	22.3%	0.49	0.84	1.65	2.05	1.80	1.34
Stock price – high ($)	—	15.00	16.50	18.38	21.75	28.50	20.88
Stock price – low ($)	—	8.00	9.63	13.13	14.75	15.38	15.38
Stock price – close ($)	15.5%	9.75	15.50	16.38	21.75	17.38	20.00
P/E – high	—	31	20	11	11	16	16
P/E – low	—	16	12	8	7	9	12
Dividends per share ($)	7.6%	0.25	0.25	0.26	0.30	0.32	0.36
Book value per share ($)	12.2%	7.80	8.46	9.71	11.37	12.82	13.87
Employees	13.8%	—	—	1,900	2,459	2,743	2,800

1995 YEAR-END
Debt ratio: 2.4%
Return on equity: 10.0%
Cash (mil.): $36.6
Current ratio: 2.74
Long-term debt (mil.): $2.8
No. of shares (mil.): 17.4
Dividends
  Yield: 1.8%
  Payout: 26.9%
Market value (mil.): $348.2

BROADCAST MUSIC INC.

OVERVIEW

"Do you have a license to play that song?" Broadcast Music Inc. (BMI) wants to know. The company, headquartered in New York City, controls 45% of the performance rights copyright market; the American Society of Composers, Authors and Publishers (ASCAP) controls about 53%. BMI collects royalties on music played or offered by more than 435,000 radio and TV stations, national and cable TV networks, shopping malls, hospitals, restaurants, online services, video-on-demand providers, and even aerobics studios. BMI's portfolio of music artists is the largest in the industry, with more than 160,000 songwriters, composers, and publishers, including some 70% of Academy Award–winning songwriters and 75% of Rock & Roll Hall of Fame inductees.

BMI was created in 1939 by music broadcasters as an alternative to ASCAP, which had tight restrictions regarding whom it would license (e.g., a writer had to have 5 published hits before being allowed to join). The company's goals were to provide an opportunity for artists to become licensed more easily and to provide an additional music source for broadcasters. By the end of 1940, BMI had signed on some 650 radio stations. As the company expanded its catalog of music, more stations defected from ASCAP to purchase their licenses from BMI, thus deciding not to play songs by ASCAP artists.

The firm's open-door policy to new artists, plus its innovative logging procedure (which produced a more comprehensive record of the songs played on the radio), attracted both songwriters and licensees to BMI. In 1968 its annual income reached $27 million.

More than 1,000 college radio stations joined BMI's logging system in 1989, enabling it to pay royalties to alternative songwriters who may not have otherwise seen money for their work. In the early 1990s the company extended its list of licensees to include such nontraditional broadcasters as amusement parks, banks, health clubs, and shopping malls.

In 1995 BMI signed a licensing contract with OnRamp Inc., allowing the Internet service provider to play digital music on the World Wide Web.

WHO

Chairman: Donald Thurston
President: Frances Preston
SVP and General Counsel: Marvin Berenson
SVP and Special Counsel: Thea Zavin
SVP Licensing: John Shaker
SVP Finance and Operations and CFO: Fred Willms
SVP International: Ekke Schnabel
VP Corporate Relations: Robbin Ahrold
VP Human Resources: Edward Chapin
Auditors: Arthur Andersen & Co, SC

WHERE

HQ: 320 W. 57th St., New York, NY 10019
Phone: 212-586-2000
Fax: 212-830-8329
Web site: http://www.bmi.com

WHAT

Selected Past and Present Artists

Ace of Base	Michael Stipe
Carla Bley	Allen Toussaint
Michael Bolton	Hank Williams
Mariah Carey	Anthony Wilson
Ray Charles	
Chuck D	**Selected Licensee Establishments**
Aretha Franklin	
Barry Gibb	Aerobics studios
Tom T. Hall	Amusement parks
Janet Jackson	Banks
Michael Jackson	Bars
John Lennon	Health clubs
E. B. Marks	Hospitals
Paul McCartney	Internet access providers
Roger Miller	Radio and TV stations and networks
Joni Mitchell	Restaurants
Alanis Morrisette	Retail stores
Willie Nelson	Satellite TV delivery services
Roy Orbison	Shopping malls
Joan Osborne	Video-on-demand providers
Dolly Parton	
Ralph Peer	
Paul Simon	

KEY COMPETITORS

ASCAP
JASRAC (Japan)

HOW MUCH

Not-for-profit organization FYE: June 30	Annual Growth	1990	1991	1992	1993	1994	1995
Sales ($ mil.)	6.8%	256.1	270.0	281.1	287.6	313.8	355.2
Employees	—	—	—	—	—	—	568

BRØDERBUND SOFTWARE, INC.

OVERVIEW

Brøderbund is bundling fun and education. The Novato, California-based firm is a leading publisher and distributor of entertainment, educational, and personal productivity software. Its titles include the geography "edutainment" program Where in the World Is Carmen Sandiego? (which inspired the Emmy-winning PBS series), the adventure game Myst (developed by Cyan), and Print Shop, which lets computer users create cards, posters, and flyers.

Brothers Doug and Gary Carlston started Brøderbund (a hybrid Scandinavian word meaning "brotherhood") in 1980 to market some computer games Doug had programmed while practicing law. (Doug owns 10% of Brøderbund; Gary left the company in 1989.) Brøderbund's first big hit came in 1984 with Print Shop. The next year it released Where in the World Is Carmen Sandiego?, which teaches geography by having users track down a spy-turned-thief. The company went public in 1991. The following year it acquired PC Globe, an electronic atlas publisher, and expanded its list of affiliated labels (software it exclusively distributes for other publishers). The company formed a joint venture with Random House in 1994 to create Living Books, a line of interactive children's storybook CD-ROMs.

In 1995 Brøderbund completed the transfer of its product line to CD-ROM. That year the company tried to acquire the Learning Company, a leading educational software developer, but lost out to SoftKey.

With the confusion created by Windows 95, the Internet stealing consumer attention, and pricing pressures among CD-ROM publishers, Brøderbund experienced weakened sales in early 1996; in response, the company announced it was looking for a new CEO, freeing up chairman Doug Carlston to develop online business opportunities.

WHO

Chairman and CEO: Douglas G. Carlston, age 48, $790,881 pay
President and COO: William M. McDonagh, age 39, $638,354 pay
SVP Brøderbund Studios: Harry R. Wilker, age 49, $454,093 pay
SVP Marketing and Sales: Jan L. Gullet, age 41
VP Business Development, General Counsel, and Secretary: Thomas L. Marcus, age 42, $376,138 pay
VP Sales: Rodney D. Haden, age 45, $286,779 pay
VP Finance and CFO: Michael J. Shannahan, age 47
VP Engineering: M. W. Mantle
VP Educational Sales and Marketing: Pat Walkington
Director Human Resources: Patsy Murphy
Auditors: Ernst & Young LLP

WHERE

HQ: 500 Redwood Blvd., Novato, CA 94948-6121
Phone: 415-382-4400
Fax: 415-382-4582
Web site: http://www.broderbund.com

WHAT

	1995 Sales
	% of total
Print Shop	30
Entertainment	24
Living Books	13
Carmen Sandiego	10
Early Learning	10
Other	13
Total	**100**

KEY COMPETITORS

3DO	Electronic Arts	Nintendo
Accolade	Gametek	Rand McNally
Activision	Golden Books	Scholastic
Creative	Grolier	SEGA
Technology	id Software	SoftKey
Davidson &	Knowledge	Sony
Associates	Adventure	Spectrum
Edmark	LucasArts	HoloByte
Educational	Maxis	T-HQ
Insights	Microsoft	Tribune

HOW MUCH

Nasdaq symbol: BROD FYE: August 31	Annual Growth	1990	1991	1992	1993	1994	1995
Sales ($ mil.)	27.8%	50.4	55.8	75.1	95.6	111.8	171.6
Net income ($ mil.)	62.4%	3.2	7.1	9.7	13.6	11.1	36.2
Income as % of sales	—	6.3%	12.7%	12.9%	14.2%	9.9%	21.1%
Earnings per share ($)	58.9%	0.17	0.38	0.50	0.68	0.55	1.72
Stock price – high ($)	—	—	13.25	24.63	29.63	47.25	78.75
Stock price – low ($)	—	—	6.25	9.25	14.88	15.75	42.25
Stock price – close ($)	51.6%	—	11.50	21.25	17.25	46.75	60.75
P/E – high	—	—	35	49	44	86	46
P/E – low	—	—	16	19	22	29	25
Dividends per share ($)	—	—	0.00	0.00	0.00	0.00	0.00
Book value per share ($)	29.5%	—	2.22	2.38	3.26	4.09	6.25
Employees	20.1%	—	271	338	402	438	563

1995 YEAR-END
Debt ratio: 0.0%
Return on equity: 34.6%
Cash (mil.): $126.5
Current ratio: 4.68
Long-term debt (mil.): $0.0
No. of shares (mil.): 20.6
Dividends
　Yield: —
　Payout: —
Market value (mil.): $1,252.9
R&D as % of sales: 13.3%

CADMUS COMMUNICATIONS

OVERVIEW

Cadmus Communications provides a full range of printing, marketing, and publishing services. The Richmond, Virginia-based firm is North America's #1 producer of scientific, technical, medical, and scholarly journals, providing such services as typesetting, editing, printing, packaging, and distribution. Cadmus also prepares financial documents; designs and markets promotional materials, directories, and catalogs; provides production services to publishers of professional, trade, and consumer magazines; publishes its own line of magazines; and makes folding cartons, mailers, and other promotional packaging.

The company began in the 1960s as the William Byrd Press, a printing company that focused on medical and technical journals. It spent heavily in the 1970s to upgrade equipment as printing technologies switched from engraved type to offset printing and photocomposition. The company was renamed Cadmus Communications (for the mythological figure who introduced the alphabet to Greece) when it went public in 1983. It started to expand and diversify through its 1984 merger with Washburn Graphics and its purchases of American Graphics (advertising materials, 1986) and Three Score (direct mail and catalogs, 1987). In 1992 Cadmus moved into publishing by buying Marblehead Communications (newsletters and magazines) and Tuff Stuff Publications (specialty magazines).

In 1995 it acquired PeachWeb (Internet applications), Software Factory (packaging and media-duplication), and Mowry (direct marketing). Also that year it created a new media unit to serve electronic markets.

The next year Cadmus bought journal publisher Lancaster Information Group. The company's earnings slipped below $6 million in 1996; sales rose to nearly $337 million.

WHO

Chairman, President, and CEO: C. Stephenson Gillispie Jr., age 53, $457,500 pay
VP and CFO: Michael Dinkins, age 41, $272,000 pay
VP and Regional Manufacturing Officer: John H. Phillips, age 51, $248,000 pay
VP Human Resources and Quality: Gregory Moyer, age 47, $245,000 pay
VP Law and Development: Bruce V. Thomas, age 38, $238,000 pay
VP Information Technologies: Edward B. Fernstrom
VP and Treasurer: David E. Bosher
Auditors: Andersen Worldwide

WHERE

HQ: Cadmus Communications Corporation, 6620 W. Broad St., Ste. 500, PO Box 27367, Richmond, VA 23261-7367
Phone: 804-287-5680
Fax: 804-287-6267
Web site: http://journals.at-home.com/

WHAT

	1995 Sales	
	$ mil.	% of total
Printing	203.1	73
Marketing	57.1	20
Publishing	19.4	7
Total	**279.6**	**100**

Printing
Financial documents
Journals
Magazines
Promotional materials
Specialty packaging

Marketing
Catalogs
Direct marketing materials

Interactive marketing materials
Point-of-purchase marketing materials

Publishing
Custom publishing services
Special-interest magazines

KEY COMPETITORS

Banta	Graphic	Quebecor
Bowne	Industries	R. R. Donnelley
Courier	Merrill Corp.	World Color
Devon Group	Quad/Graphics	

HOW MUCH

Nasdaq symbol: CDMS FYE: June 30	Annual Growth	1990	1991	1992	1993	1994	1995
Sales ($ mil.)	10.4%	170.4	177.7	188.0	198.1	247.7	279.6
Net income ($ mil.)	11.3%	4.4	3.0	3.9	4.5	4.8	7.5
Income as % of sales	—	2.6%	1.7%	2.1%	2.3%	1.9%	2.7%
Earnings per share ($)	10.9%	0.72	0.50	0.65	0.76	0.79	1.21
Stock price – high ($)	—	10.00	8.50	10.25	14.50	19.50	29.88
Stock price – low ($)	—	6.00	5.75	6.00	8.50	13.50	14.50
Stock price – close ($)	32.4%	6.63	6.00	9.25	14.00	15.75	27.00
P/E – high	—	14	17	16	19	25	25
P/E – low	—	8	12	9	11	17	12
Dividends per share ($)	0.0%	0.20	0.20	0.20	0.20	0.20	0.20
Book value per share ($)	7.3%	7.23	7.51	7.97	8.52	9.03	9.99
Employees	5.5%	1,820	1,860	1,895	1,780	2,400	2,380

1995 YEAR-END
Debt ratio: 54.3%
Return on equity: 29.5%
Cash (mil.): $0.2
Current ratio: 1.74
Long-term debt (mil.): $54.0
No. of shares (mil.): 6.2
Dividends
  Yield: 0.7%
  Payout: 16.5%
Market value (mil.): $167.3

CARMIKE CINEMAS, INC.

OVERVIEW

Taking care of the little guys has translated into big profits for Carmike Cinemas. The Columbus, Georgia-based company is the nation's largest motion picture exhibitor (measured by number of screens), with more than 2,300 movie screens in 32 states, most of them in towns and cities with populations under 100,000. Carmike often operates the only movie theater in the area, and while the towns served are small, there is nothing small about attendance. In 1995 the company counted some 65 million viewers at its cinemas. Carmike operates more than 100 of its theaters as discount cinemas and runs 2 restaurants through wholly owned subsidiary Wooden Nickel Pub, Inc.

The chain was founded in 1982, when Mike Patrick and his father, Carl, bought Martin Theatres from Fuqua Industries in an LBO. Renamed Carmike for Carl's sons, Carl and Mike, the chain began expanding when many industry observers were predicting the demise of theaters because of home video. Carmike concentrated on building and acquiring theaters in cities its larger competitors passed over. It bought dozens of screens each year during the 1980s; in the 1990s it bought hundreds more.

To keep administrative costs down, Carmike developed its own computer system and customized software. Dubbed the IQ-Zero, the system connects the theaters to company headquarters, forwards ticket sales every night, and analyzes theater profitability.

In 1995, with the addition of 377 acquired screens and 113 new screens, Carmike surpassed United Artists Theatre to become the largest exhibitor in the US. In 1996, Carmike opened a new theater in Lexington, Kentucky, with a different spin: the cinema shows only vintage movies.

WHO

Chairman: C. L. Patrick, age 77, $269,000 pay
President and CEO: Michael W. Patrick, age 45, $607,138 pay
VP Finance, CFO, and Treasurer: John O. Barwick III, age 46, $202,500 pay
VP Film: Anthony J. Rhead, age 54, $175,000 pay
VP Informational Systems and Secretary: Larry M. Adams, age 52, $155,000 pay
VP Development: Prentiss Lamar Fields, age 41
VP Advertising: Marilyn B. Grant, age 48
VP Technical: James R. Davis, age 57
Director Human Resources: Sadie Harper
Auditors: Ernst & Young LLP

WHERE

HQ: 1301 First Ave., Columbus, GA 31901-2109
Phone: 706-576-3400
Fax: 706-576-3471

	1995 Theater Operations	
	No. of theaters	No. of screens
North Carolina	75	299
Tennessee	48	259
Georgia	39	208
Pennsylvania	35	156
Florida	33	158
Texas	30	120
Alabama	29	160
Other states	230	1,023
Total	**519**	**2,383**

WHAT

	1995 Sales	
	$ mil.	% of total
Admissions	253.7	70
Concessions & other	111.0	30
Total	**364.7**	**100**

KEY COMPETITORS

AMC Entertainment	Regal Cinemas
Cinemark USA	Samuel Goldwyn
Cineplex Odeon	Sony
GC	United Artists Theatre
National Amusements	Viacom

HOW MUCH

NYSE symbol: CKE FYE: December 31	Annual Growth	1990	1991	1992	1993	1994	1995
Sales ($ mil.)	23.4%	127.4	145.7	172.0	241.8	327.6	364.7
Net income ($ mil.)	15.8%	6.3	5.7	6.1	11.9	17.0	13.1
Income as % of sales	—	4.9%	3.9%	3.5%	4.9%	5.2%	3.6%
Earnings per share ($)	6.7%	0.84	0.75	0.80	1.50	2.00	1.16
Stock price – high ($)	—	16.38	17.25	17.00	20.75	24.38	25.50
Stock price – low ($)	—	7.25	9.00	10.50	12.88	16.38	18.75
Stock price – close ($)	17.6%	10.00	15.50	14.25	18.00	23.00	22.50
P/E – high	—	20	23	21	14	12	22
P/E – low	—	9	12	13	9	8	16
Dividends per share ($)	—	0.00	0.00	0.00	0.00	0.00	0.00
Book value per share ($)	14.4%	8.47	9.23	10.02	11.77	15.65	16.58
Employees	22.2%	3,700	5,440	6,455	6,600	8,060	10,082

1995 YEAR-END
Debt ratio: 55.5%
Return on equity: 7.3%
Cash (mil.): $18.8
Current ratio: 0.71
Long-term debt (mil.): $218.0
No. of shares (mil.): 11.2
Dividends
Yield: —
Payout: —
Market value (mil.): $251.2

CENTRAL NEWSPAPERS, INC.

OVERVIEW

Here's a big fish with 2 small ponds. Central Newspapers publishes the primary daily newspapers in Indianapolis and Phoenix. Although the company publishes both morning and evening papers under different names in both places, there is only one editorial staff in each city. To cut costs in 1995, separate morning and evening staffs were combined. It also owns other small daily and weekly papers in its home state of Indiana. The founding Pulliam family (of which former Vice President Dan Quayle is a member) owns more than 30% of the company's stock.

Central Newspapers was founded in 1934 by journalist Eugene Pulliam to buy papers, and it soon owned several in Arizona. In 1945, moving northeast, the company bought the *Indianapolis Star* (founded in 1903) and 3 years later the *Indianapolis News* (founded in 1934), both of which had statewide circulation. Pulliam, who remained at the helm until his 1975 death, came from a generation in which newspapers were blatantly political. He used the papers to promote his conservative politics, including support of the Vietnam War (in which his grandson, Quayle, avoided service). The company went public in 1989, although effective control remained in family hands.

The newspaper industry has been under assault in the past 2 decades from declining readership, industry consolidation, and rising costs. Central Newspapers has survived by virtue of its lock on newspaper ad revenues in its 2 major markets (Phoenix is one of the US's fastest-growing areas). It has also acquired smaller local papers and chains and moved into electronic publishing via the Internet. In 1996 Central Newspapers bought Louisiana's McCormick & Co., which owns the Alexandria (Louisiana) *Daily Town Talk* and printing company McCormick Graphics.

WHO

Chairman: Frank E. Russell, age 75
President and CEO: Louis A. Weil III, age 54, $567,398 pay (prior to promotion)
EVP; President, Phoenix Newspapers, Inc.; Publisher, *Indianapolis Star* and *Indianapolis News*: Eugene S. Pulliam, age 81, $99,728 pay
President and General Manager, Indianapolis Newspapers, Inc.: Malcolm W. Applegate, age 60, $357,975 pay
Treasurer and CFO: Thomas K. MacGillivray, age 35
Auditors: Geo. S. Olive & Co. LLC

WHERE

HQ: 135 N. Pennsylvania St., Ste. 1200, Indianapolis, IN 46204-2400
Phone: 317-231-9200
Fax: 317-231-9208
Web site: http://www.azcentral.com

WHAT

	1995 Sales	
	$ mil.	% of total
Advertising	446.7	77
Circulation	129.5	22
Other	3.7	1
Total	**579.9**	**100**

Selected Subsidiaries

Central Newspapers, Inc. **(Indiana papers)** *The North Knox News* **Indianapolis Newspapers, Inc.** *Indianapolis News* *Indianapolis Star* **Muncie Newspapers, Inc.** **(Indiana papers)** *The Muncie Star*	**Phoenix Newspapers, Inc.** *The Arizona Business Gazette* *The Arizona Republic* *The Phoenix Gazette* **Topics Newspapers, Inc.** **(Indianapolis-area papers)** *The Daily Ledger* **13 community weeklies**

KEY COMPETITORS

Cox Enterprises
Gannett
Tribune

HOW MUCH

NYSE symbol: ECP FYE: December 31	Annual Growth	1990	1991	1992	1993	1994	1995
Sales ($ mil.)	6.1%	431.7	420.4	433.6	466.6	519.7	579.9
Net income ($ mil.)	13.8%	28.3	25.9	23.4	32.1	41.3	54.0
Income as % of sales	—	6.6%	6.2%	5.4%	6.9%	7.9%	9.3%
Earnings per share ($)	13.7%	1.07	0.98	0.88	1.21	1.55	2.03
Stock price – high ($)	—	23.50	21.38	23.75	27.75	30.00	32.63
Stock price – low ($)	—	13.88	16.75	19.00	20.88	24.63	24.13
Stock price – close ($)	13.2%	16.88	19.00	22.88	27.75	28.13	31.38
P/E – high	—	22	22	27	23	19	16
P/E – low	—	13	17	22	17	16	12
Dividends per share ($)	8.6%	0.39	0.40	0.41	0.45	0.50	0.59
Book value per share ($)	5.6%	4.95	5.22	4.85	5.28	5.81	6.51
Employees	(1.5%)	5,600	4,973	4,860	5,000	5,030	5,188

1995 YEAR-END
Debt ratio: 0.7%
Return on equity: 15.9%
Cash (mil.): $129.5
Current ratio: 2.83
Long-term debt (mil.): $2.7
No. of shares (mil.): 55.1
Dividends
　Yield: 2.0%
　Payout: 30.5%
Market value (mil.): $1,727.9

CHANCELLOR BROADCASTING COMPANY

OVERVIEW

Chancellor Broadcasting likes its chances in the big cities. The company owns and operates 34 stations (22 FM and 12 AM) in more than a dozen major markets. The Dallas-based company, one of the largest radio broadcasting companies in the US, operates mainly in the nation's 25 biggest radio markets, including Atlanta, Denver, Detroit, Los Angeles, New York, and San Francisco. The company believes that the number of stations it owns and the diversity of its programming minimize its dependence on local economies and types of advertisers. Chancellor stations offer a range of program formats, including adult contemporary, country, news/talk, rock, and sports. The company seeks to own and operate radio stations in the largest 40 markets in the US. These markets accounts for a disproportionate share of radio advertising revenue. Investment firm Hicks, Muse, Tate & Furst owns approximately 57% of the company.

Radio veteran Steven Dinetz founded the company in 1993. Dinetz teamed up with Hicks, Muse to acquire Denver stations KOSI-FM and KEZW-AM from Group W Broadcasting in a leveraged buyout. The company was named Chancellor by Dinetz, after the road he lived on as a child and the elementary school he attended. Chancellor kept making acquisitions, targeting the top 40 radio markets in the US. In 1994 it bought 11 stations from the American Media Station Group, plus 2 Sacramento stations.

The company continued its geographic expansion in 1995 with its acquisition of 19-station Shamrock Broadcasting, a private group owned by Roy Disney (the nephew of entertainment pioneer Walt), for $395 million. However, it failed in its attempt to take over station operator SFX Broadcasting.

Chancellor went public in 1996. That year the company agreed to swap a Houston station for 2 Denver stations owned by Secret Communications. It also agreed to buy 8 Florida stations (one AM and 7 FM) from Omniamerica for $178 million.

WHO

Chairman: Thomas O. Hicks
President and CEO: Steven Dinetz, age 48, $340,000 pay
EVP, General Manager, and Regional Manager:
Rick Eytcheson, age 45, $338,616 pay
EVP, General Manager, and Regional Manager:
George C. Toulas, age 43, $305,000 pay
EVP Regional Manager: Skip Weller
SVP Finance: Eric W. Neumann, age 30, $144,000 pay
SVP and CFO: Jacques D. Kerrest, age 49
Director Human Resources: Karen DuBois
Auditors: Coopers & Lybrand L.L.P.

WHERE

HQ: 12655 N. Central Expwy., Ste. 405, Dallas, TX 75243
Phone: 214-239-6220
Fax: 214-239-0220

Chancellor has 34 radio stations serving 14 of the US's top 40 radio markets.

WHAT

Markets and Stations
Atlanta (WFOX-FM)
Cincinnati (WUBE-AM/FM, WYGY-FM)
Denver (KALC-FM, KIMN-FM, KXKL-AM/FM, KZDG-FM)
Detroit (WDFN-AM, WWWW-FM)
Los Angeles (KLAC-AM, KZLA-FM)
Minneapolis-St. Paul (KDWB-FM, KEEY-FM, KFAN-AM, KTCJ-AM, KTCZ-FM)
Nassau-Suffolk, NY (WALK-AM/FM)
New York City (WHTZ-FM)
Orlando (WOCL-FM)
Phoenix (KMLE-FM)
Pittsburgh (WWSW-AM/FM)
Riverside-San Bernardino, CA (KGGI-FM, KMEN-AM)
Sacramento (KFBK-AM, KGBY-FM, KHYL-FM)
San Francisco (KABL-AM, KBGG-FM, KNEW-AM, KSAN-FM)

KEY COMPETITORS

American Radio Systems
Capital Cities/ABC
Citicasters
Clear Channel
Cox Enterprises
Evergreen Media
Gannett
Jacor Communications
Park Communications
SFX Broadcasting
Tribune
Viacom
Westinghouse

HOW MUCH

Nasdaq symbol: CBCA FYE: December 31	Annual Growth	1990	1991	1992	1993	1994	1995
Sales ($ mil.)	44.8%	10.1	10.4	12.1	14.7	26.3	64.3
Net income ($ mil.)	124.9%	(0.2)	(0.4)	(0.4)	1.5	(0.1)	(11.5)
Income as % of sales	—	1.8%	—	3.3%	9.9%	—	—
Employees	—	—	—	—	—	—	236

1995 YEAR-END
Debt ratio: 75.9%
Return on equity: —
Cash (mil.): $1.3
Current ratio: 1.14
Long-term debt (mil.): $168.1

CHRIS-CRAFT INDUSTRIES, INC.

OVERVIEW

One-time boat maker Chris-Craft now floats a TV network. The New York City-based company's United Paramount Network (UPN), a joint venture with Viacom, reaches 91% of US households through more than 150 affiliates. Chris-Craft operates 8 TV stations in major US markets. It also makes plastic film products primarily for the chemical and health care industries. Earnings dipped in 1995 due to UPN's start-up expenses. Chris-Craft is controlled by chairman Herbert Siegel, EVP Evan Thompson, and directors Lawrence Barnett and James Rochlis.

The company started in 1928 as National Automotive Fibers to make upholstery and interior trim for cars. Investor Paul Shields took it over in 1956, diversifying into oil, gas, and broadcasting. In 1960 it purchased boat builder Chris-Craft (founded in the 1880s by backwoods brothers Harry and Christopher Columbus Smith) and adopted the Chris-Craft name 2 years later. Chemical manufacturer and Chris-Craft's largest stockholder, Baldwin-Montrose, led by Herbert Siegel, took over the company in 1968, and Siegel became chairman. It was the world's largest producer of DDT by 1972 when the government banned the deadly chemical. During the 1970s Chris-Craft invested in Paramount, which led to the ownership of TV stations through United Television, Inc. In 1981 the company sold its boat division, but kept the Chris-Craft brand name. Two years later it became the largest stockholder of Warner Communications, leading to the creation of BHC Communications, a 70%-owned subsidiary that owns Chris-Craft's Television Division. Through the early 1990s the company built its station portfolio. In 1995 UPN began broadcasting 4 hours per week (increased to 6 in 1996) of prime-time programming targeted at young men.

WHO

Chairman and President: Herbert J. Siegel, age 67, $3,413,600 pay
EVP; President, Television Division: Evan C. Thompson, age 53, $3,516,090 pay
SVP: William D. Siegel, age 41, $880,000 pay
SVP: John C. Siegel, age 43, $880,000 pay
VP, CFO, and Treasurer: Joelen K. Merkel, age 44, $575,000 pay
General Counsel and Secretary: Brian C. Kelly, age 44
Auditors: Price Waterhouse LLP

WHERE

HQ: 767 Fifth Ave., 46th Fl., New York, NY 10153
Phone: 212-421-0200
Fax: 212-935-8462

WHAT

	1995 Sales	
	$ mil.	% of total
Television Division	454.7	96
Industrial Division	17.4	4
Total	**472.1**	**100**

Television Stations
KBHK-TV (UPN; San Francisco)
KCOP-TV (UPN; Los Angeles)
KMOL-TV (NBC; San Antonio)
KMSP-TV (UPN; Minneapolis)
KPTV-TV (UPN; Portland, Oregon)
KTVX-TV (ABC; Salt Lake City)
KUTP-TV (UPN; Phoenix)
WWOR-TV (UPN; Secaucus, New Jersey)

Selected Industrial Division Products
Plastic film
Polyvinyl alcohol film
Water-soluble laundry bags

KEY COMPETITORS

Capital Cities/ABC	Gannett	News Corp.
Chronicle Publishing	Harte Hanks Communications	Time Warner
Cox Enterprises	NBC	Tribune
E.W. Scripps	New World Communications	Washington Post
		Westinghouse

HOW MUCH

NYSE symbol: CCN FYE: December 31	Annual Growth	1990	1991	1992	1993	1994	1995
Sales ($ mil.)	(12.2%)	903.7	283.8	331.5	439.7	481.4	472.1
Net income ($ mil.)	(40.4%)	291.7	58.3	65.2	149.1	64.7	22.0
Income as % of sales	—	32.3%	20.5%	19.7%	33.9%	13.4%	4.7%
Earnings per share ($)	(40.9%)	7.48	1.51	1.70	3.76	1.63	0.54
Stock price – high ($)	—	30.76	28.23	31.01	40.90	40.30	44.91
Stock price – low ($)	—	21.09	19.78	22.21	28.50	31.07	31.56
Stock price – close ($)	13.6%	22.19	22.88	29.87	34.53	33.50	42.00
P/E – high	—	4	19	18	11	25	83
P/E – low	—	3	13	13	8	19	58
Dividends per share ($)	—	0.00	0.00	0.00	0.00	0.00	0.00
Book value per share ($)	5.6%	34.38	37.62	39.90	43.23	44.19	45.06
Employees	3.5%	1,050	941	1,276	1,277	1,174	1,246

1995 YEAR-END
Debt ratio: 0.0%
Return on equity: 1.7%
Cash (mil.): $1,523.4
Current ratio: 7.76
Long-term debt (mil.): $0.0
No. of shares (mil.): 29.1
Dividends
  Yield: —
  Payout: —
Market value (mil.): $1,223.0

CHRONICLE PUBLISHING

OVERVIEW

The *San Francisco Chronicle* left it to other newspapers to chronicle the lawsuit that its publisher's former chairman Nan Tucker McEvoy brought against her 16 cousins when they voted her off the board in 1995. The 76-year-old McEvoy owns 26% of the closely held San Francisco-based company, which owns 3 newspapers (including its flagship, the *Chronicle*), 4 TV stations and 2 book publishing firms.

McEvoy's grandfather Michael de Young co-founded the *San Francisco Chronicle* in 1865 with his brother Charles. In 1879 a headline comparing the preacher Isaac Kalloch, who was running for mayor, to an "unclean leper" was countered by a sermon that accused de Young's family of being the "progeny of a whore." The enraged Charles shot the preacher. Twice. Kalloch survived, but his son shot de Young dead in revenge. (He was acquitted.) After the death of Michael in 1925, the paper experienced a decline in advertising in the 1930s. This was turned around following the hiring in 1936 of Paul Smith as editor. Smith revitalized the newspaper, giving a priority to international news.

Readership began to drift away in the late 1940s and early 1950s. The Sunday editor, Scott Newhall, took over the editor slot in 1952 and brought back readers with a number of promotions and giveaways. Under Newhall the paper established a network of correspondents around the world. In 1965 the paper and archrival Hearst's *San Francisco Examiner* formed an agency to handle their operations jointly, with the exception of the editorial departments. The Hearst paper also moved to an afternoon publication. McEvoy became chairman in 1974, and in 1977 Michael de Young's great-grandson Richard Tobin Thieriot took over as publisher.

Facing tough economic times, the company brought in an outsider, John Sias, in 1993 to right the ship. The former EVP of Capital Cities/ABC set about cutting costs. In 1995 the board of directors established an age limit that ousted McEvoy, prompting her lawsuit (which she subsequently dropped in exchange for a director emeritus title).

In 1996 the company sold its cable TV systems to cable poobah TCI.

WHO

Chairman and President: John B. Sias
SVP and CFO: Alan H. Nichols
Editor, *San Francisco Chronicle*: William German
Director Human Resources: Michael O'Neil

WHERE

HQ: The Chronicle Publishing Company, Inc., 901 Mission St., San Francisco, CA 94103-2988
Phone: 415-777-1111
Fax: 415-777-7131
Web site: http://www.sfgate.com

WHAT

Newspapers
Pantagraph (Bloomington, IL)
San Francisco Chronicle
Worcester Telegram and Gazette (Massachusetts)

TV Stations
KAKE-TV, Wichita, KS
KLBY-TV, Colby, KS (satellite station)
KRON-TV, San Francisco
WOWT-TV, Omaha, NE

Book Publishing
Chronicle Books (San Francisco)
Motorbooks International (Osceola, WI)

Other
Chronicle Features Syndicate
CityLine (Bay area information service, with the *San Francisco Examiner*)

KEY COMPETITORS

Advance Publications
Bertelsmann
Capital Cities/ABC
Chris-Craft
Cox Enterprises
Dow Jones
Gannett
Hearst
Knight-Ridder
New York Times
News Corp.
Pulitzer Publishing
Time Warner
Tribune
Viacom

HOW MUCH

Private company FYE: December 31	Annual Growth	1990	1991	1992	1993	1994	1995
Sales ($ mil.)	7.5%	—	—	430.0	491.0	492.0	534.0
Employees	(5.9%)	—	—	3,000	3,100	2,700	2,500

San Francisco Chronicle

CKS GROUP, INC.

OVERVIEW

Cyberspace is CKS's playground. The Cupertino, California-based company has created World Wide Web sites for *The Tonight Show* and insurance company TransAmerica. CKS designs and implements multimedia marketing programs for other companies' products and services, offering advertising, direct mail, media placement, and other brand promotion services. It offers new media marketing programs designed for the World Wide Web, online services, and other digital formats. Clients range from small communications and technology companies to corporate giants such as MCI (which accounted for 18% of CKS's 1995 sales), Dun & Bradstreet, Fujitsu, and Microsoft.

Former Apple Computer employees Bill Cleary, Mark Kvamme, and Tom Suiter are the "C," the "K," and the "S" in the company's name. Cleary founded the company in 1987 as Cleary Communications, initially concentrating on the development and implementation of marketing plans and programs. The firm created its first interactive marketing program, for Apple, in 1988. Kvamme joined the group in 1989 and Suiter in 1991. In 1992 United Airlines hired CKS to revamp its logo and create a new look for its planes, printed materials, and ticket counters. The company began CKS Interactive in 1994 to provide new media services. Production unit CKS Pictures began that year as well.

Rapid growth in new media has created a market niche for CKS. In 1994 it developed the strategy and implementation plan for MCI's online service, internetMCI. The following year CKS designed the user interface environments for Hewlett-Packard's Personal Page computer screens and went public. In 1996 CKS acquired New York advertising and marketing firm Schell/Mullaney, Inc., whose clients include software powerhouse Computer Associates International. Also that year it created a New Media division, containing both CKS Interactive and CKS Pictures and headed by Delrina (PC fax software) co-founder Lou Ryan.

WHO

Chairman, President, and CEO: Mark D. Kvamme, age 34, $236,370 pay
Chief Creative Officer: Thomas K. Suiter, age 41, $219,517 pay
Chief Marketing Officer: William T. Cleary, age 48, $182,490 pay
EVP, COO, CFO, and Secretary: Carlton H. Baab, age 38, $170,174 pay
President, CKS New Media: Lou Ryan
Manager Human Resources: Sharon Fitzsimmons
Auditors: KPMG Peat Marwick LLP

WHERE

HQ: 10441 Bandley Dr., Cupertino, CA 95014
Phone: 408-366-5100
Fax: 408-366-5120
Web site: http://www.cks.com

WHAT

Selected Services
Advertising
Collateral systems
Consumer promotions
Corporate identity and product branding
Direct mail
Media placement services
New media
Packaging
Strategic corporate and product positioning
Trade promotions

KEY COMPETITORS

ADVO
Bronner Slosberg
Cordiant
Eagle River Interactive
Harte Hanks Communications
Heritage Media
International Post
Interpublic Group
Leap Group
M/A/R/C Group
Maritz
Modem Media
Omnicom Group
Organic Online
SOFTBANK
True North
WPP Group
Young & Rubicam

HOW MUCH

Nasdaq symbol: CKSG FYE: November 30	Annual Growth	1990	1991	1992	1993	1994	1995
Sales ($ mil.)	60.8%	—	5.2	6.7	12.0	22.9	34.8
Net income ($ mil.)	93.4%	—	0.1	0.2	0.3	0.3	1.4
Income as % of sales	—	—	2.9%	2.2%	2.3%	1.3%	4.0%
Employees	149.7%	—	—	—	30	104	187

1995 YEAR-END
Debt ratio: 14.6%
Cash (mil.): $1.5
Current ratio: 1.38
Long-term debt (mil.): $0.4

CLEAR CHANNEL COMMUNICATIONS

OVERVIEW

With all the legal static tuned out, Clear Channel Communications is raising its antenna to look for acquisitions. Since the radio station ownership cap was removed by the 1996 Telecommunications Act, the San Antonio-based company has cranked up the volume of its station purchases. It has filled its dial with 119 outlets (in 56 markets in the US, Australia, and New Zealand) making it the #1 US station owner, pending FCC approval. When the smoke clears, Clear Channel will also own 16 TV stations. The station absorber also operates 5 radio networks, providing news, sports, and other information services to radio stations in 6 US states. Chief stockholders include founder and CEO Lowry Mays (22%) and Texas auto dealership tycoon B. J. "Red" McCombs (16%).

Clear Channel was founded in 1972 when Mays, an investment banker, teamed up with McCombs to buy a struggling FM radio station. Mays revived the station within a year and then bought others. The company's name came from the 1975 purchase of a "clear channel" station that was part of the nation's emergency broadcast network.

In 1984 Clear Channel went public and continued to buy ailing stations under favorable terms. The company bought its first TV station in 1988. Clear Channel sold some of its smaller radio outlets in 1994 and merged with Tampa competitor Metroplex Communications. In 1995 it entered the international market with the purchase of a 50% stake in the Australian Radio Network. It owned 36 radio and 10 TV outlets at year's end.

In 1996 the cash-rich company enlarged its station roster by making major acquisition agreements with US Radio Inc. (18 stations), the New Zealand government (41 stations), and Federated Media (5 stations).

WHO

Chairman, President, and CEO: L. Lowry Mays, age 60, $2,098,217 pay
EVP; COO, Clear Channel Television: William R. "Rip" Riordan, age 38, $295,064 pay
SVP Operations: Mark P. Mays, age 32
VP, Clear Channel Metroplex: Dave Ross, age 45, $259,558 pay
VP, Clear Channel: Jack Peck, age 39, $230,432 pay
VP, Clear Channel Television: Josh McGraw, age 45, $191,100 pay
VP and Treasurer: Randall T. Mays, age 30
VP and Controller (HR): Herbert W. Hill Jr., age 36
Auditors: Ernst & Young LLP

WHERE

HQ: Clear Channel Communications, Inc., 200 Concord Plaza, Ste. 600, San Antonio, TX 78216
Phone: 210-822-2828
Fax: 210-822-2299

Clear Channel operates radio stations in the US, Australia, and New Zealand, and TV stations in the US.

WHAT

	1995 Sales	
	$ mil.	% of total
Radio	141.7	58
Television	102.1	42
Total	**243.8**	**100**

KEY COMPETITORS

American Radio Systems	Paxson Communications
Capital Cities/ABC	Renaissance
Chancellor Broadcasting	Communications
Cox Enterprises	SFX Broadcasting
Evergreen Media	Spanish Broadcasting
Gannett	Tichenor Media
Jacor Communications	Viacom
Park Communications	Westinghouse

HOW MUCH

NYSE symbol: CCU FYE: December 31	Annual Growth	1990	1991	1992	1993	1994	1995
Sales ($ mil.)	28.5%	69.6	74.1	94.5	135.7	200.7	243.8
Net income ($ mil.)	—	(0.3)	1.1	4.3	9.1	22.0	32.0
Income as % of sales	—	—	1.5%	4.6%	6.7%	11.0%	11.3%
Earnings per share ($)	—	(0.02)	0.05	0.15	0.30	0.64	0.91
Stock price – high ($)	—	3.07	3.97	7.24	18.45	26.00	44.25
Stock price – low ($)	—	1.94	2.69	3.46	6.48	15.70	25.06
Stock price – close ($)	74.6%	2.72	3.62	6.52	18.40	25.38	44.13
P/E – high	—	—	79	48	62	41	49
P/E – low	—	—	54	23	22	25	28
Dividends per share ($)	—	0.00	0.00	0.00	0.00	0.00	0.00
Book value per share ($)	108.5%	0.12	0.87	1.05	2.90	3.79	4.73
Employees	15.2%	764	800	1,150	1,354	1,549	1,549

1995 YEAR-END
Debt ratio: 67.1%
Return on equity: 21.8%
Cash (mil.): $5.4
Current ratio: 1.96
Long-term debt (mil.): $334.2
No. of shares (mil.): 34.4
Dividends
  Yield: —
  Payout: —
Market value (mil.): $1,517.9

COMSAT CORPORATION

OVERVIEW

COMSAT envisions a world in which you can reach out and touch someone — from anywhere on the globe. The Bethesda, Maryland-based company builds communications networks and provides voice, data, fax, telex, e-mail, video, and other information services to users in remote locations away from standard communications equipment. Subsidiary Ascent Entertainment provides on-demand movies and other programming to US hotels and motels, produces films and television programs, and owns 2 professional sports teams (the NBA's Denver Nuggets and the NHL's Colorado Avalanche). Another subsidiary, COMSAT International Ventures, manages telecommunications companies in emerging markets in Asia, Europe, and Latin America. The US government (led by the Department of Defense) accounted for 45% of the company's 1995 sales. California investor Joseph Harrosh owns 8% of the company.

The US government created public enterprise Communications Satellite Corp. in 1963 to link the country's phone companies to the INTELSAT satellite network. By 1989 the prevalence of fiber-optic networks challenged the company's primary business and led to a strategy of diversification. That year it bought a controlling stake of the Denver Nuggets (it gained full control in 1992). After purchasing 47% of On Command Video (which delivers movies via satellite to hotel rooms) in 1991, it increased its ownership to 74%. The company adopted the name COMSAT in 1993.

In 1995 COMSAT purchased the Quebec Nordiques NHL hockey team, which was moved to Colorado and renamed the Avalanche. In 1996 COMSAT introduced the Planet 1 mobile satellite communications terminal, which enables personal voice and data communications from anywhere in the world.

WHO

Chairman: Melvin R. Laird
President and CEO: Betty C. Alewine, age 48, $366,923 pay
SVP Business Development: Ronald J. Mario, age 52, $307,500 pay
President, Ascent Entertainment Group, Inc.: Charles Lyons, age 41, $478,461 pay
President, COMSAT RSI, Inc.: Richard E. Thomas, age 69, $455,071 pay
President, COMSAT Laboratories: John V. Evans, age 62
VP and CFO: Allen E. Flower, age 52
VP, General Counsel, and Secretary: Warren Y. Zeger, age 49
VP Human Resources and Organization Development: Steven F. Bell, age 46
Auditors: Deloitte & Touche LLP

WHERE

HQ: 6560 Rock Spring Dr., Bethesda, MD 20817
Phone: 301-214-3000
Fax: 301-214-7100
Web site: http://www.comsat.com

WHAT

Selected Business Segments
Entertainment (on-demand entertainment programming, NHL team Colorado Avalanche and NBA team Denver Nuggets)
International Communications (satellite communications services and telecommunications company management)
Mobile Communications (satellite communications)
Technology Services (communications network design)

KEY COMPETITORS

AMSC
Andrew Corp.
AT&T Corp.
California Microwave
Graft Pay-Per-View
Hughes Electronics
IDB Mobile
  Communications

INMARSAT
LodgeNet Entertainment
Scientific-Atlanta
SpectraVision
Walt Disney

HOW MUCH

NYSE symbol: CQ FYE: December 31	Annual Growth	1990	1991	1992	1993	1994	1995
Sales ($ mil.)	13.3%	456.8	522.9	563.6	640.4	826.9	852.1
Net income ($ mil.)	—	(16.3)	71.4	42.9	74.0	77.6	37.8
Income as % of sales	—	—	13.7%	7.6%	11.6%	9.4%	4.4%
Earnings per share ($)	—	(0.44)	1.80	1.09	1.82	1.64	0.79
Stock price – high ($)	—	19.25	19.00	24.44	35.25	30.00	24.63
Stock price – low ($)	—	10.19	11.44	17.13	23.75	17.50	17.63
Stock price – close ($)	9.2%	12.00	17.19	23.81	29.75	18.63	18.63
P/E – high	—	—	11	22	19	18	31
P/E – low	—	—	6	16	13	11	22
Dividends per share ($)	3.4%	0.66	0.67	0.70	0.74	0.76	0.78
Book value per share ($)	3.4%	14.84	15.36	15.80	16.87	17.66	17.58
Employees	13.8%	1,569	1,645	1,644	1,527	2,894	2,991

1995 YEAR-END
Debt ratio: 48.7%
Return on equity: 4.5%
Cash (mil.): $124.2
Current ratio: 2.08
Long-term debt (mil.): $664.6
No. of shares (mil.): 46.8
Dividends
  Yield: 4.2%
  Payout: 98.7%
Market value (mil.): $870.8
R&D as % of sales: 2.2%

CONSOLIDATED GRAPHICS, INC.

OVERVIEW

Houston-based Consolidated Graphics, one of the fastest-growing printing companies in the US, is actually a network of 10 printing companies serving 5 metropolitan markets. The company's print houses can exploit the buying power and management depth of a large firm while offering customers local service. The companies together boast 27 sheet-fed and 5 web presses and offer a full menu of complementary services, from electronic prepress to distribution.

Consolidated Graphics was founded by CPA Joe Davis, a veteran of both Price Waterhouse and Houston's Arthur Andersen office, where he had become a partner at age 33. Davis left Arthur Andersen in 1979 to become VP of finance and administration at International Paper. He left that firm and purchased his first printing company, Western Lithographic, in 1985. Since then Davis has concentrated on acquiring established small to medium-sized printers (those with annual sales between $2 million and $15 million) that have a reputation for quality and a strong customer base. All of the print shops specialize in printing recurring materials such as financial, promotional, and sales pieces. In 1993 it bought Gulf Printing, one of Houston's largest printers, from SBC Communications. The company went public in 1994. Davis owns about 32% of the company.

Davis continues selectively acquiring local printers. In 1994 Consolidated Graphics entered the Dallas market with the purchase of the Jarvis Press. It also added 2 Denver-area companies — Gritz-Ritter Graphics and Frederic Printing. In 1995 it acquired Heritage Graphics (Phoenix) and Clear Visions (San Antonio). The following year it acquired Emerald City Graphics (Seattle), Precision Litho (San Diego), and Tulsa Litho (Tulsa).

WHO

Chairman and CEO: Joe R. Davis, age 52, $228,000 pay (prior to promotion)
President, Chas. P. Young Co.: Scott L. Fordham, age 36, $166,000 pay
President, Gulf Printing: W. Mark Rand, age 36, $125,000 pay
SVP: Mary K. Collins, age 38, $115,000 pay
VP Mergers and Acquisitions and CFO: G. Christopher Colville
VP Human Resources: Janet Swikard
Auditors: Andersen Worldwide

WHERE

HQ: 2210 W. Dallas St., Houston, TX 77019
Phone: 713-529-4200
Fax: 713-525-4305

WHAT

	1995 Sales % of total
Commercial printing	96
Financial printing	4
Total	**100**

Selected Services
Distribution
Electronic prepress
Finishing, folding, and binding
Packaging
Printing
Warehousing

Subsidiaries
Chas. P. Young Co. (Houston)
Clear Visions (San Antonio)
Frederic Printing Co. (Denver)
Gritz-Ritter Graphics, Inc. (Boulder)
Grover/Houston Litho Co. (Houston)
Gulf Printing Co. (Houston)
Heritage Graphics (Phoenix)
The Jarvis Press, Inc. (Dallas)
Tewell Warren Printing Co. (Denver)
Western Lithographic Co. (Houston)

KEY COMPETITORS

Banta
Bowne
Graphic Industries
Hart Graphics
Merrill Corp.
Quad/Graphics
Quebecor
R. R. Donnelley
World Color

HOW MUCH

Nasdaq symbol: COGI FYE: March 31	Annual Growth	1991	1992	1993	1994	1995	1996
Sales ($ mil.)	41.7%	14.9	20.5	28.9	48.6	57.2	85.1
Net income ($ mil.)	34.8%	0.9	0.8	2.1	3.5	4.5	4.0
Income as % of sales	—	—	—	7.2%	7.2%	7.9%	4.7%
Earnings per share ($)	(10.6%)	—	—	—	0.90	0.90	0.72
Stock price – high ($)[1]	—	—	—	—	—	22.50	26.13
Stock price – low ($)[1]	—	—	—	—	—	9.75	9.50
Stock price – close ($)[1]	131.1%	—	—	—	—	11.25	26.00
P/E – high	—	—	—	—	—	25	36
P/E – low	—	—	—	—	—	11	13
Dividends per share ($)	—	—	—	—	0.00	0.00	0.00
Book value per share ($)	61.6%	—	—	—	3.22	6.99	8.41
Employees	45.1%	—	—	—	474	702	998

[1] Stock prices are for prior calendar year.

1996 YEAR-END
Debt ratio: 29.9%
Return on equity: 9.1%
Cash (mil.): $3.1
Current ratio: 2.50
Long-term debt (mil.): $20.1
No. of shares (mil.): 5.9
Dividends
  Yield: —
  Payout: —
Market value (mil.): $154.2

THE COPLEY PRESS, INC.

OVERVIEW

The Copley Press lives off the copy desk. Headquartered in La Jolla, California, the family-owned and -operated business runs the *San Diego Union-Tribune* and more than 40 other daily and nondaily papers, mostly in the Chicago and Los Angeles areas. Copley Press also has interests in newsprint production and owns stakes in resort and telecommunications businesses. The company is owned by descendants of James Copley, the adopted son of founder Colonel Ira Copley.

The newspapers started as a sideline to Ira Copley's gas company, which his family had taken over in Aurora, Illinois, in 1867. Copley graduated from Yale and attended law school in Chicago but returned to Aurora to revive the family's failing business. In 1905 Copley bought his first newspaper, the faltering *Aurora Daily Beacon*, and turned it around. He absorbed 3 other Aurora newspapers and bought and combined 2 newspapers in Joliet (1915) and Elgin (1926). Copley bought Springfield's *State Journal-Register* in 1927. In 1928 Copley bought a collection of small papers in Los Angeles and San Diego. The Copley Press was incorporated that year.

Copley died in 1947 at age 83. Despite financial problems, the company stayed intact. Ownership was divided between Copley's 2 sons, James and Bill; James became chairman. The Copley News Service was created in 1955, the same year Bill sued to liquidate the company. To settle the suit, James bought out the remainder of the Copley stock in 1959.

James died in 1973 and was succeeded by his widow, Helen, as publisher and CEO; their son David became president in 1988. In 1991 Copley Press purchased 5 suburban Chicago newspapers and merged its 2 San Diego papers into the *San Diego Union-Tribune*, thus creating one of the US's largest privately owned newspapers. The company formed a joint venture in 1994 to develop a high-speed fiber-optic network in San Diego County.

Copley Press agreed in 1996 to buy 2 Illinois newspapers, the *Peoria Journal Star* and the *Galesburg Register-Mail*. Their combined daily circulation of nearly 100,000 would boost Copley's total daily circulation in Illinois to more than 300,000.

WHO

Chairman and CEO: Helen K. Copley
President: David C. Copley
EVP and CFO: Charles F. Patrick
General Counsel: Judith L. Fanshaw
VP Finance and Treasurer: Dean P. Dwyer
VP Legal Affairs: Harold W. Fuson Jr.
VP Human Resources: Carmi Hodge

WHERE

HQ: 7776 Ivanhoe Ave., La Jolla, CA 92037
Phone: 619-454-0411
Fax: 619-454-5014
Web site: http://www.uniontrib.com

WHAT

Daily Newspapers
The Beacon-News (Aurora, IL)
The Courier (Lincoln, IL)
The Courier-News (Elgin, IL)
Daily Breeze (Torrance, CA)
The Herald-News (Joliet, IL)
News-Pilot (San Pedro, CA)
The News-Sun (Waukegan, IL)
The Outlook (Santa Monica, CA)
The San Diego Union-Tribune
The State Journal-Register (Springfield, IL)

Other Operations
Fiber-optic telecommunications (joint venture with Linkatel Communications)
La Casa del Zorro (resort; Borrego Springs, CA)
Newsprint manufacturing

KEY COMPETITORS

Advance Publications
Cox Enterprises
Dow Jones
E.W. Scripps
Freedom Communications
Gannett
Hearst
Hollinger Inc.
Knight-Ridder
Media General
New York Times
Reuters
Times Mirror
Tribune

HOW MUCH

Private company FYE: December 31	Annual Growth	1990	1991	1992	1993	1994	1995
Sales ($ mil.)	1.4%	—	376.4	363.0	365.0	384.0	398.0
Employees	0.0%	—	—	3,500	3,500	3,500	3,500

CORBIS CORPORATION

OVERVIEW

At Corbis, image is everything. The Bellevue, Washington-based company (owned by Microsoft genius Bill Gates) maintains the world's largest collection of digitized visual content, with some 700,000 images reproduced in electronic form. The library contains scanned copies of prints, artistic and journalistic photographs, and associated text. Corbis plans to expand the collection to include video, audio, graphics, and other media. The images are licensed for use in print publications and in various types of electronic media.

The company's Bettmann division handles rights to the famed Bettmann Archive, which contains more than 16 million images, including such classic photos as the exploding *Hindenberg* and a skirt-clad Marilyn Monroe over a subway air vent. The Corbis Media division supplies stock images (including Mathew Brady's Civil War photographs, Picasso paintings, and images from NASA and the Smithsonian) for use by advertisers, graphic designers, and print and electronic publishers. The Corbis Publishing division develops CD-ROMs and documentary products for the World Wide Web.

In 1989 Gates founded Interactive Home Systems (later Continuum Productions) and began buying the rights to digitize images from museums, archival collections, private collectors, publications, and others. The company changed its name in 1995 to Corbis Corporation (corbis is Latin for "woven basket" and symbolizes the company as a container for high-quality images). That year Corbis bought one of the world's largest collections of historical photos — the Bettmann Archive — which includes the photo library (through 1990) of United Press International. In 1995 it also bought the rights to the artwork of Russia's Hermitage Museum, which includes some 3 million works. Such moves prompted concern about the extent of Corbis's (and Gates's) control over world art treasures.

Corbis acquired exclusive rights in 1996 to photographer Ansel Adams's works (some 40,000 images) for CD-ROM and online distribution. Also that year it reached a licensing agreement with Mariners' Museum in Newport News, Virginia (with 650,000 photographic images).

WHO

President and CEO: Doug Rowan
VP Finance and Operations: Tony Rojas
VP Business and Legal Affairs: Steve Davis
Director Sales and Marketing: Mike Martucci
Director Technology: Steve White
General Manager and Executive Producer, Corbis Productions: Curtis Wong
General Manager, Corbis Publishing: Nana Kuo
Marketing Manager: Scott Sedlik
Sales Manager: Mark Daniel
Manager Human Resources: Tica Gordon

WHERE

HQ: 15395 SE 30th Place, Ste. 300, Bellevue, WA 98007
Phone: 206-641-4505
Fax: 206-746-1618
Web site: http://www.corbis.com

WHAT

Divisions
Bettmann (handles rights to the Bettmann Archive, which contains more than 16 million images)
Corbis Media (licenses visual content and stock photography for use by advertisers, graphic designers, and print and electronic publishers)
Corbis Publishing (publishes CD-ROM and online documentary consumer products)

Selected Image Archive Subjects
Fine arts
Geography
History
Natural history
Sciences
Technology
World cultures

KEY COMPETITORS

Agence France-Presse
Archive Photos
Associated Press
Dorling Kindersley
EMME Interactive
IBM
Image Bank
Image Smith
Index Stock Photography
Knight-Ridder
LookingGlass Technologies
Media Photographers Copyright Agency
Photodisc
Picture Network International
StarPress

HOW MUCH

Private company FYE: December 31	Annual Growth	1990	1991	1992	1993	1994	1995
Sales ($ mil.)	—	—	—	—	—	—	8.0
Employees	0.0%	—	—	—	—	270	270[1]

[1] Estimated

PUBLIC BROADCASTING

OVERVIEW

Big Bird, baseball, and Bill Moyers all have a place under the Corporation for Public Broadcasting (CPB) umbrella. Headquartered in Washington, DC, CPB is an independent, nonprofit organization created by Congress to provide high-quality educational, informational, and cultural programming. Neither the Public Broadcasting Service (PBS) nor National Public Radio (NPR) is a CPB subsidiary (they are owned by member stations), but CPB does provide some funding for those entities to acquire programming. Most CPB funding goes in the form of unrestricted grants to nearly 1,000 public radio and television stations. Lately CPB has been under heavy fire from conservatives in Congress seeking to cut or end its funding.

Public broadcasting in the US traces its roots back to the early 1900s, when many universities began broadcasting. With commercial radio beginning to fill the dial, the FCC in 1945 reserved 20 channels from 88 to 92 FM for noncommercial educational broadcasts. In 1953 KUHT-TV in Houston became the first noncommercial educational television station. Public television spread rapidly; by 1965 there were 124 public TV stations. That year, with backing from President Lyndon Johnson and the Carnegie Corporation, the Carnegie Commission on Educational Television was established to study the financial needs of educational television. The commission called for the establishment of a Corporation for Public Television (excluding radio) to acquire public TV programs and distribute them nationally, with a new emphasis on both general interest and educational programs. After lobbying from public radio, CPB was created in 1967 with the passage of the Public Broadcasting Act. In 1969 PBS was formed to unite public television stations, and in 1970 NPR was created.

Increased scrutiny from Congress has brought changes to CPB. In 1995 it reduced its staff by almost 25%. The next year it instituted performance criteria including listenership and community financial support minimums for public radio stations seeking grants. CPB is considering a similar plan for public TV.

WHO

Chairman: Henry Cauthen
President and CEO: Richard W. Carlson
EVP and COO: Robert Coonrod
SVP System and Station Development: Frederick L. DeMarco
SVP Government and Community Relations: Lillian Fernandez
SVP Programming: Eugene Katt
SVP Education: Carolynn Reid-Wallace
SVP Corporate Communications: Michael Schoenfeld
Corporate Treasurer and Director, Office of Budget: E. Renee Ingram
Acting General Counsel and Secretary: Sylvia Winik
Director Human Resources: Miriam Crawford
Auditors: KPMG Peat Marwick LLP

WHERE

HQ: Corporation for Public Broadcasting, 901 E St. NW, Washington, DC 20004
Phone: 202-879-9600
Fax: 202-879-1039
Web site: http://www.cpb.org

WHAT

	1995 Revenues	
	$ mil.	% of total
Federal appropriations	285.6	91
Grants & contracts	10.2	3
Interest income	11.9	4
Royalties & other	4.5	2
Total	**312.2**	**100**

Selected Programs Funded

Radio	Austin City Limits
American Profiles	Barney and Friends
Jazz From Lincoln Center	Frontline
Latino USA	Mister Rogers'
Marketplace	Neighborhood
Television	Nova
American Playhouse	Sesame Street

KEY COMPETITORS

A&E Networks
BET
Capital Cities/ABC
Discovery
 Communications
International Family
 Entertainment

NBC
News Corp.
Time Warner
Viacom
Westinghouse/CBS

HOW MUCH

Not-for-profit organization FYE: September 30	Annual Growth	1990	1991	1992	1993	1994	1995
Sales ($ mil.)	4.4%	251.2	318.1	340.6	339.0	294.3	312.2
Net income ($ mil.)	(6.9%)	—	(8.4)	10.1	34.6	(12.3)	(6.3)
Income as % of sales	—	—	—	3.0%	10.2%	—	—
Employees	(0.3%)	104	101	112	110	112	109

COURIER CORPORATION

OVERVIEW

This courier has good news. Lowell, Massachusetts-based printer Courier Corporation has introduced new electronic products, invested in state-of-the-art technology, and improved and streamlined its operations. In addition to its traditional printing, binding, distribution, and fulfillment services, Courier has made a commitment to electronic services (including the production of computer disks and CD-ROMS) and information management services (like its Copyright Management Service, a system for managing intellectual property information). But Courier's largest customer (27% of sales) is the Gideon Society, which distributes free Bibles on good old-fashioned paper. CEO James Conway owns about 12% of the company.

William Baldwin began publishing the *Chelmsford* (Massachusetts) *Journal* in 1824. When it was 70 years old, the paper became part of Courier-Citizen Co., which branched out into telephone directories. In 1941 the company's newspaper operations were sold to the publisher of the *Lowell Sun*, and Courier-Citizen continued as a printer. James F. Conway Jr. became CEO in 1966. The company went public in 1972 as Courier Corporation. James F. Conway III took over Courier after his father died in 1992.

Courier has faced increased competition in the 1990s with the consolidation of the printing industry. It has made heavy investments in technology to meet the increased call for jobs with short lead times and small press runs. Courier formed an electronic publishing center (EPIC) in 1992, and it launched its New Media subsidiary in 1994 to create electronic products.

Sales declined slightly in 1995, but profits increased as Courier focused on revenue sources with long-term potential.

WHO

Chairman, President, and CEO: James F. Conway III, age 43, $314,000 pay
SVP and Chief Marketing Officer: Thomas G. Osenton, age 42, $247,500 pay
SVP and CFO: Robert P. Story Jr., age 44, $242,225 pay
VP; President, National Publishing Company: George Q. Nichols, age 66, $300,000 pay
VP and Controller: Peter M. Folger, $128,000 pay
Director Human Resources: Charlie Van Horn
Auditors: Deloitte & Touche LLP

WHERE

HQ: 165 Jackson St., Lowell, MA 01852
Phone: 508-458-6351
Fax: 508-453-0344

Courier has 7 book manufacturing plants and warehouses in Indiana, Massachusetts, and Pennsylvania.

WHAT

Selected Services
Commercial printing and binding (books, manuals, technical documentation)
Custom printing (short run and on-demand)
Disk and CD-ROM production
Information management and electronic publishing
Order fulfillment
Platemaking
Product assembly and packaging
Product design
Project management services

KEY COMPETITORS

Applied Graphics	Meehan-Tooker
Astronics	Merrill Corp.
Banta	Quad/Graphics
Cadmus Communications	Quebecor
Champion Industries	Queens Group
Consolidated Graphics	R. R. Donnelley
Devon Group	Taylor Corp.
Duplex Products	World Color Press
Graphic Industries	Zomax
Hart Graphics	

HOW MUCH

Nasdaq symbol: CRRC FYE: September 30	Annual Growth	1990	1991	1992	1993	1994	1995
Sales ($ mil.)	2.8%	105.3	124.2	121.9	115.2	122.7	120.7
Net income ($ mil.)	—	(2.2)	1.3	(6.0)	2.2	3.7	5.2
Income as % of sales	—	—	1.0%	—	1.9%	3.0%	4.3%
Earnings per share ($)	—	(1.24)	0.75	(3.44)	1.20	1.92	2.60
Stock price – high ($)	—	20.00	15.00	14.00	20.00	19.50	27.00
Stock price – low ($)	—	10.00	10.25	6.00	7.25	14.50	16.25
Stock price – close ($)	12.5%	13.00	13.25	7.25	19.00	16.50	23.38
P/E – high	—	—	20	—	17	10	10
P/E – low	—	—	14	—	6	8	6
Dividends per share ($)	0.0%	0.40	0.40	0.30	0.00	0.20	0.40
Book value per share ($)	2.4%	16.31	16.46	12.74	13.68	16.15	18.34
Employees	(4.7%)	1,402	1,396	1,155	1,165	1,093	1,103

1995 YEAR-END
Debt ratio: 21.2%
Return on equity: 15.2%
Cash (mil.): $1.1
Current ratio: 1.65
Long-term debt (mil.): $9.5
No. of shares (mil.): 2.0
Dividends
  Yield: 1.7%
  Payout: 15.4%
Market value (mil.): $46.9

COWLES MEDIA COMPANY

OVERVIEW

Cowles Media Company is a Minneapolis-based, newspaper publishing company with stakes in magazines and information services. Providing about 2/3 of its revenues is the *Star Tribune*, its flagship newspaper and one of the US's top 20 metropolitan newspapers. The company's Cowles Business Media division produces a variety of products and services for the direct marketing, media, publishing, information, and travel markets. (Its core properties are *Folio:, Inside Media, Catalog Age*, and *Direct* magazines.) Cowles Magazines, which publishes 27 consumer magazines, reaches about 3 million readers in narrowly focused niche markets. Although Cowles's stock is traded through some brokerages, a family trust controls about 60% of the company's voting stock; the Washington Post owns almost 28%.

Country banker Gardner Cowles ventured into newspapers in 1903 and later bought the *Des Moines Register* (sold in 1985). His son John moved to Minneapolis to acquire the *Minneapolis Star* (1935), the *Minneapolis Journal* (1939), and the *Minneapolis Tribune* (1941). The Cowles family built a newspaper and media empire around its Minneapolis newspapers. But that empire, which had included several newspapers and magazines such as *Look*, began to unravel in the early 1980s. When costs outstripped revenues, 3rd-generation chairman John Cowles Jr. merged the *Star* and *Tribune* in 1982 and cut staff. Still unsatisfied with the company's performance, the Cowles board (consisting mainly of family members) in 1983 replaced him as CEO with cousin David Kruidenier. David Cox became president in 1984 and CEO in 1985.

Since 1988 the Cowles Business Media division has created a niche that includes 14 magazines, online services, newsletters, and conferences.

The company has continued to expand its nonnewspaper offerings with the recent acquisition of new consumer magazines (*Southwest Art* and *Walking*, among others), "how to" books (Cy DeCosse), and business media magazines (*On Demand* and *Pre*).

WHO

Chairman: John Cowles III
President and CEO: David C. Cox, age 57, $786,749 pay
Secretary: William R. Busch Jr.
Treasurer: Georgina Y. Stephens
President and CEO, Cowles Magazines, Inc.: Bruce A. Barnet
Publisher and President, Star Tribune: Joel R. Kramer, age 47, $408,924 pay
President and CEO, Weissman Travel Reports: Arnie Weissman
VP and CFO: James J. Viera, age 55, $301,600 pay
VP Administration: James A. Alcott, age 64, $215,867 pay
VP Human Resources: Pamela J. Sveinson, age 42, $208,204 pay
Auditors: KPMG Peat Marwick LLP

WHERE

HQ: 329 Portland Ave., Minneapolis, MN 55415-1112
Phone: 612-673-7100
Fax: 612-673-7020
Web site: http://www.cowles.com

WHAT

Operating Groups and Selected Products & Services

Cowles Business Media
Cowles Event Management
Direct Marketing (*Catalog Age, Direct*)
Interactive Cowles (Cowles/SIMBA Media Daily, Inside Media Online, On Demand)
Magazine publishing (*Folio, Mobile Office, Pre*)
Media (*Cable World, Inside Media, On Demand*)
Travel (*Weissman Travel Reports*)

Cowles Magazines Inc.
Collectibles (*British Heritage, Figurines & Collectibles*)
Distribution services
Healthy Lifestyles (*Country Journal, Vegetarian Times, Walking*)
Reference Books Series (*Microwave Cooking Library, A Photographic History of the Civil War*)
Video and creative services

Star Tribune
Minneapolis Star Tribune (404,757 daily circulation)
Star Tribune Online

KEY COMPETITORS

Advanstar Communications	Landmark Communications
Crain Communications	Mecklermedia
Forbes	Reed Elsevier
Gannett	VNU
Lagardère	

HOW MUCH

OTC symbol: CWMD FYE: March 31	Annual Growth	1991	1992	1993	1994	1995	1996
Sales ($ mil.)	9.9%	307.6	303.6	334.6	358.2	449.7	492.6
Net income ($ mil.)	33.3%	5.8	10.2	16.4	19.4	22.5	24.4
Income as % of sales	—	1.9%	3.4%	4.9%	5.4%	5.0%	5.0%
Employees	—	—	—	—	3,280	3,300	—

COWLES MEDIA COMPANY

CRAIN COMMUNICATIONS INC

OVERVIEW

Crain Communications is spreading its wings and taking off into international markets. The Chicago-based publisher of business, consumer, and trade journals has been looking into expanding the presence of its publications around the world. Crain publishes *Advertising Age* (its flagship), *Crain's Chicago Business*, *Crain's New York Business*, *American Laundry Digest*, *Automotive News*, and *TIRE BUSINESS*. Crain also provides content from its magazines to electronic databases. Other interests include a Florida radio station (WWUS-FM) and the Crain News Service, which provides business information to the media. The company is controlled by the founding Crain family.

Gustavus Dedman (G. D.) Crain founded his publishing company with a staff of 3 in 1916 in Louisville, Kentucky (later that year moving to Chicago). The firm produced 2 publications — *Class* (renamed *Business Marketing*) and *Hospital Management* (sold in the 1950s). In 1930 the company launched the *Advertising Age* trade magazine and adopted the name Advertising Publications Inc.

Over time the company broadened its publications beyond advertising, and in 1969 it changed its name to Crain Communications. G. D. Crain led the company until his death in 1973. That year veteran employee Sidney Bernstein, who had served as president since 1964, gave up the presidency to Rance Crain, G. D.'s elder son. Crain's widow, Gertrude, became chairman, and Keith Crain (Rance's brother) was subsequently appointed VC.

In 1986 Crain purchased *Media World*, the UK's #1 media magazine at that time. By the early 1990s the company was publishing 3 magazines in Europe. It bought *RCR Radio Communications Report* (wireless communications tabloid) in 1992. The next year it began sending subscribers daily fax updates on electronic media and auto industry news.

Crain hatched a new magazine (its 26th) in 1995, *Waste News*, covering the waste disposal business. That year Joe Cappo became SVP of international operations, taking charge of the marketing of Crain's business publications outside the US. In 1996 longtime chairman Gertrude Crain died at the age of 85.

WHO

Chairman: Keith E. Crain
President: Rance E. Crain
EVP Operations: William A. Morrow
SVP International: Joseph C. Cappo
VP and Group Publisher: Gloria Scoby
VP and Corporate Production Director: Robert C. Adams
VP Circulation: William Strong
VP: J. Clifford Mulcahy
Corporate Controller: Thomas M. Marantette Jr.
Treasurer: Mary Kay Crain
Secretary: Merillee P. Crain
Director Personnel: Frances Scott

WHERE

HQ: 740 N. Rush St., Chicago, IL 60611-2590
Phone: 312-649-5200
Fax: 312-280-3179
Web site: http://www.adage.com

WHAT

Publications	Publications of Crain Associated Enterprises, Inc.
Advertising Age	
Automotive News	*American Clean Car*
AutoWeek	*American Coin-Op*
Business Insurance	*American Dry Cleaner*
Business Marketing	*American Laundry Digest*
Crain's Chicago Business	*RCR Radio*
Crain's Cleveland Business	*Communications Report*
Crain's Detroit Business	
Crain's New York Business	**Other Operations**
Detroit Monthly	Crain News Service (news and information)
Electronic Media	Crain Subscription Services (subscription fulfillment)
Euromarketing (UK)	
European Rubber Journal (UK)	Crain's List Rental Service (subscriber information rental)
Franchise Buyer	
Modern Healthcare	WWUS (FM), Florida Keys
Pensions & Investments	
Plastics News	
Rubber & Plastics News	
TIRE BUSINESS	
Urethanes Technology (UK)	
Waste News	

KEY COMPETITORS

Advance Publications	CMP Publications	Mecklermedia
Advanstar Communications	Cowles Media	Pittway
	Dow Jones	Reed Elsevier
Associated Press	Forbes	Reuters
Bloomberg	Lagardère	Time Warner
	McGraw-Hill	VNU

HOW MUCH

Private company FYE: December 31	Annual Growth	1990	1991	1992	1993	1994	1995
Sales ($ mil.)	3.9%	150.0	145.0	151.6	157.0	170.7	181.8
Employees	(0.4%)	998	945	970	953	939	979

Crain's

CROWN BOOKS CORPORATION

OVERVIEW

The Hafts are trying to settle down so as not to break their Crown. The Landover, Maryland-based discount book retailer, sidetracked by a power struggle within the Haft family (which holds a controlling interest), is working to get back to business. The company sells books in print, books on tape, newspapers, magazines, videos, software, reference materials, and other items at its Classic Crown Books and Super Crown Books stores, which are located in metropolitan areas of California, Illinois, Washington, and Washington, DC. Crown has been reducing the number of its stores and has also shifted toward operating supersized stores to entice more consumers.

Robert Haft started Crown Books, the subject of his Harvard Business School thesis, in 1977. In 6 years the company grew into a chain with a market value of over $210 million. Crown went public in 1983 and continued to expand through the 1980s and early 1990s. In 1993 Robert was ousted by his father, chairman Herbert, in a power struggle, and replaced by his brother, Ronald. The next year Robert sued the retailing concern Dart Group (owned by the Hafts, it holds 51% of Crown's stock), along with Crown for breach of contract. He won a jury award of $34 million and immediately promised never to be involved again with the family's business affairs. In a move that removed the Hafts' influence from Crown's day-to-day affairs, Ronald stepped down from the top position in 1995, leaving COO Steve Stevens to run the company.

Crown closed nearly 40 Classic Books stores in 1995 and opened 16 Super Crown Books stores, leaving it with about 170 stores in all. Dart Group said in 1996 that it could face a shortage of cash if the courts obligate it to pay the judgment to Robert.

WHO

Chairman: Herbert H. Haft, age 75
President and CEO: E. Steve Stevens, age 40, $271,100 pay
SVP and General Merchandising Manager: Marc J. Joseph, age 44, $150,000 pay
VP and CFO: Donald J. Pilch, age 37, $155,000 pay
VP and Chief Information Officer: Keith Hammer
Director Human Resources: Anne Levinton
Auditors: Andersen Worldwide

WHERE

HQ: 3300 75th Ave., Landover, MD 20785
Phone: 301-731-1200
Fax: 301-731-1340
Web site: http://www.crownbooks.com

	1996 Stores
	No.
Los Angeles	51
Washington, DC	43
Chicago	32
San Francisco	20
Seattle	11
San Diego	9
Houston	6
Total	172

WHAT

Selected Products
Audio books
Magazines
Newspapers
Print books
Reference materials
Software
Videos

KEY COMPETITORS

Barnes & Noble
Books-A-Million
Borders
Cody's Books
Half Price Books
Kmart
Lauriat's
Price/Costco
Stacey's
Walgreen
Wal-Mart

HOW MUCH

Nasdaq symbol: CRWN FYE: January 30	Annual Growth	1991	1992	1993	1994	1995	1996
Sales ($ mil.)	5.2%	220.3	232.5	240.7	275.1	305.6	283.5
Net income ($ mil.)	(19.0%)	10.6	10.3	4.3	(0.2)	(19.4)	3.7
Income as % of sales	—	4.8%	4.4%	1.8%	—	—	1.3%
Earnings per share ($)	(19.4%)	2.03	1.97	0.82	(0.04)	(3.60)	0.69
Stock price – high ($)[1]	—	22.25	21.00	20.25	26.50	23.00	16.00
Stock price – low ($)[1]	—	13.25	13.00	17.50	18.50	14.00	9.00
Stock price – close ($)[1]	(1.6%)	13.25	19.25	20.00	23.25	15.50	12.25
P/E – high	—	11	11	25	—	—	23
P/E – low	—	7	7	21	—	—	13
Dividends per share ($)	—	0.00	0.00	0.00	0.00	0.00	0.00
Book value per share ($)	0.0%	16.20	18.22	18.76	18.87	15.46	16.24
Employees	4.6%	2,238	2,376	2,475	3,010	2,930	2,800

1996 YEAR-END
Debt ratio: 1.8%
Return on equity: 4.3%
Cash (mil.): $35.0
Current ratio: 1.94
Long-term debt (mil.): $1.6
No. of shares (mil.): 5.4
Dividends
  Yield: —
  Payout: —
Market value (mil.): $66.0

[1]Stock prices are for the prior calendar year.

DESKTOP DATA, INC.

OVERVIEW

If you are a news junkie, Desktop Data could be the ultimate pusher, delivering the goods right to you at work. Headquartered in Burlington, Massachusetts, the company provides a service called NewsEDGE, which delivers news from more than 500 different sources in real time directly to users' PCs via their companies' local area networks (LANs). Different from an online service, which requires users to dial out and retrieve news, NewsEDGE sends news directly to users, automatically monitoring and filtering the information according to preset preferences. When a story breaks that fits the user's criteria, a message is sent to that customer's PC. Desktop Data sells its service to financial institutions, including Merrill Lynch, Moody's Investment Services, and NationsBank; other corporate customers, such as AT&T and NYNEX; and government organizations, including the Department of Defense and the Department of the Treasury. Founder Donald McLagan owns 26.7% of the company.

A former executive with software maker Lotus and economic information provider Data Resources, McLagan combined his experience with computers and information to form Desktop Data in 1988. The following year the company introduced NewsEDGE. It entered a marketing agreement with IBM in 1990, with Big Blue selling NewsEDGE to its customers. The company went public in 1995.

Desktop Data distinguishes itself from the competition in two ways: it keeps costs low because it does not require special (expensive) terminals and it uses a company's existing LAN; and it gathers news from an array of sources, instead of pushing one particular source. In 1996 it launched NewsEDGE/WEB, making its services available to intranet users.

WHO

Chairman, President, and CEO: Donald L. McLagan, age 53, $115,500 pay
VP Finance and Operations and Treasurer: Edward R. Siegfried, age 50, $115,500 pay
VP Sales and Marketing: Clifford M. Pollan, age 38, $115,500 pay
VP and Chief Technology Officer: Daniel F.X. O'Reilly, age 48, $115,500 pay (prior to promotion)
Director Human Resources: Jessica Wasner
Auditors: Andersen Worldwide

WHERE

HQ: 80 Blanchard Rd., Burlington, MA 01803
Phone: 617-229-3000
Fax: 617-229-3030
Web site: http://www.desktopdata.com

WHAT

	1995 Sales	
	$ mil.	% of total
Subscriptions & royalties	21.8	94
Other	1.4	6
Total	**23.2**	**100**

Selected News Sources	Selected Customers
The Associated Press	Andersen Worldwide
Financial Times (UK)	AT&T
Forbes	Citibank
FORTUNE	Compaq
Knight-Ridder	The Executive Office of the
The New York Times	President of the U.S.
Nihon Keizai Shimbun	Merrill Lynch
(*Nikkei English News*)	Microsoft
Reuters	NYNEX
USA Today	Royal Dutch/Shell
The Wall Street Journal	Standard & Poor's

KEY COMPETITORS

America Online	IBM	OneSource
Applix	Individual	Pearson
Bloomberg	Knight-Ridder	Prodigy
CompuServe	M.A.I.D	Reed Elsevier
Comtex	Mainstream Data	Reuters
Dow Jones	Microsoft	Thomson Corp.
Gannett	New York Times	Unilever

HOW MUCH

Nasdaq symbol: DTOP FYE: December 31	Annual Growth	1990	1991	1992	1993	1994	1995
Sales ($ mil.)	115.4%	0.5	2.0	4.2	7.7	14.4	23.2
Net income ($ mil.)	—	(2.5)	(1.8)	(1.4)	(1.3)	(0.3)	3.3
Income as % of sales		—	—	—	—	—	14.1%
Earnings per share ($)	—	—	—	—	—	(0.06)	0.43
Stock price – high ($)		—	—	—	—	—	38.00
Stock price – low ($)		—	—	—	—	—	21.00
Stock price – close ($)		—	—	—	—	—	24.50
P/E – high		—	—	—	—	—	88
P/E – low		—	—	—	—	—	49
Dividends per share ($)		—	—	—	—	0.00	0.00
Book value per share ($)		—	—	—	—	(2.31)	2.89
Employees		—	—	—	—	—	130

1995 YEAR-END
Debt ratio: 3.0%
Return on equity: 14.5%
Cash (mil.): $32.5
Current ratio: 2.59
Long-term debt (mil.): $0.5
No. of shares (mil.): 8.5
Dividends
  Yield: —
  Payout: —
Market value (mil.): $207.8
R&D as % of sales: 12.5%

DICK CLARK PRODUCTIONS, INC.

OVERVIEW

dick clark productions is the umbrella for the 3 businesses of America's oldest teenager. It includes an independent TV programming production company that supplies awards shows, made-for-TV movies, and various specials and series to broadcast and cable networks, syndicators, and advertisers. New York- and Burbank-based dick clark corporate productions uses its entertainment connections and production expertise for corporate events, trade shows, and film and video production. Customers include Apple Computer, BMW, Honda, Hyundai, IBM, and others. dick clark restaurants operates the American Bandstand Grill, a chain of 5 restaurants that showcase Clark's music memorabilia. Clark owns 75% of the company stock.

In 1956 Clark, a radio DJ and entrepreneur, started in TV production when he took over *Bandstand*, a local music program in Philadelphia that focused on a new genre called rock-and-roll. Clark formed his company in 1957, the same year ABC gave the program, renamed *American Bandstand*, national exposure. Clean-cut Clark showcased hit records, film clips of recording stars, and kids having a good time. The show, TV's longest-lived variety program, was the first to feature black entertainers, including the Supremes, Johnny Mathis, and James Brown. The show was canceled in 1989. Clark also worked independently in record and concert promotions, acting, and hosting game shows.

The company went public in 1987. In 1994 it established a record label (CLICK Records) with Sony. Growth across all of the company's business lines led to 1996 sales of $74 million and earnings of about $5.6 million. In 1996 the company produced a new game show, *No Relation*, for 20th Century Fox's cable network fX.

WHO

Chairman and CEO: Richard W. Clark, age 65, $1,350,640 pay
President and COO: Francis C. La Maina, age 56, $793,480 pay
VP, CFO, and Treasurer (HR): Kenneth H. Ferguson, $201,380 pay
VP Development and Marketing: Phillip Fenty
VP Administration: Karen W. Clark, age 53
Auditors: Andersen Worldwide

WHERE

HQ: 3003 W. Olive Ave., Burbank, CA 91505-4590
Phone: 818-841-3003
Fax: 818-954-8609

WHAT

	1995 Sales		1995 Operating Income	
	$ mil.	% of total	$ mil.	% of total
Entertainment	33.1	71	6.0	87
Restaurants	13.5	29	0.9	13
Total	**46.6**	**100**	**6.9**	**100**

Selected Businesses and Affiliates
C & C Joint Venture (51%, Blooper series production)
dick clark corporate productions, inc. (corporate events and marketing)
dick clark restaurants, inc. (Dick Clark's American Bandstand Grill, entertainment-themed restaurants in Indianapolis, IN; Overland Park, KS; and Columbus, OH)
Dick Clark's American Bandstand Club (51%, dance club)
Selected Products
Annual TV award specials
Made-for-TV movies
TV series development and marketing

KEY COMPETITORS

All American Communications	King World	Spelling Entertainment
Carabiner	Kushner-Locke	Time Warner
International Family Entertainment	MCA	Viacom
Jack Morton Productions	NBC	Walt Disney
	News Corp.	Westinghouse/CBS
	Planet Hollywood	
	Sony	

HOW MUCH

Nasdaq symbol: DCPI FYE: June 30	Annual Growth	1990	1991	1992	1993	1994	1995
Sales ($ mil.)	7.7%	32.1	46.2	36.6	43.4	58.3	46.6
Net income ($ mil.)	24.0%	1.4	2.9	3.1	3.2	4.9	4.1
Income as % of sales	—	4.4%	6.3%	8.5%	7.4%	8.4%	8.8%
Earnings per share ($)	25.1%	0.16	0.35	0.37	0.39	0.59	0.49
Stock price – high ($)	—	8.25	8.00	5.75	7.50	10.75	10.25
Stock price – low ($)	—	2.75	3.00	3.25	3.50	5.25	7.50
Stock price – close ($)	25.3%	3.00	4.75	4.00	6.50	7.75	9.25
P/E – high	—	52	23	16	19	18	21
P/E – low	—	17	9	9	9	9	15
Dividends per share ($)	—	0.00	0.00	0.00	0.00	0.00	0.00
Book value per share ($)	14.3%	2.34	2.69	3.06	3.45	4.07	4.57
Employees	39.5%	90	75	57	160	500	475

1995 YEAR-END
Debt ratio: —
Return on equity: 11.4%
Cash (mil.): $29.1
Current ratio: 3.88
Long-term debt (mil.): $0.0
No. of shares (mil.): 8.3
Dividends
  Yield: —
  Payout: —
Market value (mil.): $76.6

DIRECTV, INC.

OVERVIEW

Television doesn't get much sharper than DIRECTV, at least for the moment. A division of Hughes Electronics (itself a part of General Motors), the El Segundo, California-based company is on the cutting edge of the direct broadcast satellite (DBS) business. For about $900 you can purchase a receiver and a hubcap-sized satellite dish. In addition to the basic 40-channel cable service, priced at $30 per month, the company offers pay-per-view movies and sports events with crisp digital picture and sound.

Upon the demise of the Soviet threat, Hughes Electronics redesigned its guided missile and defense satellite image for a kinder, gentler world; DIRECTV was the eventual result. After a failed DBS venture with media giants NBC, News Corp., and Cablevision Industries in 1990, Hughes decided to put the pieces together for its own DBS venture. In 1991 Hughes and rival digital satellite broadcasting company United States Satellite Broadcasting agreed to develop a common DBS system and share satellite space. The next year electronics manufacturer RCA-Thomson agreed to develop the hardware (digital decoder boxes and inexpensive satellite dishes) in return for the right to sell the first million units. Also that year Hughes signed a $50 million deal with Sony to develop the brains of the operation — digital videotape machines — to broadcast the programs via satellite.

The floodgate opened for DIRECTV after the 1992 Cable Regulation Act, which mandated that cable programming must be available to competing cable companies; in 1993 entertainment bigwigs Walt Disney and Paramount agreed to provide programming. DIRECTV introduced its 175-channel service in mid-1994.

In the first 18 months of DIRECTV service, over 1.25 million households subscribed (mainly videophiles and sports junkies), making it the fastest-growing product in consumer electronics history.

AT&T paid $137.5 million for a 2.5% stake in the company in 1996. Also that year Hughes signed a deal with Microsoft, enabling DIRECTV subscribers to access new data services, including select Internet content and multimedia magazines via PC.

WHO

President: Eddy Hartenstein
SVP Finance: Louise Wildee
President, DIRECTV International Inc.: Kevin N. McGrath, age 42
Director Administration (HR): Jim Rebman

WHERE

HQ: 2230 E. Imperial Hwy., El Segundo, CA 90245
Phone: 310-535-5000
Fax: 310-535-5225
Web site: http://www.DIRECTV.com

WHAT

Selected Programming

Family/Children	Music
Cartoon Network	CMT: Country Music
Discovery Channel	Television
The Disney Channel	MuchMusic
The Learning Channel	TNN: The Nashville
Sci-Fi Channel	Network

General Entertainment

Arts & Entertainment (A&E)
Black Entertainment Television (BET)
Bravo
E! Entertainment Television
The History Channel
Home Shopping Network
Turner Broadcasting
Superstation TBS
Turner Network Television (TNT)
USA Network

Movies

American Movie Classics (AMC)
Encore
Independent Film Channel
Turner Classic Movies

News and Information

CNBC
CNN
Court TV
The Weather Channel

Pay-Per-View

Up to 60 channels of movies, sports, and special events

Special Interest

Playboy TV
TV Asia

Sports

ESPN
ESPN2
MLB Extra Innings
NBA League Pass
NFL Sunday Ticket

KEY COMPETITORS

Adelphia Communications
American Telecasting
Cablevision Systems
Century Communications
Comcast
Continental Cablevision
Cox Communications
EchoStar Communications
PRIMESTAR
TCA Cable
TCI
Teledesic
Time Warner
United States Satellite Broadcasting
United Video Satellite
U S WEST Media
Viacom

HOW MUCH

Division FYE: December 31	Annual Growth	1990	1991	1992	1993	1994	1995
Estimated sales ($ mil.)	250.0%	—	—	—	—	150.0	525.0
Employees	—	—	—	—	—	—	602

DISCOVERY COMMUNICATIONS, INC.

OVERVIEW

Offering programs such as *The Wonderful World of Dung* and *Shark Week*, Discovery Communications knows that documentaries should be anything but boring. The Bethesda, Maryland-based company owns the Discovery Channel, which is one of the 5 largest cable channels in the US and reaches more than 63 million homes around the world. Another of the company's cable offerings is the Learning Channel (TLC), which focuses on educational programs, humanities, and theoretical science. The firm also offers videos, CD-ROMs, and other items through its World Wide Web site and Discovery Channel retail stores. Cable companies Tele-Communications Inc. (TCI) and Cox Communications own 49% and 24% of the company, respectively.

Discovery Communications was founded in 1985 by John Hendricks, a University of Alabama history graduate who noticed that the growing cable market was lacking in his favorite programming: documentaries. The Discovery Channel, devoted entirely to documentaries and nature shows, premiered that year in 156,000 US homes. Two years later it reached 20 million households. Cox Cable Communications, TCI, and NewChannels acquired controlling interest in 1989, the same year Discovery expanded into Europe. In 1991 the company acquired TLC, whose audience has grown from 14 million to 43 million viewers in the past 4 years. Discovery introduced Your Choice TV, a service giving viewers the freedom to watch programs at their convenience rather than in scheduled time slots, in test markets in 1993. The company expects to spend another 2 years developing Your Choice TV before making it available to the public.

In 1995 Discovery grew beyond television programming. It is focusing on international expansion and retailing company merchandise such as CD-ROMs, videos, computer software, and other natural science products. Discovery added Latin America and Asia to its international viewership during the year and launched its World Wide Web site.

Discovery continued its expansion in 1996 by purchasing the Nature Company retail chain (117 stores; books, toys, games, and other items) for $40 million from CML Group.

WHO

Chairman and CEO: John Hendricks, age 43
President and COO: Judith McHale, age 46
President and Chief Editorial and Creative Officer: Gregory Moyer, age 42
EVP and CFO: Greg Durig, age 40
Director Human Resources: Pandit Wright

WHERE

HQ: 7700 Wisconsin Ave., Bethesda, MD 20814
Phone: 301-986-1999
Fax: 301-986-1889
Web site: http://www.discovery.com

WHAT

Cable Channels
The Discovery Channel
The Learning Channel

Retail Products and Services
CD-ROMs
Discovery Channel Stores
Natural science products
Nature Company stores
Videos
Your Choice TV

KEY COMPETITORS

A&E Networks
BET
Coldwater Creek
Corporation for Public Broadcasting
Dorling Kindersley
International Family Entertainment
Learningsmith
National Geographic
Natural Wonders
NBC
News Corp.
Time Warner
Toys "R" Us
Viacom
Walt Disney
Westinghouse/CBS

HOW MUCH

Private company FYE: December 31	Annual Growth	1990	1991	1992	1993	1994	1995
Sales ($ mil.)	68.8%	—	—	52.0	52.0	200.0	250.0
Employees	(5.9%)	—	—	600	600	400	500

DORLING KINDERSLEY HOLDINGS PLC

OVERVIEW

Dorling Kindersley disdains dull reference books. The London-based international publisher instead produces illustrated titles for adults and children on subjects ranging from herbs to castles to travel to sex. The company's DK Multimedia division, which produces and markets CD-ROM titles, is Europe's largest creator of multimedia products. The company's DK Vision department turns out videos and television series. Through its DK Direct division, the company produces books and multimedia products with other companies and for direct mail catalogs, while the DK Family Library division handles the direct marketing of titles to homes and schools. Dorling Kindersley distributes to Australia, continental Europe, the Far East, and South America as well as in the UK and US, and the company licenses publication rights to publishers outside the UK.

Dorling Kindersley was founded as a book packager in 1974 by Christopher Dorling (now retired) and current company chairman Peter Kindersley. At first the company operated out of a back room of Kindersley's London home. By 1982 the company had shifted its focus to publishing and opened a New York office.

Expansion into the children's book market came in 1988 with the unveiling of the *Eyewitness* series, and DK Multimedia was born in 1991 when Kindersley sold Microsoft on the idea of producing new CD-ROMs for the company. Microsoft subsequently bought a stake in Dorling Kindersley (sold in 1995). Dorling Kindersley went public in 1992.

The company entered the US multimedia market in 1994 with the release of 5 CD-ROM titles for kids. In 1995 Dorling Kindersley released its first CD-ROM titles in foreign languages (French and Spanish), and its *Eyewitness* series was broadcast in the US on PBS.

WHO

Chairman: Peter Kindersley
Deputy Chairman: Christopher Davis
CEO: John Sargent
CFO: Tom Altier
Group Managing Director: Rod Hare
Group Legal Director: Giles Cunningham
Group Finance Director: Peter Gill
VP and Publisher: Chuck Lang
VP Sales: Bill Kelly
VP Finance and Operations: Charlie Generelli
VP and Publisher, DK Multimedia: Bror Saxberg

WHERE

HQ: 9 Henrietta St., Covent Garden, London, WC2E 8PS, UK
Phone: +44-01-71-836-5411
Fax: +44-01-71-836-7570
Web site: http://www.dk.com
US HQ: 232 Madison Ave., New York, NY 10016
US Phone: 212-213-4800
US Fax: 212-213-5240

WHAT

	1995 Sales % of total
DK Adult	53
DK Children's	32
DK Multimedia	9
Other	6
Total	**100**

KEY COMPETITORS

Bertelsmann	Houghton Mifflin	Pearson
Brøderbund	Intervisual Books	Reed
Discovery	Lagardere	Scholastic
Communications	McGraw-Hill	Time Warner
Golden Books	National	Tribune
Groupe de la Cite	Geographic	Viacom
HarperCollins	PAGES	W.W. Norton

HOW MUCH

Principal exchange: London FYE: June 30	Annual Growth	1990	1991	1992	1993	1994	1995
Sales (£ mil.)	38.7%	27.0	42.8	70.9	87.4	107.1	138.8
Net income (£ mil.)	16.8%	—	4.3	4.7	6.3	5.8	8.0
Income as % of sales	—	—	10.0%	6.6%	7.2%	5.4%	5.8%
Earnings per share (p)	31.6%	—	4	9	10	9	12
Stock price – high (p)	—	—	—	286	354	322	560
Stock price – low (p)	—	—	—	240	210	255	293
Stock price – close (p)	23.9%	—	—	281	263	321	534
P/E – high	—	—	—	32	35	36	47
P/E – low	—	—	—	27	21	28	24
Dividends per share (p)	(75.7%)	—	—	2	3	3	4
Book value per share (p)	13.7%	—	—	51	64	66	75
Employees	24.4%	—	—	—	569	745	880

1995 YEAR-END
Debt ratio: 5.7%
Return on equity: 17.2%
Cash (mil.): L8.6
Current ratio: 0.82
Long-term debt (mil.): L2.0
No. of shares (mil.): 67.3
Dividends
 Yield: 0.7%
 Payout: 32.5%
Market value (mil.): $573.4
Sales (mil): $221.5

DOVE AUDIO INC.

OVERVIEW

Dove Audio, a pioneer and industry leader in books-on-tape, is cooing with joy since lining its corporate nest with new operations. The Beverly Hills-based company uses its library of book titles as resources to develop movies and miniseries and is building a mini-studio to produce its films and TV shows. Dove's library contains more than 1,000 audio books, comprising best-selling fiction and nonfiction, classics, humor, and movie-related titles. The company also produces print books; the best-known include *New York Times* bestseller *Nicole Brown Simpson: The Private Diary of a Life Interrupted* by Faye D. Resnick.

Chairman Michael Viner (an author, filmmaker, and record producer — he produced Sammy Davis's platinum hit *Candy Man*) and his actress wife Deborah (*Haywire*) started the company in 1985 using, in part, $8,000 Michael won playing backgammon with his friend, novelist Sydney Sheldon. The idea for making books-on-tape came from Viner's uncle, who had heard one read by David Niven. Viner, with many friends in show business, focused on having famous actors read the material. His first releases were 2 Sheldon bestsellers read by actor friend Roger Moore (1987). Other friends like Julie Andrews and Michael York read books as favors during Dove's early years. In 1993 the company signed an agreement with Mexico's Grupo Televisa to distribute audio books in Spanish. In 1994 Dove went public. That same year the company entered the printed book market.

In 1995 Dove bought the rights to films from the Skouras Pictures library and formed a film distribution subsidiary (Dove Pictures). That year Reader's Digest bought the rights to distribute audio books around the globe through direct mail operations. In 1996 the company announced it would change its name to Dove Entertainment.

WHO

Chairman and CEO: Michael Viner, age 52, $234,955 pay
VP: Deborah Raffin Viner, age 43
COO: Charles Weber
CFO: Simon R. Baker
President and CEO, Dove Pictures: Tom Skouras
President, Dove Entertainment Distribution and Marketing: William A. Shields
Office Manager (HR): Carol Jacobs
Auditors: KPMG Peat Marwick LLP

WHERE

HQ: 301 N. Cañon Dr., Ste. 203, Beverly Hills, CA 90210
Phone: 310-273-7722
Fax: 310-273-0365
Web site: http://www.doveaudio.com

WHAT

Selected Audio Titles
The Middle Heart by Bette Bao Lord, read by the author
The Presidents: A Bird's-Eye View by Eddie the Eagle
The Prince and the Pilgrim by Mary Stewart, performed by Samantha Eggar
The Private Diary of My Life with Lana by Eric Root, read by the author
The Wind in the Willows by Kenneth Grahame, performed by Jeremy Irons

Selected Book Titles
The Cambridge Lectures by Stephen W. Hawking
Foetal Attraction by Kathy Lette
Happy at the Bel-Air by Gwen Davis
Inside the N.R.A. by Jack Anderson
The Long Journey of the Little Seed by Annie Reiner
Nicole Brown Simpson: The Private Diary of a Life Interrupted by Faye D. Resnick
The Private Diary of an O. J. Juror by Michael Knox

KEY COMPETITORS

Advance Publications
All American Communications
Audio Partners
Bertelsmann
Hearst
King World
Kushner-Locke
MCA
MGM
Pearson
Time Warner
Viacom
Walt Disney

HOW MUCH

Nasdaq symbol: DOVE FYE: December 31	Annual Growth	1990	1991	1992	1993	1994	1995
Sales ($ mil.)	23.3%	3.9	9.5	9.3	7.8	12.4	11.1
Net income ($ mil.)	0.0%	0.1	(2.3)	1.2	0.1	0.1	0.1
Income as % of sales	—	1.8%	—	13.2%	1.4%	1.1%	0.8%
Earnings per share ($)	0.0%	0.02	(0.72)	0.38	0.03	0.04	0.02
Stock price – high ($)	—	—	—	—	—	11.00	13.25
Stock price – low ($)	—	—	—	—	—	8.50	6.63
Stock price – close ($)	43.1%	—	—	—	—	9.00	12.88
P/E – high	—	—	—	—	—	275	—
P/E – low	—	—	—	—	—	213	—
Dividends per share ($)	—	—	—	—	—	0.00	0.00
Book value per share ($)	36.6%	—	—	—	—	1.83	2.50
Employees	33.0%	—	—	—	26	29	46

1995 YEAR-END
Debt ratio: 13.4%
Return on equity: 0.9%
Cash (mil.): $5.1
Current ratio: 1.82
Long-term debt (mil.): $0.0
No. of shares (mil.): 4.7
Dividends
  Yield: —
  Payout: —
Market value (mil.): $60.1

DREAMWORKS SKG

OVERVIEW

This Hollywood megaproduction isn't a film, it's a firm. DreamWorks SKG is the brainchild of Steven Spielberg, Jeffrey Katzenberg, and David Geffen. The trio formed the multimedia company in late 1994 to produce interactive software, movies, records, television programming, and toys. Spielberg, Katzenberg, and Geffen have each invested more than $30 million and retain about 2/3 combined ownership of the company. Microsoft cofounder Paul Allen anted up $500 million for an 18.5% stake. South Korea's One World Media put up $300 million, worth nearly 11% of the new firm.

Before pooling their interests, each of the 3 partners had established a phenomenal entertainment industry track record. Spielberg made blockbusters such as *E.T.* and *Jurassic Park*. Katzenberg guided Walt Disney's return to animation (*The Lion King*, *Aladdin*) before falling out with Disney CEO Michael Eisner. Music guru Geffen helped make superstars of the Eagles and Nirvana. Now, Spielberg's Amblin Entertainment has become part of DreamWorks, and he is overseeing the new company's film production. Geffen heads its music arm, and Katzenberg runs the animation and TV units.

Early successes for the nascent company include a $100 million programming partnership with Capital Cities/ABC, a 10-year HBO licensing agreement worth an estimated $1 billion, a $30 million joint venture with Microsoft to develop interactive software products, and a $50 million animation studio cofounded with Silicon Graphics.

In late 1995 the city of Los Angeles offered the company a major tax break to build a 100-acre studio near Los Angeles International Airport. (Native Americans protested the site as sacred ground, while others identified it as an environmentally sensitive wetland.)

Champs, a TV comedy series that premiered in January 1996, was the company's first project out of the gate. That was followed by the SKG label's release of pop star George Michael's first album in 5 years; and the signing of former CBS co-anchor Connie Chung and her husband, talk show host Maury Povich, to do a news program by late 1998.

WHO

Partner: David Geffen, age 52
Partner: Jeffrey Katzenberg, age 44
Partner: Steven Spielberg, age 48
Senior Executive, Business and Legal Affairs: Helene Hahn
CFO: Ronald L. Nelson, age 42
Senior Executive, Strategic Marketing and Special Projects: Terry Press, age 35
Senior Executive, DreamWorks Consumer Products: Brad Globe
Senior Executive, DreamWorks SKG Music: Mo Ostin
Senior Executive, Television Division: Dan McDermott
Manager Human Resources: Cassie Thomas

WHERE

HQ: 100 Universal Plaza, Lakeside Bldg., Universal City, CA 91608
Phone: 818-733-7000
Fax: 818-733-6153

WHAT

Selected Projects
DreamWorks film production (3 releases scheduled in 1996 and at least 5 in 1997 and 1998)
DreamWorks Interactive (joint venture with Microsoft Corp. to develop interactive and multimedia entertainment)
DreamWorks Records
Joint venture with Capital Cities/ABC, Inc., to produce 5 television series and 4 first-run programs
Joint venture with Silicon Graphics Inc. to build a digital animation studio
Joint venture with Sega Enterprises Ltd. and MCA Inc. to design and build high-tech arcades
Licensing agreement with Home Box Office, Inc., for DreamWorks-produced films
SKG Records

KEY COMPETITORS

Activision	News Corp.
All American	Nintendo
Communications	Pixar
Bertelsmann	PolyGram
Carsey-Werner	Rank
Creative Technology	Savoy Pictures
Discreet Logic	Sony
Electronic Arts	Spectrum HoloByte
Film Roman	Spelling Entertainment
King World	THORN EMI
Lucas Digital	Time Warner
LucasArts	Viacom
LucasFilm	Virgin Group
MGM	Walt Disney
NBC	Westinghouse/CBS

HOW MUCH

Private company FYE: December 31	Annual Growth	1990	1991	1992	1993	1994	1995
Estimated value ($ mil.)	—	—	—	—	—	—	2,700
Employees	—	—	—	—	—	—	400

DREAMWORKS

EDELMAN WORLDWIDE

OVERVIEW

Chicago-based Edelman "we don't do advertising" Public Relations operates 29 offices and has 60 affiliates, making it one of the largest public relations-only firms on the globe. Founder and chairman Daniel Edelman is a staunch supporter of the separation of public relations and advertising and proudly boasts his company's independence from any advertising firm.

The agency specializes in providing public relations for consumer interest campaigns, crisis management, events marketing, and public affairs positioning and in disseminating messages for financial, medical, and technology companies. Its client list includes such high-profile companies as Coca-Cola, RJR Nabisco, Time Warner, and Visa. The privately owned firm is controlled by the founding family, including Daniel Edelman and son and president Richard.

Edelman, educated in journalism and decorated for his service in the US Army during World War II, worked as a reporter and newswriter before going into public relations. He was a PR director with razormaker Gillette before founding his own 3-person agency in Chicago in 1952. The company first expanded into New York (1960) and has been stretching out ever since, including moves into the UK (1968), Germany (1971), Asia (1985), and Australia (1987). Richard, who joined the firm in 1978, became president in 1985. That year the company acquired investor relations agency ECOM. By the late 1980s the New York office had overtaken the Chicago office in sales. In the early 1990s the agency grew quickly, outpacing the growth rate of the world's top 5 PR firms.

The company opened offices in Vietnam in 1994 and in Spain the next year. Also in 1995 the firm launched Edelman I-Wire, an Internet clipping service.

The agency formed 2 new consumer divisions in 1996 to focus on the growing markets for electronic publishing and products for senior citizens. That year Ed Rollins, a former advisor to President Ronald Reagan and to Ross Perot during his 1992 presidential bid, was hired as EVP and general manager of public affairs.

WHO

Chairman and Co-CEO: Daniel J. Edelman
President and Co-CEO: Richard W. Edelman
Deputy Chairman; President, Edelman New York: Michael Morley
EVP; General Manager, Edelman Milan: Rosanna D'Antona
EVP; Co-General Manager, Edelman Chicago: Valerie Woods
EVP; Co-General Manager, Edelman Chicago: Robert A. Kornecki
EVP; Managing Director, Edelman Global Technology: Paul T. Bergevin
EVP; General Manager Public Affairs: Edward J. Rollins, age 53
CFO: Paul Mitchell
President, Edelman West: Pam Talbot
HR: John Edelman

WHERE

HQ: Edelman Public Relations Worldwide, 200 E. Randolph Dr., 63rd Fl., Chicago, IL 60601
Phone: 312-240-3000
Fax: 312-240-2900
Web site: http://www.edelman.com

Edelman Public Relations operates 29 offices and has affiliates worldwide.

WHAT

Public Relations
  Business Segments
Business to business
Consumer
Corporate/financial
Event/sports marketing
Medical/health care
Public affairs
Technology
Travel, tourism, and hospitality

Selected Clients
AT&T
Bausch & Lomb
Bristol Myers Squibb
British Airways
Coca-Cola Foods
Hertz
Mexican Ministry of Tourism
Nike
Philip Morris
RJR Nabisco
Tenneco
Time Warner
UPS
Visa
Xerox

KEY COMPETITORS

Bozell, Jacobs
Business Wire
Cordiant
Dentsu
Fleishman-Hillard
Fogarty & Klein
Grey Advertising
Havas
Leo Burnett
Omnicom Group
Ruder Finn
True North
WPP Group
Young & Rubicam

HOW MUCH

Private company FYE: June 30	Annual Growth	1990	1991	1992	1993	1994	1995
Estimated sales ($ mil.)	18.8%	—	—	—	63.4	74.1	89.5
Employees	23.3%	—	—	—	—	730	900

EDMARK CORPORATION

OVERVIEW

Edmark is making its mark on education. The Redmond, Washington-based company develops and publishes educational software and other educational products for use at home and in school, with most of its products designed for young children. Following a year of losses due to high product development and marketing costs, the business returned to profitability in 1995. Director Richard Thorp owns 6% of the company.

Edmark was founded in 1970 to make reading materials for special-education classes. The operation focused on print products until 1985, when it introduced a software version of the Edmark Reading Program for Apple computers. The corporation went public that year. It expanded in 1988 with the acquisition of the rights to TouchWindow, a touch-sensitive screen. In 1989 the company named Sally Narodick, a management consultant, CEO. She focused on expanding its offerings outside special education and into early-learning products and the retail market.

In late 1992 Edmark introduced its first retail education software products, Millie's Math House and KidDesk. To raise cash for its push into retail markets, Edmark sold $5.5 million of its stock to venture capital firms Kleiner Perkins Caufield & Byers and Roanoke Investors, which still own 13% and 10%, respectively, of the company. In 1994 it signed an alliance with Harcourt Brace School Publishers to develop multimedia educational software.

The company continues to focus on building its presence in the consumer market. In 1995 it introduced 4 new titles (Thinkin' Things Collection 2) as well as 3 additions to the Imagination Express series. Edmark's earnings held at $2 million in 1996 on increased sales of $32 million.

WHO

Chairman and CEO: Sally G. Norodick, age 50, $304,800 pay
VP Product Development: Donna G. Stanger, age 52, $225,000 pay
VP Consumer Sales: Daniel P. Vetras, age 36, $141,251 pay
VP Finance and Administration, CFO, Treasurer, and Secretary: Paul N. Bialek, age 35, $130,313 pay
VP Operations: John R. Moore, age 45
Manager Human Resources: Diane Coplentz
Auditors: KPMG Peat Marwick LLP

WHERE

HQ: 6727 185th Ave. NE, Redmond, WA 98052-3218
Phone: 206-556-8400
Fax: 206-556-8430
Web site: http://www.edmark.com

WHAT

	1995 Sales	
	$ mil.	% of total
Multimedia software products	14.3	63
Special-education products	7.1	31
Other	1.3	6
Total	**22.7**	**100**

Selected Early-Childhood Products
Bailey's Book House (language development)
KidDesk Family Edition (graphical menu)
Millie's Math House (math skills)

Special-Education Products
Edmark Reading Program (language development)
TouchWindow (attachable touch-sensitive screen)

KEY COMPETITORS

Apple Computer	Microsoft
Brøderbund	Nintendo
Capitol Multimedia	Sanctuary Woods
Davidson & Associates	Scholastic
Educational Insights	SEGA
EduSoft	Sierra On-Line
Gametek	SoftKey
Knowledge Adventure	Tiger Electronics
Maxis	Walt Disney

HOW MUCH

Nasdaq symbol: EDMK FYE: June 30	Annual Growth	1990	1991	1992	1993	1994	1995
Sales ($ mil.)	51.6%	—	4.3	6.0	8.7	11.7	22.7
Net income ($ mil.)	60.7%	—	0.3	0.4	0.1	(1.9)	2.0
Income as % of sales	—	—	7.0%	6.7%	1.1%	—	8.8%
Earnings per share ($)	37.3%	—	0.09	0.11	0.03	(0.40)	0.32
Stock price – high ($)	—	—	2.50	7.84	12.34	10.34	50.50
Stock price – low ($)	—	—	2.00	2.33	6.34	6.50	9.67
Stock price – close ($)	88.4%	—	2.50	7.67	6.84	10.34	31.50
P/E – high	—	—	28	71	—	—	158
P/E – low	—	—	22	21	—	—	30
Dividends per share ($)	—	—	0.00	0.00	0.00	0.00	0.00
Book value per share ($)	51.1%	—	0.48	0.88	1.71	2.09	2.50
Employees	58.1%	—	25	45	88	121	156

1995 YEAR-END
Debt ratio: 0.0%
Return on equity: 16.3%
Cash (mil.): $8.2
Current ratio: 4.81
Long-term debt (mil.): $0.0
No. of shares (mil.): 5.5
Dividends
  Yield: —
  Payout: —
Market value (mil.): $172.6
R&D as % of sales: 20.3%
Advertising as % of sales: 15.2%

ELECTRONIC ARTS INC.

OVERVIEW

Electronic Arts (EA) can really push your buttons. The San Mateo, California-based creator and distributor of recreational software makes live-action sports and adventure video games, such as PGA TOUR Golf and Wing Commander (which is actually an interactive movie that lets the viewer help influence the outcome of the show), for 14 different game systems. It also produces the audio and visual components used in its products. While nearly 60% of its revenues come from video cartridges (for Sega and Nintendo systems), EA is focusing on producing more titles on CD-ROM.

After 4 years with Apple Computer, video game pioneer Trip Hawkins left in 1982, raised $5 million from private investors, and founded a company that would explore the entertainment potential of PCs. In 1990 EA began designing games for the Sega Genesis video game system, and sales exploded.

In 1992 the company formed a joint venture with a unit of consumer electronics business JVC to market EA products in Japan. A merger attempt by gamemaker Brøderbund Software failed in 1994, the same year Hawkins resigned to devote time to his new venture, game system maker 3DO. (Hawkins still owns 5% of EA.) Also in 1994 EA expanded its direct distribution capabilities in Europe with the purchase of Spanish software supplier DROSoft.

In 1995 the company announced it would gradually sell off its 18% stake in 3DO, which developed the first 32-bit CD-ROM game system, as it evolves into a competitor in the market for video games. Also that year EA purchased Germany-based video game distributor Kingsoft and acquired Bullfrog Productions, a UK-based video game developer. EA purchased entertainment software developer Manley & Associates in 1996.

WHO

Chairman, President, and CEO: Lawrence F. Probst III, age 45, $592,314 pay
EVP, EA Studios: William Bingham Gordon, age 45, $367,640 pay
SVP and Chief Financial and Administrative Officer (HR): E. Stanton McKee Jr., age 50, $354,542 pay
SVP International: Mark S. Lewis, age 45, $308,331 pay
SVP Sales: Nancy L. Smith, age 42, $301,021 pay
VP, General Counsel, and Secretary: Ruth A. Kennedy, age 40
Auditors: KPMG Peat Marwick LLP

WHERE

HQ: 1450 Fashion Island Blvd., San Mateo, CA 94404-2064
Phone: 415-571-7171
Fax: 415-571-6375
Web site: http://www.ea.com

	1996 Sales	
	$ mil.	% of total
North America	306.2	57
Europe	158.0	30
Japan	45.9	9
Australia	21.8	4
Total	**531.9**	**100**

WHAT

Selected Titles	
FIFA International Soccer	Road Rash
John Madden Football	Shock Wave
Magic Carpet	Theme Park
NBA Live 95	U.S. Navy Fighters
PGA TOUR Golf	Wing Commander III
Road & Track Presents:	
The Need for Speed	

KEY COMPETITORS

3DO	LucasArts	Sierra On-Line
Acclaim	Maxis	Sony
Entertainment	Microsoft	Spectrum
Accolade	Mindscape	HoloByte
Activision	Nintendo	Spelling
Brøderbund	Pearson	Entertainment
id Software	SEGA	WMS Industries

HOW MUCH

Nasdaq symbol: ERTS FYE: March 31	Annual Growth	1991	1992	1993	1994	1995	1996
Sales ($ mil.)	39.4%	101.8	162.1	298.4	418.3	493.3	531.9
Net income ($ mil.)	37.5%	9.1	15.7	30.9	44.7	55.7	40.5
Income as % of sales	—	8.9%	9.7%	10.4%	10.7%	11.3%	7.6%
Earnings per share ($)	28.1%	0.23	0.37	0.65	0.90	1.07	0.75
Stock price – high ($)[1]	—	4.22	9.63	21.75	42.00	33.50	42.25
Stock price – low ($)[1]	—	1.53	2.22	9.19	19.75	12.75	15.38
Stock price – close ($)[1]	50.2%	2.34	9.56	20.63	30.00	19.25	26.13
P/E – high	—	18	26	34	47	31	56
P/E – low	—	7	6	14	22	12	21
Dividends per share ($)	—	0.00	0.00	0.00	0.00	0.00	0.00
Book value per share ($)	38.4%	1.15	1.56	2.39	3.61	4.66	6.11
Employees	33.0%	300	470	910	1,077	1,172	1,500

[1]Stock prices are for the prior calendar year.

1996 YEAR-END
Debt ratio: 0.0%
Return on equity: 14.5%
Cash (mil.): $185.9
Current ratio: 2.98
Long-term debt (mil.): $0.0
No. of shares (mil.): 52.7
Dividends:
 Yield: —
 Payout: —
Market value (mil.): $1,377.9
R&D as % of sales: 18.7%

FOLLETT CORPORATION

OVERVIEW

Follett Corporation is the oldest and largest operator of college bookstores in the US, with more than 400 stores serving colleges and universities in 46 states. The company is privately owned and managed by the Follett family, which has been involved with the company for 4 generations. Follett's stores don't rely solely on students' cravings for knowledge. About 1/3 of its on-campus business derives from food, snacks, and other nontextbook items. Follett is expanding into custom academic publishing, establishing many copy centers on campuses. The company is also a leading wholesaler of books to elementary and high school libraries.

Follett began in 1873 as a small bookstore opened by the Reverend Charles Barnes in his home in Wheaton, Illinois. C. W. Follett acted as both salesman and stock clerk. In 1917 Follett bought into the company when Barnes's son, William, moved to New York (he started what became one of Follett's biggest competitors, Barnes & Noble). Follett took control of the company in 1923. During WWII the company began publishing children's books, which were in demand because of a shortage of metal toys.

C. W. died in 1952, and his son, Dwight, took over. In 1957 the firm organized into divisions, and Follett Corporation was created as the parent company. During the 1960s Follett developed the first multiracial textbook series, depicting ethnically diverse characters. Dwight built Follett to $50 million in annual sales by 1977, when he retired. He was succeeded by his son, Robert, who led the company through tremendous growth in the 1980s. In 1990 Follett acquired Brennan College Service, adding 57 stores to its chain. Robert's son-in-law Richard Traut, named chairman in 1994, was the first person without the Follett name to hold that position.

In 1994 Follett introduced Sneak Preview Plus, a CD-ROM product designed to enhance the acquisition process in libraries. That year Follett also launched a custom academic publishing line. Textbook publisher McGraw-Hill in 1995 dropped a lawsuit accusing Follett of reselling books that were supposed to be destroyed. In 1996 Follett acquired used textbook reseller Western Textbook Exchange.

WHO

Chairman: Richard M. Traut
President and CEO: P. Richard Steve Litzsinger
EVP: Laverne Hosek
VP Finance and CFO: Kenneth J. Hull
VP Operations: Richard Waichler
Treasurer: Robert O'Brian
Director Human Resources: Louis Monosealco
Auditors: Andersen Worldwide

WHERE

HQ: 2233 West St., River Grove, IL 60171-1895
Phone: 708-583-2000
Fax: 708-452-9347
Web site: http://fcrfour.follett.com

Divisions

Follett Campus Resources
2211 West St., River Grove, IL 60171-1800

Follett College Stores
400 W. Grand Ave., Elmhurst, IL 60126

Follett Collegiate Graphics
2233 West St., River Grove, IL 60171-1895

Follett Educational Services
5563 S. Archer Ave., Chicago, IL 60638

Follett Library Resources
4506 Northwest Hwy., Crystal Lake, IL 60014

Follett Software Company
809 N. Front St., McHenry, IL 60050

WHAT

Selected Products and Services
Custom academic course packs
Data management systems for libraries
On-campus reprographics
Software development for libraries
Textbook distribution
Wholesale books
Workbook (elementary and high school use) distribution

KEY COMPETITORS

Baker & Taylor
Barnes & Noble
Borders
Chancery Software
Crown Books
Data Research
Ingram
Kinko's
McGraw-Hill

HOW MUCH

Private company FYE: March 31	Annual Growth	1991	1992	1993	1994	1995	1996
Sales ($ mil.)	13.5%	432.2	548.7	611.9	646.4	712.8	812.7
Employees	6.0%	5,758	6,198	6,500	6,800	7,200	7,700

FORBES, INC.

OVERVIEW

Malcolm S. "Steve" Forbes Jr., Forbes Inc. president and editor-in-chief of its eponymous magazine, became nationally known as a self-funded, "flat tax" Republican presidential candidate. The biweekly business magazine *Forbes*, the company's flagship, is 2nd only to *PC Magazine* in advertising pages. Forbes also publishes other magazines (*Forbes FYI, Forbes ASAP, Audacity, American Heritage*, and *MediaGuide*) and weekly newspapers in suburban New Jersey (Forbes Newspapers). The family-owned New York City-based company also owns a palace in Morocco and other properties in Fiji, France, and the US, most of which were picked up by Forbes's father, Malcolm.

Scottish immigrant and journalist B. C. Forbes launched *Forbes* ("devoted to doers and doings") in 1917. Son Malcolm, who harbored ambitions to become US president, began to focus on the family business after being badly wounded in WWII. In 1949 Malcolm convinced B. C. to introduce an annual feature highlighting top corporations. This feature would evolve into annual in-depth reports ranking the top 500 US corporations, special issues that would garner millions of dollars of advertisements. Malcolm's brother Bruce ran the business following the death of B. C. in 1954, while Malcolm made an unsuccessful run for governor of New Jersey in 1957. After Bruce died of cancer in 1964, Malcolm took over the business. Over the next 25 years he grew the magazine into a leading business publication, keeping the company's name in the spotlight with his own extroverted antics, such as riding around the world on a Harley-Davidson and an extravagant birthday party in Morocco. Malcolm persuaded Caspar Weinberger, the former defense secretary, to become publisher of *Forbes* in 1989. Malcolm Forbes died in 1990, and his eldest son Steve, deputy editor-in-chief of *Forbes* since 1982, took over the business.

In 1995 Steve Forbes took a leave of absence from *Forbes* to run for president. His national exposure helped the magazine. The first 5 issues of *Forbes* in 1996 posted a 12% gain in total pages over the same period in 1995, while rivals *FORTUNE* and *Business Week* saw declines.

WHO

Chairman: Caspar W. Weinberger
VC: Christopher Forbes
President and Editor-in-Chief: Malcolm S. "Steve" Forbes Jr., age 48
COO; President, *American Heritage*: Timothy C. Forbes
EVP: Leonard H. Yablon
VP Finance and Administration: Scott R. Yablon
VP and Treasurer: Joel B. Redler
VP and General Counsel: Terrence O'Connor
Manager Personnel: Rose Ateniese
Publisher, *Forbes*: Jeffrey M. Cunningham
Editor, *Forbes*: James W. Michaels
Managing Editor, *Forbes*: Lawrence Minard
Executive Editor, *Forbes*: William Baldwin

WHERE

HQ: 60 Fifth Ave., New York, NY 10011
Phone: 212-620-2200
Fax: 212-206-5534
Web site: http://www.forbes.com

WHAT

Magazines
American Heritage (history periodical)
Audacity (business/lifestyle quarterly)
Forbes (business biweekly)
Forbes ASAP (technology supplement)
Forbes FYI (lifestyle quarterly for executives)
MediaGuide (news analysis quarterly)

Newspapers
Forbes Newspapers (suburban weeklies in New Jersey)
Bound Brook Chronicle
Buyers Guide
The Chronicle (Middlesex)
Cranford Chronicle
Franklin Focus
Greenbrook-North Plainfield Journal
Highland Park Herald
Hills-Bedminster Press
Metuchen-Edison Review
Piscataway Review
Scotch Plains Fanwood Press
Somerset Messenger-Gazette
South Plainfield Reporter
Warren-Watchung Journal
Westfield Record

Other
Real estate holdings in Fiji, France, Morocco, and the US.

KEY COMPETITORS

Dow Jones	Knight-Ridder
The Economist	McGraw-Hill
FMR	New York Times
Hearst	Time Warner

HOW MUCH

Private company FYE: December 31	Annual Growth	1990	1991	1992	1993	1994	1995
Sales ($ mil.)	12.9%	—	—	200.0	245.1	266.5	287.5
Employees	—	—	—	—	—	—	502

FRANKLIN ELECTRONIC PUBLISHERS

OVERVIEW

Fair dinkum, mate! You soon won't have to drive your ute (utility vehicle) to the uni (university) to check out the *Macquarie Dictionary* (the authoritative guide to Australian English). Franklin, the world's #1 electronic book publisher, is developing an electronic version. The Burlington, New Jersey-based company has sold more than 12 million "electronic books." These handheld, battery-powered keyboard devices incorporate the text of a reference book or database and allow readers to access selected portions on an LCD screen. Franklin electronic books and IC-ROM cards include thesauruses, dictionaries, encyclopedias, and medical publications, as well as the Bible.

The company was founded as Franklin Computer, a maker of general-purpose PCs, in 1981. Under the leadership of Morton David, who became CEO in 1984, the business moved into the electronic publishing market. In 1986 it introduced an $80 spellchecker called Spelling Ace, one of the first electronic books released in the US. Franklin Computer introduced increasingly sophisticated versions of thesauruses and dictionaries in 1987 and 1988, capturing around 80% of the market. Facing growing competition from companies such as Apple, Seiko, Sharp, and Sony, Franklin Computer increased the range and quality of its products. In 1990 the company adopted its current name.

In 1995 Franklin teamed up with Intuit to build a mobile, wallet-sized version of Intuit's personal-finance software, Quicken. In a move away from single hard-wired products, it also launched its new BOOKMAN product line, which comes bundled with a built-in database and a slot for a 2nd cartridge. In 1996 electronics firm Brother International planned to introduce several word processor models with built-in BOOKMAN slots.

WHO

Chairman, President, and CEO: Morton E. David, age 59, $804,000 pay
EVP: Michael R. Strange, age 48, $227,500 pay
SVP and Secretary: Gregory J. Winsky, age 46, $227,500 pay
President, Medical Division: Bruno Bieler
Managing Director, Franklin Electronic Publishers (Europe) Ltd.: Michael Kemp, age 48, $222,160 pay
VP Finance and Treasurer: Kenneth H. Lind, age 43, $222,500 pay
VP Manufacturing: Barry J. Lipsky, age 45
VP International Sales: Peter J. Hudson
Chief Scientist: Edgar T. Irons
Auditors: Feldman Radin & Co., P.C.

WHERE

HQ: Franklin Electronic Publishers, Incorporated, One Franklin Plaza, Burlington, NJ 08016
Phone: 609-261-4800
Fax: 609-261-2984
Web site: http://www.franklin.com

	1996 Sales % of total
US	82
Other countries	18
Total	**100**

WHAT

Selected Titles
The Bible
Concise Columbia Encyclopedia
Merriam-Webster's Tenth Collegiate Dictionary
Parker's Wine Guide
Physician's Desk Reference

KEY COMPETITORS

Apple Computer
Aurora Impex
Casio
Hewlett-Packard
MathSoft

Royal Business Products
Seiko
Sharp
Sony
Texas Instruments

HOW MUCH

NYSE symbol: FEP FYE: March 31	Annual Growth	1991	1992	1993	1994	1995	1996
Sales ($ mil.)	13.1%	54.4	53.8	65.4	66.1	83.3	100.8
Net income ($ mil.)	—	(5.8)	3.1	7.1	8.1	12.4	10.4
Income as % of sales	—	—	5.8%	10.9%	12.3%	14.9%	10.3%
Earnings per share ($)	—	(0.89)	0.44	0.92	1.06	1.52	1.25
Stock price – high ($)[1]	—	6.25	7.25	16.25	19.75	21.50	44.25
Stock price – low ($)[1]	—	3.00	1.38	5.63	10.75	10.50	20.25
Stock price – close ($)[1]	56.6%	3.13	5.88	15.25	13.25	21.13	29.50
P/E – high	—	—	17	18	19	14	35
P/E – low	—	—	3	6	10	7	16
Dividends per share ($)	—	0.00	0.00	0.00	0.00	0.00	0.00
Book value per share ($)	25.9%	2.64	3.18	4.22	5.33	7.00	8.34
Employees	13.3%	166	156	170	206	271	310

[1]Stock prices are for the prior calendar year.

1996 YEAR-END
Debt ratio: 0.0%
Return on equity: 17.3%
Cash (mil.): $10.8
Current ratio: 3.61
Long-term debt (mil.): $0.0
Number of shares (mil.): 7.9
Dividends
  Yield: —
  Payout: —
Market value (mil.): $231.9
R&D as % of sales: 5.5%

FREEDOM COMMUNICATIONS, INC.

OVERVIEW

Freedom rings with news, information, and entertainment through the power of the press. The Irvine, California-based media conglomerate owns 25 daily newspapers (including its flagship paper, Southern California's *Orange County Register*), 34 weeklies, and 6 television stations. It also has an interest in IT Network, a developer of interactive TV. Through its media outlets Freedom Communications encourages personal productivity, entrepreneurship, and a libertarian philosophy.

Starting as a printer's devil at $2 per week, founder R. C. Hoiles worked his way up to buy the *Bucyrus (Ohio) Telegram* in 1927 and the *Santa Ana (California) Register* in 1935. He formed Freedom Newspapers in 1950 with 7 papers; when Hoiles died in 1970, the company owned 19. His son Clarence succeeded him. In 1978 Bob Segal became the first nonfamily member to run the business. Freedom bought its first TV station in 1981 and added 4 more by 1985.

Clarence's death in 1981 sparked a bitter family feud over control of the company. When R. C.'s other son, Harry, was bypassed as CEO, he sued to divide the firm's assets but lost his case in 1990. That year Freedom launched the 24-hour Orange County NewsChannel and started buying small weekly newspapers in Orange County. Stanford provost James Rosse succeeded Segal as president and CEO in 1992. Also that year Freedom launched a Spanish-language weekly (the *Excelsior*) in Orange County. In 1993 the company became a major investor in IT Network, formed a magazine subsidiary, and changed its name to Freedom Communications to reflect its diversification.

To expand its broadcast operations, the company purchased CBS affiliate WPEC in West Palm Beach, Florida, in 1995. The next year Freedom sold its Orange County NewsChannel to Los Angeles cable system and cellular telephone system operator Century Communications. Also in 1996 Freedom made a multimillion dollar investment (believed to be as high as $15 million) in young men's magazine *P.O.V.*

WHO

Chairman: Robert C. Hardie
President and CEO: James N. Rosse
SVP and CFO: David Kuykendall
SVP, Orange County Publications: R. David Threshie
President, Newspaper East: Jonathan Segal
President, Newspaper West: Scott Fischer
President, Broadcast Division: Alan Bell
President, Magazine Division: Samuel Wolgemuth
VP Human Resources: Mark Ernst

WHERE

HQ: 17666 Fitch Ave., Irvine, CA 92714
Phone: 714-553-9292
Fax: 714-474-4943

WHAT

Selected Newspapers
The Brownsville Herald (Texas)
Clovis News-Journal (New Mexico)
Colorado Springs Gazette Telegraph (Colorado)
Daily News (Jacksonville, NC)
Delta Democrat-Times (Greenville, MS)
The Gaston Gazette (North Carolina)
The Lima News (Ohio)
The Monitor (McAllen, TX)
The News Herald (Panama City, FL)
The Odessa American (Texas)
The Orange County Register (Santa Ana, CA)
Seymour Daily Tribune (Indiana)
Valley Morning Star (Harlingen, TX)

Selected Magazines
USA Exports (trade directory)
World Trade (in-flight trade magazine)

Television Stations
KFDM-TV (Beaumont/Port Arthur, TX)
KTVL-TV (Medford, OR)
WLNE-TV (Providence, RI)
WPEC-TV (West Palm Beach, FL)
WRGB-TV (Albany/Schenectady/Troy, NY)
WTVC-TV (Chattanooga, TN)

Other Interests
IT Network (interactive television)
MicroVoice (900-number voice personals)

KEY COMPETITORS

Advance Publications
A. H. Belo
Copley Press
Cox Enterprises
Daily Journal
Gannett
Harte-Hanks Communications
Hearst
Journal Communications
LIN Broadcasting
Media General
Meredith
New York Times
Providence Journal
Times Mirror
Tribune

HOW MUCH

Private company FYE: December 31	Annual Growth	1990	1991	1992	1993	1994	1995
Sales ($ mil.)	1.8%	485.0[1]	464.0[1]	477.0[1]	479.0	501.0	530.0
Employees	1.1%	5,200	5,200	5,500	6,800	6,800	5,500

[1]Estimated

GAYLORD ENTERTAINMENT COMPANY

OVERVIEW

How-dee! Gaylord Entertainment's flagship business, the *Grand Ole Opry* live country music show, said goodbye to its best-known greeter in 1996 with the death of veteran comedienne Minnie Pearl, a show regular for more than 50 years. The Nashville-based company has parlayed its *Grand Ole Opry* show into an entertainment, cable TV, and broadcast conglomerate. Gaylord's other offerings include *General Jackson* (the world's largest paddlewheel showboat), the Opryland theme park and hotel (one of the world's largest), 4 cable TV networks, and TV and radio broadcasting stations. The Gaylord and Dickinson families own 62% of the company.

The 2 families set up a newspaper in 1903 in Oklahoma Territory, incorporating as the Oklahoma Publishing Co. in 1925. It bought a radio station in Oklahoma City in 1928 and later a number of TV stations. In 1983 the company purchased the *Grand Ole Opry* and related properties, including the Nashville Network, for $250 million. The *Grand Ole Opry* radio show had been running since 1925. The *Opry*, the "Mother Church of Country Music," became an institution for country music performers and fans.

In 1991 Gaylord Entertainment was formed as a holding company for Oklahoma Publishing's broadcasting and entertainment businesses. That year Gaylord went public and moved its headquarters to Nashville.

The company is nurturing a global cable TV audience of country music fans. Its successful 1992 debut of Country Music Television (CMT) Europe was followed by similar launches in the Asia/Pacific region (1994) and Latin America (1995).

In 1996 Gaylord sold Houston station KHTV and its 14% stake in the Fiesta Texas theme park in San Antonio.

WHO

Chairman: Edward L. Gaylord, age 76, $510,000 pay
President and CEO: Earl W. Wendell, age 68, $940,256 pay
EVP and COO: Richard H. Evans, age 51, $627,987 pay
SVP, Chief Administrative Officer, and CFO: Terry E. London, age 46
SVP, Secretary, and General Counsel: Francis M. Wentworth Jr., age 51
Director Corporate Human Resources: Elwyn Taylor
Auditors: Andersen Worldwide

WHERE

HQ: One Gaylord Dr., Nashville, TN 37214
Phone: 615-316-6000
Fax: 615-316-6320

WHAT

	1995 Sales	
	$ mil.	% of total
Entertainment	294.2	42
Cable networks	282.7	40
Broadcasting	130.6	18
Total	**707.5**	**100**

Entertainment
General Jackson (entertainment showboat)
Grand Ole Opry (live country music show)
Opryland (theme park)
Opryland Hotel
Ryman Auditorium
Wildhorse Saloon

Cable Networks
CMT

CMT International
TNN
Z Music

Broadcasting
KSTW-TV, Tacoma/Seattle
KTVT-TV, Fort Worth/Dallas
WSM (AM/FM), Nashville
WWTN (FM), Manchester, TN

KEY COMPETITORS

A&E Networks
A. H. Belo
Anheuser-Busch
International Family Entertainment
Lifetime Television
LIN Television
MCA
NBC
News Corp.
Providence Journal
Time Warner
Six Flags
Tribune
Viacom
Walt Disney
Westinghouse/CBS

HOW MUCH

NYSE symbol: GET FYE: December 31	Annual Growth	1990	1991	1992	1993	1994	1995
Sales ($ mil.)	4.2%	—	600.9	643.7	622.6	687.9	707.5
Net income ($ mil.)	178.6%	—	1.8	29.4	36.1	63.1	108.5
Income as % of sales	—	—	0.3%	4.6%	5.8%	9.2%	15.3%
Earnings per share ($)	146.6%	—	0.03	0.33	0.40	0.69	1.11
Stock price – high ($)	—	—	14.04	19.52	27.61	30.94	27.61
Stock price – low ($)	—	—	10.35	12.55	17.14	18.45	20.23
Stock price – close ($)	17.1%	—	14.04	19.52	26.78	21.66	26.42
P/E – high	—	—	—	59	69	45	25
P/E – low	—	—	—	38	43	27	18
Dividends per share ($)	56.5%	—	0.05	0.19	0.20	0.25	0.30
Book value per share ($)	19.8%	—	2.18	2.33	2.52	3.69	4.49
Employees	3.5%	—	8,700	9,100	9,100	9,450	10,000

1995 YEAR-END
Debt ratio: 44.8%
Return on equity: 28.6%
Cash (mil.): $12.1
Current ratio: 1.04
Long-term debt (mil.): $302.6
No. of shares (mil.): 91.8
Dividends
 Yield: 1.1%
 Payout: 26.7%
Market value (mil.): $2,547.4

GC COMPANIES, INC.

OVERVIEW

GC Companies brings together popcorn, candy, and Hollywood for an entertaining combination. The Chestnut Hill, Massachusetts-based company is among the top 3 US operators of multiscreen theaters in large suburban and urban areas, using the name General Cinema Theaters. The company operates 196 theaters with a total of 1,180 screens in 25 states; over 30% of its theaters and screens are located in California, Florida, and Texas. More than 75% of General Cinema's screens are located in theaters that have 6 to 14 screens. In addition to popcorn, soft drinks, and candy, many General Cinema theaters offer branded fast-food products including Taco Bell and Pizzeria Uno.

Philip Smith founded the company in 1922 as Philip Smith Theatrical Enterprises and opened 2 of the first drive-in theaters in the US in 1938. It opened one of the first mall theaters in 1951. In 1961 Smith died, and his son Richard took over the company's operations. The company's name changed to General Cinema in 1964. In the late 1960s the company began purchasing a number of bottling franchises, especially for Pepsi Cola, and it became the US's largest independent bottler (it sold the bottling division in 1989). In 1984 General Cinema bought 37% of Carter Hawley Hale, which controlled Neiman Marcus, and in 1991 it bought publisher Harcourt Brace Jovanovich. The company was renamed Harcourt General, which spun off its movie theater division in 1993 as GC Companies. The Smith family owns 28% of the company.

General Cinema closed several smaller, less productive theaters in 1993, resulting in decreased revenue and patronage in 1994. Patronage declined further in 1995 as General Cinema sold or closed 12 of its theaters, totaling 54 screens.

WHO

Chairman and CEO: Richard A. Smith, age 71
President and COO: Robert A. Smith, age 36
SVP and Chief Investment Officer: John G. Berylson, age 42, $324,000 pay
President and CEO, General Cinema Theatres: Paul R. Del Rossi, age 53, $491,657 pay
EVP and COO, General Cinema Theatres: William B. Doeren, age 48
VP and CFO: G. Gail Edwards, age 40
VP and Treasurer: Paul F. Gibbons, age 44
VP and Controller: Stephen C. Richards, age 40
VP Human Resources: Daniel Stravinski
Auditors: Deloitte & Touche LLP

WHERE

HQ: 27 Boylston St., Chestnut Hill, MA 02167
Phone: 617-277-4320
Fax: 617-278-5397

WHAT

	1995 Sales	
	$ mil.	% of total
Admissions	309.6	69
Concessions	132.1	29
Other	9.6	2
Total	**451.3**	**100**

KEY COMPETITORS

AMC Entertainment
Carmike Cinemas
Cinemark USA
Cineplex Odeon
Edwards Theatres
Magic Cinemas
National Amusements
Regal Cinemas
Samuel Goldwyn
Sony
United Artists Theatre
Viacom

HOW MUCH

NYSE symbol: GCX FYE: October 31	Annual Growth	1990	1991	1992	1993	1994	1995
Sales ($ mil.)	(0.5%)	461.8	467.9	457.2	495.0	452.6	451.3
Net income ($ mil.)	—	(31.0)	4.8	6.2	10.5	13.6	8.7
Income as % of sales	—	—	1.0%	1.3%	2.1%	3.0%	1.9%
Earnings per share ($)	(35.8%)	—	—	—	—	1.73	1.11
Stock price – high ($)	—	—	—	—	—	38.50	35.25
Stock price – low ($)	—	—	—	—	—	24.75	26.00
Stock price – close ($)	27.6%	—	—	—	—	26.25	33.50
P/E – high	—	—	—	—	—	22	32
P/E – low	—	—	—	—	—	14	23
Dividends per share ($)	—	—	—	—	—	0.00	0.00
Book value per share ($)	6.0%	—	—	—	—	19.16	20.31
Employees	0.7%	—	—	—	—	7,350	7,400

1995 YEAR-END
Debt ratio: 17.0%
Return on equity: 5.6%
Cash (mil.): $71.3
Current ratio: 0.84
Long-term debt (mil.): $31.8
No. of shares (mil.): 7.8
Dividends
  Yield: —
  Payout: —
Market value (mil.): $261.7

GENERAL MEDIA INTERNATIONAL, INC.

OVERVIEW

Like the plastic wrapper that holds its most famous creation, *Penthouse* magazine, General Media International (GMI) is the bag that holds a racier collection of businesses than its name might suggest. Headquartered in New York City and headed by Bob Guccione, GMI is the holding company for General Media, Inc., which publishes *Penthouse* as well as a number of affiliated publications, including *Hot Talk* and *Variations*. Although *Penthouse* (with monthly circulation of around 1.1 million) lags behind rival *Playboy* (which averages more than 3 million), Guccione claims leadership in at least one category: he says *Penthouse* is "the single, biggest-selling magazine in the Pentagon." Guccione and his family own GMI.

Brooklyn-born Guccione settled in London in the early 1960s and started *Penthouse* in 1965. His first ad manager was Kathy Keeton, a dancer and actress whom he turned down for a photo shoot. Keeton, who is VC of GMI, and Guccione married in 1988. Guccione brought the magazine to the US in 1969. In 1971 *Penthouse* introduced its monthly pictorials of *Pets*. During the 1970s GMI began to acquire other magazines, including auto and computer publications. In 1978 it launched science magazine *Omni*. *Penthouse* circulation, which had peaked at 4.7 million in 1979, fell sharply in 1986 when Attorney General Edwin Meese's antipornography report prompted many convenience stores to stop selling the magazine. During the 1980s GMI expanded into other media, including video. In 1989 it began publication of health magazine *Longevity*.

The company, however, is struggling. Nothing has materialized from Guccione's $145 million investment in a planned Atlantic City casino. In addition to the declining circulation of *Penthouse*, the company has faced rising paper costs and postal rates. General Media recently laid off nearly a quarter of its staff, and in 1996 GMI announced plans to suspend publication of the print versions of *Omni* and *Longevity* while keeping both available online.

WHO

Chairman, Group Publisher, and CEO: Robert C. Guccione, age 65, $1,530,000 pay
VC and COO: Kathryn Keeton Guccione, age 56, $450,000 pay
President Marketing, Sales, and Circulation: William F. Marlieb, age 65, $355,491 pay
EVP Operations and CFO: Patrick J. Gavin, age 43, $363,600 pay
Director Human Resources: Iris Frank
Auditors: Grant Thorton LLP

WHERE

HQ: 277 Park Ave., New York, NY 10172
Phone: 212-702-6000
Fax: 212-702-6262
Web site: http://www.penthousemag.com

WHAT

Selected Holdings

General Media
Magazines
Drag Racing Monthly
Four Wheeler
The Girls of Penthouse
Hot Talk
Men's Adventure Comix
Open Wheel
Penthouse
Penthouse Comix
Penthouse Forum
Penthouse Letters
Stock Car Racing
Super Stock & Drag Illustrated
Variations

Multimedia
CD-ROMs
Low-budget erotic feature films
Pay-per-call telephone lines

Pay-per-view programming
Videocassettes
World Wide Web site

General Media Fine Arts
Collection of Impressionist, modern, and Old Master paintings; antiques

General Media Real Estate
Properties in Atlantic City and New York City

Health and Science Group
Longevity (online only)
Omni (online only)
Saturday Review (online only)

KEY COMPETITORS

Advance Publications
Graff Pay-Per-View
Metro Global Media
Hearst
LFP
Playboy
Times Mirror

HOW MUCH

Private company FYE: December 31	Annual Growth	1990	1991	1992	1993	1994	1995
Sales ($ mil.)	1.5%	111.7	116.7	114.8	111.9	123.2	120.4
Net income ($ mil.)	—	4.6	7.7	5.9	7.7	1.6	(9.5)
Income as % of sales	—	4.1%	6.6%	5.1%	6.9%	1.3%	—
Employees	(10.0%)	—	—	—	—	250	225

1995 YEAR-END
Debt ratio: 100.0%
Return on equity: —
Cash (mil.): $4.4
Current ratio: 0.89
Long-term debt (mil.): $79.1

GOLDEN BOOKS

OVERVIEW

Richard Snyder (former head of publishing company Simon & Schuster) is hoping to prevent Golden Books from becoming just another poky little publisher. The struggling New York City-based company (formerly Western Publishing) is the nation's largest publisher of children's books. It also prints catalogs, tax forms, and trading cards and produces BEACH and CONTEMPO tableware, party favors, and stationery. In 1996 an investment group led by Snyder and media mogul Barry Diller paid $65 million for a 23% stake in Western Publishing, which changed its name to Golden Books Family Entertainment.

E. H. Wadewitz and Roy Spencer started West Side Printing in 1907 in the basement of a jewelry store. In 1916 the company, then called Western Lithographic and Printing, took over a flailing publisher of children's books. Western began printing for Walt Disney in 1932. In 1958 Western and distributor Pocket Books bought Simon & Schuster's Golden Books collection and began to grow the list of titles, with such classics as the *The Poky Little Puppy*, *Pat the Bunny*, and *Tootle*. Two years later the firm adopted the name Western Publishing. In 1979 toy-maker Mattel acquired Western.

Innovative market research helped the company become the #1 seller of children's books by the 1980s. In 1984 Richard Bernstein bought the company and took it public in 1986. Through the early 1990s Western enjoyed its status as a leading publisher, but in 1994, sales started to fall as the company failed to bring new products to market on time, and losses began to mount. Lower sales of electronic books and other products led to another loss in 1996. That year Snyder replaced Bernstein as chairman.

WHO

Chairman, President, and CEO: Richard E. Snyder, age 63
EVP, Treasurer, and CFO: Steven M. Grossman, age 35, $207,000 pay
SVP Legal Affairs and Secretary: James A. Cohen, age 50, $212,500 pay
VP Business Development and Corporate Communications (HR): Ira A. Gomberg, age 52, $238,500 pay
VP Special Projects: Ilan K. Reich, age 41, $212,500 pay
VP and General Counsel: Dale Gordon, age 48
Auditors: Deloitte & Touche LLP

WHERE

HQ: Golden Books Family Entertainment Inc., 444 Madison Ave., New York, NY 10022
Phone: 212-688-4500
Fax: 212-888-5025
Web site: http://www.goldenbooks.com/

WHAT

Selected Products	Stationery
Arts and crafts supplies	Video- and audiocassettes
Coloring books	
Electronic books	**Selected Titles**
Gift wrap	*Golden Treasury of*
Giftware	*Children's Literature*
Musical storybooks	*Pat the Bunny*
Paper doll books	*The Poky Little Puppy*
Party favors	*Richard Scarry's Best*
Picture books	*Word Book Ever*
Pop-up books	*Tootle*

KEY COMPETITORS

Advance Publications	PAGES
American Greetings	Pearson
Bertelsmann	R. R. Donnelley
Dorling Kindersley	Scholastic
GoodTimes Entertainment	Time Warner
Hallmark	Troll
Harcourt General	Viacom
Houghton Mifflin	Walt Disney
MCA	

HOW MUCH

Nasdaq symbol: GBFE FYE: Saturday nearest Jan. 31	Annual Growth	1991	1992	1993	1994	1995	1996
Sales ($ mil.)	(5.3%)	491.1	552.4	652.2	613.5	398.4	374.3
Net income ($ mil.)	—	8.3	13.7	17.5	(41.0)	(17.6)	(67.0)
Income as % of sales	—	1.7%	2.5%	2.7%	—	—	—
Earnings per share ($)	—	0.36	0.62	0.80	(1.99)	(0.88)	(3.23)
Stock price – high ($)[1]	—	19.88	16.13	23.75	21.00	20.88	15.13
Stock price – low ($)[1]	—	9.13	9.25	14.63	12.25	9.25	7.75
Stock price – close ($)[1]	(5.6%)	10.50	14.88	20.88	19.25	9.50	7.88
P/E – high	—	55	26	30	—	—	—
P/E – low	—	25	15	18	—	—	—
Dividends per share ($)	—	0.00	0.00	0.00	0.00	0.00	0.00
Book value per share ($)	(17.7%)	9.10	9.56	10.28	7.57	6.70	3.43
Employees	(10.7%)	3,700	3,800	5,000	5,000	3,350	2,100

1996 YEAR-END
Debt ratio: 66.8%
Return on equity: —
Cash (mil.): $45.2
Current ratio: 3.86
Long-term debt (mil.): $149.8
No. of shares (mil.): 21.7
Dividends
  Yield: —
  Payout: —
Market value (mil.): $170.6

[1] Stock prices are for the prior calendar year.

GRAFF PAY-PER-VIEW INC.

OVERVIEW

Spice is the variety of life that Graff Pay-Per-View dishes up on its TV channels. The New York City-based company produces 4 North American adult entertainment pay-per-view channels (Spice, Spice 2, Cable Video Store, and Theatre VisioN) and operates a subsidiary in the UK, the Home Video Channel Ltd., which provides 2 subscription networks (the Home Video Channel and the Adult Channel). These channels reach an audience of 15 million customers in North America and 4.5 million in the UK. The company also has an adult channel based in Denmark. It delivers programs through cable, direct-to-home satellite dishes, and hotels. Founder Mark Graff owns about 10% of the firm.

Graff, a 20-year veteran of the film, TV, and home video industries, set up the business in 1988. Two years later the company acquired the Jerrold Electronics Cable Video Store and Reiss Media's Guest Cinema hotel service. The following year Roger Faherty, a former consultant to investment bankers and an instrumental figure in the 1990 acquisitions, was appointed chairman. In 1992 the company moved into Europe with the purchase of more than 20% of HVC, the UK-based operator of the Home Video Channel and the Adult Channel. Graff Pay-Per-View went public that year.

In 1995 the company launched Eurotica, an adult channel headquartered in Denmark. It also acquired US competitor Adam & Eve. Graff posted a loss in 1995 because of restructuring charges and costs related to investments in American Gaming Network, a joint venture with Multimedia Games to develop bingo games. In a boardroom shake-up early in 1996, founder and VC Graff and the other VC, Lloyd Nolan, were removed from their executive positions. The 2 remain with the company as directors.

WHO

Chairman and CEO: J. Roger Faherty, age 57, $475,161 pay
President and COO: Edward M. Spector, age 63
EVP and CFO: Philip J. Callaghan, age 43, $200,371 pay
EVP Sales and Marketing: Steven Saril, age 43, $198,814 pay
SVP Operations: Richard Kirby, age 35
SVP, Secretary, and General Counsel: Daniel J. Barsky, age 40
SVP Business Development: Eric M. Spector, age 31
VP Finance and Controller: Irene Merlo Posio, age 28
Director Office Services (HR): Joan Simari
Auditors: Coopers & Lybrand L.L.P.

WHERE

HQ: 536 Broadway, New York, NY 10012
Phone: 212-941-1434
Fax: 212-941-4746

WHAT

Selected Channels
Adam & Eve
The Adult Channel (UK)
Cable Video Store
Eurotica (Denmark)
The Home Video Channel (UK)
Spice
Spice 2
Theatre VisioN

KEY COMPETITORS

COMSAT
Creative Programming and Technology
General Media
LodgeNet Entertainment
Playboy
Rendez-Vous
SpectraVision
Spi-Holding

HOW MUCH

Nasdaq symbol: GPPV FYE: December 31	Annual Growth	1990	1991	1992	1993	1994	1995
Sales ($ mil.)	59.2%	5.0	12.0	15.0	18.6	40.4	51.1
Net income ($ mil.)	42.2%	(2.6)	2.4	0.9	(1.9)	3.8	(15.1)
Income as % of sales	—	—	20.3%	6.1%	—	9.4%	—
Earnings per share ($)	—	—	0.49	0.10	(0.30)	0.37	(1.29)
Stock price – high ($)	—	—	—	6.77	9.00	12.75	12.00
Stock price – low ($)	—	—	—	2.50	7.44	6.13	3.75
Stock price – close ($)	(8.5%)	—	—	6.05	8.13	11.25	4.63
P/E – high	—	—	—	68	—	35	—
P/E – low	—	—	—	25	—	17	—
Dividends per share ($)	—	—	—	0.00	0.00	0.00	0.00
Book value per share ($)	30.4%	—	—	0.32	0.80	2.14	0.71
Employees	51.8%	—	29	30	63	100	154

1995 YEAR-END
Debt ratio: 90.8%
Return on equity: —
Cash (mil.): $1.5
Current ratio: 0.85
Long-term debt (mil.): $73.1
No. of shares (mil.): 11.4
Dividends
 Yield: —
 Payout: —
Market value (mil.): $52.5

HARPO ENTERTAINMENT GROUP

OVERVIEW

From Afghanistan to Zimbabwe, when Oprah talks, people listen. Oprah Winfrey's talk show is just one of the ventures produced by her Chicago-based Harpo Entertainment production company, which takes its name from "Oprah" spelled backwards. The company also produces films (she acts in some of them) and other media offerings. Winfrey is the 3rd woman in US history (after Mary Pickford and Lucille Ball) and the first African-American woman to own her own production studio. Her empire is built upon the success of *The Oprah Winfrey Show*, the highest-rated talk show in TV history. It is seen in about 120 countries.

Winfrey began her broadcasting career in 1973 at age 19 as a news anchor at Nashville's WTVF-TV. She became an evening news co-anchor in Baltimore, where she was recruited to co-host WJZ-TV's local talk show, *People Are Talking*. In the early 1980s Winfrey moved to Chicago to host ABC affiliate WLS-TV's *AM Chicago*, which quickly became the city's top morning talk show (it was later renamed *The Oprah Winfrey Show*). What made *Oprah* distinctive from other talk shows was its focus on ordinary people.

Winfrey's success has allowed her to assume increasing control over her show. In 1986 her agent, Jeffrey Jacobs (now Harpo president and COO), secured syndication rights to the show and started distributing it through King World Productions. Harpo Entertainment was founded that year. Winfrey's performance in *The Color Purple* won her an Oscar nomination and boosted her ratings when *Oprah* debuted nationally that same year in 138 cities. In 1988 Winfrey obtained full ownership of the program. Two years later Harpo Films was created, and Winfrey bought a Chicago studio to produce *Oprah*.

Although *Oprah* remains the leader in the increasingly crowded talk show field, Winfrey's ratings have slipped recently, partly because of competition and partly because of her decision to abandon seamier tabloid TV topics. In 1995 Winfrey agreed to continue hosting her daytime show for at least another 2 years. Also that year she signed with Capital Cities/ABC to produce or star in 6 made-for-TV movies over 3 years.

WHO

Chairman and CEO: Oprah Winfrey, age 41
President and COO: Jeffrey Jacobs
President, Harpo Productions: Tim Bennett
CFO: Doug Pattison
Director of Development, Harpo Films: Valerie Scoon
Director of Media and Corporate Relations: Deborah Johns
VP Development and Production: Kate Forte

WHERE

HQ: 110 N. Carpenter St., Chicago, IL 60607
Phone: 312-633-1000
Fax: 312-633-1111

Harpo has offices in Chicago and Los Angeles.

WHAT

Selected Operations
Harpo Films (film and TV production company, based in Los Angeles)
Oprah Online (online talk show on America Online, underwritten with Capital Cities/ABC)
Oprah Winfrey Presents (made-for-TV films)
The Oprah Winfrey Show (daily TV talk show)

KEY COMPETITORS

All American Communications
BET
dick clark productions
Dove Audio
Dreamworks SKG
Essence Communications
Gannett
International Family Entertainment
Kushner-Locke
Lancit Media
Spelling Entertainment
Tribune

HOW MUCH

Private company FYE: December 31	Annual Growth	1990	1991	1992	1993	1994	1995
Sales ($ mil.)	7.4%	—	—	105.0	110.1	120.0	130.0
Employees	10.9%	—	—	—	135	141	166

HARRY W. SCHWARTZ BOOKSHOPS

OVERVIEW

In order to compete with the bookstore industry giants, Harry W. Schwartz Bookshops has adapted by homing in on business books, which account for 20% of company sales. The Milwaukee-based company operates 6 stores in Illinois and Wisconsin (2 under the name Dickens Discount Books), but most of its $2 million plus in annual sales of business books comes from volume sales to companies who buy the books for their own employees. Schwartz markets its business books through a semiannual catalog and an international subscription service for overseas customers. The company's stores, averaging 8,500 square feet, feature coffee bars, reading chairs, and appearances by leading authors. Business book division head Zack Covert has stayed true to his roots (he owned a record store) by producing a monthly top 25 list of the best-selling business books.

Harry Schwartz and his partner, Paul Romaine (who later sold out), opened their first bookstore, called Casanova Book Sellers, in Milwaukee in 1927. The 2 were equipped with their own personal libraries but little money. Schwartz borrowed from his mother to pay the shipping charges on their first shipment of books. In 1937 he moved the store to a downtown site; he relocated to the company's present headquarters in 1950. Schwartz retired in 1972 and sold the business to his son David. The company merged with competitor Avin Domnitz in 1984, keeping the Schwartz name. Two years later David Schwartz discovered that the company was not keeping up with changes in the industry, which was being dominated by companies like the rapidly expanding B. Dalton (now a unit of Barnes & Noble) and Waldenbooks (now owned by Borders). Tight financial controls were imposed on the company for the first time, and inventory was tracked more closely.

The company closed 2 underperforming stores in 1994 and opened 2 new ones, including a 10,000-square-foot store in Mequon, Wisconsin, and the 8,000-square-foot Shorewood store in Milwaukee.

The company focuses its efforts on selling to learning institutions and hospitals and developing new business through direct mail and telemarketing.

WHO

Chairman and CFO: Avin Domnitz
President and CEO: A. David M. Schwartz
VP: William Orenstein
Secretary: Stephen Churnoff
President, Schwartz Business Books: Jack Covert
General Manager, Schwartz Business Books: John E. Decker
Director Marketing: Nancy Williamsen
Manager Human Resources: Shawn Quinn

WHERE

HQ: 209 E. Wisconsin Ave., Milwaukee, WI 53202
Phone: 414-274-6400
Fax: 414-274-6408

Harry W. Schwartz Bookshops Locations
Brookfield
Loehmann's Plaza, 17145-D W. Bluemound Rd., Brookfield, WI 53005
Historic Iron Block
209 E. Wisconsin Ave., Milwaukee, WI 53202
Mequon
The Pavilion, 10976 N. Port Washington Rd., Mequon, WI 53092
Shorewood
4093 N. Oakland Ave., Milwaukee, WI 53211

Dickens Discount Books Locations
Gurney Mills
6170 W. Grand St., Gurney Mills, IL 60031
Kenosha
7700 120th Ave., Kenosha, WI 53142

WHAT

Schwartz Business Books Classic Best-Sellers
1. *The Goal* by Eliyahu M. Goldratt and Jeff Cox
2. *The Team Handbook* by Peter Scholtes
3. *The 7 Habits of Highly Effective People* by Stephen R. Covey
4. *Reengineering the Corporation* by Michael Hammer and James Champy
5. *Zapp!: The Lightning of Empowerment* by William Byham and Jeff Cox
6. *The Fifth Discipline Handbook* by Peter M. Senge
7. *Control Your Destiny or Someone Else Will* by Noel M. Tichy and Stradford Sherman
8. *Getting to Yes* by Roger Fisher and William L. Ury
9. *First Things First* by Stephen R. Covey
10. *1001 Ways to Reward Employees* by Bob Nelson

KEY COMPETITORS

Barnes & Noble
Borders
Crown Books

MTS
W H Smith
Wal-Mart

HOW MUCH

Private company FYE: June 30	Annual Growth	1990	1991	1992	1993	1994	1995
Sales ($ mil.)	21.8%	—	5.0	—	—	—	11.0
Employees	16.5%	—	76	81	87	110	140

HARRY W.
SCHWARTZ
BOOKSHOPS
SINCE 1927

HARTE-HANKS COMMUNICATIONS, INC.

OVERVIEW

It may be junk mail to you, but to Harte-Hanks it's cold, hard cash. The San Antonio-based communications company is posting higher sales in its direct mail business, which sends advertising shoppers to 7 million homes each week (in California, Florida, and Texas), while de-emphasizing its newspaper and broadcasting operations. Besides direct mail, Harte-Hanks's other marketing functions include analysis, creative, media, research, and strategy services. The company publishes 6 daily newspapers (in South Carolina and Texas) and some 25 nondaily community and supplemental papers and owns San Antonio's KENS-TV (CBS) and KENS-AM radio. Principal stockholders include brothers Houston H. Harte (21%) and Edward Harte (10%) and *Abilene Reporter-News* chairman Andrew Shelton (15%). Executive officers and directors own a total of 56% of the company.

Harte-Hanks was founded by the brothers' father (Houston) and Bernard Hanks in the early 1920s as a newspaper company. It went public in 1972 and over the next 12 years diversified and expanded outside Texas. In 1984, 5 executives took the company private again, adding $700 million in debt in the process. In 1986 Harte-Hanks consolidated operations to reduce its debt and focus on fewer, larger markets; by 1988 it had sold off half of its holdings and bought others in California, Dallas, and Boston. In 1993 the company went public a 2nd time. Also that year it suffered a hefty loss attributable to its 14 suburban Boston newspapers. (They were sold in 1995.) In 1994 Harte-Hanks acquired Select Marketing, which served the high-tech industry.

The firm bought marketing group Steinert & Associates in 1995. The company went shopping again in 1996, acquiring full-service marketing agency DiMark.

WHO

Chairman: Houston H. Harte, age 69
President and CEO: Larry Franklin, age 53, $1,300,000 pay
EVP; President, Harte-Hanks Direct Marketing: Richard M. Hochhauser, age 51, $549,100 pay
EVP: Peter E. Gorman, age 47
SVP Legal and Secretary: Donald R. Crews, age 52, $459,000 pay
SVP Finance, CFO, and Accounting Officer: Richard L. Ritchie, age 49, $438,600 pay
SVP; President, Harte-Hanks Television: Michael J. Conly, age 44
SVP; President, Harte-Hanks Newspapers: Stephen W. Sullivan, age 49
Director Employee Benefits (HR): Carolyn Oatman
Auditors: KPMG Peat Marwick LLP

WHERE

HQ: 200 Concord Plaza Dr., Ste. 800, San Antonio, TX 78216
Phone: 210-829-9000
Fax: 210-829-9403
Web site: http://www.harte-hanks.com

WHAT

	1995 Sales	
	$ mil.	% of total
Direct marketing	197.6	37
Shoppers	185.1	35
Newspapers	125.1	23
TV & radio	25.2	5
Total	**532.9**	**100**

Advertising Shoppers
The Flyer (Miami/Ft. Lauderdale)
The Original PennySaver (Southern California)
Potpourri (Northern California)
The Shopper's Guide (Dallas/Fort Worth)

KEY COMPETITORS

ADVO	Gannett	R. R. Donnelley
A. H. Belo	Greenston	Times Mirror
Bronner Slosberg	Roberts	Tribune
Catalina	Hearst	Washington Post
Marketing	Knight-Ridder	

HOW MUCH

NYSE symbol: HHS FYE: December 31	Annual Growth	1990	1991	1992	1993	1994	1995
Sales ($ mil.)	4.6%	426.3	416.2	423.3	463.5	513.6	532.9
Net income ($ mil.)	—	(18.3)	(7.0)	2.3	(45.5)	23.8	34.0
Income as % of sales	—	—	—	0.5%	—	4.6%	6.4%
Earnings per share ($)	—	(0.91)	(0.38)	0.13	(2.33)	0.80	1.10
Stock price – high ($)	—	—	—	—	13.01	14.42	22.59
Stock price – low ($)	—	—	—	—	10.09	11.76	12.42
Stock price – close ($)	23.2%	—	—	—	13.01	13.01	19.75
P/E – high	—	—	—	—	—	18	21
P/E – low	—	—	—	—	—	15	11
Dividends per share ($)	—	—	—	0.00	0.00	0.00	0.07
Book value per share ($)	34.5%	—	—	2.26	3.50	3.91	5.50
Employees	(5.2%)	—	—	5,825	6,150	6,225	4,957

1995 YEAR-END
Debt ratio: 57.1%
Return on equity: 24.9%
Cash (mil.): $6.7
Current ratio: 1.61
Long-term debt (mil.): $220.0
No. of shares (mil.): 30.0
Dividends
  Yield: 3.4%
  Payout: 59.8%
Market value (mil.): $592.3

HERITAGE MEDIA CORPORATION

OVERVIEW

Even if you've never seen or heard Heritage Media's TV or radio broadcasts, you've probably noticed the company's displays in the grocery store. That's because Dallas-based Heritage's subsidiary, ACTMEDIA, is the world's #1 provider of such in-store promotions as electronic coupon dispensers, audio advertising, printed shopping-cart ads, and product demonstrations — found in more than 37,000 US grocery, drug, and mass-merchandise stores. Heritage's DIMAC subsidiary (acquired in 1996) is the nation's top full-service direct marketing firm, providing research, creative planning, telemarketing, and related services. Heritage also owns 5 network-affiliated TV stations and operates 15 radio stations. Chairman Jim Hoak owns 6% of the company.

Heritage Media was formed in 1987 when the #1 US cable TV provider, Tele-Communications, Inc., bought Heritage Communications, Inc. (HCI), because of its cable systems. Investors led by HCI managers (including Hoak and Heritage CEO David Walthall) created Heritage Media as a spin-off for HCI's 13 TV and radio stations.

The company went public in 1988. The next year Heritage merged with ACTMEDIA and moved heavily into the market for in-store promotions. Through the early 1990s the company expanded internationally, acquiring complementary firms in Canada (1990), the Netherlands (1992), and Australia and New Zealand (1994). In 1992 ACTMEDIA introduced its INSTANT COUPON MACHINE (ICM), which delivers coupons from a shelf-mounted dispenser. In 1995 Heritage expanded its marketing business through the purchase of Powerforce Services, which builds in-store displays and resets shelves for product manufacturers. In 1996 it acquired 2 radio stations in Knoxville, Tennessee.

WHO

Chairman: James M. Hoak, age 51, $360,000 pay
President and CEO: David N. Walthall, age 49, $577,000 pay
CFO: Douglas N. Woodrum, age 37
EVP; President, ACTMEDIA, Inc.: Wayne W. LoCurto, age 51, $430,400 pay
EVP; President, Television Group: James J. Robinette, age 61, $346,500 pay
EVP; President, Radio Group: Paul W. Fiddick, age 45, $298,550 pay
Manager Human Resources: Candi Farley
Auditors: KPMG Peat Marwick LLP

WHERE

HQ: 13355 Noel Rd., Ste. 1500, Dallas, TX 75240
Phone: 214-702-7380
Fax: 214-702-7382

WHAT

	1995 Sales	
	$ mil.	% of total
In-store marketing	346.4	80
Television	45.6	10
Radio	43.8	10
Total	**435.8**	**100**

Television	Radio (cont.)
KEVN-TV, Rapid City, SD	KKSN (AM/FM), Portland, OR
KOKH-TV, Oklahoma City	KRPM (AM/FM), Seattle
WCHS-TV, Charleston, WV	WBBF (AM), Rochester, NY
WEAR-TV, Pensacola, FL	WBEE (FM), Rochester, NY
WNNE-TV, Hanover, NH	WEMP (AM), Milwaukee
(satellite of WPTZ-TV)	WEZW (FM), Milwaukee
	WIL (FM), St. Louis
Radio	WKLX (FM) Rochester, NY
KCFX (FM), Kansas City, MO	WMYX (FM), Milwaukee
KIHT (FM), St. Louis	WOFX (FM), Cincinnati
	WRTH (AM), St. Louis

KEY COMPETITORS

ADVO
Catalina Marketing
E.W. Scripps
Evergreen Media
Gannett
Hearst
HMG Worldwide Information Resources
NBC
Viacom
Walt Disney
Westinghouse/CBS

HOW MUCH

AMEX symbol: HTG FYE: December 31	Annual Growth	1990	1991	1992	1993	1994	1995
Sales ($ mil.)	16.4%	203.9	222.4	250.9	291.2	317.6	435.8
Net income ($ mil.)	—	(28.8)	(19.7)	(15.0)	0.1	22.3	26.6
Income as % of sales	—	—	—	—	0.0%	7.0%	6.1%
Earnings per share ($)	—	(3.08)	(2.43)	(1.51)	(0.32)	0.15	1.50
Stock price – high ($)	—	22.50	20.00	15.50	19.88	27.63	32.50
Stock price – low ($)	—	10.50	9.50	5.63	8.38	15.75	23.75
Stock price – close ($)	14.0%	13.50	14.00	8.63	19.88	26.88	26.00
P/E – high	—	—	—	—	—	184	22
P/E – low	—	—	—	—	—	105	16
Dividends per share ($)	—	0.00	0.00	0.00	0.00	0.00	0.00
Book value per share ($)	3.1%	5.84	4.02	4.40	4.31	5.09	6.80
Employees	14.6%	—	14,200	14,200	15,300	16,300	24,500

1995 YEAR-END
Debt ratio: 74.1%
Return on equity: 25.4%
Cash (mil.): $2.0
Current ratio: 1.08
Long-term debt (mil.): $334.8
No. of shares (mil.): 17.7
Dividends
  Yield: —
  Payout: —
Market value (mil.): $460.5

HOOVER'S, INC.

OVERVIEW

Reaching more than 2 million readers each month through a variety of formats, including online, Internet, CD-ROM, and print (including this book), Hoover's, Inc., is a leading provider of company information to the mass market. Its Hoover's Company Profiles (covering more than 2,600 companies) provide information on the operations, strategies, histories, financial performance, and products of major US and global public and private companies. Hoover's Company Capsules provide basic information on roughly 15,000 companies worldwide.

Hoover's books are sold through bookstores in the US (through Warner Books) and abroad and directly to libraries, corporate training and marketing organizations, and business and investment professionals. The company publishes its information on the Internet through Hoover's Online (http://www.hoovers.com) and makes it available through America Online, Bloomberg, CNNfn, CompuServe, Dow Jones, LEXIS-NEXIS, Microsoft Network, Reuters, and other electronic information services. The company also distributes 3rd-party-published, low-priced, high-quality business information products.

Gary Hoover (founder of BOOKSTOP, which was sold to Barnes & Noble in 1989) began the company as The Reference Press in 1990. That year it published its first business reference book, *Hoover's Handbook 1991: Profiles of Over 500 Major Corporations*. It soon began to add titles, both by publishing its own books and by entering distribution agreements with other companies. Patrick Spain succeeded Hoover as CEO in 1992 and led the company's move into direct sales markets and electronic publishing. In 1994 The Reference Press began publishing its catalog on the Internet and providing its Hoover's Company Profiles to CompuServe. In 1995 it launched Hoover's Online, a World Wide Web site featuring access to Hoover's Company Profiles and Hoover's Company Capsules. That year it partnered with over a dozen companies to make its information available through their electronic services.

In 1996 the company started its IPO Central Web site, offering information on companies registering to go public, and changed its name to Hoover's, Inc.

WHO

Chairman, President, CEO, and Publisher: Patrick J. Spain, age 44
SVP Sales and Marketing: Dana L. Smith, age 35
VP Finance & Administration and CFO (HR): Lynn Atchison, age 36
VP Electronic Publishing: Tom Linehan, age 40
Senior Managing Editor: James R. Talbot, age 32
Senior Managing Editor Production: George Sutton, age 53
Senior Contributing Editor: Alan Chai, age 44

WHERE

HQ: 1033 La Posada Dr., Ste. 250, Austin, TX 78752
Phone: 512-374-4500
Fax: 512-374-4501
Web site: http://www.hoovers.com

WHAT

Products	1996 Sales % of total
Print	67
Electronic media	33
Total	**100**

Book Sales Channels	1996 Sales % of total
Distribution	54
Direct	46
Total	**100**

Selected Print Products

Cyberstocks: An Investor's Guide to Internet Companies	$24.95
Fortune Guide to the 500 Largest U.S. Corporations	$14.95
Hoover's 500	$29.95
Hoover's Guide to Computer Companies	$34.95
Hoover's Guide to Media Companies	$29.95
Hoover's Handbook of Private Companies	$99.95
Hoover's Handbook of American Business (2 vols.)	$84.95
Hoover's Handbook of Emerging Companies	$44.95
Hoover's Handbook of World Business	$44.95
Hoover's MasterList of Major U.S. Companies	$79.95
Hoover's Top 2,500 Employers	$22.95

CD-ROM and Disk Software Products

Hoover's Company and Industry Database on CD-ROM with quarterly updates for a year	$449.95
Hoover's MasterList on Disk	$249.95

KEY COMPETITORS

Dun & Bradstreet
K-III
McGraw-Hill
Morningstar, Inc.
Primark
Thomson Corp.
Value Line

HOW MUCH

Private company FYE: March 31	Annual Growth	1991	1992	1993	1994	1995	1996
Sales ($ mil.)	39.1%	0.5	0.5	0.5	1.0	1.6	2.6
Employees	34.3%	11	7	9	13	21	48

Hoover's

HOUGHTON MIFFLIN COMPANY

OVERVIEW

In an era when most of the grand old publishing houses have been ensnared by the tentacles of media octopi, Boston-based Houghton Mifflin remains independent. The venerable publisher of Thoreau and Emerson is today a major educational publisher, producing books for students from kindergarten to college. It also produces and distributes children's books, dictionaries and other reference books, educational testing materials, and consumer multimedia products. Although its trade fiction and nonfiction lines are small, they remain prestige operations.

The publisher began as a printing company in 1832. Printer Henry Houghton bought part of the enterprise in 1848. The company grew by acquiring other printers' booklists and by 1880 was deeply in debt. George Mifflin (who had joined the firm in 1868 and was independently wealthy) became a partner, and the company, then known as Houghton Osgood, became Houghton Mifflin.

Houghton Mifflin's text sales from the 1950s to the 1970s followed the curve of the baby boom, from elementary and high school to college publishing. In the 1980s and 1990s the company grew through acquisitions that included the purchase of Rand McNally's education unit (1980) and textbook publisher McDougal, Littell & Co. (1994). In 1994 it spun off 60% of its computer software division as InfoSoft International. The cash from the IPO allowed the company to make its largest purchase ever — D.C. Heath, Raytheon's textbook publishing operation — in 1995.

But acquisition costs, a failed attempt to outsource distribution operations, and disarray in the trade book area sent Houghton Mifflin into the red in 1995. A period of management instability ensued as several officers came and went quickly in 1995 and 1996.

WHO

Chairman, President, and CEO: Nader F. Darehshori, age 59, $638,750 pay
EVP School Division: William J. Wisneski, age 48, $354,320 pay
EVP College Division: June Smith, age 51, $258,500 pay
EVP; President, The Riverside Publishing Co.: John H. Oswald, age 45, $244,300 pay
EVP; President, McDougal Littell, Inc.: Julie A. McGee
EVP Trade and Reference Division: Wendy J. Strothman, age 46
EVP, CFO, and Treasurer: Gail Deegan, age 49
SVP, General Counsel, and Secretary: Paul D. Weaver, age 52, $257,118 pay
SVP Human Resources: Margaret M. Doherty, age 57
Auditors: Ernst & Young LLP

WHERE

HQ: 222 Berkeley St., Boston, MA 02116-3764
Phone: 617-351-5000
Fax: 617-351-1105
Web site: http://www.hmco.com

WHAT

	1995 Sales	
	$ mil.	% of total
Textbooks & educational materials	359.5	68
General publishing	87.2	16
College publishing	82.3	16
Total	**529.0**	**100**

Selected Subsidiaries and Divisions
Clarion Books (children's books)
Great Source Education Group (multimedia products)

KEY COMPETITORS

Andrews & McMeel	Harcourt General	Steck-Vaughn
Axel Springer Verlag	Holtzbrink	Thomson Corp.
	John Wiley	Time Warner
Bertelsmann	Lagardère	Tribune
Encyclopædia Britannica	McGraw-Hill	Viacom
	News Corp.	William H. Sadlier
Everyday Learning	Pearson	
	Reed Elsevier	
	Scholastic	

HOW MUCH

NYSE symbol: HTN FYE: December 31	Annual Growth	1990	1991	1992	1993	1994	1995
Sales ($ mil.)	4.6%	421.6	466.8	454.7	463.0	483.1	529.0
Net income ($ mil.)	—	18.0	25.1	19.1	31.4	52.4	(7.2)
Income as % of sales	—	4.3%	5.4%	4.2%	6.8%	10.8%	—
Earnings per share ($)	—	1.27	1.75	1.35	2.27	3.79	(0.52)
Stock price – high ($)	—	34.38	30.38	39.88	50.38	53.00	54.75
Stock price – low ($)	—	18.38	22.25	26.63	36.38	36.13	39.63
Stock price – close ($)	11.7%	24.75	28.50	39.88	48.63	45.38	43.00
P/E – high	—	27	17	30	22	14	—
P/E – low	—	15	13	20	16	10	—
Dividends per share ($)	5.5%	0.71	0.75	0.79	0.83	0.87	0.93
Book value per share ($)	1.9%	14.69	15.63	13.86	15.43	16.94	16.13
Employees	1.0%	2,236	2,187	2,096	1,920	2,023	2,350

1995 YEAR-END
Debt ratio: 70.9%
Return on equity: —
Cash (mil.): $17.0
Current ratio: 1.08
Long-term debt (mil.): $426
No. of shares (mil.): 14.5
Dividends
  Yield: 2.2%
  Payout: —
Market value (mil.): $622.9

INFINITY BROADCASTING

OVERVIEW

Station-hungry Infinity Broadcasting was given a license to eat with the passage of the Telecom Act of 1996, which allows companies to own more than the previous limit of 20 AM and 20 FM radio stations. The deal cleared the way for the ravenous New York City-based company to grow its station collection, well, infinitely. However, it was not the only one licking its chops. In mid -1996 Westinghouse announced plans to buy Infinity. The deal will raise Westinghouse's roster of radio stations to more than 80. The deal also includes Infinity's 22% stake in Westwood One, the country's #1 radio program producer (with shows by Larry King, Rush Limbaugh, and Howard Stern) and parent company of NBC Radio Network and Mutual Broadcasting System.

Founded in 1972 by Michael Wiener and Gerald Carrus, the firm bought its first radio station in 1973. Mel Karmazin joined the company in 1981 and championed the push to capture major markets. Infinity grew by buying underperforming radio stations in key markets and turning them around, acquiring stations in New York, Chicago, Boston, and Houston before going public in 1986. Wiener, Carrus, and Karmazin bought out the company in 1988 and took it public again in 1992. Also that year Infinity bought New York City's WFAN-AM. In 1994 the company merged with syndication monolith Westwood One.

In 1995 Infinity bought Dallas's KLUV-FM and 7 radio stations from Alliance Broadcasting. Also in 1995 Infinity paid the FCC $1.7 million to settle broadcast indecency claims leveled against Howard Stern. In 1996 it purchased TDI Worldwide, a provider of billboard, mass transit, and other outdoor advertising (#2 in the US). That year the company agreed to acquire 12 radio stations from Granum Holdings for $410 million.

WHO

Chairman and Treasurer: Gerald Carrus, age 70, $250,000 pay
Co-chairman and Secretary: Michael A. Wiener, age 58, $250,000 pay
President and CEO: Mel Karmazin, age 52, $3,250,000 pay
VP Finance and CFO: Farid Suleman, age 44, $850,000 pay
Business Manager (HR): Tom Gesimondo
Auditors: KPMG Peat Marwick LLP

WHERE

HQ: Infinity Broadcasting Corporation, 600 Madison Ave., New York, NY 10022
Phone: 212-750-6400
Fax: 212-371-0835

WHAT

Selected Markets	San Francisco/San Jose
Atlanta	Tampa/St. Petersburg
Baltimore	Washington, DC
Boston	
Chicago	**Selected Radio**
Dallas/Fort Worth	**Personalities**
Detroit	Don Imus
Houston	G. Gordon Liddy
Los Angeles	Howard Stern
New York	Larry King
Orlando	Rush Limbaugh
Philadelphia	

KEY COMPETITORS

A. H. Belo	EZ Communications
American Radio Systems	Hearst
Capital Cities/ABC	Heritage Media
Century Communications	Jacor
Chancellor Broadcasting	Park Communications
Clear Channel	SFX Broadcasting
Cox Enterprises	Tribune
Evergreen Media	Viacom
E.W. Scripps	

HOW MUCH

NYSE symbol: INF FYE: December 31	Annual Growth	1990	1991	1992	1993	1994	1995
Sales ($ mil.)	23.8%	112.2	135.3	150.2	204.5	274.1	325.7
Net income ($ mil.)	—	(39.7)	(24.0)	(9.4)	14.3	33.2	54.5
Income as % of sales	—	—	—	—	7.0%	12.1%	16.7%
Earnings per share ($)	—	(1.75)	(0.73)	(0.13)	0.15	0.33	0.53
Stock price – high ($)	—	—	—	5.25	15.88	15.02	25.68
Stock price – low ($)	—	—	—	3.12	4.55	9.01	13.46
Stock price – close ($)	72.4%	—	—	4.85	13.46	14.01	24.85
P/E – high	—	—	—	—	106	46	49
P/E – low	—	—	—	—	30	27	25
Dividends per share ($)	—	—	0.00	0.00	0.00	0.00	0.00
Book value per share ($)	—	—	(10.11)	(2.60)	(0.33)	(0.34)	3.33
Employees	25.9%	—	420	420	675	1,114	1,055

1995 YEAR-END
Debt ratio: 49.4%
Return on equity: 43.9%
Cash (mil.): $20.3
Current ratio: 2.04
Long-term debt (mil.): $267.4
No. of shares (mil.): 83.4
Dividends
  Yield: —
  Payout: —
Market value (mil.): $2,070.5

INSO CORPORATION

OVERVIEW

tHis sentunce uSe kould some hlpe frum INSO's prawducks. Headquartered in Boston, INSO makes document proofing programs such as International CorrectSpell and CorrectText Grammar Correction System. Its software is loaded into some 50 million computers around the world as parts of such programs as Microsoft Word and Office and Lotus WordPro and Notes. The company also produces Inso Search Wizard, a software tool used to perform targeted searches of the World Wide Web that weed out nonrelevant information. In addition, INSO makes Quick View software, used to view and print files from online sources without having to first download them to the computer's memory system. Sales to Microsoft account for about half of the company's revenues. Publisher Houghton Mifflin owns nearly 34% of INSO.

The company was formed in 1982 as the Software Division of Houghton Mifflin. It developed the first commercial spell-checking system and created reference materials based on Houghton Mifflin's print products and products licensed from others. Although the division's products received praise for their design, Houghton Mifflin was having trouble getting sales jump-started. In 1990 the company hired Steven Vana-Paxhia, a former marketing director with Macmillan, to head the Software Division. He improved the unit's marketing and added original equipment manufacturers (OEMs) to the customer list. With the software unit growing beyond Houghton Mifflin's core operations, the company spun it off as InfoSoft in 1994. It took the name INSO the next year.

To grab a bigger market share, the company purchased file viewing technology firm Systems Compatibility in 1995 and computer graphics concern ImageMark Software Labs in 1996.

WHO

President and CEO: Steven R. Vana-Paxhia, age 48, $296,703 pay
VP Business Development: Kirby A. Mansfield, age 41, $191,458 pay
VP; General Manager, Tools and Technologies: Jeffrey J. Melvin
VP Engineering: Sunanda Mathai, age 44, $183,699 pay
VP, CFO, and Treasurer: Betty J. Savage, age 37, $174,691 pay
VP, General Counsel, and Secretary: Bruce G. Hill, age 32
Director Human Resources: Judith Tavano-Finkle
Auditors: Ernst & Young LLP

WHERE

HQ: 31 St. James Ave., Boston, MA 02116-4101
Phone: 617-753-6500
Fax: 617-753-6666
Web site: http://www.inso.com

WHAT

Selected Products

Information Management
ImageStream (file importer and exporter)
Inso Search Wizard (Internet search tool)
Outside In (file viewer for OEMs)
Quick View Plus (file viewer and printer)

Tools and Technologies
CorrectEnglish (for non-native English writers)
CorrectText Grammar Correction System (English grammar proofer)
CyberSpell (e-mail spelling checker)
International CorrectSpell (spelling checker)
International ProofReader (multilingual proofer)
InWords (expanded dictionary)

KEY COMPETITORS

Encyclopædia Britannica	Novell
Excite	Research Information
Infoseek	Sherpa Systems
Lotus	SoftArt
Lycos	SoftKey
Microlytics	

HOW MUCH

Nasdaq symbol: INSO FYE: December 31	Annual Growth	1990	1991	1992	1993	1994	1995
Sales ($ mil.)	48.5%	6.0	7.7	9.5	13.8	23.5	43.4
Net income ($ mil.)	64.4%	0.5	1.1	1.6	2.6	5.7	6.0
Income as % of sales	—		7.5%	14.1%	16.4%	18.7%	24.1%	13.8%
Earnings per share ($)	48.7%	—	—	0.14	0.23	0.48	0.49
Stock price – high ($)		—	—	—	—	17.88	47.50
Stock price – low ($)		—	—	—	—	8.57	16.53
Stock price – close ($)		—	—	—	—	17.57	42.50
P/E – high		—	—	—	—	37	97
P/E – low		—	—	—	—	18	34
Dividends per share ($)		—	—	—	—	0.00	0.00
Book value per share ($)		—	—	—	—	2.38	5.80
Employees	45.6%	—	—	—	83	118	176

1995 YEAR-END
Debt ratio: 7.8%
Return on equity: 11.7%
Cash (mil.): $62.6
Current ratio: 4.46
Long-term debt (mil.): $0.0
No. of shares (mil.): 13.0
Dividends
  Yield: —
  Payout: —
  Market value (mil.): $551
R&D as % of sales: 20.4%

INTERNATIONAL FAMILY

OVERVIEW

Millions of parents and kids sitting around the house watching hours of TV makes for one big happy International Family. Led by conservative TV evangelist Pat Robertson, International Family Entertainment (IFE), based in Virginia Beach, operates cable TV networks and produces and distributes television programming that ostensibly emphasizes and reflects traditional family values. The company's flagship Family Channel is one of the nation's top 10 cable channels, delivering dramas, comedies, and other shows to more than 64 million US households (99% of all homes with cable TV). Regional versions of the Family Channel are distributed in Asia and Latin America. IFE's FiT TV (formerly Cable Health Club) is the only cable channel providing 24-hour health and fitness programming. The company's MTM division distributes such TV series as the *Mary Tyler Moore Show* and *St. Elsewhere* and produces original programming for the Family Channel and other outlets. Subsidiary Calvin Gilmore Productions manages live musical variety shows. Robertson and his son, CEO Tim, own 16.5% of the company. A subsidiary of cable service monolith Tele-Communications, Inc. owns 26%.

The Robertsons founded the Family Channel in 1977 as part of the Christian Broadcasting Network (CBN). In 1989 they formed IFE to buy the Family Channel. IFE went public in 1992 and the next year bought MTM, giving it a programming library and production capabilities. A joint venture with English distributor Flextech brought the Family Channel to the UK in 1993.

In 1995 the company entered the Latin American market with the Family Channel De Las Americas. In 1996 IFE agreed to sell its interest in the Family Channel (UK) to Flextech.

WHO

Chairman: M. G. Robertson, age 65, $472,542 pay
President and CEO: Timothy B. Robertson, age 41, $739,970 pay
CEO, MTM Entertainment, Inc.: Anthony D. Thomopoulos, age 58, $762,811 pay
SVP Marketing and Corporate Communications: John B. Damoose, age 49, $426,057 pay
SVP and CFO: Larry W. Dantzler, age 40, $410,777 pay
SVP, General Counsel, and Secretary: Louis A. Isakoff, age 41
SVP Investor Relations and Strategic Planning: David R. Humphrey, age 39
Director Personnel: Carol Kleiber
Auditors: KPMG Peat Marwick LLP

WHERE

HQ: International Family Entertainment, Inc., 2877 Guardian Ln., Virginia Beach, VA 23452
Phone: 757-459-6000
Fax: 757-459-6486

WHAT

	1995 Sales	
	$ mil.	% of total
The Family Channel	198.4	64
Production & distribution	87.3	28
International networks	12.7	4
Live entertainment	10.5	3
FiT TV	3.3	1
Adjustments	(17.3)	—
Total	**294.9**	**100**

KEY COMPETITORS

A&E Networks
BET
Cablevision Systems
Capital Cities/ABC
Carsey-Werner
Corporation for Public Broadcasting
Discovery Communications
Gaylord Entertainment
Hearst
King World
MCANBC
News Corp.
Sony
Time Warner
Tribune
Univision Holdings
Viacom
Westinghouse/CBS

HOW MUCH

NYSE symbol: FAM FYE: December 31	Annual Growth	1990	1991	1992	1993	1994	1995
Sales ($ mil.)	25.9%	93.4	113.7	131.7	208.2	242.1	294.9
Net income ($ mil.)	5.4%	14.4	19.8	29.6	17.3	14.8	18.7
Income as % of sales	—	15.4%	17.4%	22.5%	8.3%	6.1%	6.3%
Earnings per share ($)	(25.8%)	0.71	0.83	0.90	0.39	0.30	0.16
Stock price – high ($)	—	—	—	12.30	20.10	17.80	16.50
Stock price – low ($)	—	—	—	7.30	10.90	9.70	9.90
Stock price – close ($)	5.4%	—	—	11.20	16.60	10.10	13.10
P/E – high	—	—	—	14	52	59	103
P/E – low	—	—	—	8	28	32	62
Dividends per share ($)	—	—	—	0.00	0.00	0.00	0.00
Book value per share ($)	—	—	(7.23)	0.24	3.66	3.57	3.80
Employees	35.4%	—	250	280	692	737	840

1995 YEAR-END
Debt ratio: 55.3%
Return on equity: 11.7%
Cash (mil.): $41.2
Current ratio: 2.43
Long-term debt (mil.): $176.8
No. of shares (mil.): 45.1
Dividends
  Yield: —
  Payout: —
Market value (mil.): $590.9

INTERNATIONAL POST LIMITED

OVERVIEW

International Post won't get your letter overseas, but it will definitely make sure you get the message. The New York City-based postproduction company puts razzle-dazzle effects into TV commercials and provides video restoration, editing, and tape transfer services for most major advertising companies (including J. Walter Thompson and Saatchi & Saatchi) and broadcast and cable networks. Founding investors Terrence Elkes and Kenneth Gorman control more than 50% of the company's stock.

In 1979 Martin Irwin and Louis Siracusano founded Video Services Corp. (VSC) to provide video production services. During the 1980s, while VSC was growing in the competitive New York market, Elkes and Gorman were working at Viacom. In 1987 they formed Apollo Partners, which invested in the media industry. The 4 men joined forces in 1992 when Apollo formed Manhattan Transfer/Edit Co. and bought VSC's postproduction business, with Irwin in charge.

In 1994 Apollo Partners took the new business public (simultaneously buying Audio Plus Video International) as International Post Limited. The company used the IPO proceeds to fund more acquisitions. The combined effects of these acquisitions and a slowdown in advertising activities brought a decline in profits in 1995. In response, the company began a cost-cutting campaign, which included the consolidation of some facilities.

As one of the few public companies in the highly fragmented postproduction industry, International Post is also one of the few with deep pockets. In 1995 the company bought Miami-based Post Edge, which serves the Latin American and Spanish television markets (MTV Latino and Discovery Channel Latin America are 2 of its clients).

WHO

Chairman: Terrence A. Elkes, age 61
President and CEO: Martin Irwin, age 59, $221,868 pay
EVP and CFO: Jeffrey J. Kaplan, age 47, $221,866 pay
VP; President, Manhattan Transfer/Edit, Inc.:
Daniel Rosen, age 57, $251,066 pay
VP; President, Audio Plus Video International, Inc.:
Adrien Macaluso, age 50, $226,505 pay
VP: Sylvester Timpanaro, age 62, $151,804 pay
VP: Dominic Pandolfino, age 44, $151,769 pay
Director Human Resources: Carla Moxham
Auditors: Andersen Worldwide

WHERE

HQ: 545 Fifth Ave., New York, NY 10017
Phone: 212-986-6300
Fax: 212-986-1364

WHAT

Subsidiaries
Audio Plus Video International, Inc. (video postproduction services and distribution, international format conversions)
Big Picture/Even Time Ltd. (TV commercial production)
International Post Finance Limited
Manhattan Transfer/Edit, Inc. (TV commercial postproduction services, film-to-tape transfer, corporate Web site design)
The Post Edge, Inc. (production, postproduction, and broadcast services for the Latin American and Spanish television markets)

KEY COMPETITORS

Allied Digital Technologies
CKS
Four Media
Harmony Holdings
Laser-Pacific Media
Leap Group
Modem Media
Northwest Teleproductions
Todd-AO
United Video Satellite
Ziff-Davis

HOW MUCH

Nasdaq symbol: POST FYE: July 31	Annual Growth	1990	1991	1992	1993	1994	1995
Sales ($ mil.)	29.8%	10.4	11.2	11.6	20.8	27.8	38.3
Net income ($ mil.)	32.0%	0.4	0.2	0.0	0.5	3.3	1.6
Income as % of sales	—	3.6%	2.1%	0.3%	0.5%	11.9%	4.2%
Earnings per share ($)	41.4%	—	—	—	0.13	0.70	0.26
Stock price – high ($)	—	—	—	—	—	12.00	7.63
Stock price – low ($)	—	—	—	—	—	3.50	3.13
Stock price – close ($)	(13.1%)	—	—	—	—	4.75	4.13
P/E – high	—	—	—	—	—	17	29
P/E – low	—	—	—	—	—	5	12
Dividends per share ($)	—	—	—	—	—	0.00	0.00
Book value per share ($)	5.8%	—	—	—	—	4.49	4.75
Employees	41.9%	—	—	—	—	227	322

1995 YEAR-END
Debt ratio: 49.7%
Return on equity: 5.6%
Cash (mil.): $0.4
Current ratio: 0.92
Long-term debt (mil.): $25.2
No. of shares (mil.): 6.2
Dividends
Yield: —
Payout: —
Market value (mil.): $25.6

IWERKS ENTERTAINMENT, INC.

OVERVIEW

Going to the movies just isn't what it used to be, especially if you go to an IWERKS theater. Burbank, California-based IWERKS Entertainment is a leading producer of high-tech specialty systems and software for ride simulators and for 3-D, giant-screen, and 360-degree movie attractions. Major clients include theme park operators, world expositions, museums, and visitor centers. IWERKS owns and operates 17 touring ride-simulation theaters.

Donald Iwerks's father, Ubbe, was Walt Disney's first animator and is credited with creating Mickey Mouse. Donald, who worked in Disney's machine shop, eventually became head of the department. When the company began building Disneyland, his department built steam locomotives and other vehicles and later developed projection equipment. Iwerks and Stanley Kinsey, a Disney VP, founded IWERKS Entertainment in 1986 and developed a ride simulator system, the Turbo Tour Theater.

The company went public in 1993 with a $47 million stock offering that was gobbled up amid a feeding frenzy for anything "multimedia." After significant losses in 1994, the company froze the development of its Cinetropolis project, entertainment centers featuring theaters with 360-degree screens, digital sound, moving seats, and on-site restaurants and shops. Only 2 Cinetropolis centers were built, one in Connecticut and one in Japan.

Heavy outlays for R&D, coupled with the lack of market response to Cinetropolis, left IWERKS in the red in 1995, despite a 23% increase in revenues. The firm moved to make itself profitable with corporate restructuring, streamlining of management, and a dramatic layoff of 31% of its workforce. Cofounder Kinsey resigned as CEO in 1995.

Sales inched up to $48.5 million in 1996 as IWERKS made a $3 million profit.

WHO

Co-chairman: Paula T. Douglass, age 42
Co-chairman, President, and CEO: Roy A. Wright, age 52, $143,492 pay (prior to promotion)
VC and Chief Technical Officer: Donald W. Iwerks, age 65, $125,000 pay
EVP Operations: W. Thomas Gimple, age 33, $120,000 pay
EVP Special Projects: Michael R. Dulion, age 42, $120,000 pay
EVP and CFO: Francis T. Phalen, age 56
EVP Sales and Marketing: William Battison
VP National Account Sales: George K. Wade, $130,769 pay
VP Human Resources and Administrative Services: Catherine Giffen
Auditors: Ernst & Young LLP

WHERE

HQ: 4540 W. Valerio St., Burbank, CA 91505-1046
Phone: 818-841-7766
Fax: 818-841-7847

	1995 Sales	
	$ mil.	% of total
US	20.4	45
Far East	23.0	51
Other regions	1.6	4
Total	**45.0**	**100**

WHAT

Attractions
CineDome (giant-screen theaters)
Cinetropolis (entertainment center)
IWERKS 870 and 1570 (giant-screen theaters)
IWERKS VideoDrome (360-degree theater)
Reactor (portable motion-simulation theater)
TurboRide (fixed-base ride simulation theater)
Virtual Adventures (3-D interactive adventure)

KEY COMPETITORS

DreamWorks SKG	Namco Virtual	Silicon Graphics
Gaylord	World	Sony
Entertainment	SEGA	Virtual World
Imax	Showscan	Virtuality Ltd.
MCA	Entertainment	

HOW MUCH

Nasdaq symbol: IWRK FYE: June 30	Annual Growth	1990	1991	1992	1993	1994	1995
Sales ($ mil.)	57.1%	4.7	5.8	18.2	32.2	36.6	45.0
Net income ($ mil.)	—	(0.4)	(0.8)	0.3	1.2	(8.1)	(13.5)
Income as % of sales	—	—	—	1.3%	3.7%	—	—
Earnings per share ($)	79.9%	(0.07)	(0.15)	(0.04)	0.18	(1.05)	(1.32)
Stock price – high ($)	—	—	—	—	37.00	29.25	6.88
Stock price – low ($)	—	—	—	—	22.25	3.88	2.88
Stock price – close ($)	(51.1%)	—	—	—	26.75	4.75	6.39
P/E – high	—	—	—	—	206	—	—
P/E – low	—	—	—	—	124	—	—
Dividends per share ($)	—	—	—	—	0.00	0.00	0.00
Book value per share ($)	—	—	—	—	(0.23)	6.25	4.76
Employees	3.6%	—	—	—	163	253	175

1995 YEAR-END
Debt ratio: 7.3%
Return on equity: —
Cash (mil.): $18.4
Current ratio: 1.58
Long-term debt (mil.): $2.1
No. of shares (mil.): 10.6
Dividends
  Yield: —
  Payout: —
Market value (mil.): $67.7
R&D as % of sales: 1.9%

JACOR COMMUNICATIONS, INC.

OVERVIEW

That swoosh you heard after President Clinton signed the Telecommunications Act of 1996 was Jacor Communications hustling to buy more radio stations. The company quickly made deals that would give the Cincinnati-based station-gobbler 50 radio outlets (10 more than the previous limit), including 7 in its hometown and 8 (the new per-market limit) in Denver. Jacor also operates Georgia Radio News Service, which delivers news, sports, and informational programming to more than 140 stations. Through the Zell/Chilmark investment partnership, former chairman David Schulte and wily Chicagoan Samuel Zell own about 2/3 of the company.

Terry Jacobs left a successful career at insurance provider American Financial Corp. to start his own business, choosing radio after research revealed it as a growing industry. He started Jacor (named after himself) in 1979 and acquired 3 religious radio stations in the early 1980s. These small stations did well, prompting Jacobs to expand the business through the 1980s by buying others, going into debt in the process. In 1986 Jacor merged with upstart station owner Republic Broadcasting, bringing its leader, Randy Michaels, on board as well. A sluggish economy in the early 1990s led Jacor to sell most of the company to Zell/Chilmark in 1993. That year it went public and Jacobs left to start another radio venture, Regent Communications. Zell/Chilmark partner David Schulte became chairman (later replaced by Sheli Rosenberg) and Michaels became president.

In 1996 Jacor planned to increase its radio holdings by more than twofold, agreeing to merge with Citicasters (19 radio and 2 TV stations) and Noble Broadcast Group (12 radio stations).

WHO

Chairperson: Sheli Z. Rosenberg, age 54
President and Co-COO: Randy Michaels, age 43, $411,993 pay
Co-COO: Robert L. Lawrence, age 43, $404,430 pay
SVP and CFO (HR): R. Christopher Weber, age 40, $269,892 pay
SVP and Treasurer: Jon M. Berry, age 49, $148,368 pay
Auditors: Coopers & Lybrand L.L.P.

WHERE

HQ: 1300 PNC Ctr., 201 E. Fifth St., Cincinnati, OH 45202
Phone: 513-621-1300
Fax: 513-621-0090

WHAT

	1995 Radio Stations
	No.
Jacksonville, FL	5
Cincinnati	4
Denver	4
Tampa	4
Atlanta	2
San Diego	1
Total	**20**

Other Operations
Georgia Radio News Service (delivers news, sports, and information broadcasting to more than 140 stations)
Joint sales agreements (advertising sales for 4 radio stations)

KEY COMPETITORS

American Radio Systems
Capital Cities/ABC
Century Communications
Chancellor Broadcasting
Cox Enterprises
Evergreen Media
EZ Communications
Gannett
Heritage Media
Media General
SFX Broadcasting
Tribune
Westinghouse/CBS

HOW MUCH

Nasdaq symbol: JCOR FYE: December 31	Annual Growth	1990	1991	1992	1993	1994	1995
Sales ($ mil.)	8.2%	80.0	64.2	70.5	89.9	107.0	118.9
Net income ($ mil.)	—	(20.7)	1.5	(23.7)	1.4	7.9	11.0
Income as % of sales	—	—	2.3%	—	1.6%	7.4%	9.3%
Earnings per share ($)	—	—	—	—	0.10	0.37	0.52
Stock price – high ($)	—	—	—	—	19.50	17.00	19.25
Stock price – low ($)	—	—	—	—	8.13	10.50	12.00
Stock price – close ($)	10.3%	—	—	—	14.38	13.25	17.50
P/E – high	—	—	—	—	195	46	37
P/E – low	—	—	—	—	81	28	23
Dividends per share ($)	—	—	—	0.00	0.00	0.00	0.00
Book value per share ($)	—	—	—	—	7.22	7.61	7.66
Employees	28.1%	—	426	574	498	844	1,147

1995 YEAR-END
Debt ratio: 24.6%
Return on equity: 7.6%
Cash (mil.): $7.0
Current ratio: 3.00
Long-term debt (mil.): $45.5
No. of shares (mil.): 18
Dividends
  Yield: —
  Payout: —
Market value (mil.): $317.8

JOHN WILEY & SONS, INC.

OVERVIEW

John Wiley is looking for wily new ways to while through the Computer Age. The New York City-based publisher specializes in professional and consumer books, textbooks and educational materials, and scientific and technical publications. It publishes the *Ernst & Young Tax Guide* on America Online. About 40% of the company's sales come from outside the US, with additional growth forecast in Asia and Europe. Sixth-generation executive Bradford Wiley II is chairman. The Wiley family owns about 19% of the firm.

The company was founded as a bookstore in 1807 by 25-year-old Charles Wiley, who began printing and marketing books for local authors in return for a share of the profits. Soon, prominent writers began meeting in the store's back room (known as "The Den"), which attracted more attention to the business. By the end of the Civil War, the firm (renamed John Wiley & Sons, after Charles's son) had become an established publisher of books on science and technology. Wiley pioneered technical textbooks that became industry standards. In 1899 it published Charles Davenport's *Statistical Methods* and in 1947 Hans Liepmann's *Aerodynamics of a Compressible Fluid*, among others. The company went public in 1962.

In 1994 Wiley sold its Canadian high school and Australian primary school textbook subsidiaries. Wiley teamed with publisher Adweek Magazines in 1995 to print media and marketing books under the name Adweek Books.

Wiley in 1996 agreed to acquire Preservation Press and a 90% stake in Germany's VCH Publishing Group. Wiley's earnings increased to nearly $25 million in fiscal 1996 on sales of almost $363 million.

WHO

Chairman: Bradford Wiley II, age 54
President and CEO: Charles R. Ellis, age 60, $662,832 pay
SVP Professional, Reference and Trade Publishing Group: Stephen A. Kippur, age 48, $386,113 pay
SVP Finance and CFO: Robert D. Wilder, age 47, $316,554 pay
SVP Educational Publishing Group: William J. Pesce, age 44, $310,039 pay
SVP and General Counsel: Richard S. Rudick, age 56, $230,053 pay
VP Finance and Controller: Peter W. Clifford, age 49
VP Human Resources: William J. Arlington, age 46
Auditors: Andersen Worldwide

WHERE

HQ: 605 Third Ave., New York, NY 10158-0012
Phone: 212-850-6000
Fax: 212-850-6088
Web site: http://www.wiley.com

	1996 Sales	
	$ mil.	% of total
US	280.0	71
Other countries	112.3	29
Adjustments	(29.6)	—
Total	**362.7**	**100**

WHAT

Selected Products
Educational textbooks and instructional materials
Professional books (accounting, architecture, computing, construction, engineering, and law)
Scientific, technical, and medical products (journals, reference books, CD-ROMs)

KEY COMPETITORS

Bertelsmann	Plenum	Tribune
Harcourt General	Publishing	Viacom
Holtzbrinck	Reed Elsevier	West Publishing
Houghton Mifflin	Scholastic	Wolters Kluwer
Lagardère	Thomson Corp.	W.W. Norton
McGraw-Hill	Times Mirror	

HOW MUCH

NYSE symbol: JWA FYE: April 30	Annual Growth	1991	1992	1993	1994	1995	1996
Sales ($ mil.)	8.9%	236.9	248.2	272.9	294.3	331.1	362.7
Net Income ($ mil.)	43.2%	4.1	3.6	7.7	12.1	18.3	24.7
Income as % of sales	—	1.7	1.5	2.8	4.1	5.5	6.8%
Earnings per share ($)	44.1%	0.24	0.23	0.50	0.76	1.12	1.49
Stock price – high ($)[1]	—	13.38	10.06	12.56	18.50	23.00	35.00
Stock price – low ($)[1]	—	6.47	7.13	7.75	10.50	17.50	21.88
Stock price – close ($)[1]	34.3%	7.50	8.13	12.56	17.75	22.13	32.75
P/E – high	—	56	44	25	24	21	23
P/E – low	—	27	31	16	14	16	15
Dividends per share ($)	4.6%	0.28	0.28	0.28	0.28	0.31	0.35
Book value per share ($)	6.3%	5.39	4.56	4.63	5.23	6.21	7.32
Employees	3.2%	1,560	1,600	1,660	1,680	1,770	1,830

[1] Stock prices are for the prior calendar year.

1996 YEAR-END
Debt ratio: 0.0%
Return on equity: 22.8%
Cash (mil.): $55.3
Current ratio: 1.23
Long-term debt (mil.): $0.0
No. of shares (mil.): 16.1
Dividends
  Yield: 1.1%
  Payout: 23.5%
Market value (mil.): $528.1

JONES INTERCABLE, INC.

OVERVIEW

Jones Communications is one of the US's 10 largest cable TV providers, with more than 1.3 million subscribers in 22 states. The Englewood, Colorado-based company also operates Mind Extension University (MEU), a 24-hour cable TV network offering educational programming that lets people earn undergraduate and graduate degrees from big-name colleges and universities. MEU is part of Jones Education Networks, which also includes the Jones Computer Network. The company is trying to position itself as the leading provider of educational programming and long-distance education. Jones Intercable also provides FM radio programming to cable TV stations, owns a brokerage that concentrates on cable stocks, and produces communications encryption devices. Chairman Glenn Jones controls 41% of the company's voting stock; BCE, Canada's largest telecommunications company, owns a 30% stake in the company.

Jones, an attorney, went into the cable business in 1967. He got a $400 loan on his Volkswagen to make a down payment on a Colorado cable system that served 150 homes. Jones Intercable was incorporated in 1970.

During the 1970s and 1980s, the company grew quickly. Jones pioneered the use of limited partnerships to finance cable operations; he also was one of the first to buy geographic "clusters" of cable systems, expand his cable operations overseas, and install fiber-optic networks. He founded MEU in 1987.

In 1994 BCE bought its stake in Jones Intercable for $400 million and an option to take control of the company in 8 years. In 1995 the company unveiled an advanced cable TV system in Alexandria, Virginia, that will offer Internet access, expanded pay-for-view movies, and interactive services.

WHO

Chairman and CEO: Glenn R. Jones, age 65, $1,160,420 pay
VC: Derek H. Burney, age 55
President and COO: James B. O'Brien, age 45, $249,068 pay
Group VP Finance and CFO: Kevin P. Coyle, age 43, $213,559 pay
Group VP Technology: Christopher J. Bowick, age 39, $198,458 pay
Group VP Operations: Ruth E. Warren, age 45
Group VP Human Resources: Raymond L. Vigil, age 48
VP, General Counsel, and Secretary: Elizabeth M. Steele, age 43, $217,207 pay
Auditors: Andersen Worldwide

WHERE

HQ: 9697 E. Mineral Ave., PO Box 3309, Englewood, CO 80155-3309
Phone: 303-792-3111
Fax: 303-790-0533
Web site: http://www.jic.com

WHAT

Selected Subsidiaries
Jones Earth Segment, Inc. (ground-to-satellite uplink facility)
Jones Financial Group, Ltd. (cable TV systems sales and financing)
Jones Galactic Radio, Inc. (radio holding company)
The Jones Group, Ltd. (brokerage firm)
Jones Infomercial Networks, Inc. (advertising on cable TV systems)
Jones Interactive, Inc. (information management and data processing services)

KEY COMPETITORS

Adelphia Communications	Century Communications	PRIMESTAR TCA Cable
American Telecasting	Comcast	TCI
Apollo Group	Continental Cablevision	Telecommunications Systems
Bell Atlantic	Cox	Time Warner
CINet Cablevision	Communications	United States Satellite
Systems	DIRECTV	Broadcasting

HOW MUCH

Nasdaq symbol: JOIN FYE: December 31	Annual Growth	1990	1991	1992	1993	1994	1995
Sales ($ mil.)	13.8%	99.0	131.0	122.6	132.4	150.9	188.8
Net income ($ mil.)	—	(33.6)	19.6	(52.9)	(25.3)	(4.0)	(21.0)
Income as % of sales	—	—	14.9%	—	—	—	—
Earnings per share ($)	—	(2.77)	1.59	(3.71)	(1.43)	(0.16)	(0.67)
Stock price – high ($)	—	16.25	13.25	14.00	20.25	17.50	17.50
Stock price – low ($)	—	4.75	5.75	9.25	1.50	10.75	11.75
Stock price – close ($)	12.3%	7.00	13.00	13.75	17.25	11.88	12.50
P/E – high	—	—	8	—	—	—	—
P/E – low	—	—	4	—	—	—	—
Dividends per share ($)	—	0.00	0.00	0.00	0.00	0.00	0.00
Book value per share ($)	—	(0.22)	1.97	1.85	3.14	8.49	9.35
Employees	3.5%	3,000	2,750	2,780	2,850	3,480	3,686

1995 YEAR-END
Debt ratio: 62.7%
Return on equity: —
Cash (mil.): $12.1
Current ratio: 0.64
Long-term debt (mil.): $462.7
No. of shares (mil.): 31.3
Dividends
  Yield: —
  Payout: —
Market value (mil.): $391.6

KATZ MEDIA GROUP, INC.

OVERVIEW

In show business, everybody needs an agent — even the media. New York City-based Katz Media Group sells advertising time for more than 1,300 cable systems, 1,900 radio stations, and 350 television stations in the US, representing radio broadcasters such as Capital Cities/ABC, Cox Enterprises, and Tribune Broadcasting, and television broadcasters such as Gannett, Viacom, and Scripps Howard. Investment house Donaldson, Lufkin & Jenrette owns 49% of the company.

Founder Emanuel Katz got his start in New York selling advertising in William Randolph Hearst's San Francisco newspapers. In 1888 he founded the E. Katz Special Advertising Agency, the first media representation firm in the US. Katz added radio stations to his client list during the 1930s, and in 1947 the company signed up its first television station. The firm stopped representing newspapers in 1969 to focus on broadcast media. By 1985 it was the largest media representation firm in the US. In 1992 the company purchased rival television representative Seltel, which operates as a subsidiary. That year Katz purchased an interest in Cable Media Corp. and entered the cable TV field. It formed Katz International in London in 1993 to pursue media representation in Europe.

Katz went public in 1995, the same year it joined with Comcast, Continental Cablevision, Cox Communications, and Time Warner Entertainment to form National Cable Communications, L.P., the largest cable representation firm in the US. Katz, whose Cable Media Corp. cable representation subsidiary was merged into the new venture, owns 50%. In 1996 the company added Cable One, a cable advertising agency representing systems in 30 markets, to its client roster.

WHO

President and CEO: Thomas F. Olson, age 47, $575,000 pay
SVP, Chief Financial and Administrative Officer, and Treasurer: Richard E. Vendig, age 48, $252,000 pay
VP and Secretary: James E. Beloyianis, age 46, $425,000 pay
VP: Stuart Olds, age 46, $450,000 pay
VP: L. Donald Robinson, age 57, $420,000 pay
Manager Human Resources: Anne Strafaci
Auditors: Price Waterhouse LLP

WHERE

HQ: 125 W. 55th St., New York, NY 10019
Phone: 212-424-6000
Fax: 212-424-6110
Web site: http://www.katz-media.com

WHAT

Selected Operations

Cable Television Representation	Katz American Television
National Cable	Katz Continental
Communications, L.P.	Television
(50%)	Katz National Television
	Seltel
Radio Representation	**Other**
Banner Radio	Katz International
Christal Radio	(European media sales)
Eastman Radio	Katz Millennium
Katz Hispanic Media	Marketing (Internet and
Katz Network	Web sites, interactive
Katz Radio	television, and online
Sentry Radio	services)
	Media Marketing Services
Television Representation	
Katz Television	

KEY COMPETITORS

CNI	SOFTBANK
Interep Radio Store	Tele Rep/HRP/MMT
Petry Inc./Blair Television	Westinghouse/CBS

HOW MUCH

AMEX symbol: KTZ FYE: December 31	Annual Growth	1990	1991	1992	1993	1994	1995
Sales ($ mil.)	12.0%	—	117.5	146.0	156.9	179.5	184.7
Net income ($ mil.)	(43.8%)	—	(7.0)	(12.5)	2.1	(1.5)	(0.7)
Income as % of sales	—	—	—	—	1.3%	—	—
Earnings per share ($)	(50.0%)	—	—	—	—	(0.10)	(0.05)
Stock price – high ($)	—	—	—	—	—	—	21.88
Stock price – low ($)	—	—	—	—	—	—	14.63
Stock price – close ($)	—	—	—	—	—	—	17.63
P/E – high	—	—	—	—	—	—	—
P/E – low	—	—	—	—	—	—	—
Dividends per share ($)	—	—	—	—	—	—	0.00
Book value per share ($)	—	—	—	—	—	—	0.13
Employees	—	—	—	—	—	—	1,600

1995 YEAR-END
Debt ratio: 92.9%
Return on equity: —
Cash (mil.): $2.4
Current ratio: 1.49
Long-term debt (mil.): $179.5
No. of shares (mil.): 107.4
Dividends
  Yield: —
  Payout: —
Market value (mil.): $1,893.6

K-TEL INTERNATIONAL, INC.

OVERVIEW

Pray tell, what will K-tel think of next? Minneapolis-based K-tel International, the company that introduced the world to the Veg-O-Matic, primarily markets prerecorded music (mainly compilations from various artists) from its proprietary collection and under license from 3rd parties. The company sells its products through TV advertisements and, more recently, through retail outlets. K-tel still markets the Veg-O-Matic and a host of other gadgets. Higher costs and lower margins on its music products led to a loss in 1995. Founder and CEO Philip Kives owns approximately 75% of the company.

K-tel was founded as Syndicate Product Lines in 1962 by Kives and his brother Ted. Early products included a nonstick frying pan and the oft-imitated but never equaled Veg-O-Matic food slicer. While sitting in a hotel room in 1965, Philip saw a country-and-western album advertised on television. He cut a deal with the record's advertisers to sell the album in Canada. K-tel (short for Kives Television) started in the US in 1968. The following year it released a collection of polka classics; the album sold over a million copies. The record was followed by such hits as *Hooked on Classics*, which the company marketed primarily through late-night TV ads.

K-tel went public in 1971. It filed for bankruptcy in 1984 after unprofitable ventures into oil exploration and shopping center development. Management then refocused the company on its strength — product marketing.

In 1995 K-tel joined with books-on-tape producer Dove Entertainment to publish audio books for children. Philip's nephew, then-CEO Mickey Elfenbein, planned in 1995 to buy out the company's video and entertainment division, but K-tel rejected the bid early the next year, leading to his resignation.

WHO

Chairman and CEO: Philip Kives, age 66
SVP Purchasing and Operations: Jeffrey Koblick, age 48, $177,482 pay
SVP: David Weiner, age 38, $117,500 pay
VP Finance, CFO, and Treasurer: Mark Dixon, age 36, $97,500 pay
Manager Human Resources: Lindee Weed
Auditors: Andersen Worldwide

WHERE

HQ: 2605 Fernbrook Ln. North, Minneapolis, MN 55447-4736
Phone: 612-559-6888
Fax: 612-559-6848
Web site: http://www.k-tel.com

	1995 Sales	
	$ mil.	% total
North America	36.6	56
Europe & Pacific	29.3	44
Total	**65.9**	**100**

WHAT

Selected Consumer Products	Instant Hair
Bacon Krisper	Kid-Tel Audio Books
Christmas Cartoons	Micro-Chip
Dog Trick Videos	Miracle Duster
Foot Massager	Pasta & Dough Maker
Glare Blocker	Veg-O-Matic

KEY COMPETITORS

Barnes & Noble	MCA	Time Warner
Bertelsmann	Musicland	Trans World
Best Buy	PolyGram	Entertainment
Comcast	Reader's Digest	Viacom
Hastings Books	Ronco	Virgin Group
Home Shopping	Sony	Wal-Mart
Network	Thomas Nelson	Walt Disney

HOW MUCH

Nasdaq symbol: KTEL FYE: June 30	Annual Growth	1990	1991	1992	1993	1994	1995
Sales ($ mil.)	9.1%	42.6	35.3	48.2	55.7	54.3	65.9
Net income ($ mil.)	—	0.7	0.6	1.9	2.7	0.4	(2.5)
Income as % of sales	—	1.6%	1.6%	3.9%	4.8%	0.7%	—
Earnings per share ($)	—	0.18	0.15	0.50	0.72	0.10	(0.67)
Stock price – high ($)	—	—	—	—	10.75	7.25	6.13
Stock price – low ($)	—	—	—	—	6.50	3.00	3.00
Stock price – close ($)	(20.3%)	—	—	—	6.50	4.25	4.13
P/E – high	—	—	—	—	15	73	—
P/E – low	—	—	—	—	9	30	—
Dividends per share ($)	—	—	—	—	0.00	0.00	0.00
Book value per share ($)	(23.7%)	—	—	—	1.15	1.21	0.67
Employees	13.9%	97	94	118	142	149	186

1995 YEAR-END
Debt ratio: 50%
Return on equity: —
Cash (mil.): $2.7
Current ratio: 1.03
Long-term debt (mil.): —
No. of shares (mil.): 3.7
Dividends
 Yield: —
 Payout: —
Market value (mil.): $15.3
Advertising as % of sales: 17.6%

LANDMARK COMMUNICATIONS, INC.

OVERVIEW

Norfolk, Virginia-based Landmark Communications communicates to readers and viewers nationwide through its 4 metropolitan daily newspapers, 35 community newspapers, and 2 CBS affiliate TV stations. The company also owns the Weather Channel, a 24-hour cable weather information provider, and the Travel Channel Networks, with viewers in the US and abroad. Landmark's specialty publications subsidiary produces national publications for antique dealers and collectors. The company is also a provider of marketing information to the consumer packaged goods industry through its Promotion Information Management division. Chairman Frank Batten and his family own most of Landmark's stock. Company executives own about 30% of the company.

Landmark was established in 1905 as Norfolk Newspapers, Inc., by Batten's uncle, S. L. Slover. The company expanded into radio broadcasting in 1932. Entry into the TV market came with the launch of a local NBC affiliate station in 1950.

Upon the death of his publisher in 1954, Slover appointed 27-year-old Batten to fill the post. Batten first set out to raise the standards of the company's reporting before continuing its expansion. In 1964 he acquired 2 cable TV franchises. In 1967 the business was renamed Landmark Communications after a defunct Norfolk paper. Two years later it added the *Roanoke Times & World-News* to its publishing portfolio.

Broadcast expansion continued with the 1978 purchase of KLAS-TV of Las Vegas, and the company moved into the national cable market with the 1982 launch of the Weather Channel. In 1992 Landmark acquired Antique Trader Publications and WTVF-TV, a CBS affiliate in Nashville, and it bought the Travel Channel, expanding into the international cable market. The company teamed up in 1994 with Wyvern Technologies, an Internet access provider, to form InfiNet, a provider that puts newspapers online. In 1995 Landmark launched a 24-hour Spanish-language Travel Channel network for Latin America.

WHO

Chairman: Frank Batten Sr.
CEO and President: John O. Wynne
EVP; President, Landmark Broadcasting: Donald H. Patterson Jr.
President, Landmark Publishing Group; President and Publisher, *The Roanoke Times*: Walter Rugaber
President, The Weather Channel: Michael J. Eckert
President, The Travel Channel Networks: Kevin D. Senie
CFO: Alfred Ritter
VP Human Resources: Charlie Hill

WHERE

HQ: 150 W. Brambleton Ave., Norfolk, VA 23510
Phone: 804-446-2000
Fax: 804-664-2163

WHAT

Broadcasting and Video Enterprises
KLAS-TV, Las Vegas
WTVF-TV, Nashville
The Travel Channel Networks
The Weather Channel

Community Newspapers
4 dailies
4 triweeklies
7 semiweeklies
20 weeklies

Metropolitan Newspapers
The Ledger-Star (Norfolk, VA)
The News & Record (Greensboro, NC)

The Roanoke Times & World-News (Virginia)
The Virginian-Pilot (Norfolk, VA)

Special Publications
The Antique Trader Weekly
Antiques & Collectibles Price Guide
Baby Boomer Collectibles
Big Reel
Collector Magazine & Price Guide
DISCoveries
Military Trader
Postcard Collector
Toy Trader

KEY COMPETITORS

Advance Publications
Central Newspapers
Cox Enterprises
E.W. Scripps
Freedom Communications
Gannett
Hollinger Inc.
Journal Communications
Knight-Ridder
McClatchy Newspapers

Media General
MediaNews
Meredith
NBC
New York Times
Primark
Times Mirror
Tribune
Washington Post

HOW MUCH

Private company FYE: December 31	Annual Growth	1990	1991	1992	1993	1994	1995
Sales ($ mil.)	7.2%	354.4	379.9	407.3	436.6	467.0	500.6
Employees	0.0%	—	—	—	—	4,500	4,500

LUCASARTS ENTERTAINMENT COMPANY

OVERVIEW

LucasArts Entertainment is one of a trio of entertainment companies owned by visionary filmmaker George Lucas. The San Raphael, California-based company, a pioneer in entertainment software, develops and publishes games for PCs (it is the #1 PC game maker) and Macintoshes as well as Nintendo and Sega machines. Its computer games and CD-ROMS combine high-tech visual effects, 3-D animation, and digital sound with elements of movie-making. In addition to exploiting Lucas's *Star Wars* and *Indiana Jones* properties, the company has developed original titles that include zany adventures (for example, Maniac Mansions and Day of the Tentacle) and appealing characters (Sam & Max Hit the Road and Full Throttle). LucasArts also designs and produces educational software. It has teamed up with such partners as Apple Computer and the National Geographic Society to teach reading, geography, language, financial management, and environmental science to schoolchildren. Lucas is the sole investor in the company.

The company was founded in 1982 as a subsidiary of Lucasfilm Ltd., which Lucas created in 1975 to produce the special effects for *Star Wars*. Its early games, created for PCs, were published by other companies. In 1987 LucasArts adopted the innovative "point-and-click" interface that became an industry standard. Two years later it developed a video game based on the movie *Indiana Jones and the Last Crusade*. The company created a patented sound system (iMUSE) in 1991. Lucasfilm spun off LucasArts as one of 3 principal companies in a 1993 restructuring.

In 1994 the company launched Rebel Assault, which has become the best-selling CD-ROM title in history; also that year LucasArts underwent a management shakeup in which Randy Komisar, named CEO in 1993, resigned and was succeeded by Jack Sorensen. To increase its market share, in 1995 LucasArts announced it would adapt all its games for the Macintosh as well as video game consoles. In 1996 the company introduced its first game created just for children, Mortimer and the Riddles of the Medallion, which runs on Nintendo, Sega, and Sony platforms.

WHO

Chairman: George Lucas, age 50
President: Jack Sorensen
CFO: Tom McCarthy
Director Human Resources: Karen Chelini
General Counsel: Robert Roden

WHERE

HQ: PO Box 10307, San Rafael, CA 94912
Phone: 415-472-3400
Fax: 415-662-2460
Web site: http://www.lucasarts.com

WHAT

Selected Products

Games	
Battlehawks 1942	The Secret Weapons of the Luftwaffe
Dark Forces	Star Wars
Day of the Tentacle	Super Return of the Jedi
Defenders of Dynatron City	Super Star Wars
The Dig	Their Finest Hour: The Battle of Britain
The Empire Strikes Back	TIE Fighter
Full Throttle	X-Wing
Ghoul Patrol	Zak McKracken and the Alien Mindbenders
Indiana Jones' Greatest Adventures	

Indiana Jones and his Desktop Adventures
Indiana Jones and the Fate of Atlantis
Indiana Jones and the Last Crusade
Monkey Island 2: LeChuck's Revenge
Mortimer and the Riddles of the Medallion
Night Shift
Pipe Dream
Rebel Assault
Sam & Max Hit the Road
The Secret of Monkey Island

Educational Multimedia Products
Choices & Decisions: Taking Charge of Your Life
GTV (Geographic TV)
Life Story: The Race for the Double Helix
Mac Magic
Night of the Living Statues
Paul Parkranger & the Mystery of the Disappearing Ducks
Treasury of Literature — Tiger Tales

KEY COMPETITORS

7th Level	id Software
Acclaim Entertainment	Interplay Productions
Accolade	Learning Co.
Activision	Maxis
Atari	Nintendo
Brøderbund	SEGA
Cyan	Sierra On-Line
Electronic Arts	Sony
Gametek	Spectrum HoloByte
Knowledge Adventure	Spelling Entertainment

HOW MUCH

Private company FYE: April 30	Annual Growth	1990	1991	1992	1993	1994	1995
Estimated sales ($ mil.)	(10.6%)	—	150.0	140.0	140.0	125.0	130.0
Employees	(24.3%)	—	—	—	250	220	230

MARVEL ENTERTAINMENT GROUP, INC.

OVERVIEW

Comics are serious business at Marvel, the world's #1 comic book publisher. The New York City-based company has parlayed its pantheon of superheroes into an empire of books, comics, trading cards, and toys. It also makes products based on other company's characters, including those from Walt Disney and *Star Trek*. Marvel's chairman, financier Ronald Perelman, owns 80% of the company.

Marvel was founded in 1932 as Western Publishing and it issued its first Marvel comics in 1939. Two years later Captain America was introduced to fight Nazis, and Stanley Martin Lieber (Stan Lee, the creator of Spider-Man, Incredible Hulk, and X-Men) came on board.

The company was incorporated as Marvel Entertainment Group in 1986. Perelman bought into Marvel in the late 1980s and the company went public in 1991. During the next few years the company expanded by acquiring trading card and confectionery maker Fleer, toy maker Toy Biz, rival Malibu Comics Entertainment, Welsh Publishing Group (now Marvel Family Publishing), Panini stickers and adhesives, and the distribution operations of Superhero Enterprises (now Heroes World). In 1994 the company signed a deal with the celebrity-backed restaurant chain Planet Hollywood to create a chain of comic-themed restaurants.

In 1995 Marvel bought trading card competitor SkyBox International. That year Toy Biz went public; Marvel retained 37%. Costs related to acquisitions, consolidation of operations, and provisions for a slump in sports card sales (the result of strikes in professional baseball and hockey) gave Marvel a loss for the year. With comic sales slumping, in 1996 Marvel cut its staff, eliminated 20 weak comic titles, and said it would de-emphasize comics and focus on licensing its characters.

WHO

Chairman: Ronald O. Perelman, age 53
Chairman and Publisher, Marvel Comics:
  Stan Lee, age 73
President and CEO: William C. Bevins Jr., age 49, $1,000,000 pay
EVP: Terry C. Stewart, age 50, $700,000 pay
EVP; CEO, Fleer/SkyBox International: Jeffrey L. Kaplan, age 34, $455,000 pay
EVP; President, Marvel Comics Group and Marvel Software: Gerard S. Calabrese, age 47, $440,288 pay
EVP, General Counsel, and Chief Administrative Officer: Paul E. Shapiro, age 54, $400,000 pay
EVP and CFO: Bobby G. Jenkins, age 34
EVP; CEO, Marvel Software: Scott C. Marden, age 41
Managing Director, Panini S.p.A.: Aldo H. Sallustro
VP Administration and Human Resources:
  D. Erik Pogue
Auditors: Ernst & Young LLP

WHERE

HQ: 387 Park Ave. South, New York, NY 10016
Phone: 212-696-0808
Fax: 212-576-8598

WHAT

Proprietary Characters	Iron Man
Captain America	Silver Surfer
Daredevil	Spider-Man
Dr. Strange	Thor
Fantastic Four (Human	X-Men (Bishop, Cable,
Torch, Invisible Woman,	Colossus, Cyclops,
Mr. Fantastic, Thing)	Gambit, Nightcrawler,
Ghost Rider	Phoenix, Storm,
Incredible Hulk	Wolverine)

KEY COMPETITORS

Acclaim	Lance	Topps
Entertainment	Mars	Upper Deck
Big	Mattel	Viacom
Entertainment	Megacards	Warner-Lambert
Harvey	RJR Nabisco	Wizards of the
Entertainment	Score Board	Coast
Hasbro	Time Warner	Wrigley

HOW MUCH

NYSE symbol: MRV FYE: December 31	Annual Growth	1990	1991	1992	1993	1994	1995
Sales ($ mil.)	59.2%	81.1	115.1	223.8	415.2	514.8	829.3
Net income ($ mil.)	—	5.4	16.1	32.6	56.0	61.8	(48.4)
Income as % of sales	—	6.7%	14.0%	14.6%	13.5%	12.0%	—
Earnings per share ($)	—	0.06	0.16	0.33	0.55	0.60	(0.48)
Stock price – high ($)	—	—	6.09	13.00	35.75	30.38	17.75
Stock price – low ($)	—	—	2.27	5.44	8.56	13.50	10.50
Stock price – close ($)	22.8%	—	5.72	12.56	27.38	14.25	13.00
P/E – high	—	—	38	39	65	51	—
P/E – low	—	—	14	16	16	23	—
Dividends per share ($)	—	—	0.00	0.00	0.00	0.00	0.00
Book value per share ($)	41.4%	—	0.51	0.88	1.51	2.41	2.04
Employees	47.9%	230	278	775	725	1,600	1,625

1995 YEAR-END
Debt ratio: 73.8%
Return on equity: —
Cash (mil.): $37.0
Current ratio: 1.57
Long-term debt (mil.): $581.3
No. of shares (mil.): 101.7
Dividends
  Yield: —
  Payout: —
Market value (mil.): $1,322.1

MECKLERMEDIA CORPORATION

OVERVIEW

Mecklermedia has given itself a subtitle: The Internet Media Company. Circulation for the Westport, Connecticut-based publisher's flagship magazine, *Internet World*, hit 250,000 in late 1995, and the company has added 2 new publications, *Web Developer* and *Web Week*. Mecklermedia's site on the World Wide Web, iWorld, is a top source of online Internet information, receiving more than a million hits a week. The firm also conducts trade shows in nearly a dozen countries for Internet and World Wide Web users and developers. Founder and CEO Alan Meckler owns about 31% of the company; VP James Mulholland III and his family own about 15%.

Meckler started the Meckler Corporation in 1971 to publish library science journals and reference books. As information technology evolved in the 1980s, the company moved into new areas, such as CD-ROMs. In the early 1990s the firm sold many of its library titles and began focusing on the Internet, CD-ROMs, and virtual reality. It launched *Internet World* and *VR World* in 1993. That year the Mulhollands purchased about 1/3 of Meckler Corporation. The company became Mecklermedia in December 1993 and went public in 1994. It launched MecklerWeb (now iWorld) in 1994 with plans to help companies develop online advertising. When advertisers failed to materialize, Meckler limited the service to putting Mecklermedia magazines online and selling advertising.

In 1995 Mecklermedia sold off more directories, publications (including *VR World*), and trade shows as it continued to narrow its focus to the Internet. That year it launched an Internet book publishing project and iWorld debuted motion video on the Web. In 1996 the company formed Mecklermedia Internet Consulting to provide Internet business services.

WHO

Chairman, President, and CEO: Alan M. Meckler, age 50, $191,800 pay
EVP and CFO: Christopher S. Cardell, age 36
SVP Internet Business Development: Bill H. Washburn, age 49, $100,100 pay
President and COO, Trade Show Group: Carl S. Pugh, age 41
Executive Director Development, iWorld: Tristan Louis
VP Administration and Secretary: James S. Mulholland III, age 35
Manager Marketing: Matthew Kurtz
Director Technology: Lance Rosen
Auditors: Andersen Worldwide

WHERE

HQ: 20 Ketchum St., Westport, CT 06880
Phone: 203-226-6967
Fax: 203-454-5840
Web site: http://www.iworld.com

	1995 Sales	
	$ mil.	% of total
US	14.1	97
Europe	0.4	3
Total	**14.5**	**100**

WHAT

	1995 Sales	
	$ mil.	% of total
Magazines & journals	8.1	56
Trade shows	5.3	37
Books & directories	0.6	4
Mailing list rentals	0.5	3
Total	**14.5**	**100**

KEY COMPETITORS

CMP Publications
Cowles Media
HyperMedia
International Data Group
McGraw-Hill
Sendai Media Group
SOFTBANK

United News & Media
Upside Publishing
VNU
Wired
Wolff New Media
Ziff-Davis

HOW MUCH

Nasdaq symbol: MECK FYE: September 30	Annual Growth	1990	1991	1992	1993	1994	1995
Sales ($ mil.)	74.7%	—	—	—	—	8.3	14.5
Net income ($ mil.)	(35.0%)	—	—	—	—	(2.0)	(1.3)
Income as % of sales	—	—	—	—	—	—	—
Earnings per share ($)	(46.9%)	—	—	—	—	(0.32)	(0.17)
Stock price – high ($)	—	—	—	—	—	6.50	24.38
Stock price – low ($)	—	—	—	—	—	2.13	2.63
Stock price – close ($)	365.1%	—	—	—	—	3.44	16.00
P/E – high	—	—	—	—	—	—	—
P/E – low	—	—	—	—	—	—	—
Dividends per share ($)	—	—	—	—	—	0.00	0.00
Book value per share ($)	386.4%	—	—	—	—	0.44	2.14
Employees	51.2%	—	—	—	35	49	80

1995 YEAR-END
Debt ratio: 0.1%
Return on equity: —
Cash (mil.): $19.4
Current ratio: 2.94
Long-term debt (mil.): $0.0
No. of shares (mil.): 8.4
Dividends
 Yield: —
 Payout: —
Advertising as % of sales: 33.9%
Market Value (mil.): $134.4

MEDIA GENERAL INC.

OVERVIEW

While its media may be general (newspapers, cable TV, broadcast TV, amagazine, and online services), Media General is showing a distinct interest in boosting its television holdings along with its print operations. The Richmond, Virginia-based company publishes the *Tampa Tribune* and 7 other dailies in Florida, North Carolina, and Virginia and owns a 40% stake in Denver Newspapers, Inc., the MediaNews subsidiary that publishes the *Denver Post*. Its plan to purchase Park Acquisitions would add 10 TV stations to the 3 it owns in Florida and South Carolina. Other Media General operations include 2 cable TV companies in Virginia, a business magazine, a commercial printing company, and a financial data services firm. It is also the largest US producer of 100% recycled newsprint. The Bryan family, including CEO Stewart Bryan, controls 15% of the voting stock but is entitled to elect 70% of the board of directors.

The firm was founded in 1879 by Joseph Bryan as the Dispatch Co., publisher of the *Richmond Dispatch*. Bryan purchased the *Richmond Times* in 1887 and later merged the papers as the *Richmond Times-Dispatch*. In 1940 it acquired the publisher of the *Richmond News Leader* (closed in 1992) to form Richmond Newspapers, Inc. The publisher, which had set up its first AM radio station in 1937, launched an FM station in 1949. In 1966 Richmond Newspapers went public, and it created Media General as a holding company in 1969. In the 1980s it bought TV stations in Florida and South Carolina. In 1995 the firm bought several dailies and other publications in central Virginia from Worrell Enterprises.

In 1996 it said it would buy Park Acquisitions, parent of Park Communications. The $710 million deal also includes 28 smaller daily and 82 weekly newspapers.

WHO

Chairman of the Executive Committee: D. Tennant Bryan, age 89
Chairman, President, and CEO: J. Stewart Bryan III, age 57, $813,127 pay
VC: James S. Evans, age 74
SVP and CFO: Marshall N. Morton, age 50, $450,608 pay
VP: H. Graham Woodlief Jr., age 51, $310,961 pay
VP: Robert W. Pendergast, age 56
General Counsel and Secretary: George L. Mahoney, age 43, $271,042 pay
Treasurer: Stephen R. Zacharias, age 46, $179,601 pay
Director Administrative Services: Edward C. Tosh
Auditors: Ernst & Young LLP

WHERE

HQ: 333 E. Grace St., Richmond, VA 23219
Phone: 804-649-6000
Fax: 804-649-6898
Web site: http://www.media-general.com

WHAT

| | 1995 Sales | |
	$ mil.	% of total
Newspapers	350.9	50
Newsprint	140.1	20
Cable television	134.2	19
Broadcast television	69.3	10
Other	13.3	1
Total	**707.8**	**100**

KEY COMPETITORS

Advance Publications	Fletcher Challenge	News Corp. Pope & Talbot
Boise Cascade	Gannett	Thomson Corp.
Bowater	Hearst	Time Warner
Capital Cities/ABC	Jacor Communications	Times Mirror Tribune
Cox Communications	Jefferson Smurfit Knight-Ridder	Viacom Washington Post
Cox Enterprises	Market Guide	Westinghouse
Dow Jones	McGraw-Hill	Weyerhaeuser
E.W. Scripps	Meredith	

HOW MUCH

AMEX symbol: MEGA FYE: December 31	Annual Growth	1990	1991	1992	1993	1994	1995
Sales ($ mil.)	2.9%	613.2	585.9	577.7	600.8	626.2	707.8
Net income ($ mil.)	15.8%	25.5	(62.1)	18.3	25.7	117.0	53.2
Income as % of sales	—	4.2%	—	3.2%	4.3%	18.7%	7.5%
Earnings per share ($)	15.5%	0.98	(2.39)	0.70	0.98	4.45	2.01
Stock price – high ($)	—	31.75	23.13	22.88	31.63	30.25	38.38
Stock price – low ($)	—	15.25	16.50	14.00	17.50	21.38	27.25
Stock price – close ($)	10.1%	18.75	17.13	17.38	29.38	28.38	30.38
P/E – high	—	32	—	33	32	7	19
P/E – low	—	16	—	20	18	5	14
Dividends per share ($)	1.8%	0.44	0.44	0.44	0.44	0.44	0.48
Book value per share ($)	6.1%	10.58	7.74	8.04	8.59	12.68	14.25
Employees	(0.5%)	7,700	7,500	7,300	7,300	7,300	7,500

1995 YEAR-END

Debt ratio: 46.4%
Return on equity: 15.0%
Cash (mil.): $3.4
Current ratio: 1.22
Long-term debt (mil.): $326.8
No. of shares (mil.): 26.5
Dividends
  Yield: 1.6%
  Payout: 23.9%
Market value (mil.): $803.8

MEDIANEWS GROUP, INC.

OVERVIEW

Ouch! Paper cuts can really hurt, especially when they're made by newspaper predator MediaNews. The Denver-based company, known for ruthlessly closing down unprofitable newspapers, publishes some 80 papers (including dailies, weeklies, and shoppers) in 12 states. Its flagship is the *Denver Post*, of which it owns 60% (Virginia-based Media General owns the rest); the paper is Colorado's largest, with a 50,000-copy lead in Sunday circulation over rival *Rocky Mountain News*. CEO Dean Singleton and the family of chairman Richard Scudder each own half of MediaNews.

In 1966, when 14-year-old Singleton started in the mailroom of a newspaper in Graham, Texas, he dreamed of owning his own paper. He worked as a reporter at nights while attending college. In 1975, following a failed attempt to revive the struggling *Fort Worth Press*, he was pelted with beer cans as he told the staff of its demise. He joined the newspaper division of Allbritton Communications in 1976 and became president in 1978.

In 1983 he teamed with 3rd-generation newspaper owner Scudder, co-inventor of the newsprint recycling process, and formed Gloucester County-Times Inc. They purchased their first paper, New Jersey's *Gloucester County-Times*, from Harte-Hanks Communications. The duo then bought 5 more dailies, in New Jersey and Ohio, and formed Garden State Newspapers in 1985. Next they started MediaNews Group as a corporate rubber band for all the company's papers, many of which had been purchased with backing from Media General. Through subsidiary Affiliated Newspapers Investments, the firm bought and sold newspapers, amassing an ever-increasing portfolio. MediaNews acquired the now-closed *Dallas Times Herald* in 1986 (sold in 1988). A year later it bought the *Denver Post* and the *Houston Post*. MediaNews bought out all of Media General's interest in its operations (except for the stake in the *Post*) in 1994.

In 1995 the company sold the *Houston Post* to Hearst, owner of the rival *Houston Chronicle*. Hearst stopped the presses at the *Post*. Also in 1995 the company moved its corporate headquarters from Houston to Denver.

WHO

Chairman: Richard B. Scudder
VC, President, and CEO: William Dean Singleton
EVP and CFO: Joseph J. Lodovic IV
VP Human Resources: Nick Lebra

WHERE

HQ: 1560 Broadway, Ste. 1450, Denver, CO 80202
Phone: 303-837-0886
Fax: 303-894-9327

MediaNews publishes newspapers in 12 states.

WHAT

Selected Newspapers
Bennington Banner (Vermont)
Berkshire Eagle (Pittsfield, MA)
Brattleboro Reformer (Vermont)
The Denver Post (60%)
Fairbanks Daily News-Miner (Alaska)
Manchester Journal (Vermont)
North Jersey Herald-News (Passaic, NJ)
The Oakland Tribune (California)

KEY COMPETITORS

Advance Publications
E.W. Scripps
Gannett
Hearst
Knight-Ridder
New York Times
Times Mirror
Tribune

HOW MUCH

Private company FYE: June 30	Annual Growth	1990	1991	1992	1993	1994	1995
Sales ($ mil.)	2.4%	—	450.0	525.0	575.0	525.0	495.0
Employees	(8.9%)	—	—	7,943	7,950	6,000	6,000

≡MediaNews Group

MEREDITH CORPORATION

OVERVIEW

With its headquarters in Des Moines, Iowa, Meredith may not fit in with the Manhattan-based media conglomerates, but the Midwest is just fine for a company that calls itself "America's leading home and family media company." Meredith's flagship publication is the venerable *Better Homes and Gardens*. Other Meredith publications include *Ladies' Home Journal*, *Country Home*, and *Successful Farming*. It also publishes a line of home and family service books, primarily under the Better Homes and Gardens imprint. Meredith owns several TV stations, including CBS affiliates in Kansas City and Phoenix, and a residential real estate marketing company. The Meredith family controls the company.

The business was founded in 1902 when Edwin Thomas Meredith launched the magazine *Successful Farming*, whose circulation reached nearly one million before 1920. In 1922 the company launched *Fruit, Garden and Home*, aimed at people who had moved from farms to cities; the name was changed to *Better Homes and Gardens* in 1924. The company went public in 1946, and in 1948 it entered the TV broadcasting business, acquiring WHEN-TV in Syracuse, New York (since sold). The real estate operation was launched in 1978, and the firm acquired *Ladies' Home Journal* in 1986.

Jack Rehm, who became CEO in 1989, has focused on building the Better Homes and Gardens brand and strengthening the broadcast operations. He has also worked to take advantage of one of the company's biggest assets — its mailing list, a database of more than 60 million names. Meredith formed a cable TV company in 1991, but in 1995 it announced plans to sell it. The company had earnings of $51 million and sales of $867 million in 1996.

WHO

Chairman of the Executive Committee: E. T. Meredith III, age 62
Chairman and CEO: Jack D. Rehm, age 62, $1,175,000 pay
President and COO: William T. Kerr, age 54, $930,000 pay
President, Publishing Group: Christopher M. Little, age 54, $668,000 pay
President, Broadcasting Group: Philip A. Jones, age 51, $595,000 pay
President, Real Estate Group: Allen L. Sabbag, age 51
VP Finance (CFO): Larry D. Hartsook, age 52, $358,000 pay
Corporate Manager Employee Services: Denise Rock
Auditors: KPMG Peat Marwick LLP

WHERE

HQ: 1716 Locust St., Des Moines, IA 50309-3023
Phone: 515-284-3000
Fax: 515-284-2700
Web site: http://www.home-and-family.com

WHAT

	1995 Sales	
	$ mil.	% of total
Publishing	683.3	77
Broadcasting	125.7	14
Cable	51.2	6
Real estate	24.4	3
Total	**884.6**	**100**

KEY COMPETITORS

Advance Publications	Lagardère	Virgin Group
Bertelsmann	Landmark Communications	Walt Disney
Cox Enterprises	Media General	Washington Post
Dow Jones	New York Times	Westinghouse/
Dun & Bradstreet	News Corp.	CBS
E.W. Scripps	Reader's Digest	
Gannett	Reed Elsevier	
General Electric	Thomson Corp.	
Hearst	Time Warner	
Heritage Media	Times Mirror	
Knight-Ridder	Tribune	

HOW MUCH

NYSE symbol: MDP FYE: June 30	Annual Growth	1990	1991	1992	1993	1994	1995
Sales ($ mil.)	3.8%	735.4	747.7	718.2	768.8	799.5	884.6
Net income ($ mil.)	—	(26.4)	83.1	1.0	18.6	27.2	39.8
Income as % of sales	—	—	11.1%	0.1%	2.4%	3.4%	4.5%
Earnings per share ($)	—	(0.72)	2.47	0.03	0.61	0.96	1.44
Stock price – high ($)	—	18.06	15.13	14.06	21.75	24.56	42.50
Stock price – low ($)	—	10.31	10.63	10.94	13.13	19.38	22.63
Stock price – close ($)	28.8%	11.81	13.56	13.50	20.00	23.31	41.88
P/E – high	—	—	6	—	36	26	30
P/E – low	—	—	4	—	22	20	16
Dividends per share ($)	3.5%	0.32	0.32	0.32	0.32	0.34	0.38
Book value per share ($)	0.4%	8.59	10.18	9.57	9.58	9.39	8.77
Employees	(8.3%)	3,707	2,270	2,025	2,335	2,194	2,400

1995 YEAR-END
Debt ratio: 42.9%
Return on equity: 16.0%
Cash (mil.): $17.2
Current ratio: 0.91
Long-term debt (mil.): $166.1
No. of shares (mil.): 27.5
Dividends
  Yield: 0.9%
  Payout: 26.4%
Market value (mil.): $1,150.9

MERRILL CORPORATION

OVERVIEW

Based in St. Paul, Minnesota, Merrill is one of the top financial printers in the world. It offers round-the-clock document reproduction, typesetting, printing, distribution, and marketing communication services to the legal, financial, and corporate markets. In line with the electronics revolution, the company has diversified into related fields, including information management and document imaging and storage. Merrill operates about 20 full-service offices in major financial centers across North America, 5 regional printing plants, and printing and distribution operations in St. Cloud, Minnesota, and Monroe, Washington.

Kenneth Merrill (who owns over 6% of the company) founded K. F. Merrill with his wife Lorraine in 1968 and grew the company into a major regional printer. He turned over the reins in 1984 to CEO John Castro (now holder of a 14% stake), who had worked his way up from production manager. Castro developed a "hub-and-spoke" system that cut costs and centralized printing jobs transmitted from sales offices nationwide. This helped Merrill survive after the 1987 stock crash. In 1992 the company formed a partnership with London-based Burrups, Europe's #1 financial printer.

Merrill was involved with developing the software for the SEC's pilot program for EDGAR (Electronic Data Gathering Analysis and Retrieval service), which allows companies to electronically file financial reports. This helped the company gain about 1/4 of the market among clients seeking help with electronic filings (which became mandatory in 1996).

Merrill acquired managed communications concern FMR Resource Management in 1996, as well as certain assets of Corporate Printing Co., the largest financial printer in the Northeast.

WHO

Chairman: Paul G. Miller, age 73
President and CEO: John W. Castro, age 47, $550,000 pay
EVP Operations: Rick R. Atterbury, age 42, $375,000 pay
VP: James G. Sippl, $144,000 pay
VP, General Counsel, and Secretary: Steven J. Machov, age 45, $134,167 pay
VP Client Services Development: Roxanne E. Iserman, $100,000 pay
VP Finance, CFO, and Treasurer: Kay A. Barber, age 45
VP Human Resources: Kathleen A. Larkin, age 36
Auditors: Coopers & Lybrand L.L.P.

WHERE

HQ: One Merrill Circle, St. Paul, MN 55108-5267
Phone: 612-646-4501
Fax: 612-649-1348
Web site: http://www.merrillcorp.com

WHAT

	1996 Sales % of total
Financial	36
Corporate	30
Commercial & other	21
Document management services	13
Total	**100**

Selected Products	
Annual reports	Newsletters
Booklets	Prospectuses
Catalogs	Proxy materials
Directories	SEC registration
Magazines	statements
Merrill Internet Services	Tabloids

KEY COMPETITORS

American Banknote	Consolidated Graphics	Kinko's
Arandell	Courier	Moore Corp.
Bowne	Dimark	Pitney Bowes
Cadmus Communications	Graphic Industries	Quad/Graphics
		R. R. Donnelley
		Xerox

HOW MUCH

Nasdaq symbol: MRLL FYE: January 31	Annual Growth	1991	1992	1993	1994	1995	1996
Sales ($ mil.)	19.4%	101.0	125.3	147.7	181.6	236.9	245.3
Net income ($ mil.)	31.7%	2.7	6.5	8.6	13.2	12.0	10.7
Income as % of sales	—	2.7%	5.2%	5.8%	7.3%	5.1%	4.4%
Earnings per share ($)	29.4%	0.37	0.86	1.12	1.65	1.50	1.34
Stock price – high ($)[1]	—	5.50	13.13	15.75	28.00	32.50	21.25
Stock price – low ($)[1]	—	2.75	3.50	8.25	13.50	13.75	14.00
Stock price – close ($)[1]	31.6%	4.06	13.00	14.50	27.00	17.00	16.00
P/E – high	—	15	15	14	17	22	16
P/E – low	—	7	4	7	8	9	10
Dividends per share ($)	—	0.00	0.00	0.00	0.10	0.12	0.12
Book value per share ($)	25.3%	3.20	4.10	5.36	7.15	8.69	9.89
Employees	23.5%	784	831	1,041	1,601	1,739	2,253

[1]Stock prices are for the prior calendar year.

1996 YEAR-END
Debt ratio: 15.1%
Return on equity: 14.9%
Cash (mil.): $12.1
Current ratio: 1.98
Long-term debt (mil.): $7.0
No. of shares (mil.): 7.9
Dividends
  Yield: 0.8%
  Payout: 9.0%
Market value (mil.): $126.0

METROMEDIA INTERNATIONAL

OVERVIEW

What do you get when you merge 4 money-losing companies? Profits! At least that's what the management of Metromedia International Group (MIG) says. Atlanta-based MIG is an amalgamation of billionaire John Kluge's money-losing interests in Orion Pictures, MCEG Sterling Inc., Metromedia International Telecommunications, and the Actava Group, owner of Snapper, Inc. (lawn care equipment).

The company hopes that selling Snapper and 38% of sports equipment maker Roadmaster will allow bankrupt Orion to resume making movies and buying distribution rights to those made by others. Entities controlled by Kluge and his partner, Stuart Subotnick, own about 33% of the company.

Actava was founded as Fuqua Industries in 1965 when John Fuqua bought Natco, a brick company. Fuqua Industries bought and sold many companies in the next decades, but its mainstays were wholesale photofinishing, Snapper, and sports gear makers. After Fuqua retired in 1989, the company (renamed Actava in 1993) declined and sold most of its operations. John Phillips, a turnaround specialist who had previously worked with Kluge, became president in 1994.

Kluge had built up Metromedia Company as a collection of television stations, which he sold to Rupert Murdoch in 1984. What was left of Metromedia then became a restaurant and long-distance phone service company. He also bought up the cellular licenses that would form the core of Metromedia International Telecommunications, Inc. He later invested in Orion Pictures which had gone bankrupt in 1991 and film distributor MCEG Sterling.

Stockholders approved the merger in November 1995. In 1996 the company acquired film distributor Samuel Goldwyn Co.

WHO

Chairman: John W. Kluge, age 81
VC: Stuart Subotnick, age 54
President and CEO: John D. Phillips, age 53, $1,374,984 pay
SVP, CFO, and Treasurer: Silvia Kessel, age 45
SVP, General Counsel, and Secretary: Arnold L. Wadler, age 52
SVP: W. Tod Chmar, age 42, $470,000 pay
SVP: Robert A. Maresca, age 61
Auditors: KPMG Peat Marwick LLP

WHERE

HQ: Metromedia International Group, Inc., 945 E. Paces Ferry Rd., Ste. 2210, Atlanta, GA 30326
Phone: 404-261-6190
Fax: 404-524-4713

Metromedia International Group's joint ventures hold wireless communications licenses in Belarus, Estonia, the Republic of Georgia, Hungary, Kazakhstan, Latvia, Lithuania, Moldova, Romania, Russia, and Uzbekistan.

WHAT

	1995 Sales	
	$ mil.	% of total
Television	85.2	61
Video	43.9	32
Theatrical	4.7	3
Wireless communications	5.2	4
Other	(0.1)	—
Total	**138.9**	**100**

Subsidiaries
Metromedia International Telecommunications, Inc. (wireless communications systems)
Orion Pictures Corp. (movie production and distribution)

KEY COMPETITORS

BSkyB	MGM	TCI
COMSAT	Rogers	U S WEST Media
Deutsche	Communications	Viacom
Telekom	Sprint	Walt Disney
France Telecom	STET	
MCA	Time Warner	

HOW MUCH

AMEX symbol: MMG FYE: December 31	Annual Growth	1990	1991	1992	1993	1994	1995
Sales ($ mil.)	(32.2%)	972.3	924.6	1,148.7	1,241.1	551.8	138.9
Net income ($ mil.)	—	(1.2)	(50.8)	10.6	(43.2)	(64.2)	(380.6)
Income as % of sales	—	—	—	0.9%	—	—	—
Earnings per share ($)	—	(0.06)	(3.08)	0.64	(2.52)	(3.53)	(15.51)
Stock price – high ($)	—	25.50	14.75	17.13	14.50	13.75	19.50
Stock price – low ($)	—	10.00	9.00	9.38	6.63	5.75	8.63
Stock price – close ($)	5.2%	10.88	13.88	12.38	7.50	9.13	14.00
P/E – high	—	—	—	27	—	—	—
P/E – low	—	—	—	15	—	—	—
Dividends per share ($)	(100.0%)	0.35	0.36	0.36	0.36	0.09	0.00
Book value per share ($)	(23.0%)	17.65	14.23	14.49	11.11	7.22	4.77
Employees	—	—	—	—	—	—	289

1995 YEAR-END
Debt ratio: 78.5%
Return on equity: —
Cash (mil.): $32.3
Current ratio: 0.72
Long-term debt (mil.): $264.0
No. of shares (mil.): 42.6
Dividends
  Yield: —
  Payout: —
Market value (mil.): $596.4

MODEM MEDIA

OVERVIEW

Modem Media's "hot links" have nothing to do with sausage. The Westport, Connecticut-based cyberagency places its clients' advertising on World Wide Web sites with links that shoot the user directly to the advertiser's home page. Modem Media claims that it was the first interactive advertising agency and the largest one dedicated to interactive marketing. The company has executed more than 300 advertising campaigns, establishing a reputation for combining technical skill and marketing know-how. It built the home pages for MasterCard and J. C. Penney, and created the acclaimed Web site for Zima, the clear malt drink from brewer Adolph Coors.

The firm was started in 1987 by G. M. O'Connell and Doug Ahlers, who had worked together at electronics retailer CUC International. At CUC, O'Connell helped create Comp-u-mall, the first online shopping mall. Bob Allen, who had worked for IBM marketing Prodigy, IBM's and Sears's online service, joined the company in 1989. Modem Media spent its first years developing software and designing interactive services using a variety of media, including CD-ROMs, faxes, and on-line sites. Early clients included CBS, Federal Express, General Electric, PepsiCo, Southwestern Bell, and computer magazine publisher Ziff-Davis. Allen became a partner in 1993. The next year, Modem Media helped create Woodstock Online, the online counterpart of the Woodstock '94 concert.

Analysts predict that the rapid growth of on-line service providers is the start of a lucrative trend — an estimated 3/4 of major national brands still lack a Web presence. Corporations and advertising agencies are turning to specialists such as Modem Media. By the turn of the century online advertising services are expected to be a multibillion-dollar industry.

In 1995 the company added Delta Airlines to its client roster. It was also named AT&T's interactive agency (beating out several heavyweights, including Young & Rubicam and McCann-Erickson). That year Modem Media created a model to help advertisers make on line media-buying decisions. In 1996 True North Communications entered talks to acquire the company.

WHO

Founding Partner: Gerald M. O'Connell, age 34
Founding Partner: Doug Ahlers, age 35
Partner: Robert Allen, age 28
CFO: Peter Massey
Chief Technology Officer: John Houston
Director Human Resources: Marilyn Fidler

WHERE

HQ: 228 Saugatuck Ave., Westport, CT 06880
Phone: 203-341-5200
Fax: 203-341-5260
Web site: http://www.modemmedia.com

WHAT

Selected Interactive Media Platforms
CD-ROM/multimedia
Diskette
Interactive fax
Interactive TV
Internet
Online
Voice response

Selected Clients
Adolph Coors
AT&T
Delta Air Lines
J. C. Penney
MasterCard International

KEY COMPETITORS

Bozzell
Bronner Slosberg
CKS
Cordiant
Dentsu
Grey Advertising
Interpublic Group
International Post
J. Walter Thompson
Leap Group
Leo Burnett
Lintas
Martin Agency
McCann-Erikson
Ogilvy & Mather
Omnicom Group
Organic Online
R/GA Interactive
Site Specific
True North
Young & Rubicam
Ziff-Davis

HOW MUCH

Private company FYE: December 31	Annual Growth	1990	1991	1992	1993	1994	1995
Sales ($ mil.)	69.9%	—	0.9	1.4	1.9	3.5	7.5
Employees	178.9%	—	—	—	9	33	70

ModemMedia

MORNINGSTAR, INC.

OVERVIEW

Mutual funds have gone supernova and Morningstar is hoping for a bright future. The biweekly *Morningstar Mutual Funds* is the top mutual fund report. The company also publishes information on closed-end funds, variable annuities/life, and equities. Morningstar built its popularity by providing one-page, statistic- and analysis-rich profiles of its subjects. Information is available in print, on CD-ROM, and online.

Morningstar (the name was inspired by the last line in Thoreau's *Walden*: "The sun is but a morning star.") was founded in 1984 by Joseph Mansueto. After a stint as an analyst at money management firm Harris Associates, he used his savings to launch the quarterly *Mutual Fund Sourcebook*. The early 1980s boom in mutual funds spurred interest in Morningstar's product; 2 years later the company added the biweekly mutual fund report. The company gained recognition in 1985 when *Business Week* used it as a resource for an issue on mutual funds. Mansueto owns the company.

Morningstar's product line has grown to 10 print and 6 CD-ROM titles. In 1991 the company added a biweekly analysis of Japanese stocks (discontinued in 1994, Morningstar's only failure to date). In 1992 the company introduced a CD-ROM database covering more than 2,200 mutual funds along with a program that allows users to compare, evaluate, and track them. The following year Canadian funds were added to Morningstar reports, and in 1994 the company launched a publication on American Depository Receipts (ADRs).

Morningstar has also been creating an investors' database of US companies. In 1994 it moved closer to achieving this goal with the acquisition of MarketBase, which compiles data on the stocks of 6,000 US firms.

By the end of 1994, *Morningstar Mutual Funds* had 35,000 subscribers at $395 a year. The monthly newsletter *5-Star Investor* had 78,000 subscribers. In an ongoing feud, rival Value Line has accused Morningstar of copying its format, while Morningstar has accused Value Line of plagiarizing its analyses.

In addition, Value Line's introduction of mutual fund rating products has slowed Morningstar's growth.

WHO

CEO: Joseph Mansueto
President: Donald Phillips
CFO: Patrick Geddes
COO: Liz Michaels
Publisher, Managed Products: John Rekenthaler
Publisher, Equity Products: Cathy Gillis
Managing Editor, ADRs: Rika Yoshida
Editor, ADRs: Haywood Kelly
Editor, Closed-End Funds: Gregg Wolper
Editor, Annuities & Life: Jennifer Strickland
Auditors: Deloitte & Touche LLP

WHERE

HQ: 225 W. Wacker Dr., Chicago, IL 60606-1224
Phone: 312-696-6000
Fax: 312-696-6001
Web site:
http://networth.galt.com/www/home/mutual/morning

WHAT

Selected Products

Mutual Funds
5-Star Investor (monthly newsletter covering 500 funds)
Morningstar Mutual Fund 500 (annual book covering 500 funds)
Morningstar Mutual Funds (biweekly report covering 1,500 funds)
Morningstar No-Load Funds (monthly report covering 650 funds)
Morningstar OnDemand (as-needed fax or mail report covering 1,500 funds)
Mutual Funds OnDisc (monthly, quarterly, or annual CD-ROM covering 5,700 funds)
Mutual Fund Performance Report (monthly, quarterly, or annual book covering 5,700 funds and 1,500 money market funds)

Other
The Dow Jones Guide to the World Stock Market (book; published in association with Dow Jones & Co.)
Morningstar ADRs (biweekly report covering 700 stocks)
Morningstar Closed-End Funds
Morningstar Variable Annuities/Life (biweekly report covering 790 subaccounts and 80 policies)
U.S. Equities OnFloppy (weekly, monthly, quarterly, or annual disk covering 6,000 stocks)
Variable Annuity/Life Performance Report (monthly, quarterly, or annual report covering 2,500 subaccounts)

KEY COMPETITORS

Bloomberg
CDA/Weisenberger
Dun & Bradstreet
Investors
Business Daily
Lipper Analytical
Media General
McGraw-Hill
Micropal
Pearson
Primark
Value Line

HOW MUCH

Private company FYE: December 31	Annual Growth	1990	1991	1992	1993	1994	1995
Sales ($ mil.)	68.9%	2.4	4.5	11.2	21.2	32.0	33.0[1]
Employees	58.5%	35	70	190	280	380	350

[1]Estimated

MTS INC.

OVERVIEW

Whether you find yourself in Thailand, Argentina, Israel, or England, thanks to MTS you'll probably be able to pick up the new Springsteen CD the same day it's released. Through its Tower stores, the West Sacramento-California-based company is the 2nd largest music retailer in the US (after Musicland). MTS operates more than 160 Tower stores worldwide; its strongest international presence is in Japan, with 22 stores. Its outlets, which include Tower Books and Tower Video, stock thousands of titles, going beyond best-sellers to address a huge variety of tastes. In recent years the chain has faced increasing competition from "big-block" retailers such as Wal-Mart and Best Buy, which sell more limited selections of CDs at lower prices.

Russ Solomon took over the record inventory from his father's drug store in 1952, but after an unsuccessful attempt at wholesaling, he went broke. With a loan from his dad, he started a new retail record business, MTS (named for his son's initials), in 1960. A 2nd record shop was opened within a month, and over the next 7 years sales grew steadily. By the late 1960s Solomon saw the music industry expanding in all directions. Catering to such diverse tastes required volume, so in 1968 he opened the first Tower Records store, in San Francisco. It was an immediate hit, becoming a hangout for disenfranchised youth with disposable income. A 2nd Tower store opened in 1970 in Los Angeles.

Over the next 10 years, 26 more Tower Records stores were opened, and in 1983 the company debuted *Pulse!* magazine, an in-store freebie with record reviews and artist interviews. But the company's real expansion began in 1989, and by 1994 Tower Records had increased its presence to 127 outlets. That year it opened its first multimedia store, offering books, videos, records, and CD-ROMs.

In 1995 the company opened the largest record shop in the world (an 8-floor megastore in Tokyo) and the WOW! superstore (a joint venture with electronics retailer Good Guys) in Las Vegas. The company also opened the first Tower Records store in Canada and started selling CDs online via its Addicted to Noise electronic magazine.

WHO

President and CEO: Russell M. Solomon
VP Finance and CFO: Dee Searson
General Counsel: Michael T. Solomon, age 47
Manager Human Resources: Shauna Pompei

WHERE

HQ: 2500 Del Monte St., Bldg. C, West Sacramento, CA 95691
Phone: 916-373-2500
Fax: 916-373-2535
Web site: http://www.towerrecords.com

MTS operates more than 160 Tower stores worldwide.

WHAT

Selected Operations
Tower Books
Tower Records
Tower Video
WOW! superstore (jointly operated with Good Guys)

Selected Publications
Addicted to Noise (electronic magazine)
Pulse!

KEY COMPETITORS

Barnes & Noble
Best Buy
Blockbuster
Books-A-Million
Borders
Camelot Music
Circuit City
Crown Books
Grow Biz
Hastings Books
Maruzen
Musicland
National Record Mart
THORN EMI
Trans World Entertainment
Virgin Group
W H Smith
Wherehouse Entertainment
The Wiz

HOW MUCH

Private company FYE: July 31	Annual Growth	1990	1991	1992	1993	1994	1995
Sales ($ mil.)	15.8%	—	528.0	626.0	650.0	830.0	950.0
Employees	10.8%	—	5,040	5,800	5,269	6,700	7,600

TOWER RECORDS®

NEW WORLD COMMUNICATIONS

OVERVIEW

Producing, distributing, and broadcasting TV shows is this New World's order. The Atlanta-based company operates 12 television stations (10 of them affiliated with the Fox network) and develops and syndicates TV movies and other programming. New World also has a minority interest in infomercial producer Guthy-Renker Corporation. Multibillionaire chairman Ronald Perelman owns 37% of the company. Rupert Murdoch's News Corp. owns 20% of New World and in 1996 agreed to acquire the remaining 80%.

New World traces its history back to the 1982 founding of film producer and home video distributor Epic Productions. The next year the firm purchased the New World Entertainment (NW Entertainment) name and various distribution assets from New World Pictures. Perelman bought NW Entertainment in 1989. During the early 1990s the company produced movies for international markets and bought 6 TV stations from a company controlled by broadcasters Storer Communications and Gillett. It also purchased syndication and programming businesses, as well as a TV station in Tampa and adopted the name New World Communications Group.

In 1994 New World went public, acquired 4 more stations (from CitiCasters), and dropped 3. That year Brandon Tartikoff, the Midas of NBC in the 1980s, became the NW Entertainment division's chairman. Also in 1994 the company changed all but 2 of its stations' affiliations from CBS to Fox and sold a $500 million stake to News Corp.

The firm in 1995 bought 4 more TV stations and action-show producer Cannell Entertainment. In 1996 New World agreed to sell its 2 NBC affiliates to the network for $425 million.

WHO

Chairman: Ronald O. Perelman, age 53
CEO: William C. Bevins, age 49, $1,000,000 pay
President and COO: Arthur H. Bilger, age 43, $1,500,000 pay
EVP and Chief Administrative Officer: Terry C. Bridges, age 52
EVP, General Counsel, and Secretary: Michael H. Diamond, age 53
EVP and CFO: Joseph P. Page, age 42
Chairman, NW Entertainment: Brandon R. Tartikoff, age 47, $1,000,000 pay
CEO, NW Genesis: Wayne A. Lepoff, age 44
CEO, NW Broadcast Group: Farrell Reynolds, age 54
Director Personnel: Jim Gorman
Auditors: Ernst & Young LLP

WHERE

HQ: New World Communications Group Incorporated, 3200 Windy Hill Rd., Ste. 1100-West, Atlanta, GA 30339
Phone: 770-955-0045
Fax: 770-563-9600

WHAT

	1995 Sales	
	$ mil.	% of total
Broadcasting	376.8	62
TV production & distribution	228.2	38
Total	**605.0**	**100**

Selected Television Stations

KNSD-TV, San Diego	KTVI-TV, St. Louis
KSAZ-TV, Phoenix	WAGA-TV, Atlanta

KEY COMPETITORS

A. H. Belo	Kushner-Locke
All American Communications	NBC
Carsey-Werner	Sony
Chris-Craft	Spelling Entertainment
Gannett	Time Warner
International Family Entertainment	Tribune
Jacor Communications	Turner Broadcasting
King World	Viacom
	Walt Disney
	Westinghouse/CBS

HOW MUCH

Nasdaq symbol: NWCG FYE: December 31	Annual Growth	1990	1991	1992	1993	1994	1995
Sales ($ mil.)	20.9%	234.0	208.8	221.5	296.1	396.9	605.0
Net income ($ mil.)	—	22.9	(98.9)	(76.8)	(257.2)	(47.8)	(28.9)
Income as % of sales	9.8%	—	—	—	—	—	—
Earnings per share ($)	(38.3%)	—	—	—	—	(0.81)	(0.50)
Stock price – high ($)	—	—	—	—	—	16.00	25.00
Stock price – low ($)	—	—	—	—	—	8.38	11.63
Stock price – close ($)	48.9%	—	—	—	—	11.75	17.50
P/E – high	—	—	—	—	—	—	—
P/E – low	—	—	—	—	—	—	—
Dividends per share ($)	—	—	—	—	—	0.00	0.00
Book value per share ($)	(8.4%)	—	—	—	—	5.69	5.21
Employees	17.4%	—	—	—	—	2,300	2,700

1995 YEAR-END
Debt ratio: 52.4%
Return on equity: —
Cash (mil.): $75.0
Current ratio: 1.66
Long-term debt (mil.): $976.0
No. of shares (mil.): 68.6
Dividends
  Yield: —
  Payout: —
Market value (mil.): $1,201.0

PAGES, INC.

OVERVIEW

PAGES hopes to close the book on its recent losses. The St. Petersburg, Florida-based company publishes children's books, cassette tapes, and software, then sells them through school book fairs (it is the #2 operator of book fairs, after Scholastic). The Clyde A. Short subsidiary sells business incentive and recognition awards. Losses have led PAGES to cut its workforce, close some operations, and even look for a buyer. Chairman Robert Davis and his son Charles, company EVP, together own 34% of PAGES. Former president Richard Stimmel owns 12%.

The company was founded in 1980 as a restaurant operator called Big Bite and taken public in 1981. In 1985 the restaurants closed and the company was acquired by Davis (founder of Arthur Treacher's Fish & Chips) and Stimmel. After dabbling in dollhouse miniatures, it acquired the Clyde A. Short Co. in 1990. Its 1992 $8.5 million acquisition of the money-losing School Book Fairs more than tripled the company's revenues within 2 years and led to its new name. PAGES has grown through other acquisitions that include Parents Magazine's Read Aloud Book Club (1993) and Cornerstone Books, the Junior Library Guild, and the National Library Service from Bantam Doubleday Dell Publishing Group (1994).

Rising product distribution costs and changes in its product mix eroded PAGES's profits in 1995 and led to its 2nd straight year of losses. To reduce its overhead, PAGES cut its workforce, closed its Canadian distribution operations, and discontinued Storybook Express, which sold books to preschoolers.

In 1996 Stimmel retired due to illness. That year PAGES continued to pare its operations, selling its UK-based book fair operations to rival Scholastic.

WHO

Chairman and President: S. Robert Davis, age 57, $183,180 pay
EVP and Secretary: Charles R. Davis, age 34, $147,896 pay
VP: Randall J. Asmo, age 30
Director Human Resources: Steve Canan
Auditors: Deloitte & Touche LLP

WHERE

HQ: 801 94th Ave. North, St. Petersburg, FL 33702
Phone: 813-578-3300
Fax: 813-578-3101

	1995 Sales	
	$ mil.	% of total
US	58.2	80
International	14.6	20
Total	**72.8**	**100**

WHAT

	1995 Sales	
	$ mil.	% of total
Children's literature	50.1	69
Incentive/recognition awards	22.7	31
Total	**72.8**	**100**

PAGES Imprints
Hamburger Press
Riverbank Press
Willowisp Press
Worthington Press

KEY COMPETITORS

Addison-Wesley
Advance
   Publications
Bertelsmann
Brøderbund
Celex
Dorling
   Kindersley
Edmark
Educational
   Development
Golden Books
Good Times
   Entertainment
Harcourt General
Hearst
Houghton Mifflin
Jostens
Kane/Miller
Lagardère
McGraw-Hill
Norwood
Promotional
   Products
Pearson
Scholastic
Time Warner
Troll
Walt Disney

HOW MUCH

Nasdaq symbol: PAGZ FYE: December 31	Annual Growth	1990	1991	1992	1993	1994	1995
Sales ($ mil.)	24.5%	24.3	22.2	44.5	76.6	79.1	72.8
Net income ($ mil.)	—	0.6	0.2	1.0	1.0	(0.5)	(9.2)
Income as % of sales	—	2.5%	0.9%	2.2%	1.3%	—	—
Earnings per share ($)	—	0.14	0.04	0.19	0.18	(0.12)	(1.87)
Stock price – high ($)	—	5.45	4.60	6.60	13.75	12.25	8.00
Stock price – low ($)	—	1.13	1.90	2.80	5.80	4.00	1.63
Stock price – close ($)	(3.0%)	1.90	2.80	6.20	10.75	4.50	1.63
P/E – high	—	39	115	35	76	—	—
P/E – low	—	8	48	15	32	—	—
Dividends per share ($)	—	0.00	0.00	0.00	0.00	0.00	0.00
Book value per share ($)	(1.0%)	2.18	2.50	2.52	3.63	4.09	2.07
Employees	49.8%	110	117	485	590	879	831

1995 YEAR-END
Debt ratio: 68.4%
Return on equity: —
Cash (mil.): $1.0
Current ratio: 1.51
Long-term debt (mil.): $17.0
No. of shares (mil.): 5.2
Dividends
   Yield: —
   Payout: —
Market value (mil.): $8.0

PIXAR

OVERVIEW

Plenty of movie studios shoot on location, but few have traveled to Pixar's location — cyberspace. The Richmond, California-based company's *Toy Story* was the world's first computer-animated feature film. Pixar created the film using its proprietary software systems Marionette (modeling, animating, and lighting), Ringmaster (production management), and RenderMan (image rendering). It also makes television commercials and CD-ROMs and sells its RenderMan software to film studios, visual effects companies, and others. CEO Steven Jobs (a cofounder of Apple Computer) owns 80% of the company.

Pixar began in the early 1980s as part of Lucasfilm, where filmmaker George Lucas assembled a team to develop computer graphics systems. In 1986, 2 years after he left Apple, Jobs acquired the computer division of Lucasfilm for $10 million. The new company was named Pixar after its first product, the Pixar Image Computer, a 3-D graphics system. Pixar and Disney signed a deal in 1986 to jointly develop the Computer Animated Production System (CAPS), which uses computers to digitally color hand-drawn animation. In 1988 animator John Lasseter won an Oscar for best short film (animated) for the computer-animated *Tin Toy*. Pixar began producing TV commercials the next year to gain more production experience and to better establish its name. In 1991 it began work on *Toy Story*, with Lasseter directing. Disney and Pixar released *Toy Story* in 1995, and the movie grossed more than $300 million. Jobs took the company public just weeks after the film release in one of the hottest offerings of the year.

A CD-ROM based on *Toy Story* (also developed with Disney) sold more than 100,000 copies within weeks of its 1996 release.

WHO

Chairman and CEO: Steven P. Jobs, age 40
EVP and Chief Technical Officer: Edwin E. Catmull, age 50, $182,646 pay
EVP, CFO, and Secretary: Lawrence B. Levy, age 36
VP Creative Development: John Lasseter, age 38, $235,463 pay
VP Feature Film Production: Ralph J. Guggenheim, age 44, $160,411 pay
VP Interactive Products: Pamela J. Kerwin, age 46
Technical Director, Feature Films: William T. Reeves, age 44, $172,430 pay
Director Human Resources: Lisa Ellis
Auditors: KPMG Peat Marwick LLP

WHERE

HQ: 1001 W. Cutting Blvd., Richmond, CA 94804
Phone: 510-236-4000
Fax: 510-236-0388
Web site: http://www.pixar.com

WHAT

Software Systems	Fresca
Marionette (modeling, animating, and lighting)	GummiSavers
	Levi's Jeans
RenderMan (rendering to create photo-realistic image synthesis)	Listerine
	Selected Films
Ringmaster (production management)	*Luxo Jr.*
	Tin Toy
Selected Commercials	*Toy Story*
Coca-Cola	

KEY COMPETITORS

DreamWorks SKG	Netter Digital
Four Media	News Corp.
IBM	Samuel Goldwyn
Jim Henson Productions	Savoy Pictures
Laser Pacific Media	Silicon Graphics
LucasFilm	Sony
MCA	Time Warner
MGM	Viacom
Microsoft	Walt Disney

HOW MUCH

Nasdaq symbol: PIXR FYE: December 31	Annual Growth	1990	1991	1992	1993	1994	1995
Sales ($ mil.)	28.9%	3.4	7.3	4.2	6.8	5.6	12.1
Net income ($ mil.)	—	(9.7)	(0.9)	(3.4)	(1.2)	(2.4)	1.6
Income as % of sales	—	—	—	—	—	—	13.2%
Earnings per share ($)	—	—	—	—	—	(0.06)	0.04
Stock price – high ($)	—	—	—	—	—	—	49.50
Stock price – low ($)	—	—	—	—	—	—	22.00
Stock price – close ($)	—	—	—	—	—	—	28.88
P/E – high	—	—	—	—	—	—	—
P/E – low	—	—	—	—	—	—	—
Dividends per share ($)	—	—	—	—	—	0.00	0.00
Book value per share ($)	—	—	—	—	—	(0.05)	3.73
Employees	34.5%	—	51	64	75	86	167

1995 YEAR-END

Debt ratio: 1.7%
Return on equity: 2.3%
Cash (mil.): $97.0
Current ratio: 14.73
Long-term debt (mil.): $0.0
No. of shares (mil.): 38.3
Dividends
  Yield: —
  Payout: —
Market value (mil.): $1,106.0
R&D as % of sales: 33.6%

PLAYBOY ENTERPRISES, INC.

OVERVIEW

Built on its well-known magazine (which is known for its well-built centerfolds), Playboy Enterprises is a global publishing, entertainment, and licensing company with related operations in international and domestic cable TV networks, movies, TV programming, videos, CD-ROMS, direct marketing, and name-brand retail products (apparel, spirits, and condoms, among others). Though it is the world's leading men's magazine, with 3 million readers, *Playboy* is still shunned by some advertisers. US circulation is half its 1972 peak, and lately profits have been hurt by higher paper and postage costs. Hugh Hefner owns 70% of company voting stock.

Playboy was started in 1953 by Hefner, a former copywriter at *Esquire*, who mortgaged some belongings, borrowed $6,000 from friends, and threw in $600 of his own. The first issue, which was put together on Hefner's kitchen table, sold 51,000 copies, earning enough to publish a 2nd issue. The Playboy Club, which opened in 1960, was one of the most successful nightclub chains in history during its 20-year reign (the last club closed in 1986). In 1971 the company went public.

In 1982, when Hefner's daughter Christie was named Playboy president, the company began to diversify and greatly expand overseas. That year Playboy launched a national pay cable TV service and home video business. The company agreed to form its first overseas TV network in 1995 with Flextech. Also that year a consortium that includes Playboy was awarded a casino license on the Greek isle of Rhodes. In 1996 Playboy announced plans to add a subscriber-based service to its hugely successful Web site. Sales reached almost $277 million that year, and earnings increased to $4 million.

WHO

Founder, Chairman Emeritus, and Editor in Chief: Hugh M. Hefner, age 69, $498,493 pay
Chairman, President, and CEO: Christie Hefner, age 42, $714,332 pay
EVP and General Counsel: Howard Shapiro, age 48
EVP Publishing Group and Publisher, *Playboy:* Richard Kinsler
VP Human Resources: Denise M. Bindelglass
Auditors: Coopers & Lybrand L.L.P.

WHERE

HQ: 680 N. Lake Shore Dr., Chicago, IL 60611
Phone: 312-751-8000
Fax: 312-751-2818
Web site: http://www.playboy.com

WHAT

	1995 Sales		1995 Pretax Income	
	$ mil.	% of total	$ mil.	% of total
Publishing	127.3	51	10.7	—
Catalog	61.4	25	5.2	—
Entertainment	51.7	21	1.0	—
Product marketing	6.8	3	3.4	—
Adjustments	—	—	(17.9)	—
Total	**247.2**	**100**	**2.4**	**—**

Selected Products
900 number (Playboy-related audiotext services)
AdulTVision (pay-per-view TV channel)
Books (anthologies and compilations from Playboy)
Critics' Choice Video (movie and video catalog)
Playboy (US editions plus 16 foreign editions)
Playboy catalog (clothes, gifts, and collectibles)
The Playboy Electronic Datebook (PC-based daily planner)
Playboy Home Video
Playboy Late Night (weekly TV series)
Playboy Television (cable TV network)

KEY COMPETITORS

General Media
Graff Pay-Per-View
LFP

HOW MUCH

NYSE symbol: PLA FYE: June 30	Annual Growth	1990	1991	1992	1993	1994	1995
Sales ($ mil.)	8.1%	167.7	174.0	193.7	214.9	219.0	247.2
Net income ($ mil.)	(37.3%)	6.2	4.5	3.5	0.4	(17.0)	0.6
Income as % of sales	—	3.7%	2.6%	1.8%	0.2%	—	0.3%
Earnings per share ($)	(38.1%)	0.33	0.24	0.19	0.02	(0.86)	0.03
Stock price – high ($)	—	7.63	8.50	9.50	11.00	11.00	9.63
Stock price – low ($)	—	3.13	3.88	5.88	6.63	6.00	7.63
Stock price – close ($)	16.9%	4.00	6.88	7.38	11.00	9.50	8.75
P/E – high	—	23	35	50	—	—	—
P/E – low	—	9	16	31	—	—	—
Dividends per share ($)	—	0.00	0.00	0.00	0.00	0.00	0.00
Book value per share ($)	4.1%	1.93	2.14	2.33	2.78	2.32	2.36
Employees	1.1%	561	586	616	628	583	593

1995 YEAR-END
Debt ratio: 11.3%
Return on equity: 1.3%
Cash (mil.): $2.0
Current ratio: 1.17
Long-term debt (mil.): $1.0
No. of shares (mil.): 20
Dividends
  Yield: —
  Payout: —
Market value (mil.): $175.0

PRIMARK CORPORATION

OVERVIEW

Primark is making its mark in the information marketplace. Among the Waltham, Massachusetts-based company's 8 subsidiaries are 5 that dispense financial and business information and another that delivers real-time weather data. Information services to the US government accounted for 49% of the firm's 1995 revenues. Its 2 service subsidiaries provide systems integration and maintenance for commercial turbojets, respectively. CEO Joseph Kasputys (a former assistant secretary of commerce) and investor Neil Weisman each own 7.6% of the company.

Primark was formed as a holding company for Michigan Consolidated (MichCon), a natural gas utility that was spun off from oil & gas producer Coastal Corp. in 1982. In 1988 Kasputys refocused Primark on information technology, spun off MichCon, and sold or closed other units. In 1991 the company acquired TASC (formed in 1966), which provides the US government's defense agencies with information technology services and systems. The next year it bought Datastream (a UK company serving customers in 40 countries with online financial data) from Dun & Bradstreet.

The company bought Disclosure Group, a financial information services firm, in 1995. That purchase included I/B/E/S, which provides earnings expectations to more than 1,000 investment management firms, and a 50% interest in Worldscope, which supplies information on global public companies. Also in 1995 Primark's WSI weather data subsidiary launched the Intellicast online weather service and joined with NBC News to provide weather information to the Microsoft Network.

In 1996 Primark acquired Trapeze, a document distribution technology that allows real-time information delivery, from Bondtech International.

WHO

Chairman, President, and CEO; Chairman, TASC:
Joseph E. Kasputys, age 59, $976,180 pay
EVP; President and CEO, TASC: John C. Holt, age 55, $644,704 pay
SVP, General Counsel, and Secretary; VP and General Counsel, TASC: Michael R. Kargula, age 48, $351,916 pay
SVP and CFO: Stephen H. Curran, age 48, $292,282 pay
VP Corporate Development: Patrick G. Richmond, age 45, $252,790 pay
Manager Human Resources: Diane Robesen
Auditors: Deloitte & Touche LLP

WHERE

HQ: 1000 Winter St., Ste. 4300N, Waltham, MA 02154
Phone: 617-466-6611
Fax: 617-890-6187
Web site: http://www.primark.com

	1995 Sales	
	$ mil.	% of total
US	491.0	80
UK	63.5	10
Other countries	62.8	10
Total	**617.3**	**100**

WHAT

	1995 Sales	
	$ mil.	% of total
Information services	531.0	86
Transportation services	79.2	13
Financial services	7.1	1
Total	**617.3**	**100**

KEY COMPETITORS

American Management	Control Data	Landmark Communications
AmeriData Technologies	DEC	Market Guide
Astraea Aviation	Deloitte Touche Tohmatsu	Nichols Research
BFGoodrich	Dun & Bradstreet	Pearson
Bloomberg	Global Financial Information	Price Waterhouse
Computer Sciences	Hewlett-Packard	Thomson Corp.
	Knight-Ridder	UNC
		Unisys

HOW MUCH

NYSE symbol: PMK FYE: December 31	Annual Growth	1990	1991	1992	1993	1994	1995
Sales ($ mil.)	86.7%	27.2	153.1	309.7	444.0	477.0	617.3
Net income ($ mil.)	—	(2.4)	0.9	7.2	8.1	13.8	18.9
Income as % of sales	—	—	0.6%	2.3%	1.8%	2.9%	3.1%
Earnings per share ($)	—	(0.13)	0.02	0.30	0.34	0.62	0.85
Stock price – high ($)	—	9.50	14.75	14.75	16.38	15.00	30.25
Stock price – low ($)	—	5.63	6.00	9.00	10.50	11.00	12.75
Stock price – close ($)	35.2%	6.63	10.63	14.75	11.25	13.13	30.00
P/E – high	—	—	—	49	48	24	36
P/E – low	—	—	—	30	31	18	15
Dividends per share ($)	—	0.00	0.00	0.00	0.00	0.00	0.00
Book value per share ($)	7.3%	10.67	10.75	11.08	11.32	12.14	15.19
Employees	12.4%	2,860	3,182	3,272	3,439	3,789	5,131

1995 YEAR-END
Debt ratio: 42.2%
Return on equity: 6.5%
Cash (mil.): $62.3
Current ratio: 1.59
Long-term debt (mil.): $265.9
No. of shares (mil.): 23.3
Dividends
  Yield: —
  Payout: —
Market value (mil.): $699.5

PRIMESTAR PARTNERS L.P.

OVERVIEW

PRIMESTAR has hitched its wagon to the rising star of direct broadcast satellite (DBS) TV. The privately owned Bala Cynwyd, Pennsylvania-based company is a partnership of 6 leading cable companies (Comcast Cable, Continental Cablevision, Cox Cable Communications, Newhouse Broadcasting, Tele-Communications, and Time Warner Cable) and the American Communications division of General Electric. The latter owns the satellite used by PRIMESTAR to deliver nationwide programming, which consists of 67 channels that range from ESPN to the Disney Channel. The company has over 1.4 million subscribers.

After a 7-year stint in the US Air Force, John Cusick hired on with telecommunications firm COMSAT, helping it develop digital satellite equipment. In 1987 he joined GE American Communications and became involved in an unsuccessful effort to develop a satellite service for HBO. From this failure arose PRIMESTAR, the US's first DBS service. In 1991, a year after PRIMESTAR began operations with service in 40 markets across the US, Cusick took over as president.

The company emerged unscathed from a 2-year antitrust investigation in 1993. In 1994 heavyweight telecommunication companies Hughes Communications (DIRECTV) and Hubbard Broadcasting (United States Satellite Broadcasting) entered the DBS field, challenging PRIMESTAR's market share. That year PRIMESTAR became the first DBS service to offer digital video and audio to US consumers. It claims that its 32-39 inch umbrella dishes give better reception than competitors' smaller dishes.

In 1995 the FCC blocked PRIMESTAR's planned acquisition of key DBS frequencies formerly owned by Advanced Communications, citing Advanced's lack of efforts in developing satellite services. That year the company made a deal to begin selling its satellite TV service at 200 Radio Shack stores. Cusick resigned that year and was replaced as CEO by James Gray. In 1996 Tele-Communications announced its intention to buy out its 5 PRIMESTAR partners.

WHO

Chairman and CEO: James L. Gray, age 59
CFO: Larry Epstein
VP Marketing: Jeffrey Smith
VP Systems: Gary Traver
Director Employee Relations: Barbara Caprice

WHERE

HQ: 3 Bala Plaza West, Bala Cynwyd, PA 19004
Phone: 610-660-6100
Fax: 610-660-6112

WHAT

Selected Channels Offered

A&E	The Learning Channel
ABC	MSG
Audio services (6 channels)	NBC
Cartoon Network	NESN
CBS	PASS
Cinemax	Pay-Per-View (10 channels)
Cinemax2	PBS
CMT	PreVue
CNBC	PSN-IMW
CNN	PSN-MW
CNNfn	PSN-RM
C-Span	PSN-UMW
The Discovery Channel	PS-NW
Disney	Sci-Fi
Empire	Special pro-sports feeds
Encore	Sport South
Encore Love Stories	Sunshine
Encore Mystery	TBS
ESPN	TNN
The Family Channel	TNT
Fox	Turner Classic Movies
HBO	TV Japan (English)
HBO2	TV Japan (Japanese)
HBO3	USA Network
Headline News	The Weather Channel
HSE	X-Press (Ingenius) data
HTS	service
KBL	

KEY COMPETITORS

Alphstar	TCA Cable
American Telecasting	United States Satellite
Cablevision Systems	Broadcasting
DIRECTV	U S WEST Media
EchoStar Communications	Thomson SA
Jones Communications	Viacom
Pico Products	

HOW MUCH

Partnership FYE: December 31	Annual Growth	1990	1991	1992	1993	1994	1995
Estimated sales ($ mil.)	400%	—	—	—	—	80.0	400.0
Employees	35.3%	—	—	—	41	41	75

PRODIGY INC.

OVERVIEW

This prodigiously problematic progeny of Sears and IBM is going it alone. In 1996 Prodigy executives and cellular/Internet investment group International Wireless (largely owned by Mexican industrial firm Grupo Carso) bought the company from IBM and Sears. For the estimated $250 million purchase price — far below the billion-plus dollars invested in Prodigy by its sellers — the new owners have taken over an online also-ran. White Plains, New York-based Prodigy was the first consumer online service in the US, but it has a reputation for poor graphics and slow service, and with under 2 million subscribers it lags far behind rivals America Online and CompuServe. International Wireless CEO Paul DeLacey was named as the head of Prodigy. He plans to build the company's international online operations.

Prodigy was founded in 1984 as a joint venture by IBM, Sears, and CBS (which dropped out in 1986). Originally called Trintex and led by former IBM executive Theodore Papes, the company launched its first service in 1988. Trintex marketed itself as a shopping and banking service for households, particularly for time-pressured women. It changed its name to Prodigy in 1989 and the next year made its national debut. The company continued to add services, including a financial news database produced by Dow Jones and a classified advertising service (with *USA Today*) in 1991. However, by 1992 Prodigy users were more interested in e-mail and bulletin boards than shopping online. The company started to charge for e-mail, leading many users to switch to CompuServe and AOL.

In 1994 Prodigy began a major overhaul of its service, adding slicker graphics. The company also dropped its proprietary technology and switched to industry-standard software, making it easier for content providers to add services. In 1995 former MTV chief Ed Bennett took over as CEO, setting out to change Prodigy's stodgy image. That year, in an effort to gain a foothold on the Internet, Prodigy became the first major online service to offer access to the World Wide Web. In 1996 Bennett was named head of Prodigy Ventures, a subsidiary which will invest in entertainment, content, and technology companies.

WHO

President and CEO: Paul DeLacey
EVP and COO: William J. Lansing
EVP and General Manager, Internet Services: Gerry Mueller
SVP Content: Josh Grotstein
SVP Communications: Barry Kluger
SVP and General Manager New Product Development: Scott Danielson
VP and CFO: J. Mark Hattendorf
VP and General Counsel: Marc Jacobson
Director Human Resources: Nicolas Lapko

WHERE

HQ: 445 Hamilton Ave., White Plains, NY 10601
Phone: 914-448-8000
Fax: 914-448-8083
Web site: http://www.prodigy.com

WHAT

Selected Services
Bulletin boards
Business and finance news
Chat groups
Consumer Reports
Downloadable software
E-mail
Entertainment news
Horoscopes
Internet access
Movie/video reviews
Music reviews
National and world news
Online shopping
Reference materials
Sports news
Travel guides and reservation system
Weather forecasts

KEY COMPETITORS

America Online	MCI
ASCIINet	MFS Communications
AT&T Corp.	Microsoft
BBN	Mindspring
CompuServe	NETCOM
CUC International	News Corp.
Dow Jones	PC Van
Earthlink	People World
IDT	PSINet

HOW MUCH

Private company FYE: December 31	Annual Growth	1990	1991	1992	1993	1994	1995
Estimated sales ($ mil.)	35.6%	48.0	119.0	—	180.0	200.0	220.0
Employees	(22.7%)	—	—	1,050	800	600	485

PROVIDENCE JOURNAL COMPANY

OVERVIEW

Providence Journal is on a provident journey to succeed in the unpredictable media industry. The Rhode Island-based company publishes the *Providence Journal-Bulletin*. The Rhode Island Bible or the Conscience of New England, as the paper is sometimes called by readers, is the largest of the state's 5 daily newspapers and has 182,000 subscribers. ProJo, as the company is known, also owns or manages 12 network-affiliated and independent television stations, provides interactive TV services, and operates the Rhode Island Horizons online information service. In addition, the firm provides TV programming through 2 cable networks — TV Food Network and America's Health Network. ProJo went public in 1996. Descendants of Stephen Metcalf (president from 1904 to 1941) and other old Providence families control the company, which agreed in 1996 to be bought by Dallas publisher A.H. Belo for $1.5 billion.

The company published its first paper, the *Manufacturers' and Farmers' Journal and Providence and Pawtucket Advertiser*, in 1820. It incorporated in 1884 as the Providence Printing Company. The next year it started the *Providence Sunday Journal* and adopted the name Providence Journal Company. George Metcalf succeeded his father, Stephen, as president in 1941. ProJo started Colony Communications in 1969 to develop cable TV systems, and in 1978 it bought its first TV station — Philadelphia's WPHL. (It was sold in 1987.) In 1985 George's son, Michael, became CEO and modernized the company's printing and production processes. Michael was found critically injured next to his bicycle in 1987 on a country road near his Westport, Massachusetts, summer home. He died a week later from wounds suffered in the accident and was succeeded by current chairman Stephen Hamblett.

In 1990 the company sold its cellular communications subsidiary to GTE and started managing the Palmer Communications cable TV operations. In 1992 ProJo purchased King Broadcasting Corp.'s 5 TV stations.

The company sold its cable TV systems in 1995 to Continental Cablevision.

WHO

Chairman, CEO, and Publisher: Stephen Hamblett, age 61, $990,000 pay
EVP Broadcasting, Programming, and Electronic Media: Jack C. Clifford, age 62, $429,000 pay
SVP and General Manager Publishing: Howard G. Sutton, age 46
VP Finance and CFO: Thomas N. Matlack, age 31
VP, General Counsel, and Chief Administrative Officer: John L. Hammond, age 50, $302,000 pay
VP Human Resources: John A. Bowers, age 43, $297,000 pay
VP Television: John E. Hayes, age 54

WHERE

HQ: 75 Fountain St., Providence, RI 02902-0050
Phone: 401-277-7000
Fax: 401-277-7346
Web site: http://www.projo.com

WHAT

Selected Operations
America's Health Network (cable TV network)
Broadcast and video programming
Providence Journal-Bulletin (newspaper in Rhode Island)
Rhode Island Horizons (online information service)
Television stations (9 owned; 3 managed)
TV Food Network (46%, cable TV network)

Owned Television Stations
KGSW-TV, Albuquerque/Santa Fe, NM
KGW(TV), Portland, OR
KHNL(TV), Honolulu, HI
KING-TV, Seattle
KMSB-TV, Tucson, AZ
KREM-TV, Spokane, WA
KTVB(TV), Boise, ID
WCNC-TV, Charlotte, NC
WHAS-TV, Louisville, KY

Managed Television Stations
KFVE(TV), Honolulu, HI
KONG-TV, Seattle
KTTU(TV), Tucson, AZ

KEY COMPETITORS

Capital Cities/ABC
Cox Enterprises
Gaylord Entertainment
International Family
  Entertainment
Lifetime Television
New York Times
News Corp.
Pulitzer Publishing
Viacom
Westinghouse/CBS

HOW MUCH

NYSE symbol: PRJ FYE: December 31	Annual Growth	1990	1991	1992	1993	1994	1995
Sales ($ mil.)	(7.5%)	—	427.4	535.0	560.0	600.0	312.5
Employees	29.1%	—	—	—	1,500	1,500	2,500

1995 YEAR-END
Debt ratio: 48.1%
Cash (mil.): $0.1
Current ratio: 1.32
Long-term debt (mil.): $244.0

PULITZER PUBLISHING COMPANY

OVERVIEW

Pulitzer Publishing first succeeded in newspapers, but broadcasting is the biggest prize on the company's mantle these days. The St. Louis-based company operates 9 television stations and 2 radio stations, which account for about 3/4 of the company's profits. Pulitzer also publishes the *St. Louis Post-Dispatch* and the *Arizona Daily Star*. CEO Michael Pulitzer (grandson of the founder) and his family own more than 90% of the company.

Joseph Pulitzer, a Hungarian immigrant, acquired the bankrupt *St. Louis Evening Dispatch* in 1878, and in 1879 merged it with the *St. Louis Evening Post*, creating the *Post-Dispatch*. In 1903 Pulitzer gave Columbia University $2 million to set up a journalism school and to establish the Pulitzer Prizes. (The Pulitzer Prize Board is not affiliated with Pulitzer Publishing.) Joseph Pulitzer's son (also named Joseph) took control of the company in 1912. He expanded into broadcasting, starting a radio station in St. Louis in 1922 and a television station there in 1947. In 1955 Joseph Pulitzer Jr. (the 3rd Joseph Pulitzer) took over following his father's death. He acquired Tucson's *Daily Star* in 1971 and expanded the company's broadcasting operations, acquiring TV stations in Albuquerque (1969), Omaha (1976), and Lancaster, Pennsylvania (1979). Also in 1979 the company traded its St. Louis radio station for 2 radio stations in Phoenix. In 1986 the company went public. That year Michael, Joseph Jr.'s half brother, became CEO.

In 1993 the company acquired TV stations in Orlando and Des Moines, and the next year sold Chicago-based Pulitzer Community Newspapers. Pulitzer has taken an interest in major league baseball, buying a stake in the expansion team Arizona Diamondbacks in 1995 and the St. Louis Cardinals in 1996.

WHO

Chairman, President, and CEO: Michael E. Pulitzer, age 66, $1,241,072 pay
EVP, Pulitzer Broadcasting Company: C. Wayne Godsey, age 49, $297,103 pay
SVP Broadcast Operations: Ken J. Elkins, age 58, $568,589 pay
SVP Newspaper Operations: Nicholas G. Penniman IV, age 58, $422,624 pay
SVP Finance: Ronald H. Ridgway, age 57, $392,658 pay
VP: R. Jeffrey Edwards, age 41
Secretary: James V. Maloney, age 46
Director Human Resources: Preston Vanderford
Auditors: Deloitte & Touche LLP

WHERE

HQ: 900 N. Tucker Blvd., St. Louis, MO 63101
Phone: 314-340-8000
Fax: 314-340-3125
Web site: http://www.stlnet.com/postnet

WHAT

	1995 Sales		1995 Operating Income	
	$ mil.	% of total	$ mil.	% of total
Publishing	269.4	57	25.4	28
Broadcasting	202.9	43	66.0	72
Adjustments	—		(4.7)	
Total	**472.3**	**100**	**86.7**	**100**

Selected Television Stations
KCCI-TV (CBS; Des Moines, IA)
KETV-TV (ABC; Omaha, NE)
KOAT-TV (ABC; Albuquerque, NM)
WDSU-TV (NBC; New Orleans)
WESH-TV (NBC; Daytona Beach/Orlando, FL)
WLKY-TV (CBS; Louisville, KY)
WXII-TV (NBC; Winston-Salem, NC)

KEY COMPETITORS

Advance Publications	Chronicle Publishing	Jefferson-Pilot
A. H. Belo	Comcast	Knight-Ridder
Capital Cities/ABC	Cox Enterprises	Times Mirror
	Hearst	Tribune
		U S WEST Media

HOW MUCH

NYSE symbol: PTZ FYE: December 31	Annual Growth	1990	1991	1992	1993	1994	1995
Sales ($ mil.)	3.2%	402.8	393.4	398.4	427.0	485.6	472.3
Net income ($ mil.)	31.6%	12.5	10.6	23.9	23.0	39.9	49.3
Income as % of sales	—	3.1%	2.7%	6.0%	5.4%	8.2%	10.4%
Earnings per share ($)	28.3%	0.87	0.73	1.66	1.50	2.45	3.02
Stock price – high ($)	—	22.36	18.73	25.82	31.80	32.20	53.00
Stock price – low ($)	—	12.18	13.09	15.63	22.80	26.40	30.75
Stock price – close ($)	29.2%	13.27	16.18	25.09	28.70	32.10	47.75
P/E – high	—	26	26	16	21	13	18
P/E – low	—	14	18	9	15	11	10
Dividends per share ($)	7.2%	0.36	0.38	0.39	0.43	0.46	0.54
Book value per share ($)	20.9%	4.69	5.05	4.64	7.53	9.53	12.13
Employees	(4.5%)	3,150	2,900	2,700	2,950	2,400	2,500

1995 YEAR-END
Debt ratio: 39.3%
Return on equity: 27.9%
Cash (mil.): $100.4
Current ratio: 3.22
Long-term debt (mil.): $114.5
No. of shares (mil.): 16.5
Dividends
  Yield: 1.1%
  Payout: 17.9%
Market value (mil.): $782.4

QUARK, INC.

OVERVIEW

Quark has written a real page-turner. The Denver-based company's flagship software, QuarkXPress, is the leading page layout software, an application that helps designers assemble text and graphics into documents such as books, brochures, or newsletters. QuarkXPress has more than half of the desktop publishing market worldwide and is available for both PCs and Macintosh computers and in 24 languages. The firm is jumping from the printed page to the Internet with the release of QuarkImmedia, its Web site authoring software. Founder and chairman Tim Gill and CEO Fred Ebrahimi each own 50% of Quark.

In 1981 Gill, then 27, founded Quark after being laid off from a job at a Denver music software company. He believed "Quark" (named after the subatomic particle that got its name from James Joyce's *Finnegans Wake*) would stand out in the classified sections of magazines. Gill wrote a word processing program, called Word Juggler, for the Apple III computer, beating the competition (including Apple) to market by 6 months. Several other word processing products followed. In 1986 Gill sold half the company to Ebrahimi and handed over administrative and sales duties. The firm introduced QuarkXPress the next year. In 1992 it introduced a Windows version of QuarkXPress, launched the Quark Publishing System, and introduced QuarkXPress Passport, a multilingual version. A lower-priced configuration of its Quark Publishing System for editorial management debuted in 1994.

The company announced 2 new software programs in 1995, QuarkImmedia and QuarkXPosure. QuarkImmedia lets designers add multimedia components such as sound and video to files created in QuarkXPress for use on CD-ROMs or the Web; QuarkXPosure is electronic image manipulation software. Amid ongoing rumors that it is preparing to go public, in 1996 the company acquired a stake in Colossal Pictures, a San Francisco-based film and video special-effects and design studio whose clients include Coca-Cola and electronic game maker SEGA. The purchase moves Quark further into the realm of multimedia and is expected to help boost recognition of QuarkImmedia.

WHO

Chairman; SVP Research and Development: Timothy E. Gill, age 41
President and CEO: Farhad Fred Ebrahimi, age 56
CFO: Kenneth J. Collins, age 48
VP Research and Development: Raymond Fink
VP Product Management: Wayne Yamamoto, age 38
Manager Public Relations: Bob Monzel
Director Human Resources: D. Witonsky

WHERE

HQ: 1800 Grant St., Denver, CO 80203
Phone: 303-894-8888
Fax: 303-894-3399
Web site: http://www.quark.com

Quark has international offices in Denmark, France, Germany, Ireland, Japan, and the UK.

WHAT

Selected Products
Quark Publishing System (editorial management system for workgroups)
QuarkCopyDesk (word processing and editing)
QuarkDispatch
QuarkDispatch Administrator (configuring)
QuarkDispatch FileManager (archiving)
QuarkDispatch Planner (assigning and tracking)
QuarkDispatch XTension to QuarkXPress (connects QuarkXPress to publishing system)
QuarkImmedia (high-end multimedia and Internet design and viewing software)
QuarkXPosure (image editing)
QuarkXPress (page layout)
QuarkXPress Passport (multilingual system that supports 10 languages)

Selected Publications Produced Using Quark Products
The Calgary Herald (Canada)
Die Woche (Germany)
Eddie Bauer catalog
Esquire
FORTUNE
Hoover's Guide to Media Companies
Info-Matin (France)
La Repubblica (Italy)
Macy's catalog
The New York Times

KEY COMPETITORS

Adobe
ColorAge
Corel
Deneba
Electronics for Imaging
General Parametrics
Interleaf

Linotype-Hell
Lotus
Microsoft
Multi-Ad Services
Scitex
SoftKey

HOW MUCH

Private company FYE: June 30	Annual Growth	1990	1991	1992	1993	1994	1995
Estimated sales ($ mil.)	46.1%	30.0	50.0	80.0	120.0	168.0	200.0
Employees	53.7%	70	200	—	420	520	600

RAND MCNALLY & COMPANY

OVERVIEW

Rand McNally knows the way to San Jose, and every other city on earth. The Skokie, Illinois-based company is the world's largest commercial mapmaker, with some 10,000 different maps (its road atlas is 2nd only to the Bible in book sales). It also markets travel-related software, provides electronic geographic-information products and services, prints such books as *World Book Encyclopedia* and Merriam-Webster's dictionaries, is the 3rd largest printer of children's books, and provides a variety of publishing and other media services. Its DocuSystems unit is the world's #1 printer of airline, railroad, and baggage claim tickets. Rand McNally is a closely held private company, led by Andrew McNally IV, great-great-grandson of the founder.

William Rand cofounded a small print shop with the *Chicago Tribune* in 1856 and 2 years later hired Andrew McNally as an assistant. In 1868 Rand bought the newspaper's share and formed a new company with McNally as his partner. The 2 began making timetables and railway tickets and published their first book, a Chicago business directory, in 1870. McNally bought Rand's share of the business in 1894 upon Rand's retirement, and the firm has been held by the McNally family ever since. The publisher expanded into road atlases after McNally's grandson got lost while driving from Chicago to Milwaukee on his honeymoon. In the last 50 years, Rand McNally has been profitable every year except 1991 and 1992, when the breakup of the Soviet Union made maps outdated and slowed sales.

In 1994 Rand McNally introduced TripMaker, a vacation-planning software program on CD-ROM, which by late the following year was trampling a similar 3-year-old Microsoft product. In 1995 Rand McNally won a 10-year contract to create maps and indexes for the *Reader's Digest Illustrated Atlas of the World*. That year the firm also began a joint venture with Italian publisher De Agostini to provide geographic information for print and electronic media worldwide. In 1996 Rand McNally started its Cartographic and Information Services division to provide software enabling customers to make maps under their own brand names.

WHO

Chairman and CEO: Andrew McNally IV
President and COO: John S. Bakalar
President, Publishing and New Media Division: Henry J. Feinberg
President, Book Services: William C. Korner
President, Media Services: James T. Thaden
President, DocuSystems: Thomas J. Breen
VP and CFO: James J. Habschmidt
VP Corporate Relations and Secretary: Edward C. McNally
VP Human Resources and General Counsel: Kurt D. Steele
Chief Cartographer: Michael W. Dobson
Auditors: Andersen Worldwide

WHERE

HQ: 8255 N. Central Park Ave., Skokie, IL 60076-2970
Phone: 847-329-8100
Fax: 847-673-0539
Web site: http://www.randmedia.ie/

Rand McNally serves customers in the Middle East, North America, the Pacific Rim, Russia, and Western Europe.

WHAT

Selected Operations and Products

Book Services
Book manufacturing
Services to book and information producers

Cartographic and Information Services
Map-making software

Docusystems
Airline and surface transportation tickets
Baggage tags
Debit cards
Specialty labels and tags

Media Services
Custom packaging
Distribution and fulfillment
Invoicing and collection
Order processing
Software manufacturing

KEY COMPETITORS

AAA	Brøderbund	Microsoft
Advance Publications	DeLorme	News Corp.
	Geonex	R.L. Polk
American Banknote	Lonely Planet	Thomson Corp.
	MapInfo	Time Warner
Bertelsmann	Michelin	Tribune

HOW MUCH

Private company FYE: December 31	Annual Growth	1990	1991	1992	1993	1994	1995
Sales ($ mil.)	12.3%	262.0	306.9	341.9	395.0	438.0	468.5
Employees	3.1%	4,000	4,000	4,000	4,000	4,200	4,650

✷ RAND McNALLY

R. L. POLK & CO.

OVERVIEW

R. L. Polk manufactures the raw material for the Information Age. Headquartered in Detroit, the company provides statistics, demographics, and consumer data to businesses around the world. The oldest consumer marketing information company in the US, Polk publishes more than 1,000 city directories covering about 5,000 communities in the US and Canada. Its database has lifestyle and other demographic information on 95 million US consumer households. The company also compiles statistics on the more than 197 million cars and trucks on the road in the US and Canada in an annual census called the National Vehicle Population Profile and sells the information to the auto industry. Polk's other products include computer-readable maps, and bulk-mailing services. A privately held company, Polk is headed by Stephen Polk, the great-grandson of the company's founder.

Ralph Lane Polk founded the company in 1870 when he issued a directory of the towns served by the Detroit and Milwaukee Railroad. He later published a city directory of Detroit and a business directory of Michigan. In 1916 the company published its first bank directory, and in 1922 it began compiling statistics on automobiles. With the post WWII boom in auto sales, Polk began to concentrate its direct marketing activities on the automobile industry.

The company expanded outside the US for the first time in 1956, when it acquired a Canadian directory company. In 1965 Polk moved into the UK, and in 1971 it expanded into Germany and Australia. During the 1980s the company grew through a series of acquisitions, buying Burch Directory Company (1985), Advertising Unlimited (promotional calendars, 1987), and National Demographics & Lifestyles (1988).

In 1994 the company began a major restructuring of its marketing information business. Polk sold its bank directory business to Canadian publisher Thomson Corp.'s Thomson Financial Publishing in 1995. That year the company signed an agreement with Marketing Systems, a German firm, to provide automakers with information on motor vehicles worldwide.

WHO

Chairman and CEO: Stephen R. Polk
President and COO: Arthur L. Olson
CFO: Bob Tatum
General Counsel and Secretary: Leo A. Marx Jr.
SVP Product Management and Marketing: Robert Shapiro
SVP Human Resource: Joan Miszak
Auditors: Deloitte & Touche LLP

WHERE

HQ: 1155 Brewery Park Blvd., Detroit, MI 48207-2697
Phone: 313-393-0880
Fax: 313-393-2860

WHAT

Selected Products and Services
Calendars
Consumer database marketing
Direct marketing
Geographic mapping
Motor vehicle statistics
Newsletters
Order fulfillment
Specialty advertising products

Selected Subsidiaries
Advertising Unlimited, Inc. (specialty items)
Geographic Data Technology, Inc. (computer-readable maps)
Portica GmbH (order fulfillment and database services, Germany)
Portica Ltd. (mass mailings and order fulfillment, UK)

KEY COMPETITORS

Acxiom
ADVO
American Business Information
Database America
EquiFax
Fronteer Directory
J.D. Power
Link Marketing and Data Services
Metromail
Microlytics
Phillips Publishing
Printmailers
Rand McNally
Thomas Publishing
TRW
United Communications
Wolters Kluwer

HOW MUCH

Private company FYE: March 31	Annual Growth	1990	1991	1992	1993	1994	1995[1]
Sales ($ mil.)	3.1%	275.0	284.0	296.0	317.3	341.3	320.0
Employees	(3.6%)	6,000	7,000	7,000	6,000	6,000	5,000

[1] Estimated

THE SAMUEL GOLDWYN COMPANY

OVERVIEW

If Shakespeare were alive today, he would probably write screenplays for this company. The Los Angeles-based Samuel Goldwyn Company produces and distributes specialized motion pictures and art films. Releases in the 1990s have included *Much Ado About Nothing*, *Henry V*, and *The Wedding Banquet*. The company's TV division produces original programming for the first-run syndication market, including a remake of the dolphin TV series *Flipper*. The firm has 125 screens in 50 theaters across the country, making it the US's #1 exhibitor of art films. In 1996 Metromedia International acquired the company and the Motion Picture Corporation of America and began consolidating them into its Orion Pictures unit.

The company was founded in 1979 by Samuel Goldwyn Jr., the son of the Hollywood mogul who produced over 80 films, including *Guys and Dolls* and *Wuthering Heights*. Inheriting a library of 52 classic films from his father (who died in 1974), Goldwyn Jr. added to the collection and marketed films to cable and network TV. In the mid-1980s the company moved into art-film production and later into mass entertainment TV shows (*American Gladiators*). In 1991 the company acquired Heritage Entertainment, which operated 42 specialty movie houses. It went public that year.

Although the firm plans to release 10-15 films a year, it distributed only one film on the international market in fiscal 1995 (*The Madness of King George*). Other films (*Oleanna, To Live*, and *The Perez Family*) and TV pilots (*Wild West Showdown* and *Why Didn't I Think of That?*) bombed. Goldwyn owns 64% of the company's stock.

In 1995 the firm agreed to sell its 850-film library to PolyGram for $62 million.

WHO

Chairman and CEO: Samuel Goldwyn Jr., age 68, $258,333 pay
President and COO: Meyer Gottlieb, age 55, $434,934 pay
COO, The Samuel Goldwyn Company Theatre Group: Stephen Gilula, age 44, $210,739 pay
SVP, CFO, and Secretary: Hans W. Turner, age 47, $180,000 pay
SVP Operations: Lawrence J. Kirk Jr., age 41
VP Human Resources: Gaston Bitar
Auditors: Price Waterhouse LLP

WHERE

HQ: 10203 Santa Monica Blvd., Los Angeles, CA 90067-6403
Phone: 310-552-2255
Fax: 310-284-8493

WHAT

Selected Products and Services
Home video marketing
Motion picture distribution
Television production and distribution

KEY COMPETITORS

All American Communications
AMC Entertainment
Blockbuster
Carmike
Cinemark USA
Cinergi Pictures
GC
International Family Entertainment
King World
MCA
MGM
NBC
News Corp.
PolyGram
Regal Cinemas
Savoy Pictures
Sony
Spelling Entertainment
Time Warner
United Artists Theatre
Viacom
Walt Disney
Westinghouse/CBS

HOW MUCH

Subsidiary FYE: March 31	Annual Growth	1991	1992	1993	1994	1995	1996
Sales ($ mil.)	21.0%	41.5	61.3	107.8	108.8	91.3	107.8
Net Income ($ mil.)	51.7%	(4.1)	(3.4)	1.1	2.2	(20.1)	(32.9)
Income as % of sales	—	—	—	1.0	2.1	—	—
Employees	(26.1%)	—	900	260	260	269	269

SCHOLASTIC CORPORATION

OVERVIEW

The day the Scholastic book club box arrived was exciting. The teacher opened it up and handed out the books, and the fact that we had chosen them ourselves — and paid with our own money — made them precious.

This drama is a key to New York City-based Scholastic Corp.'s success. The company is the leading operator of children's book clubs and fairs, but it also sells books through bookstores. Other products include classroom and professional magazines, educational software, CD-ROMs, and videos. In 1995 it produced 2 movies — *The Indian in the Cupboard* and *The Baby-sitters Club* — based on its own titles. Scholastic also uses its knowledge of children to produce classroom instructional materials. CEO Richard Robinson and his family own about 18% of the company.

The enterprise was founded in 1920 by Robinson's father, Maurice, to bring the world into high school classrooms via *The Scholastic* newsletter. Scholastic introduced more classroom magazines and, in 1948, a book club. Richard became CEO of the then public company in 1975. Six years later it entered the book-fair business. After going private in a 1987 leveraged buyout, the company went public again in 1992.

Scholastic has branched out into electronic products, often with high-profile partners. Its efforts include CD-ROMs (with Microsoft), an online service (with America Online), and a TV series based on its popular *Goosebumps* children's mystery series (with Fox TV).

In the 1990s Scholastic has moved into the non-English-speaking world, with book clubs in Mexico and France. In 1996 it bought Bantam Doubleday Dell's book club division (Trumpet) and PAGES, Inc.'s UK book-fair operations. Sales that year rose 24% to $929 million.

WHO

Chairman, President, and CEO: Richard Robinson, age 58, $631,600 pay
EVP and CFO: Kevin J. McEnery, age 47
EVP Children's Book Publishing: Barbara A. Marcus, age 44, $472,442 pay
EVP Instructional Publishing Group: Margery W. Mayer, age 43, $325,710 pay
President, Scholastic Book Fairs, Inc.: David D. Yun, age 47, $346,047 pay
VP, General Counsel, and Secretary: Lynette E. Allison
VP Human Resources: Larry V. Holland, age 36
Auditors: Ernst & Young LLP

WHERE

HQ: 555 Broadway, New York, NY 10012-3999
Phone: 212-343-6100
Fax: 212-343-6928
Web site: http://www.scholastic.com

	1995 Sales % of total
US	83
Other countries	17
Total	**100**

WHAT

Selected Products
The Baby-sitters Club (series)
Cartwheel Books (imprint)
Clifford the Big Red Dog (series)
Goosebumps (mystery series)
Home Office Computing (consumer magazine)

KEY COMPETITORS

Bertelsmann
Brøderbund
Center for Applied Psychology
Davidson & Associates
Dorling Kindersley
Edmark
Educational Development
EduStar
Everyday Learning
HarperCollins
Intervisual Books
Knowledge Adventure
Lagardère
Living Books
Marvel
McGraw-Hill
PAGES
Pearson
Steck-Vaughn
Time Warner
Troll
Walt Disney

HOW MUCH

Nasdaq symbol: SCHL FYE: May 31	Annual Growth	1990	1991	1992	1993	1994	1995
Sales ($ mil.)	14.9%	374.6	422.9	489.3	552.3	631.6	749.9
Net income ($ mil.)	69.0%	2.8	13.8	13.0	28.1	32.9	38.6
Income as % of sales	—	0.7%	3.3%	2.7%	5.1%	5.2%	5.1%
Earnings per share ($)	60.9%	0.22	1.29	1.05	1.75	2.04	2.37
Stock price – high ($)	—	—	—	37.75	54.25	52.50	78.25
Stock price – low ($)	—	—	—	25.75	32.25	33.75	47.75
Stock price – close ($)	33.2%	—	—	32.88	43.50	51.00	77.75
P/E – high	—	—	—	36	31	26	33
P/E – low	—	—	—	25	18	17	20
Dividends per share ($)	—	—	—	0.00	0.00	0.00	0.00
Book value per share ($)	—	—	—	9.84	9.98	13.27	16.83
Employees	15.5%	—	3,165	3,396	3,918	4,615	5,636

1995 YEAR-END
Debt ratio: 28.8%
Return on equity: 16.9%
Cash (mil.): $3.7
Current ratio: 1.96
Long-term debt (mil.): $91.5
No. of shares (mil.): 15.7
Dividends
  Yield: —
  Payout: —
Market value (mil.): $1,156

SFX BROADCASTING, INC.

OVERVIEW

SFX Broadcasting is tuned in to some serious growth. Soon after the 1996 elimination of rules on how many radio stations a company can own, The New York City-based radio station operator struck deals that would boost its holdings to 77 stations (from 15 just a few months before), putting it in the front ranks of US station owners. Chairman Robert F. X. Sillerman controls 57% of the company.

Sillerman (whose father had founded a radio network) started his career by advising advertisers how to reach consumers under age 30. Then he began investing in radio and TV stations, cable TV, and satellite music services. In 1992 Sillerman formed SFX Broadcasting (named for a scrambling of his initials) with the purchase and merger of 8 radio stations owned by 2 companies in which he was a partner — Command Communications and Capstar Communications. The next year SFX went public. The company has increased its presence in major and midsized markets and improved operating efficiency by having more than one station in its markets.

In 1995 SFX warded off a buyout attempt by Chancellor Holdings, a station group owned by Hicks, Muse (headed by Thomas Hicks, the brother of SFX's then-COO Steven Hicks). Shortly thereafter, Hicks was promoted to CEO, replacing Sillerman, who became executive chairman. That year SFX agreed to purchase 19 stations from Liberty Broadcasting.

Following the 1996 passage of the Telecommunications Act, SFX agreed to buy 2 stations in North Carolina and the 16 stations of Prism Radio Partners. SFX also agreed to purchase Multi-Market Radio (which owns 26 stations and was also started by Sillerman). Michael Ferrel took over as CEO that year when Hicks resigned to join Hicks, Muse-owned station owner Capstar Broadcasting.

WHO

Executive Chairman: Robert F. X. Sillerman, age 48, $250,000 pay
President and CEO: Michael Ferrel
EVP and CFO: D. Geoffrey Armstrong, age 38, $150,000 pay (prior to promotion)
EVP and Secretary: Howard Tytel, age 49
Corporate Controller: Bill Schwartz
Corporate Business Manager: Kim Borron
Accounting Manager: Michele Manuel
Auditors: Ernst & Young LLP

WHERE

HQ: 150 E. 58th St., 19th Fl., New York, NY 10155-5749
Phone: 212-407-9191
Fax: 212-753-3188
Web site: http://www.sunny99.com/sfx.htm

WHAT

	1995 Stations
	No.
Greenville-Spartanburg, SC	3
Jackson, MS	3
Charlotte, NC	2
Dallas	2
Nashville	2
San Diego	2
Houston	1
Total	**15**

Selected Station Formats

70s Rock	Contemporary
Adult contemporary	Country
Album rock	News/talk
Alternative rock	Sports

KEY COMPETITORS

A. H. Belo	Cox Enterprises	Jacor
Capital Cities/ABC	EZ	Communications
Century	Communications	Tribune
Communications	Gannett	Viacom
Chancellor	Heritage Media	Westinghouse/
Broadcasting	Infinity	CBS
Clear Channel	Broadcasting	

HOW MUCH

Nasdaq symbol: SFXBA FYE: December 31	Annual Growth	1990	1991	1992	1993	1994	1995
Sales ($ mil.)	44.0%	12.4	13.4	15.0	34.2	55.6	76.8
Net income ($ mil.)	(2.5%)	(5.0)	(4.5)	(2.6)	(15.9)	1.8	(4.4)
Income as % of sales	—	—	—	—	—	3.2%	—
Earnings per share ($)	(66.6%)	—	—	—	(6.37)	0.26	(0.71)
Stock price – high ($)	—	—	—	—	17.00	18.75	30.75
Stock price – low ($)	—	—	—	—	11.75	10.75	17.00
Stock price – close ($)	54.0%	—	—	—	12.75	18.50	30.25
P/E – high	—	—	—	—	—	72	—
P/E – low	—	—	—	—	—	41	—
Dividends per share ($)	—	—	—	—	0.00	0.00	0.00
Book value per share ($)	14.8%	—	—	—	8.45	8.50	11.14
Employees	21.0%	—	—	—	—	357	432

1995 YEAR-END
Debt ratio: 49.6%
Return on equity: —
Cash (mil.): $11.9
Current ratio: 2.80
Long-term debt (mil.): $81.3
No. of shares (mil.): 7.5
Dividends
   Yield: —
   Payout: —
Market value (mil.): $225.6

SILVER KING COMMUNICATIONS, INC.

OVERVIEW

CEO Barry Diller wants Silver King's dominion to be local TV. The company (officially headquartered in Florida but with most corporate operations in Los Angeles and New York) operates 12 UHF television stations that reach 28 million homes in 8 of the 12 largest US markets. It also owns 26 low-powered television (LPTV) stations. Rather than build a national network — as he did at Fox — wheeler-dealer Diller wants to turn the company's stations into the video equivalents of alternative city newspapers. For now, most of the time slots at the Silver King stations are reserved for the Home Shopping Club (HSC), whose parent, Home Shopping Network (HSN), is controlled by Silver King. (Diller is also the chairman of HSN.) Silver King's largest shareholder is cable programming kingpin Liberty Media.

The enterprise was formed in 1986 as a unit of HSN to distribute the channel's programming, and it eventually changed its name to HSN Communications. In 1992 it was spun off from HSN, went public, and adopted its present name. The spinoff was designed to boost the value of the network, which was being acquired by Liberty Media, a unit of Tele-Communications, Inc. With financial backing from TCI, Diller took control of Silver King in 1995.

Also that year the company agreed to acquire broadcaster Savoy Pictures Entertainment for $109 million. Silver King agreed in 1996 to spend $1.3 billion to increase its ownership of HSN to 80%. (Liberty Media owns the rest.) Diller plans to find cable systems to carry HSN programming, thereby freeing up space for local news and entertainment programming on Silver King's TV stations. This programming — 2/3 of which will be generated locally — will be gradually introduced between 1997 and 1999.

WHO

Chairman and CEO: Barry Diller, age 53, $47,945 pay
VC, EVP, CFO, Chief Administrative Officer, and Treasurer: Steven H. Grant, age 35, $128,492 pay
President: James M. Lawless, age 57, $156,001 pay
EVP, General Counsel, and Secretary: Michael Drayer, age 35, $120,484 pay
EVP Compliance/Programming: Lia Afriat-Hernandez, age 51, $101,358 pay
EVP Development: Charles H. Bohart, age 60
EVP Operations and Planning: William D. Lovell, age 41
EVP Broadcasting: Adam Ware, age 30
Director Human Resources: Barbara O'Grady
Auditors: Deloitte & Touche LLP

WHERE

HQ: 12425 28th St. North, Ste. 300, St. Petersburg, FL 33716
Phone: 813-573-0339
Fax: 813-527-1488

UHF Television Stations

KHSC-TV, Los Angeles	WHSH-TV, Boston
KHSH-TV, Houston	WHSI-TV, New York City
KHSX-TV, Dallas	WHSP-TV, Philadelphia
WBHS-TV, Tampa/St.	WHSW-TV, Baltimore
Petersburg	WQHS-TV, Cleveland
WEHS-TV, Chicago	WYHS-TV, Miami
WHSE-TV, New York City	

WHAT

	1995 Sales	
	$ mil.	% of total
Broadcasting	44.5	93
Production	3.4	7
Total	**47.9**	**100**

KEY COMPETITORS

Capital Cities/ABC	Cox Enterprises	Time Warner
Chris-Craft	Gannett	Tribune
Comcast	Hearst	ValueVision
Corporation for Public Broadcasting	King World	Viacom
	LIN Broadcasting	Washington Post
	NBC	Westinghouse/
	News Corp.	CBS

HOW MUCH

Nasdaq symbol: SKTV FYE: August 31	Annual Growth	1990	1991	1992	1993	1994	1995
Sales ($ mil.)	15.8%	—	26.6	46.7	46.2	46.6	47.9
Net income ($ mil.)	—	—	(18.8)	(15.2)	(6.4)	(0.9)	0.1
Income as % of sales	—	—	—	—	—	—	0.2%
Earnings per share ($)	—	—	—	—	(0.72)	(0.10)	0.01
Stock price – high ($)	—	—	—	—	21.25	13.50	40.25
Stock price – low ($)	—	—	—	—	2.63	8.00	8.75
Stock price – close ($)	86.4%	—	—	—	10.00	10.75	34.75
P/E – high	—	—	—	—	—	—	—
P/E – low	—	—	—	—	—	—	—
Dividends per share ($)	—	—	—	—	0.00	0.00	0.00
Book value per share ($)	20.8%	—	—	—	0.72	0.29	1.05
Employees	(4.7%)	—	—	210	205	196	182

1995 YEAR-END
Debt ratio: 92.5%
Return on equity: 1.7%
Cash (mil.): $22.2
Current ratio: 1.28
Long-term debt (mil.): $97.9
No. of shares (mil.): 9.4
Dividends
  Yield: —
  Payout: —
Market value (mil.): $325.6

SOFTKEY INTERNATIONAL INC.

OVERVIEW

SoftKey plays hardball. The Cambridge, Massachusetts-based company, a leading publisher of consumer software (with more than 500 titles), has gone after acquisitions with a vengeance, adding Compton's NewMedia and the Learning Company to its team. Known for its mass-marketing approach, SoftKey packages and displays some programs in racks like music CDs. Chairman and CEO Michael Perik owns 5% of the company. Tribune Co., publisher of the *Chicago Tribune*, owns 22.5%.

The company was created in 1994 by the merger of SoftKey Software, Spinnaker Software, and WordStar International. SoftKey Software, founded in Canada in 1983 by Kevin O'Leary, focused on personal productivity programs. Spinnaker was founded by David Seuss in 1982 to manufacture educational software and entered the home office market in 1991 with the acquisition of the PFS: product line from Software Publishing Corp. WordStar was founded in 1978 (as MicroPro International) by Seymour Rubinstein to develop word processing programs and other software. The new company combined WordStar's strengths in international distribution and direct mail, Spinnaker's alliances with PC vendors, and SoftKey's broad product line and retail connections. Perik, SoftKey Software's CEO, was chosen to head the new firm, which began trading on Nasdaq in 1994. That year it introduced its Platinum line, the first consumer software sold in jewel case-only packaging and displayed on racks to encourage impulse purchases.

Merger-related charges led to a loss for 1995. That year SoftKey agreed to merge with another software publisher, Minnesota Educational Computing Corp. SoftKey paid $606 million in cash in early 1996 for the Learning Company, a leading educational software publisher.

WHO

Chairman and CEO: Michael J. Perik, age 38, $300,000 pay
President: Kevin O'Leary, age 41, $300,000 pay
CFO: R. Scott Murray, age 32, $260,000 pay
COO: Les Schmidt, age 41
EVP: Edward J. Sattizahn, $220,833 pay
EVP, SoftKey Software: Robert Gagnon, age 58
President, International: David E. Patrick, age 40, $181,008 pay
VP Human Resources: Mary De Saint Croix
Auditors: Coopers & Lybrand L.L.P.

WHERE

HQ: One Athenaeum St., Cambridge, MA 02142
Phone: 617-494-1200
Fax: 617-225-0318
Web site: http://www.softkey.com

	1995 Sales	
	$ mil.	% of total
North America	141.5	85
Europe	24.3	14
Other regions	1.2	1
Total	**167.0**	**100**

WHAT

Selected Titles

Calendar Creator Plus	The Hubble Space
Compton's Interactive	Telescope
Encyclopedia	Instant Resume
Dinosaur Discovery	Key 3D Design Center
The Exotic Garden	Key Gourmet
The Family Doctor	PFS: First Publisher

KEY COMPETITORS

Adobe	Edmark	Nintendo
Borland	Electronic Arts	Quark
Brøderbund	Encyclopædia	SEGA
Claris	Britannica	Sony
Corel	IBM	Symantec
Creative	Intuit	Viacom
Technology	Knowledge	Walt Disney
CUC International	Adventure	
Dorling Kindersley	Microsoft	

HOW MUCH

Nasdaq symbol: SKEY FYE: December 31	Annual Growth	1990	1991	1992	1993	1994	1995
Sales ($ mil.)	61.8%	—	—	39.4	50.1	121.3	167.0
Net income ($ mil.)	—	—	—	6.4	(1.5)	21.1	(66.0)
Income as % of sales	—	—	—	16.2%	—	17.4%	—
Earnings per share ($)	—	—	—	0.32	(0.06)	1.04	(2.65)
Stock price – high ($)	—	—	—	—	—	27.25	51.75
Stock price – low ($)	—	—	—	—	—	9.75	20.38
Stock price – close ($)	(9.3%)	—	—	—	—	25.50	23.13
P/E – high	—	—	—	—	—	26	—
P/E – low	—	—	—	—	—	9	—
Dividends per share ($)	—	—	—	0.00	0.00	0.00	0.00
Book value per share ($)	—	—	—	0.00	0.00	2.25	6.71
Employees	11.4%	—	—	—	625	450	775

1995 YEAR-END
Debt ratio: 70.2%
Return on equity: —
Cash (mil.): $77.8
Current ratio: 1.17
Long-term debt (mil.): $500.7
No. of shares (mil.): 32.0
Dividends
  Yield: —
  Payout: —
Market value (mil.): $739.1
R&D as % of sales: 7.5%

SOFTWARE PUBLISHERS ASSOCIATION

OVERVIEW

If you are in the software business, the SPA is more than a place to get a steam and a massage among the beautiful people. Headquartered in Washington, DC, the Software Publishers Association (SPA) is the #1 international trade organization representing the personal computer software industry and is best known for its crackdown on software pirates. The group's 1,200 members include publishers and developers of business, consumer, and educational software. It also has associate members involved in distribution, retailing, consulting, and other software publishing services. The SPA's services include market research reports and surveys, seminars, lobbying, and antipiracy litigation. In addition, each year it presents "Codie" awards to outstanding software makers.

President Ken Wasch founded the SPA in 1983 with a group of businesses including Atari Software, the Bureau of National Affairs, CBS Software, Mindscape, and Xerox Educational Products. The group opened an office in France in 1990, and in 1991 it began a campaign (including starting a copyright protection fund) to heighten awareness of software piracy. However, in 1992 several of its largest members, including Microsoft, Autodesk, Lotus, and Novell, abandoned the group's domestic software-piracy program in favor of another program run by the Business Software Alliance (BSA). While these members began to rely on the BSA to enforce software laws, they remained members of the SPA.

Enforcing laws against the illegal use of software remains a key focus for the SPA. In 1994 it estimated that nearly half of all business software (and more than 90% in Russia and China) in use was pirated. However, the group has received some criticism for its sometimes heavy-handed tactics, which have included raids by federal marshals.

In 1995 the SPA won a major test case against Global Software & Accessories, which had been allowing customers to use software for 5 days if they put down a "nonrefundable deposit." A federal court ruled that the practice constituted software rental, which is illegal.

WHO

Chairman: Phil Adam
VC: Phil Goodhew
President: Ken Wasch
CFO: Thomas Meldrum
Secretary: Kirk Loevner
Treasurer: Alan Gleicher
Manager Human Resources: Joan Luedtkey
Auditors: Lang + Associates, P.A.

WHERE

HQ: 1730 M St. NW, Ste. 700, Washington, DC 20036-4510
Phone: 202-452-1600
Fax: 202-223-8756
Web site: http://www.spa.org

	1995 Revenues	
	$ mil.	% of total
US	9.1	88
Europe	1.3	12
Total	**10.4**	**100**

WHAT

	1995 Revenues	
	$ mil.	% of total
Membership	3.3	32
Litigation settlements	2.5	24
Conferences	2.4	23
Investment income	0.4	4
Other	1.8	17
Total	**10.4**	**100**

Selected Services
Antipiracy education and litigation
Government affairs briefings and lobbying
Market research reports
Publications
Sales data
Seminars

KEY COMPETITORS

Business Software Alliance

HOW MUCH

Trade organization FYE: June 30	Annual Growth	1990	1991	1992	1993	1994	1995
Sales ($ mil.)	15.3%	5.1	3.0	8.0	9.6	9.8	10.4
Net income ($ mil.)	(12.9%)	0.4	0.1	1.4	1.9	1.5	0.2
Income as % of sales	—	7.8%	3.3%	17.5%	19.8%	15.3%	2.0%
Employees	27.5%	—	—	—	40	50	65

1995 YEAR-END
Cash (mil.): $0.3
Current ratio: 2.84

SOUTH CHINA MORNING POST

OVERVIEW

British control or Chinese control of Hong Kong matters little to South China Morning Post (Holdings) Limited, as long as there is news to print. The company's operating business, the *South China Morning Post* (SCMP), is Hong Kong's leading English-language newspaper. SCMP's circulation of about 113,000 dwarfs the handful of English-language competitors in Hong Kong (including the *Hong Kong Standard* and the *Asian Wall Street Journal*). Other interests include a 27% stake in Asia Magazines and a 20% stake in the publisher of Thailand's leading English-language daily, the *Bangkok Post*. SCMP is incorporated in Bermuda to mitigate the effects of China's 1997 takeover of Hong Kong.

SCMP was set up by Alfred Cunningham and a group of British businessmen as a mouthpiece for China's reform movement. It was first published in 1903. The company went public in 1971. Later renamed News Printing Ltd., it subsequently diversified into securities and commercial printing. It also acquired stakes in the Dow Jones *Asian Wall Street Journal* and the *Far Eastern Economic Review*. In 1987 Australian-born media maven Rupert Murdoch's News Corp. conglomerate acquired News Printing. The company went public again in 1990. Malaysian tycoon Robert Kuok Hock Nien's Kerry Media acquired 35% of the company in 1993; he became its chairman. Fellow Malaysian tycoon Khoo Kay Peng owns 23% of the company.

The firm is expanding both in Hong Kong and in the Chinese mainland, where Kuok enjoys a good relationship with government leaders. In 1996 it acquired TVE Holdings, a Hong Kong-based entertainment, leisure, retail, and travel group. In 1997 the company plans to launch the *North China Morning Post*, a financial daily focusing on China and Hong Kong.

WHO

Chairman: Robert Kuok Hock Nien, age 71
Deputy Chairman: Roberto V. Ongpin, age 58
CEO: Lindley J. Holloway, age 66
Deputy Chief Executive: Owen R. Jonathan, age 43
Company Secretary: Daniel Doo Shek Hoi, age 52
Editor: Jonathan Fenby
Manager Human Resources: Milly Liew
Auditors: Ernst & Young LLP

WHERE

HQ: South China Morning Post Holdings Ltd., Cedar House, 41 Cedar Ave., Hamilton, HM12, Bermuda
Phone: 809-295-2244
Fax: 809-292-8666
Web site: http://www.scmp.com
Hong Kong HQ: Morning Post Centre, 22 Dai Fat St., Tai Po Industrial Estate, New Territories, Hong Kong
Hong Kong Phone: +852-2-680-8888
Hong Kong Fax: +852-2-680-8855

WHAT

	1995 Sales	
	HK$ mil.	% of total
Classified advertising	646.0	51
Display advertising	414.0	33
Circulation	136.0	11
Other	57.8	5
Total	**1,253.8**	**100**

Newspapers	*Harper's Bazaar*
South China Morning Post	PC Home
Sunday Morning Post	TV Week

Chinese-Language Publications (TVE Holdings)	Affiliates
Amoeba	Asia Magazines (27%)
Automobile	The Post Publishing Co.
Champion	(20%, publisher of
Cosmopolitan	Thailand's English daily
	Bangkok Post)

KEY COMPETITORS

Gannett
International Herald Tribune
Oriental Press
Sing Tao Holdings
Singapore Press

HOW MUCH

Principal exchange: Hong Kong FYE: June 30	Annual Growth	1990	1991	1992	1993	1994	1995
Sales (HK mil.)	9.6%	793.5	807.6	921.6	1,041.2	1,221.0	1,253.8
Net income (HK mil.)	16.2%	273.9	486.4	531.7	586.4	564.1	580.1
Income as % of sales	—	34.5%	60.2%	57.7%	56.3%	46.2%	46.3%
Earnings per share (HK)	16.7%	0.18	0.32	0.36	0.39	0.38	0.39
Stock price – high (HK)	—	2.75	3.53	4.40	5.55	5.45	5.15
Stock price – low (HK)	—	2.35	2.33	3.20	3.88	3.90	4.03
Stock price – close (HK)	12.5%	2.63	3.48	3.88	4.70	4.53	4.73
P/E – high	—	15	11	12	14	14	13
P/E – low	—	13	7	9	10	10	10
Dividends per share (HK)	1.4%	0.28	0.28	0.30	0.30	0.30	0.30
Book value per share (HK)	1.7%	1.70	1.74	1.81	1.87	2.01	1.85
Employees	(3.7%)	—	—	—	—	810	780

Note: $=HK7.73 (June 30, 1995)

1995 YEAR-END
Debt ratio: 4.8%
Return on equity: 20.1%
Cash (mil.): HK16.0
Current ratio: 0.95
Long-term debt (mil.): HK0.0
No. of shares (mil.): 1,500.0
Dividends
  Yield: 6.3%
  Payout: 77.5%
Market value (mil.): $916.6
Sales (mil.): $162.1

SPELLING ENTERTAINMENT GROUP INC.

OVERVIEW

You don't have to be able to spell to understand Spelling Entertainment's TV shows. The Los Angeles-based company is an independent producer and distributor of TV series, miniseries, made-for-TV movies, video games, and feature films. Spelling's titillating assets in the entertainment field include such TV series as *Melrose Place* and *Beverly Hills 90210* (which features founder Aaron Spelling's daughter Tori as one of its stars). Recently introduced TV shows include *Malibu Shores* and *Savannah*. Media titan Viacom, which owns 78% of Spelling Entertainment, put the company on the auction block in 1995 to pay down debt, but took it off the block the next year when it couldn't find a good offer.

A former actor and writer, Spelling had his first hit show, *Zane Grey Theatre*, in 1956. He formed the Charter Company in 1959 (oil marketing; sold in 1992) and Aaron Spelling Productions in 1965. A year after the debut of *The Mod Squad* in 1968, the company signed an exclusive production agreement with the ABC television network that lasted 18 years. Throughout the 1970s Spelling produced a series of escapist TV hits: *Charlie's Angels*, *Fantasy Island*, *The Love Boat*, and *Starsky and Hutch*. In 1981 Spelling launched the prime-time soap opera *Dynasty*, which ran 9 years. The company went public in 1986.

In 1989 the company bought Laurel Entertainment and merged with Great American Communications, creating Spelling Entertainment. Video rental chain Blockbuster Entertainment bought 48% of its stock in 1993, and the company launched a cable channel, TeleUNO, in Latin America. In 1994 it bought Republic Pictures and entertainment software producer Virgin Interactive, which boosted revenues. That year Viacom (owner of Paramount Pictures) bought Blockbuster.

WHO

Chairman: Sumner M. Redstone, age 72
VC; Chairman and CEO, Spelling Television: Aaron Spelling, age 73
EVP Office of the President, CFO, and Treasurer: Thomas P. Carson, age 49, $401,077 pay
EVP Office of the President: Peter H. Bachmann, age 38, $401,077 pay
SVP General Counsel: Sally Suchil, age 45, $199,154 pay
SVP and Corporate Controller: Kathleen Coughlan, age 43, $211,654 pay
VP Human Resources: Cheryl Wingard
Auditors: Price Waterhouse LLP

WHERE

HQ: 5700 Wilshire Blvd., Los Angeles, CA 90036-3659
Phone: 213-965-5700
Fax: 213-965-6984
Web site: http://www.viacom.com/spelling

WHAT

	1995 Sales	
	$ mil.	% of total
Television	349.7	53
Interactive entertainment	212.2	32
Home video	72.2	11
Licensing & merchandising	15.8	2
International film distribution	11.4	2
Other	3.1	0
Total	**664.4**	**100**

KEY COMPETITORS

All American Communications
BET
Carsey-Werner
DreamWorks SKG
Electronic Arts
International Family Entertainment
King World
Kushner-Locke
LucasArts
MCA
Nintendo
SEGA
Silicon Graphics
Sony
Time Warner
United Video Satellite
Walt Disney

HOW MUCH

NYSE symbol: SP FYE: December 31	Annual Growth	1990	1991	1992	1993	1994	1995
Sales ($ mil.)	1.8%	608.6	122.7	258.5	274.9	599.8	664.4
Net income ($ mil.)	83.2%	0.8	8.0	5.9	19.7	24.1	16.5
Income as % of sales	—	0.1%	6.5%	2.3%	7.2%	4.0%	2.5%
Earnings per share ($)	—	0.00	0.16	0.11	0.35	0.32	0.19
Stock price – high ($)	—	4.75	8.63	8.63	10.38	12.25	14.00
Stock price – low ($)	—	3.50	3.63	5.13	4.75	8.38	9.25
Stock price – close ($)	25.6%	4.00	8.38	6.25	10.00	10.75	12.50
P/E – high	—	—	54	79	30	38	74
P/E – low	—	—	23	47	14	26	49
Dividends per share ($)	(100.0%)	0.05	0.05	0.08	0.08	0.06	0.00
Book value per share ($)	16.4%	2.91	3.13	3.71	4.62	6.01	6.23
Employees	1.1%	852	382	600	500	700	900

1995 YEAR-END

Debt ratio: 35.4%
Return on equity: 3.0%
Cash (mil.): $20.7
Current ratio: 3.14
Long-term debt (mil.): $305.7
No. of shares (mil.): 89.7
Dividends
  Yield: —
  Payout: —
Market value (mil.): $1,121.0

STECK-VAUGHN PUBLISHING

OVERVIEW

This textbook publisher seemed "steck-in-a-rut" and out of touch with educational fashions that emphasize supplemental and multi-media materials over texts. But Austin, Texas-based Steck-Vaughn hopes that issuing new supplements and buying expertise in CD-ROMs will help it remain a leader in elementary, high school, and adult remedial and vocational education. In addition to texts, workbooks, and other support materials, the company publishes and distributes reference and other books to libraries. California-based trade school operator National Educational Corp. (NEC) owns about 83% of Steck-Vaughn.

The Steck Co., an Austin printer, established a publishing division in 1936. Financier Jack Vaughn bought the firm in 1965 and spun off publishing, by then the most profitable division, as Steck-Vaughn. In 1979 NEC bought it. The corporation — having loan default problems with its schools — took Steck-Vaughn public in 1993, its best year ever.

Much of Steck-Vaughn's strength was due to the fact that its home state, Texas, traditionally bought textbooks on a statewide basis. But in the 1990s educational theory dictated a greater use of supplemental materials like literature-based readers. Teachers had more discretion in these purchases and Steck-Vaughn had not courted them. Nor had it devoted much effort to developing computer-based materials. As a result, profits dived about 20% in 1994.

Sam Yau was brought in as chairman in 1995. He beefed up the marketing staff and acquired Educational Development Laboratories (adult education supplements) and Summit Learning (supplements sold directly to teachers and consumers). In 1996 the company agreed to buy Israel-based Edunetics (edutainment software) that Steck-Vaughn intends to use to support its curriculum materials.

WHO

Chairman: Sam Yau, age 47
President and CEO: Roy E. Mayers, age 52, $234,640 pay
VP Sales: Gunnar C. Voltz, age 51, $121,876 pay
VP Finance and CFO: Floyd D. Rogers, age 58, $109,862 pay
VP Marketing: Richard Y. Blumenthal, age 48, $106,481 pay
VP and Editor-in-Chief: Leslie M. Ford, age 46, $100,817 pay
Director Human Resources: Gabriele Madison
Auditors: Price Waterhouse LLP

WHERE

HQ: Steck-Vaughn Publishing Corporation, 8701 N. MoPac Expwy., Ste. 200, Austin, TX 78759-8365
Phone: 512-343-8227
Fax: 512-795-3397
Web site: http://www.steck-vaughn.com/

Steck-Vaughn distributes its books in Australia, Canada, the Caribbean, Japan, Mexico, New Zealand, Puerto Rico, Singapore, South Korea, Taiwan, and the US.

WHAT

	1995 Sales	
	$ mil.	% of total
Elementary/High School	34.9	60
Adult Education	12.7	22
Library	10.6	18
Total	**58.2**	**100**

Selected Products

Adult Education	Science/Health
Bilingual Education	Social Studies
Mathematics	Test Preparation and
Reading and Language Arts	Assessment

KEY COMPETITORS

Davidson &	Houghton Mifflin	Scholastic
Associates	McGraw-Hill	Simon &
Everyday	Minnesota	Schuster
Learning	Educational	Tribune
Grolier	Computing	William H.
Harcourt General	NTC Publishing	Sadlier

HOW MUCH

Nasdaq symbol: STEK FYE: December 31	Annual Growth	1990	1991	1992	1993	1994	1995
Sales ($ mil.)	14.2%	30.0	38.0	45.1	53.2	53.6	58.2
Net income ($ mil.)	12.3%	3.8	5.1	7.9	8.0	6.1	6.8
Income as % of sales	—	—	12.5%	13.4%	17.5%	15.0%	11.4%	11.7%
Earnings per share ($)	(6.6%)	—	—	0.59	0.61	0.42	0.48
Stock price – high ($)	—	—	—	—	16.00	10.75	8.75
Stock price – low ($)	—	—	—	—	8.75	4.75	5.00
Stock price – close ($)	(11.3%)	—	—	—	9.38	5.75	7.38
P/E – high	—	—	—	—	26	26	18
P/E – low	—	—	—	—	14	11	10
Dividends per share ($)	—	—	—	0.00	0.00	0.00	0.00
Book value per share ($)	21.3%	—	—	2.20	3.01	3.61	3.93
Employees	16.6%	170	239	283	283	329	367

1995 YEAR-END
Debt ratio: 5.5%
Return on equity: 13.1%
Cash (mil.): $11.8
Current ratio: 5.23
Long-term debt (mil.): $2.9
No. of shares (mil.): 14.3
Dividends
  Yield: —
  Payout: —
Market value (mil.): $105.7

TATTERED COVER, INC.

OVERVIEW

Following the road less traveled, the Tattered Cover Book Store has added a new story to the book-selling business. In an age of impersonal superstores, owner Joyce Meskis has come up with a different formula: comfortable chairs in every department; a vast range of books for customers to browse, read, and buy; and an instore restaurant with booklined booths. The Tattered Cover is the largest independent new-book bookseller in the US, stocking 500,000 volumes representing 150,000 titles. Sofas and chairs for customers to sit in abound, including rocking chairs in the children's section and church pews in the religion department. Although the store has moved a couple of times within the Denver metropolitan area, customers have not only followed the store to each new location but have volunteered to help the store move.

After years of working in bookstores and libraries to support herself through college to become a teacher, Meskis woke up one morning to realize that she was already living her dream. In 1973 she poured her life savings into a small bookstore in Parker, Colorado, 20 miles southeast of Denver. Unable to make a go of the store, Meskis discovered that a 3-year-old Denver bookstore called the Tattered Cover was for sale. Borrowing from everyone she knew, Meskis bought the store in 1974 and started business with one employee. As business grew, Meskis expanded the store 7 times and moved twice, settling at the present location in the prosperous Cherry Creek area in 1986.

The Tattered Cover emphasizes large selection, personal service and a cozy atmosphere. Customers are brought into the store by weekly poetry readings, 20 or more author appearances a month, young writers' contests, storytime for children, and other special activities. Every employee receives 2 weeks of training, with the first day's training conducted by Meskis herself. To push books that might go unnoticed, the store publishes a newsletter twice a year.

In 1994 Tattered Cover opened a 7,500-square-foot store in downtown Denver; it plans to expand this location to 35,000 square feet in 1996. In 1995 it opened the Fourth Story restaurant in its Cherry Creek store.

WHO

President and Owner: Joyce Meskis, age 53
General Manager: Regina Bullock
General Manager: Barb Bush
General Manager: Geoffrey Godwin-Austen
General Manager: Roy Laird
General Manager: Cathy Langer
General Manager: Linda Millemann
General Manager: Mathew Miller
Controller: Margie Keenan
Director of Marketing and Community Relations: Heather Conn
Auditors: Causey, Demgen, & Moore

WHERE

HQ: 1628 16th St., Denver, CO 80202
Phone: 303-322-1965
Fax: 303-629-1704
Web site: http://www.tatteredcover.com

WHAT

Book Sections

Architecture	Literary Criticism
Art	Maps and Globes
Bargain Books	Metaphysics
Biography	Mythology
Blank Books	Nature
Business	New Fiction
Children's Section	New Mystery
Collecting	New Paperback Fiction
Computer Books	New Paperback Nonfiction
Cookbooks	Performing Arts
Electronics	Philosophy
Engineering	Photography
Exercise	Poetry
Fiction	Political Science
Foreign Language	Posters
Games	Psychology
Gardening	Reference
Health	Religion
Historical Documents and	Spiritual Growth
Autographs	Sports
History	Transportation
Home Repair	Travel
Humor	True Crime
Judaica	Woodworking
Large Print Books	

KEY COMPETITORS

Barnes & Noble
Between the Covers
Borders
The Boulder Bookstore
Explore Booksellers &
  Coffeehouse
McKinzey-White
  Booksellers
Off the Beaten Path

HOW MUCH

Private company FYE: December 31	Annual Growth	1990	1991	1992	1993	1994	1995	
Sales ($ mil.)	15.2%	—	—	18.0	21.5[1]	25.0	27.5[1]	
Employees	7.7%	—	—	320	348	375	400	

[1] Estimated

Tattered Cover
Book Store

TELESCAN, INC.

OVERVIEW

Telescan lets you conduct important business online — from managing your investments to golfing with your business contacts. The Houston-based company's online services help investors access financial news and information, while its Computer Sports Network serves up online golf and baseball games. Telescan provides online services in conjunction with other companies and organizations such as the American Institute of Architects and the Editor and Publisher Company. Its online database serves universities, corporations, and the US government. Microsoft cofounder Paul Allen's Vulcan Ventures owns 15% of the company. Telescan cofounder and CEO David Brown owns 9%.

While working on his doctorate in biochemical engineering, Richard Carlin created a computer program to track his investments. With seed money from Brown, a former NASA engineer who helped design landing gear for the lunar module, the pair founded Telescan in 1983. They introduced their first product, Telescan Analyzer investment software, in 1986 and an online golf game in 1987. The company added a portfolio manager in 1990 and a mutual fund search product in 1992. Telescan began trading on Nasdaq in 1993.

In 1995 Telescan developed several 3rd-party online services, including those for *Adweek* and *Billboard* magazines. It also created TIPnet, a World Wide Web investor "supersite" linking information on major international stock markets.

The company launched Wall Street City, a Web site for individual investors, in 1996. It also announced an alliance with Internet access provider NETCOM whereby NETCOM will offer access to TIPnet and include promotional information about Telescan with its NetCruiser disks.

WHO

Chairman and CEO: David L. Brown, age 55, $107,625 pay
VC and SVP: Richard K. Carlin, age 40
EVP and Acting COO: Luiz V. Alvim, age 65
SVP: Roger C. Wadsworth, age 48
SVP: Scott L. Brown
CFO: Karen R. Fohn, age 35
Director Human Resources: Brigette Dewhurst
Auditors: Hein & Associates LLP

WHERE

HQ: 10550 Richmond Ave., Ste. 250, Houston, TX 77042
Phone: 713-588-9700
Fax: 713-588-9797
Web site: http://www.telescan.com

WHAT

	1995 Sales	
	$ mil.	% of total
Online services	8.8	63
Contract & license revenues	2.8	20
Products	2.4	17
Total	**14.0**	**100**

Selected Products and Services

Computer Sports Network
General Manager (simulated baseball game)
Links Tour (computer golf tournaments)

Knowledge Express Data Systems (KEDS, online database serving the US government, universities, and corporations)

Telescan Financial
Options Search (custom options search)
QuoteLink (link with other financial service software)
Telescan Analyzer (financial database access and analysis)
Telescan Esearch (investment screening)

KEY COMPETITORS

America Online	Knight-Ridder	Reach
Bloomberg	M.A.I.D.	Reuters
CompuServe	Microsoft	Thomson Corp.
Dow Jones	OneSource	
Global Financial	Prodigy	
Information	Quote.Com	

HOW MUCH

Nasdaq symbol: TSCN FYE: December 31	Annual Growth	1990	1991	1992	1993	1994	1995
Sales ($ mil.)	41.1%	2.5	3.0	4.2	6.9	10.5	14.0
Net income ($ mil.)	32.0%	(0.3)	(0.6)	(0.3)	0.0	(2.6)	(1.2)
Income as % of sales	—	—	—	—	0.0%	—	—
Earnings per share ($)	(29.7%)	(0.70)	(0.11)	(0.05)	0.00	(0.28)	(0.12)
Stock price – high ($)	—	—	—	2.25	10.50	9.63	9.50
Stock price – low ($)	—	—	—	1.75	1.75	3.75	4.00
Stock price – close ($)	59.6%	—	—	2.00	9.13	4.38	8.13
P/E – high	—	—	—	—	—	—	—
P/E – low	—	—	—	—	—	—	—
Dividends per share ($)	—	—	0.00	0.00	0.00	0.00	0.00
Book value per share ($)	44.3%	—	0.18	0.49	0.91	0.63	0.78
Employees	39.0%	—	—	57	95	142	153

1995 YEAR-END
Debt ratio: 9.2%
Return on equity: —
Cash (mil.): $1.8
Current ratio: 2.05
Long-term debt (mil.): $0.5
No. of shares (mil.): 10.2
Dividends
  Yield: —
  Payout: —
Market value (mil.): $83.2
R&D as % of sales: 11.4%

THOMAS NELSON, INC.

OVERVIEW

These days that still, small voice you hear in the middle of the night is likely to belong to a QVC salesperson, but it might still carry a message from the Lord if the products being hawked are Bibles, books, and music published by Nashville-based Thomas Nelson. The world's leading religious publishing house, Thomas Nelson offers 9 Bible translations (4 of which it owns) and publishes more than 1,200 Bible versions and related products for targeted audiences. It also publishes and distributes other books (by the likes of Billy Graham, Pat Robertson, and Robert Schuller), music (by Amy Grant and Sandi Patty, among others), videos, and gift items. These items are distributed through religious bookstores and stores like Wal-Mart. The company's Royal Media unit operates the Morningstar Radio Network, which features country and contemporary Christian music and has 138 affiliates in the US. Founder and chairman Sam Moore owns 15% of the company.

When 19-year-old Salim Ziady came to the US from Lebanon in 1950, he financed his education by selling books door-to-door. After changing his name to Sam Moore (Ziady means "more"), in 1957 he founded National Book, which merged with Bible producer Royal Publishing and went public in 1962. In 1969 Royal bought and merged with the US operations of Thomas Nelson & Sons, a UK-based Bible publisher founded in 1798. A foray into magazine publishing and greeting cards in the 1980s was only marginally succesful. In 1992 it bought Christian publisher and record company Word from Capital Cities/ABC.

In 1996 the company sought a buyer or partner for Aspire, its newsstand magazine for women. Thomas Nelson has had better luck with gift and stationery lines, which it enlarged with the 1995 purchase of C.R. Gibson.

WHO

Chairman, President, and CEO: Sam Moore, age 64, $450,000 pay
President, Word Records and Music Division: Roland Lundy, age 45, $311,201 pay
President, Word Publishing Division: Byron D. Williamson, age 49, $266,275 pay
EVP and CFO: S. Joseph Moore, age 32, $283,847 pay
EVP and Secretary: Joe L. Powers, age 49, $249,234 pay
SVP International: Charles Z. Moore, age 61
VP and General Counsel: Stuart A. Heaton, age 39
VP Human Resources: Rusty Faulks
Auditors: Andersen Worldwide

WHERE

HQ: Nelson Place at Elm Hill Pike, Nashville, TN 37214-1000
Phone: 615-889-9000
Fax: 615-883-6353

Thomas Nelson distributes its products in Asia, Australia, Canada, Europe, Mexico, New Zealand, South Africa, South America, and the US.

	1995 Sales
	% of total
US	91
Other countries	9
Total	**100**

WHAT

	1995 Sales	
	$ mil.	% of total
Music	89.7	34
Book publishing	86.9	33
Bible publishing	58.4	22
Gifts & other	30.1	11
Total	**265.1**	**100**

KEY COMPETITORS

Allied Digital Technologies	Integrity Music International	Reader's Digest Sparrow
American Greetings	Family Entertainment	Tandycrafts Watchtower
Bertelsmann	Moody	
Hallmark	Foundation	

HOW MUCH

NYSE symbol: TNM FYE: March 31	Annual Growth	1990	1991	1992	1993	1994	1995
Sales ($ mil.)	34.9%	59.4	73.6	93.1	137.5	227.7	265.1
Net income ($ mil.)	28.8%	3.3	4.3	5.9	6.4	8.7	11.7
Income as % of sales	—	5.6%	5.8%	6.3%	4.7%	3.8%	4.4%
Earnings per share ($)	21.0%	0.32	0.42	0.48	0.49	0.66	0.83
Stock price – high ($)	—	4.74	5.87	9.47	15.80	20.80	20.20
Stock price – low ($)	—	3.27	3.27	5.34	8.27	11.40	14.20
Stock price – close ($)	37.3%	3.94	5.34	8.54	14.60	19.40	19.20
P/E – high	—	15	14	20	32	32	24
P/E – low	—	10	8	11	17	17	17
Dividends per share ($)	34.1%	0.03	0.07	0.09	0.10	0.13	0.13
Book value per share ($)	19.0%	2.27	2.61	3.78	4.19	4.69	5.41
Employees	30.4%	300	320	600	1,100	1,100	1,130

1995 YEAR-END
Debt ratio: 62.6%
Return on equity: 17.3%
Cash (mil.): $0.8
Current ratio: 3.39
Long-term debt (mil.): $120.2
No. of shares (mil.): 13.4
Dividends
  Yield: 0.7%
  Payout: 15.7%
Market value (mil.): $257.9

THE TODD-AO CORPORATION

OVERVIEW

Todd-AO made sure you had no problem hearing Tom Hanks say "Houston, we have a problem" in the movie *Apollo 13*. The San Francisco-based company provides postproduction sound services, including music recording, sound editing and mixing, and sound effects for film and television production companies. It also offers special visual effects, postproduction video, and satellite transmission services. San Francisco's Naify family owns more than 58% of the company.

The business was founded in 1952 by film producer Michael Todd, who worked with American Optical to develop a process for mixing stereo sound for a wide-screen projection system. Armed with the new technology, Todd convinced Broadway musical creators Richard Rodgers and Oscar Hammerstein to put their work on film. Soon Todd-AO helped bring *Oklahoma!*, *South Pacific*, and *The King and I* to the big screen. Todd died in a plane crash in 1958, but the company went on to provide sound services for *West Side Story* and *The Sound of Music*. The firm went public in 1974 and was later acquired by United Artists, which was controlled by Robert and Marshall Naify. In 1986 Todd-AO acquired television postproduction company Glen Glenn Sound. That year United Artists spun off Todd-AO to the public, but the Naifys still held a majority interest. In 1988 Todd-AO acquired postproduction sound company Trans-Audio.

Todd-AO focused on sound services until 1994, when Salah Hassanein, former head of Warner Brothers International Theaters, became president. Hassanein has expanded the company's postproduction business. It acquired postproduction video services company Paskal Video in 1994, and in 1995 it bought Chrysalis Television Facilities, a London-based provider of postproduction video and satellite transmission services.

WHO

Co-chairman and Co-CEO: Marshall Naify, age 75, $5,000 pay
Co-chairman and co-CEO: Robert A. Naify, age 73, $5,000 pay
President and COO: Salah M. Hassanein, age 74, $100,001 pay
SVP; President, Todd-AO Studios: Christopher D. Jenkins, age 40, $465,981 pay
SVP; EVP, Todd-AO Studios: Joseph R. DeLang, age 39, $293,942 pay
VP and Treasurer (CFO): Silas R. Cross, age 56
Director Human Resources: Kate Reck
Auditors: Deloitte & Touche LLP

WHERE

HQ: 1135 N. Mansfield Ave., Hollywood, CA 90038
Phone: 213-465-2579
Fax: 213-465-1231

	1995 Sales	
	$ mil.	% of total
US	45.1	90
Europe	4.9	10
Total	**50.0**	**100**

WHAT

Selected Services

Dialogue	Sound effects
Music mixing	Special visual effects
Music recording	Video and transmission
Narration	services
Sound editing	

KEY COMPETITORS

Digital Communications
IndeNet
International Post
Laser-Pacific Media
Lucas Digital
Sound Delux
Unitel Video

HOW MUCH

Nasdaq symbol: TODDA FYE: August 31	Annual Growth	1990	1991	1992	1993	1994	1995
Sales ($ mil.)	15.8%	24.0	28.5	28.2	27.4	32.9	50.0
Net income ($ mil.)	62.5%	0.3	2.6	2.1	1.1	1.8	3.4
Income as % of sales	—	1.3%	9.1%	7.4%	4.0%	5.5%	6.8%
Earnings per share ($)	58.5%	0.04	0.32	0.25	0.14	0.22	0.40
Stock price – high ($)	—	5.91	4.66	4.32	5.23	6.82	11.25
Stock price – low ($)	—	2.95	3.18	3.41	3.07	3.18	3.64
Stock price – close ($)	18.3%	3.35	3.64	3.64	4.09	4.32	7.75
P/E – high	—	148	15	17	37	31	28
P/E – low	—	74	10	14	22	15	9
Dividends per share ($)	0.0%	0.05	0.05	0.05	0.05	0.05	0.05
Book value per share ($)	6.8%	2.75	3.01	3.05	3.30	3.43	3.83
Employees	18.8%	165	165	180	170	240	390

1995 YEAR-END
Debt ratio: 27.9%
Return on equity: 11.5%
Cash (mil.): $6.0
Current ratio: 2.53
Long-term debt (mil.): $8.0
No. of shares (mil.): 8.2
Dividends
  Yield: 0.6%
  Payout: 12.5%
Market value (mil.): $63.0

TRUE NORTH COMMUNICATIONS INC.

OVERVIEW

Navigating the new frontiers of advertising is tricky, as Chicago-based advertising holding company True North discovered. It lost about $150 million in billings in 1996 from Colgate-Palmolive (despite a reorganization meant to improve support services), in part because its foreign operations (in about 60 countries) lacked depth. Colgate consolidated most of its worldwide accounts at the larger Young & Rubicam. True North's primary subsidiary Foote, Cone & Belding (FCB) is the #1 ad agency "brand" in the US, but the parent company is not even in the top 5 among US advertising companies. In addition to FCB, True North's subsidiaries include TN Services Inc. (agency support services); TN Media Inc. (media buying); and TN Technologies Inc. (electronic services, including Web site creation and interactive advertising). True North also owns 49% of Publicis-FCB, a European joint venture with French ad agency Publicis Communication.

FCB's predecessor was founded in 1873 by Daniel Lord. In 1881 Ambrose Thomas joined the company, which became Lord & Thomas. Executive Albert Lasker took over in 1906. In 1943 it passed to 3 managers, Emerson Foote, Fairfax Cone, and Don Belding, and became one of the top agencies worldwide. In 1988, hoping to build its international presence, FCB put its European operations into a joint venture with Publicis Communication (Publicis owns about 20% of True North). In 1991 Bruce Mason took over and created True North as FCB's parent in 1994.

Meanwhile relations with Publicis deteriorated. In 1996 after almost 2 years of arbitration, the companies declared their cooperation pact dead, but the joint venture remained nominally intact. In 1995 and 1996, True North began buying more ad agencies, including Chicago's Bayer Bess Vanderwarker.

WHO

Chairman and CEO: Bruce Mason, age 56, $1,180,000 pay
VC: Craig R. Wiggins, age 50, $670,000 pay
Chairman and CEO, Foote, Cone & Belding Advertising: J. Brendan Ryan, age 53
Chairman and CEO, TN Technologies Inc.: Jack Balousek, age 50, $720,000 pay
EVP and CFO: Terry M. Ashwill, age 51, $660,000 pay
VP and Manager Human Resources: Doris Radcliffe
Auditors: Andersen Worldwide

WHERE

HQ: 101 E. Erie St., Chicago, IL 60611-2897
Phone: 312-751-7227
Fax: 312-751-3501
Web site: http://www.fcb-tg.com/fcb-tg

	1995 Sales		1995 Pretax Income	
	$ mil.	% of total	$ mil.	% of total
US	324.0	74	41.8	100
Other countries	115.1	26	(2.5)	—
Adjustments	—	—	(24.6)	—
Total	**439.1**	**100**	**14.7**	**100**

WHAT

Services
Advertising (including specialties in health care and the Hispanic market)
Digital and interactive communications
Marketing and product research
Media buying and planning
Package design
Public relations
Sales promotion and direct marketing
Trademark and name development
Yellow pages directory advertising

KEY COMPETITORS

Ackerley Communications	Dentsu	Omnicom Group
Bozell, Jacobs	Grey Advertising	Organic Online
Cordiant	Interpublic Group	WPP Group
Corinthian Communications	Leo Burnett	Young & Rubicam
D'Arcy Masius	Modem Media	
	N W Ayer	

HOW MUCH

NYSE symbol: TNO FYE: December 31	Annual Growth	1990	1991	1992	1993	1994	1995
Sales ($ mil.)	5.4%	338.1	342.0	353.3	372.7	403.7	439.1
Net income ($ mil.)	(1.8%)	21.6	(19.1)	18.0	25.7	30.3	19.7
Income as % of sales	—	6.4%	—	5.1%	6.9%	7.5%	4.5%
Earnings per share ($)	(3.7%)	1.05	(0.91)	0.83	1.15	1.34	0.87
Stock price – high ($)	—	15.06	13.75	15.75	24.00	24.00	21.81
Stock price – low ($)	—	8.88	9.31	11.50	14.75	19.94	15.75
Stock price – close ($)	12.8%	10.13	12.75	15.69	24.00	21.50	18.50
P/E – high	—	14	—	19	21	18	25
P/E – low	—	9	—	14	13	15	18
Dividends per share ($)	0.0%	0.60	0.60	0.60	0.60	0.60	0.60
Book value per share ($)	1.7%	8.76	7.25	7.95	8.62	9.10	9.51
Employees	2.5%	3,865	3,696	3,631	3,709	3,929	4,369

1995 YEAR-END
Debt ratio: 20.0%
Return on equity: 9.1%
Cash (mil.): $57.0
Current ratio: 0.90
Long-term debt (mil.): $5.4
No. of shares (mil.): 23.4
Dividends
  Yield: 3.2%
  Payout: 69.0%
Market value (mil.): $432.2

UNITED STATES SATELLITE

OVERVIEW

United States Satellite Broadcasting (USSB) is making waves for digital TV channel surfers. The St. Paul, Minnesota-based company beams 25 channels of television programming (including the Movie Channel, HBO, Nickelodeon, MTV, and the All News Channel) to subscribers across the US, who receive the signals via an 18-inch dish antenna and receiver system (available at more than 18,000 stores for about $600). USSB, Hughes Electronics' DIRECTV (with which it shares its satellite), and PRIMESTAR dominate the market for high-power direct broadcast satellite (DBS) TV programming, though similar ventures (including one by MCI and media hulk News Corp.) are in the works. Family-owned Hubbard Broadcasting owns 52% of the company. Dow Jones owns 5%.

Hubbard Broadcasting, a radio and TV station owner founded in 1923, formed USSB in 1981 to develop a direct broadcast satellite television system. The next year the company obtained the first DBS license ever issued. Following a decade of R&D, in 1991 USSB and satellite technology company Hughes Electronics agreed to share technology for developing digital broadcasting. In 1993 the DBS-1 satellite (with 1/3 of its broadcast capacity designated for USSB) was launched into space, giving the company the backbone for its distribution system. USSB negotiated long-term contracts with major programming providers and in 1994 introduced its DBS TV service. That year it completed its state-of-the-art National Broadcast Center to control its distribution system.

At the end of 1995, USSB had some 628,000 subscribers; analysts believe the company needs more than 3 million to turn a profit. By focusing on households that are underserved by cable TV providers and offering competitive prices, USSB plans to continue increasing its customer base.

In 1996 Hubbard Broadcasting spun USSB off as a public company. For that fiscal year USSB reported a loss of $95 million on sales of $192 million.

WHO

Chairman: Stanley S. Hubbard, age 62, $100,000 pay
President and CEO: Stanley E. Hubbard, age 34, $100,000 pay
EVP: Robert W. Hubbard, age 30, $100,000 pay
SVP Marketing: Mary Pat Ryan, age 39, $275,000 pay
VP Finance and Administration: Bernard J. Weiss, age 41, $145,000 pay
VP Dealer Marketing: Carl Wegener, age 43, $136,000 pay
VP Operations: John Degan, age 63
CFO, Treasurer, and Secretary: Gerald D. Deeney, age 72
Director Human Resources: Frank Vilotta
Auditors: Andersen Worldwide

WHERE

HQ: United States Satellite Broadcasting Company, Inc., 3415 University Ave., St. Paul, MN 55114
Phone: 612-645-4500
Fax: 612-642-4314
Web site: http://www.ussbtv.com/channel1/index.html

WHAT

Selected Programming Package Offerings

USSB Essentials ($7.95 per month)	Nick at Nite
All News Channel	Nickelodeon
Comedy Channel	VH1
Lifetime	
MTV	**Entertainment Plus ($34.95)**
Nick at Nite	All News Channel
Nickelodeon	Comedy Channel
VH1	Lifetime Television
	MTV
HBO Plus ($24.95)	Multichannel Cinemax
All News Channel	Multichannel HBO
Comedy Channel	Multichannel Showtime
Lifetime Television	Multichannel The Movie
MTV	Channel
Multichannel Cinemax (3 channels)	Nickelodeon
	VH1
Multichannel HBO (5 channels)	

KEY COMPETITORS

Adelphia	Comcast	PRIMESTAR
Communications	Continental	TCI
American	Cablevision	Time Warner
Telecasting	Cox	United Video
Cablevision	Communications	Satellite
Systems	DIRECTV	U S WEST Media
Century	EchoStar	Viacom
Communications	Communications	

HOW MUCH

Nasdaq symbol: USSB FYE: June 30	Annual Growth	1990	1991	1992	1993	1994	1995
Sales ($ mil.)	—	—	0.0	0.0	0.0	0.0	42.3
Net income ($ mil.)	—	—	(1.7)	(6.9)	(4.1)	(22.2)	(74.7)
Income as % of sales	—	—	—	—	—	—	—
Employees	—	—	—	—	—	—	98

1995 YEAR-END
Debt ratio: 95.1%
Cash (mil.): $12
Current ratio: 0.72
Long-term debt (mil.): $97

UNITED VIDEO SATELLITE

Not only can United Video Satellite Group (UVSG) tell you who's on first and what's on 2nd, it can tell you what's on all your other TV channels. The Tulsa-based company operates the Prevue Networks, which provides on-screen programming guides for TV viewers in the US, Canada, Latin America, and Europe. Its UVTV unit distributes programming and information via satellite to cable TV systems. The SpaceCom unit transmits radio programming, paging, and news services via satellite to private networks. The Superstar Satellite Entertainment division markets programming to home satellite dishes, and the 70%-owned SSDS unit provides software development and systems integration for corporations. The company owns 20% of On-Demand Services, which provides the gaming industry with technology for at-home horse betting. UVSG is controlled by the #1 US cable TV operator, Tele-Communications, Inc. (TCI), which bought a 40% stake in 1996.

UVSG was founded in 1965 to develop a microwave network to provide programming to cable systems. CEO Lawrence Flinn acquired a majority interest in 1976, and 2 years later the company entered the satellite market when it began transmitting WGN. UVSG introduced its first program promotion and guide service in 1981. It went public in 1993.

The company introduced Prevue Express Plus Video (program listings and on-demand previews) in 1995. The next year it began developing promotional Web sites that enable cable systems to post programming and other information on the World Wide Web. Also in 1996 UVSG formed a joint venture with TCI's Liberty Media programming arm to create the nation's #1 provider of programming for C-band satellite receivers (installed at about 2.4 million US homes).

WHO

Chairman and CEO: Lawrence Flinn Jr., age 60
President and COO: Roy L. Bliss, age 53
EVP and CFO: Peter C. Boylan III, age 32
EVP; President, Prevue Networks: Joe D Batson, age 41
EVP; President, Superstar Satellite Entertainment: Rick Brattin, age 39
SVP and General Counsel: Charles B. Ammann, age 41
SVP: Jerry D. Henshaw
VP Human Resources: Suzanne Shepherd
Auditors: Ernst & Young LLP

WHERE

HQ: United Video Satellite Group, Inc.,
7140 S. Lewis Ave., Tulsa, OK 74136-5422
Phone: 918-488-4000
Fax: 918-488-4979
Web site: http://www.uvsg.com

WHAT

	1995 Sales	
	$ mil.	% of total
Superstar	166.3	63
Prevue Networks	39.6	15
UVTV	26.6	10
SSDS	18.0	7
SpaceCom	12.4	5
Total	**262.9**	**100**

Selected Services
Prevue Networks (on-screen program promotion and guide services for cable TV systems)
SpaceCom (satellite transmission services for radio programming, paging and news services, and others)
SSDS (70%, software development and systems integration)
Superstar (marketing and distribution of programming to home satellite dish owners)
UVTV (marketing and distribution of video and audio services to cable television systems)

KEY COMPETITORS

Gemstar International
Lenfest Group
News Corp.
StarSight

HOW MUCH

Nasdaq symbol: UVSGA FYE: December 31	Annual Growth	1990	1991	1992	1993	1994	1995
Sales ($ mil.)	41.7%	46.0	53.4	68.2	114.4	196.7	262.9
Net income ($ mil.)	38.8%	4.5	4.8	3.5	5.2	16.3	23.2
Income as % of sales	—	9.9%	8.9%	5.1%	4.5%	8.3%	8.8%
Earnings per share ($)	78.9%	—	—	0.11	0.16	0.46	0.63
Stock price – high ($)	—	—	—	—	8.50	12.50	17.94
Stock price – low ($)	—	—	—	—	6.13	5.25	10.25
Stock price – close ($)	44.1%	—	—	—	6.50	12.00	13.50
P/E – high	—	—	—	—	53	27	29
P/E – low	—	—	—	—	38	11	16
Dividends per share ($)	—	—	—	—	0.00	0.00	0.00
Book value per share ($)	54.4%	—	—	—	0.81	1.23	1.93
Employees	32.0%	275	321	351	500	700	1,100

1995 YEAR-END
Debt ratio: 28.2%
Return on equity: 41.4%
Cash (mil.): $29.0
Current ratio: 1.14
Long-term debt (mil.): $24.0
No. of shares (mil.): 35.8
Dividends
  Yield: —
  Payout: —
Market value (mil.): $483.0
R&D as % of sales: 1.4%

UPSIDE PUBLISHING CO.

OVERVIEW

Upside does more than publish a magazine; it chronicles the curious cross-culture that results when high finance meets high tech. The San Mateo, California-based company's monthly magazine, also called *Upside*, is a forum for investors, executives, and industry insiders to share information about the business of technology. The magazine's industry-savvy, irreverent attitude, and humorous artwork (caricatures of high-tech heavies are a big hit) has earned it a steadily growing readership that has topped 100,000. In addition, the company's site on the World Wide Web extends its reach from the printed page to cyberspace.

Upside was founded in 1989 by Richard Karlgaard (now editor of *Forbes* magazine's *ASAP* supplement, an *Upside* rival) and Anthony Perkins (who later started Flipside Communications's *Red Herring* magazine, another competitor) as "a magazine for Silicon Valley about Silicon Valley." The pair raised $1 million from investors and venture capitalists, but a downturn in the industry made advertising hard to come by. In 1992 the founders left Upside in the hands of an interim management team. That year the company formed an alliance with *Forbes* to create *ASAP*, but *Forbes* ended the joint venture when Karlgaard left Upside. In 1994 the firm made its first profit — just over $125,000. Also in 1994 *Upside* launched its online edition.

The company is using partnerships to increase its credibility. In 1995 it created an Entrepreneur of the Year award with financial consultants Ernst & Young, brokerage firm Merrill Lynch, and *Inc.* magazine. It also collaborated with business information specialist, Hoover's, Inc. (publisher of this profile), on *Hoover's Guide to Computer Companies*. In 1996 Upside joined with the Nasdaq market, software developer Cadence Design Systems, Ernst & Young, and investment bankers Alex Brown & Sons to sponsor the Upside Technology Summit, a meeting of technology movers and shakers.

Also that year it named David Bunnell, founder of *PC Magazine* and *PC World*, as CEO and publisher of *Upside* magazine.

WHO

Chairman: Putney Westerfield
Publisher and CEO: David Bunnell
Associate Publisher: Cheryl Lucanegro
CFO and Circulation Director: Edward A. Ring
Editor-in-Chief: Eric Nee
Executive Editor: Richard Brandt
Executive Editor: Karen Southwick
Managing Editor: Chuck Lenatti
Assistant Editor: Kora McNaughton
Art Director: Richard Merchan
Production Manager: Christine Marquez
Online Production Manager: Aaron Jones
Auditors: Grant Thornton LLP

WHERE

HQ: 2015 Pioneer Ct., San Mateo, CA 94403
Phone: 415-377-0950
Fax: 415-377-1962
Web site: http://www.upside.com

WHAT

	1995 Sales
	% of total
Magazine	85
Other	15
Total	**100**

Upside Magazine Features
High-Tech Stock Ticker
Hot Prospects
Inside Upside
Interview
Management Insights
On the Soapbox
Paradigm Shifts
Technology Trends
Venture View

Upside Online Features
Current Issue
Entrepreneur Forum
Online Feedback
Online News
Resource Center

KEY COMPETITORS

CMP Publications
Cowles Media
Dow Jones
Dun & Bradstreet
Flipside Communications
Forbes
Goldhirsh Group
Hearst
HyperMedia

International Data Group
McGraw-Hill
Mecklermedia
Reed Elsevier
Time Warner
U.S. News & World Report
Wired Ventures
Ziff-Davis

HOW MUCH

Private company FYE: December 31	Annual Growth	1990	1991[1]	1992	1993	1994	1995[1]
Sales ($ mil.)	24.6%	1.0	1.3	1.5	1.7	2.3	3.0
Employees	—	—	—	—	—	—	27

[1] Estimated

U.S. NEWS & WORLD REPORT

OVERVIEW

There's big news at *U.S. News*. The arrival of new editor James Fallows, author of a controversial book that skewered US journalists, heralded major change in both the staff and the focus of *U.S. News & World Report*, which has a circulation of 2.2 million and is 3rd after *Time* and *Newsweek* among weekly news magazines. *U.S. News*, known for its annual guides including *America's Best Colleges*, *Best Mutual Funds*, and *Best Jobs for the Future*, is owned by Mort Zuckerman, whose other publications include the traditional Bostonian political and literary magazine *Atlantic Monthly*, the punchy *New York Daily News*, and *Fast Company*, a business magazine targeted at readers under 45. Zuckerman, with associate Fred Drasner, also owns Applied Graphics Technologies, a developer of computerized graphics and magazine formats, and he controls real estate developer Boston Properties, with holdings in Boston, New York City, Washington. DC, and elsewhere.

In 1933 political columnist David Lawrence started *United States News*, a weekly newspaper that reflected his conservative views. He turned it into a magazine 7 years later, launched another magazine, *World Report*, in 1946, and merged the 2 publications in 1948.

After making millions through Boston Properties, Zuckerman bought *U.S. News* in 1984. By the next year his real estate and media holdings were worth some $400 million.

With circulation down slightly in the first half of the 1990s and ad pages dropping in 1996, *U.S. News* increased its emphasis on book and CD-ROM publishing of material including its annual consumer guides. Later that year Fallows replaced Michael Ruby and his wife, Merrill McLoughlin, co-editors for 7 years. Fallows, author of *Breaking the News: How the Media Undermine American Democracy*, immediately replaced several top editorial managers and staff and shuffled many others, saying he wanted to focus more on the substance behind the news and less on political mechanics. Among the casualties were executive editor Peter Bernstein and prominent political reporter Steven Roberts.

WHO

Chairman and Editor-in-Chief: Mortimer B. Zuckerman, age 58
President and CEO: Fred Drasner, age 53
EVP and Publisher: Thomas R. Evans
Editor: James Fallows, age 47
SVP and Business Manager: Alice Rogoff
SVP Consumer Marketing: Hilleary Hoskinson
VP and Treasurer: Joan T. Williams
Director Corporate Communications: Bruce Zanca

WHERE

HQ: 2400 N St. NW, Washington, DC 20037-1196
Phone: 202-955-2000
Fax: 202-955-2035
Web site: http://www.usnews.com

WHAT

	1996 Sales
	% of total
Advertising	69
Subscriptions	28
Newsstand sales	3
Total	**100**

Selected Zuckerman Holdings
Applied Graphics Technologies (70%, computerized graphics and magazine formatting)
The Atlantic Monthly (political and literary magazine)
Boston Properties (real estate development firm)
Fast Company (business magazine)
New Media Group (coordinates online publications)
New York Daily News (tabloid newspaper)
U.S. News & World Report (weekly news magazine, book and CD-ROM publishing)

KEY COMPETITORS

Advance Publications
Dow Jones
The Economist
Forbes
McGraw-Hill
New York Times
Time Warner
Upside Publishing
Washington Post

HOW MUCH

Private company FYE: January 31	Annual Growth	1991	1992	1993	1994	1995	1996
Sales ($ mil.)	3.1%	267.4	295.0	298.2	315.0	318.5	311.0
Employees	0.0%	500	500	500	500	500	500

VALUE LINE, INC.

OVERVIEW

Investors interested in stock splits should pay attention to Value Line. The New York City-based company produces investment-related publications, and its *Value Line Investment Survey* (one-page analyses of 1,700 companies) is one of the best-known stock-rating publications in the US. Value Line also produces an electronic version of the survey and manages 17 mutual funds. Eighty percent of Value Line is owned by a family holding company controlled by Value Line CEO Jean Bernhard Buttner, but that control has been contested by her twin brother, Van Bernhard.

Founded by their father in 1931 as Arnold Bernhard & Co., the company began ranking stocks through its Value Line Ranking System in 1965. It was reorganized under the name Value Line in 1982 and went public in 1983. Arnold Bernhard died in 1987, and Jean took over as chairman and CEO the next year.

Key to Value Line's success is its secretive ranking system. Despite claims by Buttner that her father invented the system, credit is generally given to Samuel Eisenstadt, who has been with the company since 1946.

In 1994 Value Line introduced its *Value Line Mutual Fund Survey*, thus entering true competition with Morningstar, which introduced its mutual fund survey in 1986. A 1994 *Wall Street Journal* article outlined similarities between the wording of Value Line's surveys and those of Morningstar, but the company has denied ever copying its rival.

Buttner's brother — whose feuding with his sister over their late mother's estate earned him the boot from the boards of both the family holding company and Value Line — sued her in 1996 to gain control of his share of the family business. The company earned $42 million on sales of $87 million in fiscal 1996.

WHO

Chairman, President, and CEO: Jean B. Buttner, age 61, $1,091,250 pay
SVP and Research Chairman: Samuel Eisenstadt, age 73, $225,000 pay
VP, Treasurer and Director of Compliance and Internal Audit: David T. Henigson, age 37, $198,400 pay
CFO: Paul Ehrenstein
Senior Portflio Manager: John Moore, $212,500 pay
Director of Information Technology: Dean Tencic
Secretary: Howard Brecher, age 41
Auditors: Price Waterhouse LLP

WHERE

HQ: 220 E. 42nd St., New York, NY 10017-5891
Phone: 212-907-1500
Fax: 212-818-9747

WHAT

	1995 Sales		1995 Operating Income	
	$ mil.	% of total	$ mil.	% of total
Investment information & publications	55.9	71	15.4	52
Investment management	23.2	29	14.3	48
Total	**79.1**	**100**	**29.7**	**100**

Brokerage Services
Electronic Publishing
The Value Line Daily Options Survey
Value Line Fund Analyzer
The Value Line Industry Review
Value/Screen III

Institutional Services
Selected Print Publications
The Value Line Investment Survey
The Value Line Investment Survey — Expanded Edition
The Value Line Mutual Fund Survey

KEY COMPETITORS

CDA/ Weisenberger
Dun & Bradstreet
Investor's Business Daily
Lipper Analytical
Market Guide
McGraw-Hill
Media General
Morningstar, Inc.
Multex
Primark
Thomson Corp.

HOW MUCH

Nasdaq symbol: VALU FYE: April 30	Annual Growth	1991	1992	1993	1994	1995	1996
Sales ($ mil.)	6.1%	64.7	74.6	78.4	82.1	79.1	87.1
Net Income ($ mil.)	16.3%	19.6	26.3	27.7	28.9	23.2	41.7
Income as % of sales	—	30.3	35.3	35.3	35.2	29.3	47.9%
Earnings per share ($)	16.3%	1.97	2.64	2.78	2.90	2.32	4.18
Stock price – high ($)[1]	—	25.50	27.00	40.50	42.00	40.00	39.25
Stock price – low ($)[1]	—	16.00	12.50	22.75	26.50	29.00	26.00
Stock price – close ($)[1]	19.2%	16.00	24.50	27.50	39.00	31.00	38.50
P/E – high	—	13	10	15	15	17	9
P/E – low	—	8	5	8	9	13	6
Dividends per share ($)	5.9%	0.60	0.60	0.60	0.75	0.80	0.80
Book value per share ($)	21.3%	8.45	10.49	12.68	14.78	17.36	22.18
Employees	1.9%	347	343	363	372	375	381

[1]Stock prices are for the prior calendar year.

1995 YEAR-END
Debt ratio: 0.0%
Return on equity: 21.2%
Cash (mil.): $31.8
Current ratio: 2.62
Long-term debt (mil.): $0.0
No. of shares (mil.): 10.0
Dividends
  Yield: 2.1%
  Payout: 19.1%
Market value (mil.): $384.1

THE VOYAGER COMPANY

OVERVIEW

Forget passive reading. New York City-based Voyager is a pioneer in interactive publishing, with more than 350 books and laser disc movies in its catalog. The company's interactive book formats include CD-ROMs, "expanded books" (books on disk with annotated, searchable text), and graphic novels available on the World Wide Web. The company's best-selling CD-ROM, a version of the Beatles' film *A Hard Day's Night* that includes biographies, outtakes, and musical information, has sold more than 100,000 copies.

Robert and Aleen Stein began Voyager Press in Santa Monica, California, in 1984 to distribute classic movies on laser disc. (It developed the "letterbox" format, which allows widescreen movies to be shown on television's square screens.) In 1985 Voyager partnered with international film distributor Janus Films, co-owned by Jonathan Turell and William Becker (now partners in the company with Bob Stein) and began adding interviews and outtakes to films. In 1989 Voyager created the first interactive CD-ROM, a guide to Beethoven's 9th Symphony. The company pioneered expanded books in 1992.

In 1993 the Steins separated. (Aleen founded new media publishing concern Organa in 1995.) That year Bob moved the company to Manhattan.

Voyager's early titles were exclusively for Apple computers, but by 1994 1/3 of its catalog was available for PCs, and the company announced it would convert all its titles to Windows. Voyager entered an agreement with Public Media Home Video to distribute its titles through video retail outlets (the company's primary distribution is through mail order).

In 1995 it debuted CDLink (developed with *Spin* magazine and record label Rykodisc), which links audio CDs to sites on the World Wide Web. That year it signed an agreement with Image Entertainment, the largest licensee of optical laser disc programming in the US, to copublish CD-ROMs of films, including *Citizen Kane* and *The Terminator*. The company launched The Narrative Corpse, a serial graphic novel created on the Web by more than 60 writers, in 1996.

WHO

Partner: Robert Stein
Partner: William Becker
Partner: Jonathan B. Turell
Director Marketing: Noelle Celeste
Director Sales: Kelly Cook
Auditors: Kamler, Lewis, Nourman

WHERE

HQ: 578 Broadway, Ste. 406, New York, NY 10012
Phone: 212-431-5199
Fax: 212-431-5799
Web site: http://www.voyagerco.com

WHAT

Selected Titles

Interactive CD-ROMs
The Complete Maus, Art Spiegelman
A Hard Day's Night, The Beatles
Invisible Universe, Dr. Fiorella Terenzi
Making Music, Morton Subotnick
Our Secret Century, Rick Prelinger
Van Gogh: Starry Night, Albert Boime
Who Built America?, Roy Rosenzweig and Steve Brier
With Open Eyes, The Art Institute of Chicago

Original Projects for the Web
Eric Drooker's FLOOD!
Laurie Anderson's Green Room
The Narrative Corpse

KEY COMPETITORS

Advance Publications
Allegro New Media
Bertelsmann
Brøderbund
Bureau of Electronic Publishing
Byron Preiss Multimedia
Capitol Multimedia
Dataware
Hearst
IVI Publishing
Knowledge Adventure
Microsoft
OverDrive
Pearson
R/GA Interactive
Simon & Schuster
SoftKey
Sony
Time Warner

HOW MUCH

Private company FYE: December 31	Annual Growth	1990	1991	1992	1993	1994	1995
Estimated sales ($ mil.)	14.5%	—	—	8.0	11.0	12.0	12.0
Employees	0.0%	—	—	—	100	100	100

VOYAGER

WENNER MEDIA

OVERVIEW

Jann Wenner may have tired of *Family Life*, but he's still bringing up his baby — *Rolling Stone* magazine — after nearly 3 decades. New York City-based Wenner Media, led by its namesake, publishes the profitable rock culture title as well as magazines *US* (celebrities) and *Men's Journal* (macho adventures). It also develops books around *Rolling Stone*'s name.

Wenner, then a 21-year-old Berkeley dropout, started his "little rock and roll newspaper" in 1967. The name *Rolling Stone*, derived from a blues song, was suggested by Ralph Gleason, a San Francisco music critic and Wenner's mentor. At that time, with backing of $7,500, Wenner formed Straight Arrow Publishers, taking the name from a rival counterculture rag. Straight Arrow had an approach that was right for the times: an early subscription drive offered pot paraphernalia as an enticement.

Unfazed by a string of magazine failures, Straight Arrow started a book division in 1971. That year the company saw its first profit. As the 1970s rolled on, the stature of *Rolling Stone* grew with contributions from Hunter S. Thompson and Annie Leibovitz. Straight Arrow moved to New York in 1977. More magazine failures followed, but by then it didn't matter: the company's flagship was a national icon.

Wenner purchased 25% of *US* in 1985 and launched the "Perception/Reality" campaign, which persuaded potential nonmusic advertisers that *Rolling Stone* readers were a great untapped — not unwashed — market. Rounding out that pivotal year, Wenner and his wife, Jane, began buying up Straight Arrow stock, becoming its sole owners.

Straight Arrow bought the rest of *US* in 1989 and began *Men's Journal* in 1992. It reached out to yuppie parents by delivering *Family Life* in 1993, the same year the company became Wenner Media. Jann and Jane Wenner separated in 1995, generating rampant speculation about the company's future; *Family Life* was subsequently sold. Meanwhile, both *US* and *Men's Journal* have improved at least to the brink of profitability. Rolling Stone Online, which began on CompuServe in 1995, moved to America Online the next year.

WHO

Chairman; Editor and Publisher, *Rolling Stone*: Jann S. Wenner, age 50
SVP and General Manager: Kent Brownridge
VP and CFO: John Lagana
VP; Group Publisher, *Rolling Stone*: Dana L. Fields
VP; West Coast Director, *Rolling Stone*: Bill Harper
VP; Director Marketing Communications: Linn Tanzman
VP; Creative Director: Fred Woodward
Editor, *US*: Barbara O'Dair
Editor, *Men's Journal*: John Rasmus
Editor, Rolling Stone Press: Holly George-Warren
Director Human Resources: Pamela Fox
Auditors: Ernst & Young LLP

WHERE

HQ: 1290 Avenue of the Americas, New York, NY 10104
Phone: 212-484-1616
Fax: 212-767-8205

WHAT

Magazines
Men's Journal
Rolling Stone
US

Selected Rolling Stone Press Books
Cobain
Garcia
Neil Young: The Rolling Stone Files
R.E.M.: The Rolling Stone Files
The Rolling Stone Album Guide
The Rolling Stone Encyclopedia of Rock & Roll
The Rolling Stone Illustrated History of Rock & Roll
Rolling Stone: Images of Rock & Roll
Rolling Stone: The Photography
Rolling Stone's Alt-Rock-A-Rama
U2: The Rolling Stone Files

Other Selected Operations
Men's Journal (30-minute weekly program on sports channel ESPN)
Rolling Stone Online (supplemented electronic version on America Online)

KEY COMPETITORS

Advance Publications
Camouflage Associates
Hearst
Lagardère
Mariah Media
News Corp.
Rodale Press
Stern Publishing
Time Warner

HOW MUCH

Private company FYE: December 31	Annual Growth	1990	1991	1992	1993	1994	1995
Estimated sales ($ mil.)	2.3%	178.3	160.2	159.5	161.9	190.9	200.0
Estimated employees	0.0%	—	—	—	300	300	300

WESTWOOD ONE, INC.

OVERVIEW

Even if the sound goes in one ear and out the other, the revenues from radio broadcasts often end with Westwood One. The Culver City, California-based company is one of the US's top 3 producers and distributors of radio programming, with ABC and CBS. It operates Westwood One Radio Networks, Mutual Broadcasting System, and NBC Radio Network, which broadcast entertainment, news, sports, and talk programming to more than 6,000 stations. Infinity Broadcasting owns about 22% of the company; chairman Norman Pattiz also owns a large portion. Westinghouse has announced plans to acquire Infinity and its stake in Westwood One.

After being fired from his Los Angeles TV advertising sales job in 1974, Pattiz heard a local radio station broadcast a 52-hour program of Motown music. He approached the station about syndicating a similar show, lined up advertisers, and signed on some 250 stations to air the broadcast. Pattiz soon moved the business to an office in nearby Westwood, and Westwood One was born. The company grew by giving programs to stations in exchange for a percentage of advertising revenues, instead of trying to sell the shows for cash.

In 1984 the company went public. The next year it acquired the struggling Mutual Broadcasting System radio network. Westwood One bought the National Broadcasting Co. radio networks in 1987 from General Electric. Two years later the company launched the Westwood One News and Entertainment Network. It bought Infinity's Unistar Radio Networks in 1994 in exchange for Westwood One stock and let Infinity take over management of the company.

Westwood One expanded in 1996 with the purchase of certain operations of Shadow

WHO

Chairman: Norman J. Pattiz, age 53, $1,025,000 pay
President and CEO: Mel A. Karmazin, age 52
CFO and Secretary: Farid Suleman, age 44
President, Westwood One Entertainment: Gregory P. Batusic, age 41, $329,167 pay
President, Westwood One Radio Networks: Jeffrey B. Lawenda, age 53, $338,906 pay
Director Personnel: Carolyn Jones
Auditors: Price Waterhouse LLP

WHERE

HQ: 9540 Washington Blvd., Culver City, CA 90232
Phone: 310-204-5000
Fax: 310-836-1158

Westwood One broadcasts to more than 6,000 stations around the world.

WHAT

Selected Operations
Mutual Broadcasting System (news broadcast network)
NBC Radio Network (news and entertainment broadcast network)
Radio & Records (radio and music industry publication)
Shadow Broadcast Services (regional weather, news, and sports broadcasts for radio and TV)
Unistar Radio Networks (radio production and 24-hour satellite broadcasts)
Westwood One Broadcasting Services, Inc. (traffic, news, sports, and weather programming)
Westwood One Entertainment (produces radio shows and live events)
Westwood One Radio Networks (manages radio network operations)

Selected Radio Personalities

Jim Bohannon	G. Gordon Liddy
Don Imus	Doug "The Greaseman"
Larry King	Tracht
Tom Leykis	Bruce Williams

KEY COMPETITORS

American Urban Radio Networks	Corporation for Public Broadcasting
Capital Cities/ABC	Westinghouse/CBS

HOW MUCH

Nasdaq symbol: WONE FYE: December 31	Annual Growth	1990	1991	1992	1993	1994	1995
Sales ($ mil.)	(0.0%)	145.9	144.4	137.7	99.6	136.3	145.7
Net income ($ mil.)	—	(18.2)	(16.8)	(24.1)	(23.9)	(2.7)	9.7
Income as % of sales	—	—	—	—	—	—	6.7%
Earnings per share ($)	—	(1.25)	(0.58)	(1.62)	(1.58)	(0.09)	0.28
Stock price – high ($)	—	9.75	3.00	3.63	9.50	11.63	19.50
Stock price – low ($)	—	1.50	1.13	1.47	1.59	7.13	9.63
Stock price – close ($)	51.9%	1.75	1.53	1.63	8.38	9.75	14.13
P/E – high	—	—	—	—	—	—	70
P/E – low	—	—	—	—	—	—	34
Dividends per share ($)	—	0.00	0.00	0.00	0.00	0.00	0.00
Book value per share ($)	(14.9%)	6.04	6.63	5.01	3.38	3.08	2.69
Employees	45.1%	—	—	—	269	464	566

1995 YEAR-END
Debt ratio: 54.8%
Return on equity: 10.2%
Cash (mil.): $0.0
Current ratio: 1.19
Long-term debt (mil.): $108.0
No. of shares (mil.): 31.0
Dividends
  Yield: —
  Payout: —
Market value (mil.): $441.4s

318

WILLIAM MORRIS AGENCY, INC.

OVERVIEW

If Sylvester Stallone tells you to contact his people, he's referring to William Morris. Headquartered in Beverly Hills (where else?), the talent agency represents some of the world's most famous actors, authors, musicians, and sports stars. But a client need not possess a toothy grin, magic pen, perfect voice, or amazing athletic prowess. Morris also fronts for such accidental celebrities as Kent Weeks, a Cairo professor who led a team of archaeologists in the discovery of the ancient tomb of Egyptian pharaoh Ramses II. The agency is owned by its executives and employees.

The company was started in 1898 as William Morris, Vaudeville Agent, by its 25-year-old namesake, a New York booking agent. When his acts were blacklisted by a rival, Morris built his own theater circuit and refurbished the American Music Hall to showcase them. In the early 1900s the agency invented the concept of bundling stars and performing acts and promoting them as a package. By 1922 Morris was a leading vaudeville agent. In 1927 he opened an office in California to broker talent for the new "talkies." Morris died in 1932.

Abe Lastfogel began leading the firm's New York operations in the 1930s, turning it into one of the top talent agencies in vaudeville, radio, movies, nightclubs, and books. In 1949 it combined forces with the Berg-Allenberg agency in California. In the 1950s Lastfogel became president as the company ventured into TV, supplied entertainers to a booming Las Vegas, and started the vogue in TV quiz shows. Lastfogel, who owned all of Morris's voting stock, retired in 1969, distributing the stock among top executives and employees.

Management changes and infighting in the 1970s and 1980s resulted in an exodus of key stars and staff; former Morris agents started archrival Creative Artists Agency. In the 1990s the firm regrouped by buying the Jim Halsey Co. (country music); Triad Artists (talent agency); and Charles Dorris (Christian music).

When CAA lost its top executives in 1995, William Morris was able to pick off such key clients as Whoopi Goldberg.

In 1996 Morris reached agreements with publisher Simon and Schuster and online content provider Wave Interactive to market pay-per-use software on the World Wide Web.

WHO

Chairman and CEO: Norman Brokaw
President: Jerome F. Katzman
COO, EVP, and Secretary: Walter Zifkin
EVP: Jim Griffin
EVP: Alan Kanoff
EVP: Owen Laster
EVP: Richard Rosenberg
SVP and CFO: Irving J. Weintraub
Director Human Resources: Gail Moore
Auditors: Wallin Simon & Black

WHERE

HQ: 151 El Camino Dr., Beverly Hills, CA 90212
Phone: 310-274-7451
Fax: 310-786-4462
Nashville office: 2100 W. End Ave., Ste. 1000, Nashville, TN 37203
Nashville phone: 615-963-3000
Nashville fax: 615-693-3090
New York office: 1325 Avenue of the Americas, New York, NY 10019
New York phone: 212-586-5100
New York fax: 212-246-3583

WHAT

Selected Clients

Actors	Marcia Clark
Alec Baldwin	Chris Darden
Bill Cosby	Alexandra Ripley
Clint Eastwood	Kent Weeks
Alan King	
Angela Lansbury	**Musicians**
Jack Lemmon	Bobby Brown
Walter Matthau	Digital Underground
Marie Osmond	The Eagles
Burt Reynolds	En Vogue
Annabella Sciorra	Peter Frampton
Sylvester Stallone	Whitney Houston
Christopher Walken	Barry Manilow
	Eddie Rabbitt
Authors/Personalities	John Salley
Oksana Baiul	James Taylor
Tom Clancy	Tanya Tucker

KEY COMPETITORS

Agency for the Performing Arts	InterTalent
Chief Talent Corp.	Leading Artists Agency
Creative Artists	Monterey Peninsula Artists
Elite Model Management	United Talent Agency
International Creative Management	

HOW MUCH

Private company FYE: December 31	Annual Growth	1990	1991	1992	1993	1994	1995
Sales ($ mil.)	12.3%	—	—	—	111.0	125.0	140.0
Employees	9.5%	—	—	—	500	500	600

WIRED VENTURES, INC.

OVERVIEW

San Francisco-based Wired Ventures has made a name for itself by chronicling the ever-changing, ever-growing online community. Reflecting the cyberculture it follows, the company's flagship magazine, *Wired*, offers irreverent but technologically savvy articles and a splashy graphic style. The company also offers an online version of its cyber-chronicle, HotWired, on the World Wide Web.

Wired Ventures is trying to expand its brand into other media, including books and television. To raise the cash for the move the company filed to go public in May 1996. The IPO valued the company at around $415 million. Following the offering, cofounders Louis Rossetto and Jane Metcalfe would have owned about 16% and 15%, respectively, and media holding company Advance Publications would have owned 11%. However, with Wall Street interest in Internet-related stocks cooling, Wired delayed the offering.

Metcalfe and Rossetto attempted to publish a tech-culture magazine, *Electric Pencil*, in Europe in the 1980s, but the venture failed. They brought their idea to the US and recruited MIT Media Lab founder Nicholas Negroponte as a financial backer and eventual contributor. The magazine's first issue hit newsstands in 1993. By January 1994 it had over 110,000 paid subscribers, and in March of that year upscale magazine publisher Conde Nast (Advance Publications) bought a 17% stake in the company.

Wired's online sister, HotWired, which features shorter info-bites and pieces not available in the magazine, debuted in 1994. It received more than 100,000 connections and 4,000 subscribers its first day, growing to 235,000 subscribers the next year. HotWired is supported by advertisers — including IBM, Apple, and MCI.

In 1995 Wired sold about 15% of the company to German publisher Burda, ad agency WPP, and telecommunications firm Pacific Telesis. Also in 1995 the company announced its HardWired book division, with plans to release more than 10 titles by 1997. In 1996, HotWired unveiled Hotbot, a World Wide Web search engine.

WHO

CEO; Editor and Publisher, *Wired*; **Editor-in-Chief,** *HotWired*: Louis Rossetto, age 46, $88,558 pay
President: Jane Metcalfe , age 34, $88,558 pay
CFO and Secretary: Jeffrey Simon, age 34, $110,000 pay
VP Interactive: Andrew Anker, age 32, $140,369 pay
VP Corporate and Business Development: Rex O. Ishibashi, age 32, $110,000 pay
VP and Chief Technology Officer: Jacquard W. Guenon
VP Operations: Todd Sotkiewicz
Executive Editor, *Wired*: Kevin Kelly

WHERE

HQ: 520 Third St., 4th Fl., San Francisco, CA 94107-1815
Phone: 415-222-6200
Fax: 415-222-6209
Web site: http://www.hotwired.com

WHAT

Selected *Wired* Features
"Deductible Junkets" (information technology conferences)
"Electric Word" (technology news)
"Fetish" (product news)
"Geek Page" (changing technology news)
"Net Surf" (online directory)
"Raw Data" (trivia)
"Reality Check" (news features)
"Street Cred" (product news)

Selected Hotwired Features
Coin (online marketplace)
Eye Witness (international news)

Renaissance 2.0 (gallery with art, music, videos, and written contributions)
Signal (Internet news and reviews, industry updates)
Wired (online information from the magazine)

Selected Hardwired Books
Digerati: Encounters with the Cyber Elite by John Brockman
Mind Grenades by John Plunkett and Louis Rossetto
Wired Style: Principles of English Usage in the Digital Age by the editors of *Wired*

KEY COMPETITORS

CMP Publications
C/NET
DEC
Excite
HyperMedia
Infoseek
International Data Group
Lycos
McGraw-Hill

Mecklermedia
Open Text
Upside Publishing
Wolff New Media
Yahoo
Ziff-Davis

HOW MUCH

Private company FYE: December 31	Annual Growth	1990	1991	1992	1993	1994	1995
Sales ($ mil.)	195.4%	—	—	—	2.9	9.2	25.3
Net income ($ mil.)	—	—	—	—	(1.0)	(3.5)	(6.5)
Income as % of sales	—	—	—	—	—	—	—
Employees	—	—	—	—	—	—	284

1995 YEAR-END:
Cash (mil.): $7.2
Current ratio: 0.90
Long-term debt (mil.): $1.2

WOLFF NEW MEDIA LLC

OVERVIEW

"Our goal is to deliver the friendliest, easiest-to-use, and most knowledgeable guide to the Internet and online services," says Michael Wolff, CEO of Wolff New Media. The New York City-based company, which built its business publishing the ubiquitous *Net Book Internet* guide series, is becoming a full-fledged Internet directory company through YPN (Your Personal Network), a web site that contains over 70,000 reviews of more than 600 topics and online versions of many of its NetBooks.

Since *NetGuide*, a directory to the nooks and crannies of the Internet, was published in 1994, it and other titles in the series (*NetGames, NetMusic*, and *NetTravel* and miniguides such as *NetVote*) have sold over a million copies. A consultant to such media concerns as Time Warner and CMP Publications, the firm has also been involved in the creation of *Wired*, *Out*, and *NetGuide* magazines, as well as Time Inc.'s online service, Pathfinder.

A journalist who began his career with the *New York Times* and who later wrote for *Esquire*, *Rolling Stone*, and the *Village Voice*, Michael Wolff founded Michael Wolff & Co. in 1988 to develop books and magazines that could take advantage of desktop publishing technologies. In 1990 Peter Rutten, a founder of *Electric Word* magazine, joined Wolff as creative director. Following the success of the book *NetGuide*, Wolff licensed CMP Publications its database and rights to produce *NetGuide* magazine. The series now includes *NetGames, NetChat, NetMoney, NetTrek*, and *NetSports*.

In 1996 the company changed its name to Wolff New Media and expanded its online offerings as well as the book line. It received $3.5 million in new financing that year from National Direct Marketing Corp. and investment bankers Patricof & Co. Capital Corp. With a rigorous production schedule planned for 1996, Wolff New Media decided to publish its own books. Wolff said the company would publish a new guide every 20 days in 1996, including *NetDoctor, NetKids, NetSci-Fi, NetSpy, and NetStudy*. Also in 1996 the company announced NetClock, a calendar listing some 500 online events daily.

WHO

President and CEO: Michael Wolff, age 43
EVP: Jim Morouse
CFO and General Counsel: Alison Anthoine
VP Marketing: Jay Sears, age 29
Executive Editor: Kelly Maloni, age 27
Managing Editor: Ben Greenman, age 26

WHERE

HQ: 520 Madison Ave., 11th Fl., New York, NY 10022
Phone: 212-308-8100
Fax: 212-308-8837
Web site: http://www.ypn.com

WHAT

Selected Company Projects
NetChat: Where to meet people in Cyberspace!
Net Clock (calendar of daily online events)
NetGames: What's playing in Cyberspace!
NetJobs: Use the Internet to land your Dream Job!
NetMoney: How to get rich in Cyberspace!
NetMusic: Your guide to rock and more!
NetSports: Sports mania on the Information Highway!
NetTaxes: Prepare and file your taxes electronically!
NetTech: Products! Support! Software!
NetTravel: Make your travel plans online!
NetVote: Follow the 1996 campaign online!
Resume-O-Matic: Fill out a simple form and turn your resume into a Web page
YPN (web site featuring reviews and other content)

KEY COMPETITORS

America Online
CompuServe
Excite
HyperMedia
Infoseek
International Data Group
Lycos
McGraw-Hill
Mecklermedia
Viacom
Yahoo
Ziff-Davis

HOW MUCH

Private company FYE: December 31	Annual Growth	1990	1991	1992	1993	1994	1995
Estimated sales ($ mil.)	102.7%	—	—	0.6	1.4	2.2	5.0
Employees	63.6%	—	—	8	14	21	35

W.W. NORTON & COMPANY, INC.

OVERVIEW

That weight in the book bag isn't a brick, it's a Norton Anthology. The well-known, dense tomes are just one example of W.W. Norton's determination to "publish books not for a single season, but for the years." New York City-based employee-owned Norton publishes some 300 fiction, nonfiction, and poetry books per year for the college, medical, professional, and trade markets. Its Countryman Press division produces adventure and mystery books (under the Foul Play Press imprint), while Norton Professional Books operation specializes in architecture, design, self-help, psychology, and psychotherapy books. Norton also publishes literary compilations as well as college texts for biology, computer science, economics, history, political science, and psychology.

William Warder Norton and his wife, M. D. Herter Norton, started the enterprise by publishing pamphlets of lectures given at the adult education division of New York City's Cooper Union. To appease booksellers who found the pamphlets hard to handle, Norton began packaging the lectures in book format in 1925. In 1930 the Nortons began publishing textbooks. The Depression did little to slow sales as the company added books about music, philosophy, and psychology.

As chairman of the Council on Books in Wartime during WWII, Warder Norton worked to ensure that soldiers around the world had access to books. He died in 1945. Two years later, his widow sold nearly all of the company stock to Norton's managers, who later sold it to other employees. During the 1950s the publisher developed the Norton Anthologies of literature, which have since sold more than 20 million copies. Norton began publishing paperbacks and started a series of poetry books in the 1960s. In 1974 the company acquired Liveright Publishing Corp.

Norton extended the reach of its products in the 1980s with the establishment of offices in Canada, East Asia, and Latin America. It started Norton Professional Books in 1985 to publish books on psychotherapy. In 1994 it expanded the line to include books on architecture and design.

Norton made its 2nd-ever acquisition with the 1996 purchase of Countryman Press, a 23-year-old Vermont-based publisher.

WHO

Chairman: Donald Lamm
VC: Edwin Barber
President: W. Drake McFeely
EVP and Treasurer: Victor Schmalzer
VP and Director, Subsidiary Rights: Geannie Luciano
VP and Secretary: Warren Tiley Jr.
VP Trade Sales: William F. Rusin
Director Personnel: Lisa Gaeth

WHERE

HQ: 500 Fifth Ave., New York, NY 10110
Phone: 212-354-5500
Fax: 212-869-0856
Web site: http://www.norton.com

WHAT

Selected Operations
Countryman Press (adventure books)
Foul Play Press (imprint, mystery books)
Norton Professional Books (architecture, psychology, psychotherapy, and self-help books)
W.W. Norton & Company Ltd. (international operations)

Selected Titles
AnOther Cummings (e.e. cummings)
The Coming of Age (Simone De Beauvoir)
Confession (Leo Tolstoy)
Frankenstein (Mary Shelley)
Gertrude Stein's America (Gertrude Stein)
A Little Yellow Dog (Walter Mosley)
The Metamorphosis (Franz Kafka)
The Mismeasure of Man (Stephen Jay Gould)
The Norton Anthology of Poetry (Editors: Margaret Ferguson, Mary Jo Salter, and Jon Stallworthy)
The Republic (Plato)
Virus (Luc Montagnier)
We Never Make Mistakes (Aleksandr Solzhenitsyn)
The X Factor (George Plimpton)

KEY COMPETITORS

Addison-Wesley
Advance Publications
Bertelsmann
Harcourt General
Hearst
Holtzbrinck
Houghton Mifflin
John Wiley
Lagardere
McGraw-Hill
Pearson
Plenum Publishing
Rand McNally
Reed Elsevier
Scholastic
Thomson Corp.
Times Mirror
Tribune
Universal Press
Viacom
Wolters Kluwer

HOW MUCH

Private company FYE: March 31	Annual Growth	1990	1991	1992	1993	1994	1995
Estimated sales ($ mil.)	23.1%	—	20.0	26.0	32.0	39.0	46.0
Employees	(2.2%)	—	350	320	320	320	320

W. W. NORTON
NEW YORK · LONDON & COMPANY

YAHOO! INC.

OVERVIEW

In *Gulliver's Travels* Yahoos were a dirty and backward people. Now they're trying to clean up on the Internet. Sunnyvale, California-based Yahoo! is one of the premier services for getting around the World Wide Web. Its advertiser-supported free navigational guide is featured on several online networks and leading Web sites, including CompuServe and the Microsoft Network. Among companies providing content to Yahoo! are Ziff-Davis, Reuters, Rogers Communications, and Hoovers, Inc., publisher of this profile.

Despite its meager revenues and minimal operating history, the company's estimated valuation at the time of its 1996 IPO was a staggering $300 million, and months later its valuation held steady at $500 million. Following the offering, investment firm Sequoia Capital owned 21% of the company, and founders David Filo and Jerry Yang each owned 19.5%. Other shareholders included Reuters New Media and SOFTBANK.

While graduate students at Stanford, Filo and Yang developed the Yahoo! search engine to compile a list of their favorite Internet sites. They set up their own Web index site in 1994, and it was soon being accessed by thousands of web surfers each day. Marc Andreessen, who had written the original Mosaic web browser and cofounded Netscape Communications, and Randy Adams, president of the Internet Shopping Network, stepped in to help Filo and Yang commercialize the service. Yahoo! moved to corporate offices and hired Timothy Koogle, the former head of Intermec, a maker of data collection and data communications products, as CEO. The company continued to add Web sites to its index — as many as 1,000 a day. In late 1995 Yahoo! and Ziff-Davis announced that they would codevelop products for delivery online, on CD-ROM, and in print.

By that time it was being accessed by about one million users a day. Yahoo! continues to expand its services, with Yahooligans!, an Internet navigation guide for children ages 8-14; Yahoo! Canada; Yahoo! Japan; and Yahoo! Internet Life, an online and print magazine that resulted from its Ziff-Davis partnership.

WHO

President and CEO: Timothy Koogle, age 44
Chief Yahoo: Jerry Yang, age 27
Chief Yahoo and Acting VP Engineering and Operations: David Filo, age 29
SVP Business Operations: Jeff Mallett, age 31
SVP Finance and Administration and CFO: Gary Valenzuela, age 39
Auditors: Price Waterhouse LLP

WHERE

HQ: 3400 Central Expwy., Ste. 201, Santa Clara, CA 94086
Phone: 408-731-3300
Fax: 408-731-3301
Web site: http://www.yahoo.com

	1995 Users % of total
US	70
Other countries	30
Total	**100**

WHAT

Selected Products	Selected Search Categories
Yahoo! (search engine for indexing the location of information on the Web)	Arts
	Business and Economy
	Computers and Internet
Yahoo! Canada (regional guide, with Rogers Communications)	Education
	Entertainment
	Government
Yahoo! Internet Life (online and print magazine, with Ziff-Davis)	Health
	News
	Recreation
Yahoo! Japan (Japanese-language guide, with Softbank Corp.)	Reference
	Regional
	Science
Yahooligans! (Internet navigational guide for children ages 8-14)	Social Science
	Society and Culture

KEY COMPETITORS

Excite
Infoseek
Lycos
Open Text
Verity
Wired
Wolff New Media

HOW MUCH

Nasdaq symbol: YHOO FYE: December 31	Annual Growth	1990	1991	1992	1993	1994	1995[1]
Sales ($ mil.)	—	—	—	—	—	—	1.4
Net income ($ mil.)	—	—	—	—	—	—	(0.6)
Income as % of sales	—	—	—	—	—	—	—
Employees	—	—	—	—	—	—	39

[1]10-month fiscal year

1995 YEAR-END:
Debt ratio: 1.8%
Cash (mil.): $5.3
Current ratio: 8.14
Long-term debt (mil.): $0.1
R&D as % of sales: 17.8%
Advertising as % of sales: 9.2%

Top Media Companies

A&E TELEVISION NETWORKS

235 E. 45th St.
New York, NY 10017
Phone: 212-661-4500
Fax: 212-983-4370

CEO: Nickolas Davatzes
CFO: Seymour H. Lesser
HR: Rosalind C. Carter
Employees: 315

1995 Est. Sales: $263.1 mil.
1-Yr. Sales Change: 22.9%
Ownership: Privately Held

Broadcasting - cable TV station

 See page 200 for a full profile of this company.

ABBOTT MEAD VICKERS PLC

191 Old Marylebone Rd.
London NW1 5DW, UK
Phone: +44-171-402-4100
Fax: +44-171-935-1642

CEO: Peter W. Mead
CFO: Jeremy Hicks
HR: —
Employees: 562

1995 Sales: $444.2 million
1-Yr. Sales Change: 18.1%
Exchange: London

Advertising & marketing

A.C. NIELSEN CO.

150 N. Martingale Rd.
Schaumburg, IL 60173
Phone: 708-498-6300
Fax: 708-498-7286

CEO: Nicholas L. Trivisonno
CFO: Robert J. Chrenc
HR: Michael P. Connors
Employees: 17,000

1995 Sales: $1,286.1 million
1-Yr. Sales Change: 16.7%
Ownership: Division

Business services - marketing of retail measurement services, modeling & analytical services (division of Dun & Bradstreet, being spun out to shareholders as a separate, publicly traded company)

ACCLAIM ENTERTAINMENT, INC.

One Acclaim Plaza
Glen Cove, NY 11542
Phone: 516-656-5000
Fax: 516-656-2040

CEO: Gregory E. Fischbach
CFO: Anthony R. Williams
HR: John Ma
Employees: 800

1995 Sales: $566.7 million
1-Yr. Sales Change: 17.9%
Exchange: Nasdaq
Symbol: AKLM

Video game cartridges (WWF Raw, NFL Quarterback Club, The Simpsons), PC CD-ROM games (StarGate, Batman Forever) & comic books (*Ninjak, Bloodshot*)

ACKERLEY COMMUNICATIONS, INC.

800 Fifth Ave., Ste. 3770
Seattle, WA 98104
Phone: 206-624-2888
Fax: 206-623-7853

CEO: Barry A. Ackerley
CFO: Denis M. Curley
HR: Deborah A. Stednick
Employees: 930

1995 Sales: $235.8 million
1-Yr. Sales Change: 11.3%
Exchange: AMEX
Symbol: AK

Diversified operations - advertising; broadcasting; professional basketball team (Seattle SuperSonics)

ACTV, INC.

1270 Avenue of the Americas, Ste. 2401
New York, NY 10020
Phone: 212-262-2570
Fax: 212-459-9548

CEO: William C. Samuels
CFO: Christopher C. Cline
HR: —
Employees: 17

1995 Sales: $1.3 million
1-Yr. Sales Change: 44.4%
Exchange: Nasdaq (SC)
Symbol: IATV

Leisure & recreational products - interactive TV entertainment system

ACXIOM CORPORATION

301 Industrial Blvd., PO Box 2000
Conway, AR 72033-2000
Phone: 501-336-1000
Fax: 501-336-3913

CEO: Charles D. Morgan Jr.
CFO: Robert S. Bloom
HR: —
Employees: 1,850

1996 Sales: $269.9 million
1-Yr. Sales Change: 33.3%
Exchange: Nasdaq
Symbol: ACXM

Business services - mailing lists & related software; mail-order automation software; CD-ROM telephone directories (ProCD)

A.D.A.M. SOFTWARE, INC.

1600 RiverEdge Pkwy., Ste. 800
Atlanta, GA 30328
Phone: 770-980-0888
Fax: 770-955-3088

CEO: Curtis A. Cain
CFO: Robert A. DiProva
HR: —
Employees: 72

1996 Sales: $6.4 million
1-Yr. Sales Change: 12.3%
Exchange: Nasdaq
Symbol: ADAM

Computers - educational multimedia software that provides anatomical, medical, scientific & health-related information for academic & consumer markets

ADAMS MEDIA CORPORATION

260 Center St.
Holbrook, MA 02343
Phone: 617-767-8100
Fax: 617-767-0994

CEO: Bob Adams
CFO: Allan B. Tatel
HR: Allan B. Tatel
Employees: 75

1995 Sales: $10.0 million
1-Yr. Sales Change: 25.0%
Ownership: Privately Held

Publishing - books, software & online service for job hunters (Adams JobBank, AdamsResume & Cover Letters)

ADELPHIA COMMUNICATIONS CORPORATION

5 W. Third St., PO Box 472
Coudersport, PA 16915
Phone: 814-274-9830
Fax: 814-274-8631

CEO: John J. Rigas
CFO: Timothy J. Rigas
HR: Orby G. Kelley Jr.
Employees: 2,564

1995 Sales: $361.5 million
1-Yr. Sales Change: 13.3%
Exchange: Nasdaq
Symbol: ADLAC

Cable TV; wireless personal communications, security monitoring, alternate access & programming

ADOBE SYSTEMS INCORPORATED

1585 Charleston Rd.	CEO: John E. Warnock	1995 Sales: $762.3 million
Mountain View, CA 94043-1225	CFO: M. Bruce Nakao	1-Yr. Sales Change: 27.5%
Phone: 415-961-4400	HR: Rebecca Guerra	Exchange: Nasdaq
Fax: 415-961-3769	Employees: 2,319	Symbol: ADBE

Computers - font (Postscript) & desktop publishing (Pagemaker) software

 See pages 36–37 for a full profile of this company.

ADVANCE PUBLICATIONS, INC.

950 Fingerboard Rd.	CEO: Samuel I. Newhouse Jr.	1995 Sales: $4,855.0 million
Staten Island, NY 10305	CFO: Arthur Silverstein	1-Yr. Sales Change: 3.5%
Phone: 718-981-1234	HR: —	Ownership: Privately Held
Fax: 718-981-1415	Employees: 19,000	

Publishing - newspapers, books (Random House) & magazines (*New Yorker, Conde Nast, Allure, Bon Appetit, Bride's, Conde Nast Traveler, Details, Gentlemen's Quarterly, Vanity Fair, Vogue*); cable TV

 See pages 38–39 for a full profile of this company.

ADVANCED MARKETING SERVICES, INC.

5880 Oberlin Dr., Ste. 400	CEO: Charles C. Tillinghast III	1996 Sales: $365.5 million
San Diego, CA 92121-9653	CFO: Jonathan S. Fish	1-Yr. Sales Change: 20.3%
Phone: 619-457-2500	HR: Alisa R. Judge	Exchange: Nasdaq
Fax: 619-452-2237	Employees: 407	Symbol: ADMS

Wholesale distribution - books, audio- & videocassettes for the membership warehouse club, office product superstores & other specialty retailers

 See page 201 for a full profile of this company.

ADVANCED PROMOTION TECHNOLOGIES, INC.

3001 SW 10th St.	CEO: H. Robert Wientzen	1995 Sales: $5.6 million
Pompano Beach, FL 33069-4814	CFO: Stephen L. Conkling	1-Yr. Sales Change: 27.3%
Phone: 954-969-3000	HR: Steve Curtis	Exchange: OTC
Fax: 954-970-0381	Employees: 89	Symbol: APTV

TV programming & services - in-store promotion network (Vision Value)

ADVANSTAR COMMUNICATIONS INC.

7500 Old Oak Blvd.	CEO: Gary Ingersoll	1995 Est. Sales: $150.0 mil.
Cleveland, OH 44130	CFO: David Montgomery	1-Yr. Sales Change: 5.9%
Phone: 216-243-8100	HR: Phil Stocker	Ownership: Privately Held
Fax: 216-891-2791	Employees: 1,000	

Publishing - trade & professional magazines; business exposition & conference production; marketing of database, direct marketing & reference products to the health care, pharmaceutical & communications industries

ADVO, INC.

One Univac Ln., PO Box 755	CEO: Robert Kamerschen	1995 Sales: $1,011.9 million
Windsor, CT 06095-0755	CFO: Lowell W. Robinson	1-Yr. Sales Change: 3.7%
Phone: 860-285-6100	HR: J. Thomas Van Berkem	Exchange: NYSE
Fax: 860-285-6393	Employees: 5,200	Symbol: AD

Business services - direct marketing, primarily solicitation & processing of printed advertising from retailers, manufacturers & service companies for distribution to US households

 **See page 202 for a full profile of this company.**

AEGIS GROUP PLC

11a W. Halkin St.	CEO: Charles Hochman	1995 Sales: $5,262.2 million
London SW1X 8JL, UK	CFO: —	1-Yr. Sales Change: 14.5%
Phone: +44-171-470-5000	HR: —	Exchange: Nasdaq
Fax: +44-171-470-5099	Employees: 1,764	Symbol: CAMBY (ADR)

Business services - media specialists (Carat), including media strategy, consulting, marketing, planning & buying

AFFINITY TELEPRODUCTIONS, INC.

15436 N. Florida Ave., Ste. 103	CEO: William J. Bosso	1995 Sales: $1.2 million
Tampa, FL 33613	CFO: James E. Farrell	1-Yr. Sales Change: 9.1%
Phone: 813-264-1778	HR: Elliot Bellen	Exchange: Nasdaq (SC)
Fax: 813-264-6626	Employees: 60	Symbol: AFTY

TV production & programming - commercials, infomercials & videos

AGENCE FRANCE-PRESSE

13, Place de la Bourse	CEO: Jean Miot	1995 Sales: $250.0 million
Paris 75002, France	CFO: Michel Tourmen	1-Yr. Sales Change: 8.2%
Phone: +33-140-41-4646	HR: —	Ownership: Privately Held
Fax: +33-140-41-4632	Employees: 3,100	

Business services - general newswires & financial information services

 **See page 203 for a full profile of this company.**

A. H. BELO CORPORATION

400 S. Record St.	CEO: Robert W. Decherd	1995 Sales: $735.3 million
Dallas, TX 75202	CFO: Michael D. Perry	1-Yr. Sales Change: 17.1%
Phone: 214-977-6606	HR: Jeff Lamb	Exchange: NYSE
Fax: 214-977-6603	Employees: 3,489	Symbol: BLC

Broadcasting - radio & TV; newspapers (*Dallas Morning News*)

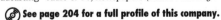 **See page 204 for a full profile of this company.**

ALL AMERICAN COMMUNICATIONS, INC.

808 Wilshire Blvd.	CEO: Anthony J. Scotti	1995 Sales: $228.8 million
Santa Monica, CA 90401-1810	CFO: Thomas Bradshaw	1-Yr. Sales Change: 99.1%
Phone: 310-656-1100	HR: Frederick J. Scotti	Exchange: Nasdaq (SC)
Fax: 310-656-7410	Employees: 245	Symbol: AACI

TV production & programming - syndicated shows (*Baywatch*, *Dating Game*); music publishing (James Brown, Weird Al Yankovich)

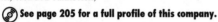 **See page 205 for a full profile of this company.**

ALLEGRO NEW MEDIA, INC.

16 Passaic Ave., Unit 6	CEO: Barry A. Cinnamon	1995 Sales: $1.4 million
Fairfield, NJ 07004	CFO: Mark E. Leininger	1-Yr. Sales Change: 40.0%
Phone: 201-808-1992	HR: —	Exchange: Nasdaq
Fax: 201-808-2645	Employees: 36	Symbol: ANMI

Publishing - interactive how-to, business & instructional CD-ROMs (Learn To Do, Berlitz Executive Travel, Entrepreneur Magazine, Business Reference, InPrint Art Library)

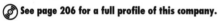 **See page 206 for a full profile of this company.**

ALLEN & CO.

711 5th Ave.	CEO: Herbert A. Allen	1996 Sales: —
New York, NY 10022	CFO: —	1-Yr. Sales Change: —
Phone: 212-832-8000	HR: —	Ownership: Privately Held
Fax: 212-832-8023	Employees: 170	

Financial - investment bankers for the media industry

ALLIANCE ENTERTAINMENT CORP.

110 E. 59th St.	CEO: Joseph J. Bianco	1995 Sales: $720.3 million
New York, NY 10022	CFO: Anil K. Narang	1-Yr. Sales Change: 34.6%
Phone: 212-750-2303	HR: Ken Butler	Exchange: NYSE
Fax: 212-935-6620	Employees: 1,426	Symbol: CDS

Wholesale distribution - prerecorded music & related products, including blank tapes, laser discs & licensed apparel

AMAZON.COM

2250 First Ave. South	CEO: Jeff Bezos	1995 Sales: —
Seattle, WA 98134	CFO: Jeff Bezos	1-Yr. Sales Change: —
Phone: 206-622-2335	HR: Nicholas Lovejoy	Ownership: Privately Held
Fax: 206-602-2405	Employees: 33	

Retail - bookstore in cyberspace with over one million titles available

AMC ENTERTAINMENT INC.

106 W. 14th St., PO Box 419615
Kansas City, MO 64141-6615
Phone: 816-221-4000
Fax: 816-480-4617

CEO: Stanley H. Durwood
CFO: Peter C. Brown
HR: Edward Moyer
Employees: 8,000

1996 Sales: $657.9 million
1-Yr. Sales Change: 16.5%
Exchange: AMEX
Symbol: AEN

Motion pictures & services - theaters (#2 in the US)

AMERICA ONLINE, INC.

8619 Westwood Center Dr.
Vienna, VA 22182-2285
Phone: 703-448-8700
Fax: 703-883-1532

CEO: Stephen M. M. Case
CFO: Lennert J. Leader
HR: Mark Stavish
Employees: 2,481

1995 Sales: $358.5 million
1-Yr. Sales Change: 243.4%
Exchange: Nasdaq
Symbol: AMER

Computers - Internet access & online services, including e-mail, conferencing, software, computing
support, interactive magazines & newspapers & online classes

 **See pages 40–41 for a full profile of this company.**

AMERICAN BANKNOTE CORPORATION

200 Park Ave.
New York, NY 10106
Phone: 212-557-9100
Fax: 212-338-0753

CEO: Morris Weissman
CFO: John T. Gorman
HR: JoAnne O. Martinez
Employees: 2,380

1995 Sales: $206.2 million
1-Yr. Sales Change: (0.9%)
Exchange: NYSE
Symbol: ABN

Printing - counterfeit-resistant documents, including food coupons, social security cards & treasury checks
for the US government; currency, passports, motor vehicle titles, birth certificates & travelers cheques

AMERICAN BAR ASSOCIATION

750 N. Lake Shore Dr.
Chicago, IL 60611
Phone: 312-988-6179
Fax: 312-988-5100

CEO: Robert A. Stein
CFO: John E. Hanle Jr.
HR: Nina B. Eidell
Employees: 750

1995 Sales: $112.9 million
1-Yr. Sales Change: (1.1%)
Ownership: Privately Held

National professional legal association with approximately 370,000 members (#1 voluntary professional
association worldwide); magazine & book publishing (ABA Press)

AMERICAN BOOKSELLERS ASSOCIATION, INC.

828 S. Broadway
Tarrytown, NY 10591
Phone: 914-591-2665
Fax: 914-591-2720

CEO: Avin M. Domnitz
CFO: Richard Howorth
HR: Deirdre Fitzsimmons
Employees: 55

1995 Sales: $8.0 million
1-Yr. Sales Change: 15.9%
Ownership: Association

Miscellaneous - association that provides weekly, monthly, quarterly & annual print, disk & online
publications, group & discount book-buying (Booksellers Order Service) & other services for booksellers

 **See page 207 for a full profile of this company.**

AMERICAN BUSINESS INFORMATION, INC.

5711 S. 86th Circle	CEO: Vinod Gupta	1995 Sales: $86.8 million
Omaha, NE 68127	CFO: Jon H. Wellman	1-Yr. Sales Change: 13.8%
Phone: 402-593-4500	HR: Jeff Bauman	Exchange: Nasdaq
Fax: 402-331-1505	Employees: 870	Symbol: ABII

Business services - business-to-business marketing information in the form of mailing labels, printed directories, computer diskettes & CD-ROMs

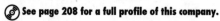 **See page 208 for a full profile of this company.**

AMERICAN LABELMARK COMPANY INC.

5724 N. Pulaski Rd.	CEO: Dwight Curtis	1995 Sales: $40.5 million
Chicago, IL 60646	CFO: Alan Schoen	1-Yr. Sales Change: 1.3%
Phone: 312-478-0900	HR: Peggy Boyd	Ownership: Privately Held
Fax: 312-478-6054	Employees: 315	

Printing - commercial labels

AMERICAN LIBRARY ASSOCIATION

50 E. Huron St.	CEO: Betty Turok	1995 Sales: $23 million
Chicago, IL 60611-2795	CFO: Gregory Calloway	1-Yr. Sales Change: —
Phone: 312-944-6780	HR: —	Ownership: Not-for-profit
Fax: 312-440-9374	Employees: 286	

Membership organization - library association (oldest & largest in the world, with 57,000 members)

AMERICAN LIST CORPORATION

330 Old Country Rd.	CEO: Martin Lerner	1996 Sales: $18.9 million
Mineola, NY 11501	CFO: Martin Lerner	1-Yr. Sales Change: 21.9%
Phone: 516-248-6100	HR: —	Exchange: AMEX
Fax: 516-248-6364	Employees: 25	Symbol: AMZ

Business services - mailing lists of children & students throughout the country

AMERICAN MEDIA, INC.

600 S. East Coast Ave.	CEO: Peter J. Callahan	1996 Sales: $295.1 million
Lantana, FL 33462	CFO: Richard W. Pickert	1-Yr. Sales Change: (6.4%)
Phone: 407-540-1000	HR: Susan Napolitano	Exchange: NYSE
Fax: 407-540-1018	Employees: 1,575	Symbol: ENQ

Publishing - periodicals (*National Enquirer*, *The Star*, *Weekly World News*, *Soap Opera Magazine*, *Country Weekly*)

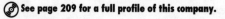 **See page 209 for a full profile of this company.**

AMERICAN MEDICAL ASSOCIATION

515 N. State St.	CEO: F. John Seward	1995 Sales: $199.2 million
Chicago, IL 60610	CFO: Bill Zimmerman	1-Yr. Sales Change: 6.8%
Phone: 312-464-5000	HR: Chris Theodore	Ownership: Privately Held
Fax: 312-464-4184	Employees: 1,175	

National voluntary service association of physicians with nearly 300,000 members; publisher of scientific & medical information (#1 worldwide: *Journal of the American Medical Association, Archives of Surgery, American Medical News*)

AMERICAN RADIO SYSTEMS CORPORATION

116 Huntington Ave.	CEO: Steven B. Dodge	1995 Sales: $97.8 million
Boston, MA 02116	CFO: Joseph L. Winn	1-Yr. Sales Change: 43.8%
Phone: 617-375-7500	HR: —	Exchange: Nasdaq
Fax: 617-375-7575	Employees: 596	Symbol: AMRD

Broadcasting - radio (8 AM & 13 FM stations in 7 markets)

AMERICAN SOCIETY OF COMPOSERS, AUTHORS AND PUBLISHERS

One Lincoln Plaza	CEO: Marilyn Bergman	1995 Sales: $436.8 million
New York, NY 10023	CFO: Jim Collins	1-Yr. Sales Change: 3.3%
Phone: 212-621-6000	HR: Sally McKinney	Ownership: Not-for-profit
Fax: 212-724-9064	Employees: 500	

Business services - licensing of music copyrights (membership society with over 68,000 members)

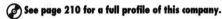 **See page 210 for a full profile of this company.**

AMERICAN TELECASTING, INC.

4065 N. Sinton Rd., Ste. 201	CEO: Robert D. Hostetler	1995 Sales: $47.5 million
Colorado Springs, CO 80907	CFO: David K. Sentman	1-Yr. Sales Change: 119.9%
Phone: 719-632-5544	HR: Sam Walker	Exchange: Nasdaq
Fax: 719-632-5549	Employees: 449	Symbol: ATEL

Cable TV - wireless cable TV (#1 in the US)

ANDERSON LITHOGRAPH CO.

3217 S. Garfield Ave.	CEO: John Fosmire	1995 Est. Sales: $120.0 mil.
Los Angeles, CA 90040	CFO: Alan Pemberton	1-Yr. Sales Change: 6.2%
Phone: 213-727-7767	HR: Betty Miyahira	Ownership: Privately Held
Fax: 213-722-2328	Employees: 398	

Printing - commercial

APPLIED GRAPHICS TECHNOLOGY, INC.

28 W. 23rd St.
New York, NY 10010
Phone: 212-929-4111
Fax: 212-929-2787

CEO: Fred Drasner
CFO: Louis Salamone Jr.
HR: Bonni Rhodes
Employees: 1,500

1995 Est. Sales: $200.0 mil.
1-Yr. Sales Change: (9.1%)
Ownership: Privately Held

Printing - prepress services

ARANDELL CORPORATION

North 82, West 13118, Leon Rd.
Menomonee Falls, WI 53051
Phone: 414-255-4400
Fax: 414-253-3162

CEO: F. E. Treis
CFO: Mike Myers
HR: Ernie Haug
Employees: 456

1995 Est. Sales: $125.0 mil.
1-Yr. Sales Change: 11.6%
Ownership: Privately Held

Printing - catalogs

ARGYLE TELEVISION, INC.

200 Concord Plaza, Ste. 700
San Antonio, TX 78216
Phone: 210-828-1700
Fax: 210-828-7300

CEO: Bob Marbut
CFO: Harry T. Hawks
HR: —
Employees: 453

1995 Sales: $46.9 million
1-Yr. Sales Change: 35.9%
Exchange: Nasdaq
Symbol: ARGL

Broadcasting - TV stations (5 network-affiliated stations in Grand Rapids, MI; Buffalo, NY; Providence, RI; Jackson, MS; Honolulu, HI)

ARISTO INTERNATIONAL CORPORATION

152 W. 57th St., 29th Fl.
New York, NY 10019
Phone: 212-586-2400
Fax: 212-586-1652

CEO: Mouli Cohen
CFO: Ed Hughes
HR: Grace Russo
Employees: 35

1995 Sales: $0.2 million
1-Yr. Sales Change: —
Exchange: Nasdaq (SC)
Symbol: ATSP

Computers - entertainment & video game software for CD-ROM-based PC & dedicated video game platforms

ARNOLDO MONDADORI EDITORE S.P.A.

Via Bianca di Savoia 12
20122 Milan, Italy
Phone: +39-2-583-011-51

CEO: Francesco Tato
CFO: —
HR: —
Employees: 5,430

1995 Sales: $1,358.9 million
1-Yr. Sales Change: 51.3%
Exchange: Milan

Publishing - books & newspapers; graphics services

ASHER/GOULD ADVERTISING, INC.

5900 Wilshire Blvd., 31st Fl.
Los Angeles, CA 90036
Phone: 213-931-4151
Fax: 213-931-3477

CEO: Bruce Silverman
CFO: Peter Nicholson
HR: Sandi Winston
Employees: 65

1995 Sales: $13.5 million
1-Yr. Sales Change: 4.7%
Ownership: Privately Held

Advertising

ASSOCIATED PRESS

50 Rockefeller Plaza
New York, NY 10020
Phone: 212-621-1500
Fax: 212-621-5447

CEO: Louis D. Boccardi
CFO: Patrick T. O'Brien
HR: James M. Donna
Employees: 3,150

1995 Sales: $426.0 million
1-Yr. Sales Change: 4.9%
Ownership: Not-for-profit

Business services - news, photos, graphics, photo technology, information & satellite services

(⚬) **See page 211 for a full profile of this company.**

ASTRAL COMMUNICATIONS, INC.

2100 Rue Ste-Catherine Ouest
Montreal, QC H3H 2T3, Canada
Phone: 514-939-5000
Fax: 514-939-1515

CEO: Ian Greenberg
CFO: Claude Gagnon
HR: —
Employees: —

1995 Sales: $252.0 million
1-Yr. Sales Change: 12.7%
Ownership: Privately Held

Broadcasting - pay & basic TV broadcasting; video & film distribution

ATC COMMUNICATIONS GROUP, INC.

5950 Berkshire Ln., Ste. 1650
Dallas, TX 75225
Phone: 214-361-9870
Fax: 214-361-9874

CEO: Michael G. Santry
CFO: Jerry L. Sims Jr.
HR: —
Employees: 2,617

1995 Sales: $61.4 million
1-Yr. Sales Change: 63.7%
Exchange: Nasdaq
Symbol: ATCT

Business services - telecommunications-based marketing & information services

AVANTI/CASE-HOYT, INC.

13449 NW 42nd Ave.
Miami, FL 33054
Phone: 800-327-7486
Fax: 305-685-3448

CEO: Jose Ariola
CFO: George San Miguel
HR: Pat Ward
Employees: 800

1995 Est. Sales: $125.0 mil.
1-Yr. Sales Change: 4.2%
Ownership: Privately Held

Printing - commercial

AVID TECHNOLOGY, INC.

One Park West	CEO: William J. Miller	1995 Sales: $406.7 million
Tewksbury, MA 01876	CFO: Jonathan H. Cook	1-Yr. Sales Change: 99.7%
Phone: 508-640-6789	HR: Judith M. Oppenheim	Exchange: Nasdaq
Fax: 508-640-1366	Employees: 1,476	Symbol: AVID

Computers - digital, nonlinear film-, video- & audio-editing systems

 See page 212 for a full profile of this company.

AXEL SPRINGER VERLAG AG

Axel-Springer-Platz 1	CEO: Juergen Richter	1995 Sales: $2,887.9 million
D-20350 Hamburg, Germany	CFO: —	1-Yr. Sales Change: 4.4%
Phone: +49-40-347-22884	HR: —	Exchange: Frankfurt
Fax: +49-40-347-25540	Employees: 13,331	

Publishing - newspapers (*Die Welt*, *Bild*) & magazines

 See pages 42–43 for a full profile of this company.

BAKER & TAYLOR, INC.

2709 Water Ridge Pkwy.	CEO: Craig M. Richards	1995 Sales: $785.0 million
Charlotte, NC 28217	CFO: Edward H. Gross	1-Yr. Sales Change: (1.9%)
Phone: 704-357-3500	HR: Chuck Mankoff	Ownership: Privately Held
Fax: 704-329-9105	Employees: 2,200	

Wholesale - books, videos & software

 See page 213 for a full profile of this company.

BANTA CORPORATION

River Place, 225 Main St.	CEO: Donald D. Belcher	1995 Sales: $1,022.7 million
Menasha, WI 54952-8003	CFO: Gerald A. Henseler	1-Yr. Sales Change: 26.1%
Phone: 414-751-7777	HR: Cheryl Spindler	Exchange: Nasdaq
Fax: 414-751-7790	Employees: 5,700	Symbol: BNTA

Printing - retail catalogs, direct mail & single-use products; books & magazines; digital imaging services; point-of purchase displays; security products

BARNES & NOBLE, INC.

122 Fifth Ave.	CEO: Leonard Riggio	1996 Sales: $1,976.9 million
New York, NY 10011	CFO: Irene R. Miller	1-Yr. Sales Change: 21.8%
Phone: 212-633-3300	HR: Mike Malone	Exchange: NYSE
Fax: 212-675-0413	Employees: 21,400	Symbol: BKS

Retail - books (#1 in the US) through superstores (Barnes & Noble, Bookstop, Bookstar) & mall stores (B. Dalton, Doubleday, Scribner's)

 See pages 44–45 for a full profile of this company.

BBN CORPORATION

150 Cambridge Park Dr.
Cambridge, MA 02140
Phone: 617-873-2000
Fax: 617-873-5011

CEO: George H. Conrades
CFO: Ralph A. Goldwasser
HR: Steven Heinrich
Employees: 2,000

1995 Sales: $215.0 million
1-Yr. Sales Change: 9.6%
Exchange: NYSE
Symbol: BBN

Computers - internetworking services & products, collaborative systems & acoustic technologies, data analysis & process optimization software products; Internet access services (BBN Planet)

BCT INTERNATIONAL, INC.

3000 NE 30th Place, 5th Fl.
Fort Lauderdale, FL 33306-1957
Phone: 954-563-1224
Fax: 954-565-0742

CEO: William A. Wilkerson
CFO: Donna M. Pagano-Leo
HR: Joann Gandalfo
Employees: 69

1996 Sales: $17.6 million
1-Yr. Sales Change: 30.4%
Exchange: Nasdaq
Symbol: BCTI

Printing - business cards & personalized products (#1 wholesale printing chain worldwide); trade thermography

BELL & HOWELL COMPANY

5215 Old Orchard Rd.
Skokie, IL 60077-1076
Phone: 847-470-7660
Fax: 847-470-9825

CEO: William J. White
CFO: Nils A. Johansson
HR: Maria T. Rubly
Employees: 5,966

1995 Sales: $820.0 million
1-Yr. Sales Change: 13.8%
Exchange: NYSE
Symbol: BHW

Diversified operations - information access, including to periodicals & scholarly papers in electronic & microfilm formats (UMI) & to technical reference information; high-volume commercial mail processing systems

BENEDEK BROADCASTING CORPORATION

308 W. State St., Ste. 210
Rockford, IL 61101
Phone: 815-987-5350
Fax: 815-987-5335

CEO: A. Richard Benedek
CFO: Ronald Lindwall
HR: Gloria Greene
Employees: 800

1995 Sales: $52.0 million
1-Yr. Sales Change: —
Ownership: Privately Held

Broadcasting - TV stations (22 network-affiliated stations)

BERLIN INDUSTRIES, INC.

175 Mercedes Dr.
Carol Stream, IL 60188
Phone: 708-682-0600
Fax: 708-682-5928

CEO: Bruce Smith
CFO: Steve Schmitt
HR: Mike Chieslewicz
Employees: 450

1995 Sales: $88.0 million
1-Yr. Sales Change: 10.0%
Ownership: Privately Held

Printing - full-service commercial

BERTELSMANN AG

Carl-Bertelsmann-Strasse 270	CEO: Mark Wossner	1995 Sales: $14,761.2 mil.
D-33311 Gutersloh, Germany	CFO: Siegfried Luther	1-Yr. Sales Change: 10.8%
Phone: +49-52-41-80-0	HR: —	Ownership: Privately Held
Fax: +49-52-41-7-51-66	Employees: 57,397	

Publishing - books (Bantam, Doubleday, Dell) & music (Arista, BMG, RCA); film, radio & TV production

 See pages 46–47 for a full profile of this company.

BEST BUY CO., INC.

7075 Flying Cloud Dr.	CEO: Richard M. Schulze	1996 Sales: $7,217.4 million
Eden Prairie, MN 55344	CFO: Allen U. Lenzmeier	1-Yr. Sales Change: 42.1%
Phone: 612-947-2000	HR: Joseph M. Joyce	Exchange: NYSE
Fax: 612-947-2422	Employees: 33,500	Symbol: BBY

Retail - consumer electronics & prerecorded music stores

BET HOLDINGS, INC.

1900 W. Place NE	CEO: Robert L. Johnson	1995 Sales: $115.2 million
Washington, DC 20018-1211	CFO: William T. Gordon III	1-Yr. Sales Change: 18.2%
Phone: 202-608-2000	HR: Crystal Gant	Exchange: NYSE
Fax: 202-608-2595	Employees: 450	Symbol: BTV

Broadcasting - cable TV networks (Black Entertainment Television, BET on Jazz); pay-per-view movies; magazines (*Emerge*); direct marketing, national spot & infomercial advertising; film production

 See page 214 for a full profile of this company.

BHC COMMUNICATIONS, INC.

767 Fifth Ave.	CEO: Herbert J. Siegel	1995 Sales: $454.7 million
New York, NY 10153	CFO: Joelin K. Merkel	1-Yr. Sales Change: (0.6%)
Phone: 212-421-0200	HR: —	Exchange: AMEX
Fax: 212-935-8462	Employees: 1,050	Symbol: BHC

Broadcasting - TV (6 VHF & 2 UHF stations); commercial TV broadcasting on 68 channels in the US (subsidiary of Chris-Craft Industries)

BIG ENTERTAINMENT, INC.

2255 Glades Rd, Ste. 237 W	CEO: Mitchell Rubenstein	1995 Sales: $6.3 million
Boca Raton, FL 33431-7383	CFO: Michael La Belle	1-Yr. Sales Change: 320.0%
Phone: 407-998-8000	HR: Beth Krumper	Exchange: Nasdaq (SC)
Fax: 407-998-2974	Employees: 150	Symbol: BIGE

Publishing - science fiction comic books; online comics

 See page 215 for a full profile of this company.

BIG FLOWER PRESS HOLDINGS, INC.

3 E. 54th St.
New York, NY 10022
Phone: 212-521-1600
Fax: 212-223-4074

CEO: Theodore Ammon
CFO: Theodore Ammon
HR: Marlene Gurrola
Employees: 4,100

1995 Sales: $896.6 million
1-Yr. Sales Change: 43.5%
Exchange: NYSE
Symbol: BGF

Printing - advertising circulars, newspaper TV listing guides, Sunday comics & magazines

BLADE COMMUNICATIONS INC.

541 Superior St.
Toledo, OH 43660
Phone: 419-245-6000
Fax: 419-245-6167

CEO: William Block Jr.
CFO: Gary J. Blair
HR: Jo Kerns
Employees: 1,600

1995 Est. Sales: $325.0 mil.
1-Yr. Sales Change: 6.9%
Ownership: Privately Held

Publishing - newspapers (*Pittsburgh Post-Gazette*); cable TV

BLOCKBUSTER ENTERTAINMENT GROUP

200 S. Andrews Ave.
Fort Lauderdale, FL 33301-1860
Phone: 954-832-3000
Fax: 954-832-4086

CEO: William R. Fields
CFO: Al Detz
HR: H. Scott Barrett
Employees: 45,000

1995 Sales: $3,333.4 million
1-Yr. Sales Change: 1.0%
Ownership: Subsidiary

Retail - video rentals; TV & film production (Spelling, Republic Pictures); software development (Virgin Interactive); children's entertainment (50.1% of Discovery Zone) (subsidiary of Viacom)

 See pages 48–49 for a full profile of this company.

BLOOMBERG L.P.

499 Park Ave.
New York, NY 10022
Phone: 212-318-2000
Fax: 212-980-4585

CEO: Michael R. Bloomberg
CFO: Wolf Boehm
HR: Geri Ingram
Employees: 2,000

1995 Est. Sales: $650.0 mil.
1-Yr. Sales Change: 36.4%
Ownership: Privately Held

Business services - online financial information; print, radio & TV news network

 **See page 216 for a full profile of this company.**

BONNIERFORETAGEN AB

Torsgatan 21
S-113 90 Stockholm, Sweden
Phone: +46-8-736-4000
Fax: +46-8-34-27-45

CEO: Carl-Johan Bonnier
CFO: —
HR: —
Employees: 5,286

1995 Sales: $1,443.0 million
1-Yr. Sales Change: 17.8%
Exchange: Stockholm

Publishing - magazines & books; business information in printed & electronic forms; broadcast media & film operations

BOOKS-A-MILLION, INC.

402 Industrial Ln.
Birmingham, AL 35211
Phone: 205-942-3737
Fax: 205-945-1772

CEO: Clyde B. Anderson
CFO: Sandra B. Cochran
HR: Christine Sanders
Employees: 2,883

1996 Sales: $229.8 million
1-Yr. Sales Change: 33.3%
Exchange: Nasdaq
Symbol: BAMM

Retail - book superstores in the southeast US

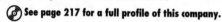 **See page 217 for a full profile of this company.**

BORDERS GROUP, INC.

500 E. Washington St.
Ann Arbor, MI 48104
Phone: 313-913-1100
Fax: 313-913-1965

CEO: Robert F. DiRomualdo
CFO: George R. Mrkonic
HR: Anne Kubek
Employees: 20,000

1996 Sales: $1,749.0 million
1-Yr. Sales Change: 15.8%
Exchange: NYSE
Symbol: BGP

Retail - mall book stores (#1 in the US: Walden Books), superstores (#2 in the US: Borders); retail music
(Planet Music)

 **See pages 50–51 for a full profile of this company.**

BOWNE & CO., INC.

345 Hudson St.
New York, NY 10014
Phone: 212-924-5500
Fax: 212-229-3420

CEO: Robert M. Johnson
CFO: Denise K. Fletcher
HR: Allen D. Marold
Employees: 2,800

1995 Sales: $392.7 million
1-Yr. Sales Change: 1.8%
Exchange: AMEX
Symbol: BNE

Printing - legal, corporate, commercial & financial documentation (#1 worldwide), specializing in securities
offerings, corporate restructurings & other financial transactions

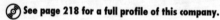 **See page 218 for a full profile of this company.**

BOZELL, JACOBS, KENYON & ECKHARDT, INC.

40 W. 23rd St.
New York, NY 10010
Phone: 212-727-5000
Fax: 212-463-8419

CEO: Charles D. Peebler Jr.
CFO: Valentine Zammit
HR: Michael Bruce
Employees: 3,931

1996 Sales: $408.0 million
1-Yr. Sales Change: 21.1%
Ownership: Privately Held

Advertising - full-service global advertising & public relations agency

BPP HOLDINGS PLC

Aldine Place, 142-144 Uxbridge Rd.
London W12 8AA, UK
Phone: +44-181-740-1111
Fax: +44-181-746-0552

CEO: Charles C. L. Prior
CFO: Lynn A. Chandler
HR: —
Employees: 1,231

1995 Sales: $101.3 million
1-Yr. Sales Change: 22.2%
Exchange: London

Publishing - language training & educational books; service organization

BRISTOL EVENING POST PLC

Temple Way
Bristol BS99 7HD, UK
Phone: +44-117-926-0080
Fax: +44-117-922-6985

CEO: A. R. Goode
CFO: Keith J. Sadler
HR: —
Employees: 1,005

1995 Sales: $97.3 million
1-Yr. Sales Change: 0.8%
Exchange: London

Publishing - newspapers (*Evening Post, Western Daily Press*)

BRITISH BROADCASTING CORPORATION PLC

Broadcasting House
London W1A 1AA, UK
Phone: +44-171-580-4468
Fax: +44-171-765-1181

CEO: John Birt
CFO: Rodney Baker-Bates
HR: —
Employees: 24,000

1995 Est. Sales: $3,000 mil.
1-Yr. Sales Change: —
Ownership: State-Owned

TV & radio broadcasting, including educational, news, entertainment & regional programs

BRITISH SKY BROADCASTING GROUP PLC

6 Centaurs Business Park, Grant Way
Isleworth, Middlesex TW7 5QD, UK
Phone: +44-171-705-3000
Fax: +44-171-705-3453

CEO: Samuel H. Chisholm
CFO: Richard J. Brooke
HR: —
Employees: 3,054

1995 Sales: $1,226.0 million
1-Yr. Sales Change: 41.4%
Exchange: NYSE
Symbol: BSY (ADR)

Broadcasting - pay-TV broadcasting service (#1 in the UK: The Movie Channel, Sky Movies Gold, Sky Sports)

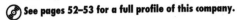 **See pages 52–53 for a full profile of this company.**

BROADCAST MUSIC, INC.

320 W. 57th St.
New York, NY 10019
Phone: 212-586-2000
Fax: 212-830-8329

CEO: Frances Preston
CFO: Fred Willms
HR: Edward Chapin
Employees: 568

1995 Sales: $355.2 million
1-Yr. Sales Change: 13.2%
Ownership: Not-for-profit

Business services - licensing of music copyrights

 **See page 219 for a full profile of this company.**

BRØDERBUND SOFTWARE, INC.

500 Redwood Blvd.
Novato, CA 94948-6121
Phone: 415-382-4400
Fax: 415-382-4582

CEO: Douglas G. Carlston
CFO: Michael J. Shannahan
HR: —
Employees: 563

1995 Sales: $171.6 million
1-Yr. Sales Change: 53.5%
Exchange: Nasdaq
Symbol: BROD

Computers - educational & game software & CD-ROMs (Carmen Sandiego, Myst, Print Shop)

See page 220 for a full profile of this company.

BURDA GMBH

Arabellastrasse 23	CEO: H. Burda	1995 Sales: $1,187.6 million
81925 Munich, Germany	CFO: —	1-Yr. Sales Change: 35.2%
Phone: +49-89-92-50-34-22	HR: —	Exchange: Frankfurt
Fax: +49-89-92-50-20-14	Employees: 5,000	

Publishing - newspapers, magazines (*Focus*, German edition of *Elle*) & advertisements

BUREAU OF ELECTRONIC PUBLISHING, INC.

619 Alexander Rd.	CEO: Larry Shiller	1995 Sales: $3.1 million
Princeton, NJ 08540	CFO: William P. Fox	1-Yr. Sales Change: 10.7%
Phone: 609-514-1600	HR: Brent Subkowsky	Exchange: Nasdaq (SC)
Fax: 609-514-1818	Employees: 23	Symbol: BEPI

Publishing - interactive multimedia CD-ROMs for the consumer & library/education markets (Inside the White House, Much Ado About Shakespeare, Multimedia World Factbook)

BUREAU OF NATIONAL AFFAIRS, INC.

1231 25th St. Northwest	CEO: Bill Beltz	1995 Est. Sales: $225.0 mil.
Washington, DC 20037	CFO: George Korphage	1-Yr. Sales Change: 4.7%
Phone: 202-452-4200	HR: Jacqueline Blanchard	Ownership: Privately Held
Fax: 202-452-4610	Employees: 1,700	

Publishing - professional periodicals, books & newsletters for human resources, environmental & health care industries

BYRON PREISS MULTIMEDIA COMPANY, INC.

24 W. 25th St., 10th Fl.	CEO: Byron Preiss	1995 Sales: $6.3 million
New York, NY 10010	CFO: James R. Dellomo	1-Yr. Sales Change: 103.2%
Phone: 212-989-6252	HR: Lois Brown	Exchange: Nasdaq (SC)
Fax: 212-989-6550	Employees: 49	Symbol: CDRM

Computers - interactive multimedia software on CD-ROM & other multimedia formats for educational, entertainment & professional uses

CABLEVISION SYSTEMS CORPORATION

One Media Crossways	CEO: James L. Dolan	1995 Sales: $1,078.1 million
Woodbury, NY 11797	CFO: Barry J. O'Leary	1-Yr. Sales Change: 28.8%
Phone: 516-364-8450	HR: Joyce E. Mancini	Exchange: AMEX
Fax: 516-364-4913	Employees: 5,801	Symbol: CVC

Cable TV

See pages 54–55 for a full profile of this company.

CADMUS COMMUNICATIONS CORPORATION

6620 W. Broad St., PO Box 27367
Richmond, VA 23261-7367
Phone: 804-287-5680
Fax: 804-287-6267

CEO: C. Stephenson Gillispie Jr.
CFO: Michael Dinkins
HR: Gregory Moyer
Employees: 2,380

1995 Sales: $279.6 million
1-Yr. Sales Change: 12.9%
Exchange: Nasdaq
Symbol: CDMS

Printing - regional special interest journals & CD-ROM products from printed materials

 **See page 221 for a full profile of this company.**

CAMELOT CORPORATION

17770 Preston Rd.
Dallas, TX 75252
Phone: 214-733-3005
Fax: 214-733-4308

CEO: Daniel Wettreich
CFO: Shirley A. Green
HR: —
Employees: 34

1995 Sales: $1.2 million
1-Yr. Sales Change: —
Exchange: Nasdaq (SC)
Symbol: CAML

Computers - CD-ROM distribution (Maxmedia Distributing); retail sales (Mr. CD-ROM); Internet telephone software (Digiphone)

CAMELOT MUSIC INC.

8000 Freedom Ave. Northwest
Canton, OH 44720-2282
Phone: 216-494-2282
Fax: 216-494-0394

CEO: James Bonk
CFO: Jack Rogers
HR: Don Groom
Employees: 3,000

1996 Est. Sales: $450.0 mil.
1-Yr. Sales Change: —
Ownership: Privately Held

Retail - prerecorded music & video stores (over 350 units)

CANAL+

85-89, quai Andre Citroen
75015 Paris Cedex 15, France
Phone: +33-1-44-25-10-00
Fax: +33-1-44-25-12-34

CEO: Pierre Lescure
CFO: Laurent Perpere
HR: Francoise Provotelle
Employees: 2,084

1995 Sales: $2,075.2 million
1-Yr. Sales Change: (1.0%)
Exchange: OTC
Symbol: CNPLY (ADR)

Cable & satellite TV; movie production (Le Studio CANAL+); publishing (CANAL+ Editions SNC)

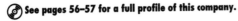 **See pages 56–57 for a full profile of this company.**

CAPITAL CITIES/ABC, INC.

77 W. 66th St.
New York, NY 10023-6298
Phone: 212-456-7777
Fax: 212-456-6850

CEO: Robert A. Iger
CFO: Ronald J. J. Doerfler
HR: William J. Wilkinson
Employees: 20,000

1995 Sales: $6,878.6 million
1-Yr. Sales Change: 7.8%
Ownership: Subsidiary

Broadcasting - radio & TV; publishing (subsidiary of Walt Disney Co.)

See pages 58–59 for a full profile of this company.

CAPITAL RADIO PLC

Euston Tower	CEO: R. A. Eyre	1995 Sales: $106.7 million
London NW1 3DR, UK	CFO: J. P. E. Taylor	1-Yr. Sales Change: 30.4%
Phone: +44-171-608-6080	HR: —	Exchange: London
Fax: +44-171-387-2345	Employees: 451	

Broadcasting - commercial radio stations & a TV studio

CAPITOL INDUSTRIES-EMI

1750 N. Vine St.	CEO: Gary Gersh	1995 Sales: $27.1 million
Hollywood, CA 90028	CFO: Charles Goldstuck	1-Yr. Sales Change: —
Phone: 213-462-6252	HR: —	Ownership: Subsidiary
Fax: 213-467-5267	Employees: 190	

Diversified operations - music & TV, rentals, technology (subsidiary of Thorn EMI)

CAPITOL MULTIMEDIA, INC.

7315 Wisconsin St., Ste. 800-E	CEO: Robert I. Bogin	1996 Sales: $4.3 million
Bethesda, MD 20814	CFO: Catherine K. Hoopes	1-Yr. Sales Change: (6.5%)
Phone: 301-907-7000	HR: —	Exchange: Nasdaq (SC)
Fax: 301-907-7000	Employees: 123	Symbol: CDIM

Computer - educational interactive consumer software & business applications focusing on the children's market within the CD-ROM interactive software industry

CARLTON COMMUNICATIONS PLC

15 St. George St., Hanover Square	CEO: June F. de Moller	1995 Sales: $2,532.8 million
London W1R 9DE, UK	CFO: B. A. Cragg	1-Yr. Sales Change: 13.9%
Phone: +44-171-499-8050	HR: —	Exchange: Nasdaq
Fax: +44-171-895-9575	Employees: 9,953	Symbol: CCTVY (ADR)

TV production & programming - video & audio production & TV broadcasting (Carlton Television, ITV & radio news, London News Network)

CARMIKE CINEMAS, INC.

1301 First Ave.	CEO: Michael W. Patrick	1995 Sales: $364.7 million
Columbus, GA 31901-2109	CFO: John O. Barwick III	1-Yr. Sales Change: 11.3%
Phone: 706-576-3400	HR: —	Exchange: NYSE
Fax: 706-576-3471	Employees: 10,082	Symbol: CKE

Motion pictures & services - theaters

See page 222 for a full profile of this company.

CARQUEVILLE GRAPHICS

2200 Estes Ave.
Elk Grove Village, IL 60007
Phone: 847-439-8700
Fax: 847-228-3953

CEO: Patrick Carney
CFO: John Nowicki
HR: —
Employees: 233

1995 Sales: $37.5 million
1-Yr. Sales Change: 19.8%
Ownership: Privately Held

Printing - labels, brochures & annual reports

CARSEY-WERNER DISTRIBUTION

4024 Radford Ave.
Los Angeles, CA 91604
Phone: 818-760-5598
Fax: 818-760-6067

CEO: Stuart Glickman
CFO: Bob Dubelko
HR: Nina Bass
Employees: 100

1995 Est. Sales: $175.0 mil.
1-Yr. Sales Change: —
Ownership: Privately Held

TV production & programming (*Cybill, Grace Under Fire, Roseanne, Third Rock From The Sun*)

CATALINA MARKETING CORPORATION

11300 Ninth St. North
St. Petersburg, FL 33716-2329
Phone: 813-579-5000
Fax: 813-570-8507

CEO: George W. Off
CFO: Phil Livingston
HR: Miller Detrick
Employees: 428

1996 Sales: $134.2 million
1-Yr. Sales Change: 18.4%
Exchange: NYSE
Symbol: POS

Business services - point-of-scan electronic marketing products & services

CD RADIO INC.

1001 22nd St. NW, 6th Fl.
Washington, DC 20037
Phone: 202-296-6192
Fax: 202-296-6265

CEO: David Margolese
CFO: Margaret E. Grayson
HR: —
Employees: 3

1995 Sales: —
1-Yr. Sales Change: —
Exchange: Nasdaq (SC)
Symbol: CDRD

Broadcasting - subscription-based satellite-to-car broadcast system

CENTRAL EUROPEAN MEDIA ENTERPRISES LTD.

Clarendon House, Church St.
Hamilton HM CX, Bermuda
Phone: 809-296-1431

CEO: Leonard M. Fertig
CFO: John Schwallie
HR: —
Employees: 1,029

1995 Sales: $98.9 million
1-Yr. Sales Change: 84.5%
Exchange: Nasdaq
Symbol: CETV

Broadcasting - national & regional commercial TV stations in Central Europe & Germany

CENTRAL NEWSPAPERS, INC.

135 N. Pennsylvania St., Ste. 1200
Indianapolis, IN 46204-2400
Phone: 317-231-9200
Fax: 317-231-9208

CEO: Louis A. Weil III
CFO: —
HR: —
Employees: 5,188

1995 Sales: $579.9 million
1-Yr. Sales Change: 11.6%
Exchange: NYSE
Symbol: ECP

Publishing - newspapers (*Indianapolis Star, Phoenix Gazette* & *Arizona Republic*)

 See page 223 for a full profile of this company.

CENTURY COMMUNICATIONS CORP.

50 Locust Ave.
New Canaan, CT 06840
Phone: 203-972-2000
Fax: 203-966-9228

CEO: Leonard Tow
CFO: Scott Schneider
HR: Claire L. Tow
Employees: 2,300

1995 Sales: $416.7 million
1-Yr. Sales Change: 11.2%
Exchange: Nasdaq
Symbol: CTYA

Cable TV - cable systems in 6 states, wireless telephone systems & one radio station

CEP COMMUNICATION SA

20, avenue Hoche
75008 Paris, France
Phone: +33-1-42-25-05-98
Fax: +33-1-42-25-16-01

CEO: Christian Bregou
CFO: J. de Menou
HR: —
Employees: 6,770

1995 Sales: $2,252.5 million
1-Yr. Sales Change: 73.4%
Exchange: Paris

Publishing - books & business & trade journals; trade show organization

CHAMPION INDUSTRIES, INC.

2450 First Ave., PO Box 2968
Huntington, WV 25728
Phone: 304-528-2791
Fax: 304-528-2765

CEO: Marshall T. Reynolds
CFO: Joseph C. Worth III
HR: Tony Atkins
Employees: 392

1995 Sales: $44.8 million
1-Yr. Sales Change: 14.6%
Exchange: Nasdaq
Symbol: CHMP

Printing - business cards, multicolored brochures, posters, binding & business forms; general office supplies

CHANCELLOR BROADCASTING COMPANY

12655 N. Central Expy., Ste. 405
Dallas, TX 75243
Phone: 214-239-6220
Fax: 214-239-0220

CEO: Steven Dinetz
CFO: Jacques D. Kerrest
HR: Karen DuBois
Employees: 236

1995 Sales: $64.3 million
1-Yr. Sales Change: 144.5%
Exchange: Nasdaq
Symbol: CBCA

Broadcasting - 34 radio stations, focused primarily on radio station ownership & operation

 See page 224 for a full profile of this company.

CHAS. LEVY COMPANIES

1200 N. North Branch
Chicago, IL 60622
Phone: 312-440-4400
Fax: 312-440-4434

CEO: Carol G. Kloster
CFO: Carol G. Kloster
HR: Jim Crawford
Employees: 2,000

1995 Sales: $320.0 million
1-Yr. Sales Change: 14.3%
Ownership: Privately Held

Wholesale distribution - books & magazines

CHARTER COMMUNICATIONS INC.

12444 Powerscourt Dr., Ste. 400
St. Louis, MO 63131
Phone: 314-965-0555
Fax: 314-965-6640

CEO: Barry Babcock
CFO: Jeffrey Sanders
HR: Dot Hoffman
Employees: 1,750

1995 Est. Sales: $275.0 mil.
1-Yr. Sales Change: 0.7%
Ownership: Privately Held

Cable TV - St. Louis area

CHASE ENTERPRISES, INC.

One Commercial Plaza
Hartford, CT 06103
Phone: 203-549-1674
Fax: 860-293-4289

CEO: David T. Chase
CFO: John Redding
HR: Sheri Lee
Employees: 250

1995 Est. Sales: $380.0 mil.
1-Yr. Sales Change: —
Ownership: Privately Held

Diversified operations - real estate; media; radio stations (Ten Eighty Corp.); cable TV in Poland (World Cable Communications, Inc.); investments; insurance

CHILDREN'S BROADCASTING CORPORATION

724 First Ave. North, 4th Fl.
Minneapolis, MN 55401
Phone: 612-338-3300
Fax: 612-338-4318

CEO: Christopher T. Dahl
CFO: James G. Gilbertson
HR: Amy Lynn
Employees: 160

1995 Sales: $5.1 million
1-Yr. Sales Change: 15.9%
Exchange: Nasdaq (SC)
Symbol: AAHS

Radio production & programming - children's radio programming (music, stories, current events, weather, interactive quizzes & interviews)

CHRIS-CRAFT INDUSTRIES, INC.

767 Fifth Ave., 46th Fl.
New York, NY 10153
Phone: 212-421-0200
Fax: 212-935-8462

CEO: Herbert J. Siegel
CFO: Joelen K. Merkel
HR: —
Employees: 1,246

1995 Sales: $472.1 million
1-Yr. Sales Change: (1.9%)
Exchange: NYSE
Symbol: CCN

Broadcasting - TV (6 VHF & 2 UHF stations, including ABC, NBC, CBS, FOX, United Paramount Network & independent affiliates)

See page 225 for a full profile of this company.

CHRISTIAN SCIENCE PUBLISHING SOCIETY

One Norway St.	CEO: J. Anthony Periton	1995 Est.Sales: $100.0 mil.
Boston, Ma 02115	CFO: John Ranson	1-Yr. Sales Change: —
Phone: 617-450-2000	HR: Stephanie McNeil	Ownership: Nonprofit
Fax: 617-450-3635	Employees: 450	

Publishing - religious books & newspaper (*Christian Science Monitor*); radio news program (*Monitor Radio*)

THE CHRONICLE PUBLISHING COMPANY, INC.

901 Mission St.	CEO: John B. Sias	1995 Sales: $418.0 million
San Francisco, CA 94103-2988	CFO: Alan H. Nichols	1-Yr. Sales Change: (15.0%)
Phone: 415-777-1111	HR: Michael O'Neil	Ownership: Privately Held
Fax: 415-777-7131	Employees: 2,500	

Publishing - newspapers (*San Francisco Chronicle*); TV stations

 **See page 226 for a full profile of this company.**

CHUBU-NIPPON BROADCASTING

1-2-8, Shinsakae, Naka-ku	CEO: Masao Hotta	1995 Sales: $377.6 million
Nagoya 460, Japan	CFO: —	1-Yr. Sales Change: 4.4%
Phone: +81-52-241-8111	HR: —	Exchange: Nagoya
Fax: +81-52-259-1331	Employees: 487	

Broadcasting - radio & TV company affiliated with TBS (Japan)

CIA GROUP

One Paris Garden	CEO: C. J. Ingram	1995 Sales: $938.3 million
London SE1 8NU, UK	CFO: Peter Toynton	1-Yr. Sales Change: 29.6%
Phone: +44-171-633-9999	HR: —	Exchange: London
Fax: +44-171-261-0188	Employees: 454	

Business services - time & space buyer for the broadcast & media markets

CINAR FILMS, INC.

1055 Rene East, 9th Fl.	CEO: Micheline Charest	1995 Sales: $31.0 million
Montreal, QC H2L 4S5, Canada	CFO: Michel S. Brunet	1-Yr. Sales Change: 41.6%
Phone: 514-843-7070	HR: —	Exchange: Nasdaq
Fax: 514-843-7080	Employees: 150	Symbol: CINRF

TV production & programming - nonviolent family entertainment programming (*The Little Lulu Show, Million Dollar Babies, Are You Afraid of the Dark*); CD-ROMs based on their TV shows

CINEMARK USA INC.

7502 Greenville Ave., Ste. 800
Dallas, TX 75231
Phone: 214-696-1644
Fax: 214-696-3946

CEO: Lee Roy Mitchell
CFO: Jeff Stedman
HR: —
Employees: 7,000

1995 Sales: $298.6 million
1-Yr. Sales Change: 5.5%
Ownership: Privately Held

Motion pictures & services - theaters

CINEMASTAR LUXURY THEATERS, INC.

431 College Blvd.
Oceanside, CA 92057
Phone: 619-630-2011
Fax: 619-630-8593

CEO: John Ellison Jr.
CFO: Alan Grossberg
HR: —
Employees: 32

1995 Sales: $10.0 million
1-Yr. Sales Change: 38.9%
Exchange: Nasdaq
Symbol: LUXY

Motion pictures & services - multiscreen theaters

CINEPLEX ODEON CORPORATION

1303 Yonge St.
Toronto, ON M4T 2Y9, Canada
Phone: 416-323-6600
Fax: 416-323-6612

CEO: Allen Karp
CFO: Ellis Jacob
HR: Cynthia Haxell
Employees: 7,661

1995 Sales: $513.2 million
1-Yr. Sales Change: (4.9%)
Exchange: NYSE
Symbol: CPX

Motion pictures & services - theaters (#2 in the US)

CINERGI PICTURES ENTERTAINMENT INC.

2308 Broadway
Santa Monica, CA 90404
Phone: 310-315-6000
Fax: 310-828-0443

CEO: Andrew G. Vajna
CFO: Warren Braverman
HR: —
Employees: 30

1995 Sales: $192.9
Exchange: Nasdaq
Symbol: CINE

Motion pictures & services - production & financing (*Medicine Man, Tombstone, Die Hard With a Vengeance, Judge Dredd*)

GROUPE DE LA CITÉ SA

20, avenue Hoche
75008 Paris, France
Phone: +33-1-44-95-56-00
Fax: +33-1-44-95-56-56

CEO: Christian Bregou
CFO: —
HR: —
Employees: 9,217

1995 Sales: $1,516.0 million
1-Yr. Sales Change: 1.8%
Exchange: Paris

Publishing - general literature, reference & textbooks

CITICASTERS INC.

One E. 4th St., Ste. 600
Cincinnati, OH 45202
Phone: 513-562-8000
Fax: 513-721-8413

CEO: John P. Zanotti
CFO: Gregory C. Thomas
HR: Suzanne J. Cook
Employees: 900

1995 Sales: $136.4 million
1-Yr. Sales Change: (30.8%)
Exchange: Nasdaq
Symbol: CITI

Broadcasting - radio & TV (10 FM & 4 AM radio stations; 2 ABC-affiliated TV stations)

CKS GROUP, INC.

10441 Bandley Dr.
Cupertino, CA 95014
Phone: 408-366-5100
Fax: 408-366-5120

CEO: Mark D. Kvamme
CFO: Carlton H. Baab
HR: Sharon Fitzsimmons
Employees: 187

1995 Sales: $34.8 million
1-Yr. Sales Change: 52.0%
Exchange: Nasdaq
Symbol: CKSG

Business services - marketing services, including strategic & corporate positioning, corporate identity & product branding, new media, packaging, collateral systems & advertising

 **See page 227 for a full profile of this company.**

CLARINET COMMUNICATIONS CORP.

4880 Stevens Creek Blvd., Ste. 206
San Jose, CA 95129-1034
Phone: 408-296-0366
Fax: 408-296-1668

CEO: Brad Templeton
CFO: Roy E. Folk
HR: Marilyn Foust
Employees: 22

1995 Est. Sales: $2.0 million
1-Yr. Sales Change: 100.0%
Ownership: Privately Held

Publishing - electronic news publication (e.News: Internet's first & largest news publication)

CLASSICS INTERNATIONAL ENTERTAINMENT, INC.

919 N. Michigan Ave., Ste. 3400
Chicago, IL 60611
Phone: 312-482-9006
Fax: 312-482-8557

CEO: Richard S. Berger
CFO: James M. Dore
HR: Lawrence A. Strauss
Employees: 93

1995 Sales: $2.8 million
1-Yr. Sales Change: (48.1%)
Exchange: Nasdaq (SC)
Symbol: CIEI

Retail - comic-book stores (Moondog's); comic-book publishing (First Classics)

CLEAR CHANNEL COMMUNICATIONS, INC.

200 Concord Plaza, Ste. 600
San Antonio, TX 78216
Phone: 210-822-2828
Fax: 210-822-2299

CEO: L. Lowry Mays
CFO: Herbert W. Hill Jr.
HR: —
Employees: 1,549

1995 Sales: $283.4 million
1-Yr. Sales Change: 63.7%
Exchange: NYSE
Symbol: CCU

Broadcasting - radio (33 stations & 3 networks) & TV (9 stations)

See page 228 for a full profile of this company.

CMG INFORMATION SERVICES, INC.

187 Ballardvale St., Ste. B110
Wilmington, MA 01887-7000
Phone: 508-657-7000
Fax: 508-988-0046

CEO: David S. Wetherell
CFO: Andrew Hajducky
HR: Susan Michelinie
Employees: 202

1995 Sales: $2.7 million
1-Yr. Sales Change: (86.1%)
Exchange: Nasdaq
Symbol: CMGI

Data collection & systems - information-based products & services to direct marketers; investments in
Internet-related technology (Lycos)

CMP PUBLICATIONS, INC.

600 Community Dr.
Manhasset, NY 11030-3847
Phone: 516-562-5000
Fax: 516-562-7830

CEO: Michael S. Leeds
CFO: Joseph E. Sichler
HR: —
Employees: 1,500

1995 Sales: $382.0 million
1-Yr. Sales Change: 19.2%
Ownership: Privately Held

Publishing - technology- & computer-related publications (*HomePC*, *InformationWeek*, *NetGuide*,
WINDOWS magazine, *Electronic Engineering Times*, *Interactive Age*); trade shows; online services

 **See pages 60–61 for a full profile of this company.**

C/NET, INC.

150 Chestnut St.
San Francisco, CA 94111
Phone: 415-395-7800
Fax: 415-395-9205

CEO: Halsey M. Minor
CFO: Shelby W. Bonnie
HR: Nancy Guilbert
Employees: 164

1995 Sales: $3.5 million
1-Yr. Sales Change: —
Ownership: Privately Held

Computers - Internet (c/net.com, shareware.com, search.com) & TV-based programming (c/net central)

CODY'S BOOKS INC.

2454 Telegraph Ave.
Berkeley, CA 94704
Phone: 510-845-7852
Fax: 510-841-6185

CEO: Andy Ross
CFO: Shane Battle
HR: —
Employees: 60

1995 Sales: $5.0 million
1-Yr. Sales Change: —
Ownership: Privately Held

Retail - bookstore with over 100,000 titles

COMCAST CORPORATION

1500 Market St., 35th Fl.
Philadelphia, PA 19102-2148
Phone: 215-665-1700
Fax: 215-981-7790

CEO: Brian L. Roberts
CFO: John R. Alchin
HR: —
Employees: 12,200

1995 Sales: $3,362.9 million
1-Yr. Sales Change: 144.5%
Exchange: Nasdaq
Symbol: CMCSA

Cable TV - cable & cellular telephone communications systems & production & distribution of cable
programming (#4 in the US)

 **See pages 62–63 for a full profile of this company.**

COMMUNICATIONS AND ENTERTAINMENT CORPORATION

1900 Avenue of the Stars, Ste. 615
Los Angeles, CA 90067
Phone: 310-556-3656
Fax: 310-556-5460

CEO: Shane O'Neil
CFO: Jay Behling
HR: —
Employees: 6

1995 Sales: $1.5 million
1-Yr. Sales Change: (89.9%)
Exchange: OTC
Symbol: CECO

Motion pictures & services - production

COMPUSERVE CORPORATION

5000 Arlington Centre Blvd.
Columbus, OH 43220
Phone: 614-457-8600
Fax: 614-457-0348

CEO: Robert J. Massey
CFO: Lawrence A. Geyenes
HR: Judy Reinhard
Employees: 2,500

1996 Sales: $793.2 million
1-Yr. Sales Change: 36.1%
Exchange: Nasdaq
Symbol: CSRV

Computers - online information service & Internet access provider

 See pages 64–65 for a full profile of this company.

COMPUTER PETROLEUM CORPORATION

30 E. Seventh St.
St. Paul, MN 55101
Phone: 612-225-9550
Fax: 612-298-0243

CEO: William G. Leonard
CFO: Gary C. Thomas
HR: —
Employees: 45

1996 Sales: $4.4 million
1-Yr. Sales Change: 12.8%
Exchange: Nasdaq (SC)
Symbol: CPCO

Business services - information network database provider servicing energy & trucking industries with customized news & commentary

COMSAT CORPORATION

6560 Rock Spring Dr.
Bethesda, MD 20817
Phone: 301-214-3000
Fax: 301-214-7100

CEO: Bruce L. Crockett
CFO: Allen E. Flower
HR: Steven F. Bell
Employees: 2,991

1995 Sales: $852.1 million
1-Yr. Sales Change: 3.0%
Exchange: NYSE
Symbol: CQ

Telecommunications services; professional basketball (Denver Nuggets) & hockey (Colorado Avalanche) teams; film production (Beacon); hotel-room movies (On Command Video)

 See page 229 for a full profile of this company.

COMTEX SCIENTIFIC CORPORATION

4900 Seminary Rd.
Alexandria, VA 22311
Phone: 703-820-2000
Fax: 703-824-8750

CEO: C. W. Gilluly
CFO: —
HR: Danie Penenburgh
Employees: 25

1995 Sales: $2.8 million
1-Yr. Sales Change: (6.7%)
Exchange: OTC

Business services - real-time online news provider

CONSOLIDATED GRAPHICS, INC.

2210 W. Dallas St.
Houston, TX 77019
Phone: 713-529-4200
Fax: 713-525-4305

CEO: Joe R. Davis
CFO: Mary K. Collins
HR: Janet Swikard
Employees: 998

1996 Sales: $85.1 million
1-Yr. Sales Change: 48.8%
Exchange: Nasdaq
Symbol: COGI

Printing - annual reports, product & capability brochures, direct-mail pieces, catalogs & other promotional material for corporate clients

 **See page 230 for a full profile of this company.**

CONSUMERS UNION OF UNITED STATES, INC.

101 Truman Ave.
Yonkers, NY 10703
Phone: 914-378-2000
Fax: 914-378-2900

CEO: Rhoda H. Karpatkin
CFO: Conrad Harris
HR: Rick Lustig
Employees: 451

1996 Sales: $136.0 million
1-Yr. Sales Change: 5.4%
Ownership: Not-for-profit

Publishing - magazines (*Consumer Reports, Consumer Reports Travel Letter, Consumer Reports on Health, Zillions: Consumer Reports for Kids*); syndicated TV programming

CONTINENTAL CABLEVISION, INC.

The Pilot House, Lewis Wharf
Boston, MA 02110
Phone: 617-742-9500
Fax: 617-742-0530

CEO: Amos B. Hostetter Jr.
CFO: Nancy Hawthorne
HR: H. Clare Muhm
Employees: 9,200

1995 Sales: $1,442.4 million
1-Yr. Sales Change: 20.2%
Ownership: Privately Held

Cable TV (#3 in the US)

CONTINENTAL WEB PRESS, INC.

1430 Industrial Dr.
Itasca, IL 60143
Phone: 708-773-1903
Fax: 708-773-1909

CEO: Kenneth W. Field
CFO: John DeBerge
HR: Michele Krahn
Employees: 450

1995 Sales: $89.0 million
1-Yr. Sales Change: 14.1%
Ownership: Privately Held

Printing - commercial web offset printing

THE COPLEY PRESS, INC.

7776 Ivanhoe Ave.
La Jolla, CA 92037
Phone: 619-454-0411
Fax: 619-454-5014

CEO: Helen K. Copley
CFO: Charles F. Patrick
HR: Carmi Hodge
Employees: 3,500

1995 Sales: $398.0 million
1-Yr. Sales Change: 1.6%
Ownership: Privately Held

Publishing - daily & nondaily newspapers (over 40: *San Diego Union-Tribune*); newsprint

 **See page 231 for a full profile of this company.**

CORBIS CORPORATION

15395 SE 30th Place, Ste. 300	CEO: Doug Rowan	1995 Sales: —
Bellevue, WA 98007	CFO: Tony Rojas	1-Yr. Sales Change: —
Phone: 206-641-4505	HR: Tica Gordon	Ownership: Privately Held
Fax: 206-746-1618	Employees: 270	

Computers - multimedia CD-ROMs (A Passion for Art: Renoir, Cezanne, Matisse, and Dr. Barnes); digital image licensing (Bettmann archive) - owned by Bill Gates

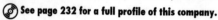 **See page 232 for a full profile of this company.**

CORDIANT PLC

83-89 Whitfield St.	CEO: Robert L. Seelert	1995 Sales: $1,177.7 million
London W1A 4XA, UK	CFO: Wendy Smyth	1-Yr. Sales Change: (1.8%)
Phone: +44-171-436-4000	HR: Albert Pendergast	Exchange: NYSE
Fax: +44-171-436-1998	Employees: 10,570	Symbol: CDA (ADR)

Advertising - media services, direct marketing & public relations

 **See pages 66–67 for a full profile of this company.**

CORINTHIAN COMMUNICATIONS, INC.

845 Third Ave.	CEO: Larry Miller	1995 Est. Sales: $225.0 mil.
New York, NY 10022	CFO: Claire Pride	1-Yr. Sales Change: —
Phone: 212-371-5225	HR: —	Ownership: Privately Held
Fax: 212-752-6594	Employees: 65	

Advertising

CORPORATION FOR PUBLIC BROADCASTING

901 E Street NW	CEO: Richard W. Carlson	1995 Sales: $312.2 million
Washington, DC 20004	CFO: E. Renee Ingram	1-Yr. Sales Change: 6.1%
Phone: 202-879-9600	HR: Miriam Crawford	Ownership: Privately Held
Fax: 202-879-1039	Employees: 95	

Broadcasting - radio & TV

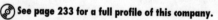 **See page 233 for a full profile of this company.**

COURIER CORPORATION

165 Jackson St.	CEO: James F. Conway III	1995 Sales: $120.7 million
Lowell, MA 01852	CFO: Robert P. Story Jr.	1-Yr. Sales Change: (2.2%)
Phone: 508-458-6351	HR: Charlie Van Horn	Exchange: Nasdaq
Fax: 508-453-0344	Employees: 1,103	Symbol: CRRC

Printing - books, manuals, diskettes & CD-ROMs

See page 234 for a full profile of this company.

COWLES MEDIA COMPANY

329 Portland Ave.
Minneapolis, MN 55415-1112
Phone: 612-673-7100
Fax: 612-673-7020

CEO: David C. Cox
CFO: James J. Viera
HR: Pamela J. Sveinson
Employees: 3,300

1995 Sales: $449.7 million
1-Yr. Sales Change: 25.5%
Exchange: OTC

Publishing - newspapers (*Minneapolis Star Tribune*), magazines (*Folio, Inside Media, Catalog Age*) & newsletters; trade publishing (*Weissmann Travel Reports*); online services (Cowles Media, SIMBA)

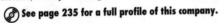 **See page 235 for a full profile of this company.**

COX COMMUNICATIONS, INC.

1400 Lake Hearn Dr.
Atlanta, GA 30319
Phone: 404-843-5000
Fax: 404-843-5975

CEO: James O. Robbins
CFO: Jimmy W. Hayes
HR: Marybeth Lemer
Employees: 4,375

1995 Sales: $1,286.2 million
1-Yr. Sales Change: 74.7%
Exchange: NYSE
Symbol: COX

Cable TV - US cable TV systems; investments in The Discovery Channel, The Learning Channel, E! Entertainment; international cable TV (UK Gold); programming; telecommunications operations

COX ENTERPRISES, INC.

1400 Lake Hearn Dr.
Atlanta, GA 30319
Phone: 404-843-5000
Fax: 404-843-5142

CEO: James Cox Kennedy
CFO: John R. Dillon
HR: Marybeth Leamer
Employees: 38,000

1995 Sales: $3,806.0 million
1-Yr. Sales Change: 29.3%
Ownership: Privately Held

Publishing - newspapers (*Atlanta Journal-Constitution, Austin American-Statesman, Palm Beach Post*); TV & radio broadcasting; cable TV (75% ownership of Cox Communications); auto auctions (Manheim)

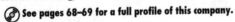 **See pages 68–69 for a full profile of this company.**

CRAIN COMMUNICATIONS INC

740 N. Rush St.
Chicago, IL 60611-2590
Phone: 312-649-5200
Fax: 312-280-3179

CEO: Gertrude R. Crain
CFO: Mary Kay Crain
HR: Frances Scott
Employees: 979

1995 Sales: $181.8 million
1-Yr. Sales Change: 6.5%
Ownership: Privately Held

Publishing - business (*Crain's Chicago Business, Crain's New York Business*), trade (*Advertising Age*) & consumer periodicals (*Automotive News*); radio station; business news service

 **See page 236 for a full profile of this company.**

CREATIVE ALLIANCE INC.

222 S. First St.
Louisville, KY 40202
Phone: 502-584-8787
Fax: 502-589-9900

CEO: Debbie Scoppechio
CFO: Wes Burgiss
HR: Carol Demeuth
Employees: 125

1995 Sales: $10.8 million
1-Yr. Sales Change: 25.6%
Ownership: Privately Held

Advertising

CREATIVE ARTISTS AGENCY, INC.

9830 Wilshire Blvd.
Beverly Hills, CA 90212
Phone: 310-288-4545
Fax: 310-288-4800

Talent agency

CEO: Rick Nicica
CFO: Ray Kurtzman
HR: Arlene Newman
Employees: 350

1995 Est. Sales: $175.0 mil.
1-Yr. Sales Change: —
Ownership: Privately Held

CREATIVE LEARNING PRODUCTS, INC.

150 Morris Ave.
Springfield, NJ 07081
Phone: 201-467-0266
Fax: 201-467-5650

CEO: Peter J. Jegou
CFO: Walter J. Krzanowski
HR: —
Employees: 17

1995 Sales: $1.5 million
1-Yr. Sales Change: 275.0%
Exchange: Nasdaq (SC)
Symbol: CLPI

Publishing - educational audio- & videocassettes; cards, placemats & workbooks

CREATIVE PROGRAMMING AND TECHNOLOGY VENTURES, INC.

7900 E. Union Ave., Ste. 1100
Denver, CO 80237
Phone: 303-694-5324
Fax: 303-694-5326

CEO: Gary R. Vickers
CFO: Gary R. Vickers
HR: —
Employees: 32

1995 Sales: $0.4 million
1-Yr. Sales Change: (85.7%)
Exchange: Nasdaq (SC)
Symbol: CPTV

Diversified - TV commercials; interactive digital entertainment; cable programming

CREATIVE TECHNOLOGY LTD.

67 Ayer Rajah
Crescent #03-18 0513, Singapore
Phone: +65-773-0233
Fax: +65-773-0353

CEO: Sim Wong Hoo
CFO: Patrick Verderico
HR: Judith Martin
Employees: 4,100

1995 Sales: $1,202.3 million
1-Yr. Sales Change: 82.7%
Exchange: Nasdaq
Symbol: CREAF

Computers - interactive CDs (A Brief History of Time), sound & video multimedia products (Sound Blaster) & voice recognition software (Voiceassist)

CROWN BOOKS CORPORATION

3300 75th Ave.
Landover, MD 20785
Phone: 301-731-1200
Fax: 301-731-1340

Retail - discount bookstores

CEO: E. Steve Stevens
CFO: Donald J. Pilch
HR: Anne Levinton
Employees: 2,800

1996 Sales: $283.5 million
1-Yr. Sales Change: (7.2%)
Exchange: Nasdaq
Symbol: CRWN

(◎) **See page 237 for a full profile of this company.**

CST ENTERTAINMENT, INC.

5901 Green Valley Circle, Ste. 400
Culver City, CA 90230
Phone: 310-417-3444
Fax: 310-417-3500

CEO: Jonathan D. Shapiro
CFO: Jeffrey M. Jacobs
HR: Maggie Chambers
Employees: 140

1995 Sales: $6.1 million
1-Yr. Sales Change: 84.8%
Exchange: AMEX
Symbol: CLR

Motion pictures & services - colorization of black & white films & TV programs; licensing & distribution of film library

CUC INTERNATIONAL INC.

707 Summer St.
Stamford, CT 06901
Phone: 203-324-9261
Fax: 203-348-4528

CEO: Walter A. Forbes
CFO: Cosmo Corigliano
HR: Fran Johnson
Employees: 8,000

1996 Sales: $1,415.0 million
1-Yr. Sales Change: 35.4%
Exchange: NYSE
Symbol: CU

Retail - membership-based consumer services & products offered by mail order, phone & online network (Comp-U-Card); educational software (Davidson Associates, Sierra On-Line)

DAI NIPPON PRINTING

1-1, Ichigaya Kagacho 1-chome
Shinjuku-ku, Tokyo 162-01, Japan
Phone: +81-3-3266-2111
Fax: +81-3-3266-2119

CEO: Yoshitoshi Kitajima
CFO: Michiji Sato
HR: Yasuo Yamaji
Employees: 33,000

1995 Sales: $14,386.6 mil.
1-Yr. Sales Change: 8.7%
Exchange: OTC
Symbol: DNPCY (ADR)

Printing - commercial (#1 worldwide)

 **See pages 70–71 for a full profile of this company.**

DAILY JOURNAL CORPORATION

355 S. Grand Ave, 34th Fl.
Los Angeles, CA 90071-1560
Phone: 213-624-7715
Fax: 213-680-3682

CEO: Gerald L. Salzman
CFO: Gerald L. Salzman
HR: —
Employees: 365

1995 Sales: $34.6 million
1-Yr. Sales Change: 3.9%
Exchange: Nasdaq
Symbol: DJCO

Publishing - newspapers (18, including *The Los Angeles Daily Journal*, *San Francisco Daily Journal*) & specialized information services

DAILY MAIL AND GENERAL TRUST PLC

Northcliffe House, 2 Derry St.
Kensington, London W8 5TT, UK
Phone: +44-171-938-6000
Fax: +44-171-938-4626

CEO: Charles J. F. Sinclair
CFO: J. P. Williams
HR: —
Employees: 9,520

1995 Sales: $1,392.6 million
1-Yr. Sales Change: 13.0%
Exchange: London

Publishing - newspapers (*Daily Mail*, Northcliffe Newspapers, Euromoney Publications)

DALE CARNEGIE TRAINING, INC.

1475 Franklin Ave.	CEO: Stuart Levine	1995 Est. Sales: $100.0 mil.
New York, NY 11530	CFO: Marc Johnston	1-Yr. Sales Change: —
Phone: 516-248-5100	HR: Kathleen Gambino	Ownership: Privately Held
Fax: 516-877-0627	Employees: 195	

School - leadership training; book publishing (*The Leader In You*)

D'ARCY MASIUS BENTON & BOWLES, INC.

1675 Broadway	CEO: Roy J. Bostock	1995 Sales: $626.0 million
New York, NY 10019	CFO: Craig D. Brown	1-Yr. Sales Change: 2.9%
Phone: 212-468-3622	HR: William L. Clayton	Ownership: Privately Held
Fax: 212-468-4385	Employees: 6,333	

Advertising

DATA BROADCASTING CORPORATION

3490 Clubhouse Dr., PO Box 7443	CEO: Alan J. Hirschfield	1995 Sales: $74.2 million
Jackson, WY 83001	CFO: Mark F. Imperiale	1-Yr. Sales Change: 11.7%
Phone: 307-733-9742	HR: Eileen Gilbert	Exchange: Nasdaq
Fax: 307-733-4935	Employees: 658	Symbol: DBCC

Business services - real-time stock market quotes, customized portfolio tracking & investor information

DATA TRANSMISSION NETWORK CORPORATION

9110 W. Dodge Rd., Ste. 200	CEO: Roger R. Brodersen	1995 Sales: $62.3 million
Omaha, NE 68114	CFO: Brian L. Larson	1-Yr. Sales Change: 35.1%
Phone: 402-390-2328	HR: Carol Pigg	Exchange: Nasdaq
Fax: 402-390-7188	Employees: 450	Symbol: DTLN

Business services - electronic information & communication services, including electronic satellite delivery of time-sensitive information

DATATIMES CORPORATION

14000 Quail Springs Pkwy, Ste. 450	CEO: Allen W. Paschal	1995 Sales: $42.0 million
Oklahoma City, OK 73134	CFO: Doug Stussi	1-Yr. Sales Change: 40.0%
Phone: 405-751-6400	HR: Doug Stussi	Ownership: Privately Held
Fax: 405-755-8028	Employees: 70	

Computers - online business information network (EyeQ); on-demand executive briefing reports sold over the World Wide Web (Avenue Technologies)

DAVIDSON & ASSOCIATES, INC.

19840 Pioneer Ave.
Torrance, CA 90503
Phone: 310-793-0600
Fax: 310-793-0601

CEO: Robert M. Davidson
CFO: Jacques R. Allewaert
HR: Lonna Lynn
Employees: 538

1995 Sales: $147.2 million
1-Yr. Sales Change: 67.5%
Exchange: Nasdaq
Symbol: DAVD

Computers - educational & entertainment software (Math Blaster, Kid CAD, Zoo Keeper)

DAVIS, BALL & COLOMBATTO ADVERTISING, INC.

865 S. Figueroa St., 12th Fl.
Los Angeles, CA 90036
Phone: 213-688-7000
Fax: 213-688-7288

CEO: Mark Davis
CFO: Steve Orenstein
HR: Susan Franceschini
Employees: 108

1995 Sales: $15.7 million
1-Yr. Sales Change: 1.9%
Ownership: Privately Held

Advertising

DAY RUNNER, INC.

15295 Alton Pkwy.
Irvine, CA 92718
Phone: 714-680-3500
Fax: 714-680-0542

CEO: Mark A. Vidovich
CFO: Dennis K. Marquardt
HR: Lee R. Coffey
Employees: 801

1995 Sales: $121.8 million
1-Yr. Sales Change: 25.6%
Exchange: Nasdaq
Symbol: DAYR

Paper - personal organizers, diaries & assignment books

DE LA RUE PLC

6 Agar St.
London WC2N 4DE, UK
Phone: +44-171-836-8383
Fax: +44-171-240-4224

CEO: Jeremy J. S. Marshall
CFO: Les G. Cullen
HR: —
Employees: 8,012

1995 Sales: $1,210.9 million
1-Yr. Sales Change: 26.0%
Exchange: London

Printing - bank notes; securities, transaction & payment systems

DELUXE CORPORATION

3680 Victoria St. N
Shoreview, MN 55126-2966
Phone: 612-483-4477
Fax: 612-481-4163

CEO: John A. "Gus" Blanchard III
CFO: Charles M. Osborne
HR: Mike Reeves
Employees: 18,000

1995 Sales: $1,858.0 million
1-Yr. Sales Change: 6.3%
Exchange: NYSE
Symbol: DLX

Paper - business forms, check printing; electronic funds transfer software

DENTSU INC.

1-11 Tsukiji, Chuo-ku	CEO: Gohei Kogure	1995 Sales: $2,026.0 million
Tokyo 104, Japan	CFO: —	1-Yr. Sales Change: 24.9%
Phone: +81-3-5551-5111	HR: —	Ownership: Privately Held
Fax: +81-3-5551-2013	Employees: 5,910	

Advertising - services including marketing & planning

(💿) **See pages 72–73 for a full profile of this company.**

DESKTOP DATA, INC.

80 Blanchard Rd.	CEO: Donald L. McLagan	1995 Sales: $23.2 million
Burlington, MA 01803	CFO: Edward R. Siegfried	1-Yr. Sales Change: 61.1%
Phone: 617-229-3000	HR: Jessica Wasner	Exchange: Nasdaq
Fax: 617-890-1565	Employees: 130	Symbol: DTOP

Computers - customized, real-time news & information delivered via LAN

(💿) **See page 238 for a full profile of this company.**

A/S DET OSTASIATISKE KOMPAGNI

Company House, 7 Midtermolen	CEO: Carsten D. Nielsen	1995 Sales: $2,602.1 million
DK 2100 Copenhagen, Denmark	CFO: —	1-Yr. Sales Change: 15.8%
Phone: +45-35-27-27-27	HR: —	Exchange: Copenhagen
Fax: +45-31-42-12-34	Employees: 12,891	

Business services - marketing; graphics machinery; consumer goods

DEVON GROUP, INC.

281 Tresser Blvd., Ste. 501	CEO: Marne Obernauer Jr.	1996 Sales: $249.0 million
Stamford, CT 06901-3227	CFO: Bruce K. Koch	1-Yr. Sales Change: 10.3%
Phone: 203-964-1444	HR: Bruce K. Koch	Exchange: Nasdaq
Fax: 203-964-1036	Employees: 1,900	Symbol: DEVN

Printing - advertising & editorial production, computerized typesetting, composition, color separation, printing, binding & related services

DICK CLARK PRODUCTIONS, INC.

3003 W. Olive Ave.	CEO: Richard W. Clark	1995 Sales: $46.6 million
Burbank, CA 91505-4590	CFO: Kenneth H. Ferguson	1-Yr. Sales Change: (20.1%)
Phone: 818-841-3003	HR: Kenneth H. Ferguson	Exchange: Nasdaq
Fax: 818-954-8609	Employees: 475	Symbol: DCPI

TV production & programming; event marketing; talent booking agency; theme restaurants; skin care products (Geviderm)

(💿) **See page 239 for a full profile of this company.**

DIRECTV, INC.

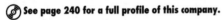

2230 E. Imperial Hwy.	CEO: Eddie Hartenstein	1995 Est. Sales: $525.0 mil.
El Segundo, CA 90245	CFO: Louise Wildee	1-Yr. Sales Change: —
Phone: 310-535-5000	HR: Jim Rebman	Ownership: Subsidiary
Fax: 310-535-5225	Employees: 602	

Satellite-to-home TV system (subsidiary of Hughes Electronics)

See page 240 for a full profile of this company.

DISCOVERY COMMUNICATIONS, INC.

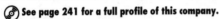

7700 Wisconsin Ave.	CEO: John Hendricks	1995 Sales: $250.0 million
Bethesda, MD 20814	CFO: Greg Durig	1-Yr. Sales Change: 25.0%
Phone: 301-986-1999	HR: Elizabeth Speziale	Ownership: Privately Held
Fax: 301-986-1889	Employees: 500	

Broadcasting - science & education cable TV programming (Discovery Channel, Learning Channel); nature- & science-themed retail stores (49% owned by TCI; 24% owned by Cox Communications)

See page 241 for a full profile of this company.

DISCREET LOGIC INC.

5505 Boulevard St. Laurent, Ste. 5200	CEO: Richard J. Szalwinski	1995 Sales: $64.5 million
Montreal, QC H2T 1S6, Canada	CFO: Douglas R. Johnson	1-Yr. Sales Change: 318.8%
Phone: 514-272-0525	HR: Garry Blagrave	Exchange: Nasdaq
	Employees: 270	Symbol: DSLGF

Computers - digital image processing systems for creating & editing special visual effects for film (*Speed, Forrest Gump, Interview with the Vampire*) & video

DISPATCH PRINTING COMPANY

34 S. 3rd St.	CEO: John F. Wolfe	1995 Est. Sales: $235.0 mil.
Columbus, OH 43215	CFO: A. Kenneth Pierce Jr.	1-Yr. Sales Change: 1.0%
Phone: 614-461-5000	HR: Mark Evans	Ownership: Privately Held
Fax: 614-461-7571	Employees: 1,300	

Publishing - newspapers (*Columbus Dispatch*); door-to-door advertisements, telemarketing & commercial printing (Dispatch Consumer Services Inc.)

DMX INC.

11400 W. Olympic Blvd., Ste. 1100	CEO: Jerold H. Rubinstein	1995 Sales: $12.8 million
Los Angeles, CA 90064-1507	CFO: J. Wendy Kim	1-Yr. Sales Change: 36.2%
Phone: 310-444-1744	HR: —	Exchange: Nasdaq
Fax: 310-444-1717	Employees: 145	Symbol: TUNE

Music publishing - commercial-free cable audio programming

DOLBY LABORATORIES INC.

100 Potrero Ave.	CEO: Bill Jasper	1995 Sales: $60.0 million
San Francisco, CA 94103	CFO: Janet Daily	1-Yr. Sales Change: —
Phone: 415-558-0200	HR: Rachel Yu	Ownership: Privately Held
Fax: 415-863-1373	Employees: 300	

Music production - noise reduction systems for improving sound quality

DORLING KINDERSLEY HOLDINGS PLC

9 Henrietta St., Covent Garden	CEO: John Sargent	1995 Sales: $221.3 million
London WC2E 8PS, UK	CFO: Tom Altier	1-Yr. Sales Change: 30.3%
Phone: +44-171-836-5411	HR: —	Exchange: London
Fax: +44-171-836-7570	Employees: 880	

Publishing - illustrated reference books; CD-ROMs; broadcast & video programs

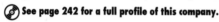 **See page 242 for a full profile of this company.**

DOVE AUDIO INC.

301 N. Canon Dr., Ste. 203	CEO: Michael Viner	1995 Sales: $11.1 million
Beverly Hills, CA 90210	CFO: Simon R. Baker	1-Yr. Sales Change: (10.5%)
Phone: 310-273-7722	HR: Carol Jacobs	Exchange: Nasdaq
Fax: 310-273-0365	Employees: 46	Symbol: DOVE

Publishing - audio books on tape & CD (including authors Sidney Sheldon, Amy Tan & Jack Higgins); film production & development

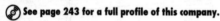 **See page 243 for a full profile of this company.**

DOW JONES & COMPANY, INC.

World Financial Center, 200 Liberty St.	CEO: Peter R. Kann	1995 Sales: $2,283.8 million
New York, NY 10281	CFO: Kevin J. Roche	1-Yr. Sales Change: 9.2%
Phone: 212-416-2000	HR: James A. Scaduto	Exchange: NYSE
Fax: 212-732-8356	Employees: 11,200	Symbol: DJ

Publishing - business newspapers (*Barron's*, *Wall Street Journal*), magazines (*SmartMoney*) & online services (Dow Jones News/Retrieval, Telerate); general-interest daily newspapers

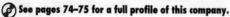 **See pages 74–75 for a full profile of this company.**

DREAMWORKS SKG

100 Universal Plaza, Lakeside Bldg.	CEO: Helene Hahn	1995 Sales: $0.0 million
Universal City, CA 91608	CFO: Ronald L. Nelson	1-Yr. Sales Change: —
Phone: 818-733-7000	HR: Cassie Thomas	Ownership: Privately Held
Fax: 818-733-6153	Employees: —	

Motion pictures & services - film production, interactive & multimedia entertainment, TV programming, record production & digital animation services

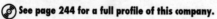 **See page 244 for a full profile of this company.**

THE DUN & BRADSTREET CORPORATION

187 Danbury Rd.	CEO: Robert E. Weissman	1995 Sales: $5,415.1 million
Wilton, CT 06897	CFO: Frank S. Sowinski	1-Yr. Sales Change: 10.6%
Phone: 203-834-4200	HR: —	Exchange: NYSE
Fax: 203-834-4201	Employees: 49,500	Symbol: DNB

Business services - marketing (A. C. Nielsen), audience measurement (Nielsen Media Research), risk management (Dun & Bradstreet Information Services, Moody's), software & directory information services

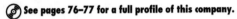 **See pages 76–77 for a full profile of this company.**

EAGLE RIVER INTERACTIVE, INC.

1060 W. Beaver Creek Blvd.	CEO: Terence Graunke	1995 Sales: $5.3 million
Avon, CO 81620	CFO: —	1-Yr. Sales Change: —
Phone: 970-845-8300	HR: —	Exchange: Nasdaq
	Employees: 66	Symbol: ERIV

Business services - interactive marketing services, including billboards, WWW site development, information & transaction kiosks, CD-ROMs & online services

E&D WEB, INC.

4633 W. 16th St.	CEO: Christopher Love	1995 Sales: $45.0 million
Cicero, IL 60650	CFO: Sophie Siek	1-Yr. Sales Change: (10.0%)
Phone: 708-656-6600	HR: —	Ownership: Privately Held
Fax: 708-656-8390	Employees: 145	

Printing - full-service, commercial web offset printing

EARLE PALMER BROWN COS.

6935 Arlington Rd.	CEO: Jeremy E. Brown	1995 Sales: $50.3 million
Bethesda, MD 20814	CFO: Charles Walsh	1-Yr. Sales Change: (0.2%)
Phone: 301-657-6000	HR: Pollyann Burkert	Ownership: Privately Held
Fax: 301-657-2590	Employees: 503	

Advertising

EAST TEXAS DISTRIBUTING INC.

7171 Grand Blvd.	CEO: Ron Eisenberg	1995 Est. Sales: $525.0 mil.
Houston, TX 77054	CFO: David Streusand	1-Yr. Sales Change: —
Phone: 713-748-2520	HR: Carol Terrando	Ownership: Privately Held
Fax: 713-747-5897	Employees: 800	

Wholesale distribution - magazines & books; videos

ECHOSTAR COMMUNICATIONS CORPORATION

90 Inverness Circle East
Englewood, CO 80112
Phone: 303-799-8222
Fax: 303-799-6222

CEO: Charles W. Ergen
CFO: Steve Schaver
HR: Donna Dunn
Employees: 508

1995 Sales: $163.9 million
1-Yr. Sales Change: (14.2%)
Exchange: Nasdaq
Symbol: DISH

Telecommunications equipment - satellite receiving dishes, integrated receivers & descramblers, programming, installation & 3rd-party consumer financing for products & services

ECRM INCORPORATED

554 Clark Rd.
Tewksbury, MA 01876
Phone: 508-851-0207
Fax: 508-851-7016

CEO: William R. Givens
CFO: Rudolf I. Bunde
HR: Andrea Bunde
Employees: 248

1995 Sales: $59.3 million
1-Yr. Sales Change: 21.8%
Exchange: Nasdaq
Symbol: ECRM

Computers - image processing systems, including imagesetters (AIR75-Advanced Image Recorder), scanners (Autokon) & related software for the printing & publishing industry worldwide

EDELMAN PUBLIC RELATIONS WORLDWIDE

200 E. Randolph Dr., 63rd Fl.
Chicago, IL 60601
Phone: 312-240-3000
Fax: 312-240-2900

CEO: Daniel J. Edelman
CFO: Darryl Salerno
HR: Sandy Harling
Employees: 900

1995 Sales: $80.0 million
1-Yr. Sales Change: 8.0%
Ownership: Privately Held

Business services - public relations

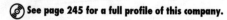 **See page 245 for a full profile of this company.**

EDITORIALE LA REPUBBLICA SPA

Piazza Indipendenza, 11B
00185 Rome, Italy
Phone: +39-6-49-821
Fax: +39-6-49-82-29-23

CEO: Marco Benedetto
CFO: —
HR: —
Employees: 730

1995 Sales: $360.5 million
1-Yr. Sales Change: 13.1%
Exchange: Milan

Publishing - newspaper (*La Repubblica*); advertising (publicly traded subsidiary of Editoriale L'Espresso SPA)

EDITORIALE L'ESPRESSO SPA

Via Po. 12
00198 Rome, Italy
Phone: +39-6-84-781
Fax: +39-6-844-3174

CEO: Marco Benedetto
CFO: —
HR: —
Employees: 2,577

1995 Sales: $707.0 million
1-Yr. Sales Change: 10.6%
Exchange: Milan

Publishing - newspapers (*La Repubblica*) & periodicals (*L'Espresso, La Sentinella*); advertising

EDMARK CORPORATION

6727 185th Ave. NE	CEO: Sally G. Norodick	1995 Sales: $22.7 million
Redmond, WA 98052-3218	CFO: Paul N. Bialek	1-Yr. Sales Change: 94.0%
Phone: 206-556-8400	HR: Diane Coplentz	Exchange: Nasdaq (SC)
Fax: 206-556-8430	Employees: 156	Symbol: EDMK

Computers - children's educational software (Millie's Math House & KidDesk) & books

◉ **See page 246 for a full profile of this company.**

EDUCATIONAL DEVELOPMENT CORPORATION

10302 E. 55th Place, PO Box 470663	CEO: Randall W. White	1995 Sales: $20.6 million
Tulsa, OK 74147-0663	CFO: W. Curtis Fossett	1-Yr. Sales Change: 60.9%
Phone: 918-622-4522	HR: W. Curtis Fossett	Exchange: Nasdaq
Fax: 918-663-4509	Employees: 68	Symbol: EDUC

Wholesale distribution - instructional children's books & educational materials for book, toy & specialty stores, educators, independent consultants & school & public libraries

EDUSOFT LTD.

19 Weissburg St.	CEO: Menachem Hasfari	1995 Sales: $11.0 million
61130 Tel Aviv, Israel	CFO: Rafi Itzaki	1-Yr. Sales Change: 10.0%
Phone: +972-3-648-2131	HR: —	Exchange: Nasdaq
Fax: +972-3-647-8095	Employees: 60	Symbol: EDUSF

Computers - educational software covering science, technology (TINA), language (English Discoveries) & early childhood development

EDWARDS THEATRES CIRCUIT, INC.

300 Newport Center Dr.	CEO: James Edwards Sr.	1995 Est. Sales: $150.0 mil.
Newport Beach, CA 92660	CFO: Joan Edwards-Randolph	1-Yr. Sales Change: —
Phone: 714-640-4600	HR: Olga Gonzales	Ownership: Privately Held
Fax: 714-721-7170	Employees: 1,800	

Motion pictures & services - theaters

ELECTRONIC ARTS INC.

1450 Fashion Island Blvd.	CEO: Lawrence F. Probst III	1996 Sales: $531.9 million
San Mateo, CA 94404-2064	CFO: E. Stanton McKee Jr.	1-Yr. Sales Change: 7.8%
Phone: 415-571-7171	HR: E. Stanton McKee Jr.	Exchange: Nasdaq
Fax: 415-571-6375	Employees: 1,172	Symbol: ERTS

Computers - interactive entertainment software & video-game players

◉ **See page 247 for a full profile of this company.**

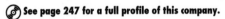

ELECTRONICS BOUTIQUE, INC.

1345 Enterprise Dr.	CEO: Joseph J. Firestone	1995 Sales: $240.0 million
West Chester, PA 19380	CFO: John Panichello	1-Yr. Sales Change: 20.0%
Phone: 610-430-8100	HR: Leslie Boris	Ownership: Subsidiary
Fax: 610-430-6574	Employees: 2,000	

Computers - software & video-game stores (over 500 worldwide: subsidiary of Anam Group)

ELECTRONICS FOR IMAGING, INC.

2855 Campus Dr.	CEO: Dan Avida	1995 Sales: $190.5 million
San Mateo, CA 94403	CFO: David Warner	1-Yr. Sales Change: 46.1%
Phone: 415-286-8600	HR: Janice Smith	Exchange: Nasdaq
Fax: 415-286-8663	Employees: 222	Symbol: EFII

Computers - workstations that connect color copiers with computer networks to enable high-quality printing in short production runs (Fiery Color Servers)

ELLER MEDIA GROUP

2122 E. Highland Ave., Ste. 425	CEO: Karl Eller	1995 Est. Sales: $225.0 mil.
Phoenix, AZ 85016	CFO: Tim Donmoyer	1-Yr. Sales Change: —
Phone: 312-254-4400	HR: —	Ownership: Privately Held
Fax: 312-927-4428	Employees: 870	

Outdoor advertising (#1 in the US)

EMAP PLC

One Lincoln Ct., Lincoln Rd.	CEO: R. W. Miller	1995 Sales: $886.7 million
Peterborough PE1 2RF, UK	CFO: D. J. Grigson	1-Yr. Sales Change: 51.1%
Phone: +44-1733-689-00	HR: —	Exchange: London
Fax: +44-1733-349-290	Employees: 6,789	

Publishing - consumer magazines, business magazines & newspapers; radio stations

EMMIS BROADCASTING CORPORATION

950 N. Meridian St., Ste. 1200	CEO: Jeffrey H. Smulyan	1996 Sales: $99.8 million
Indianapolis, IN 46204	CFO: Howard L. Schrott	1-Yr. Sales Change: 49.4%
Phone: 317-266-0100	HR: Carolyn Herald	Exchange: Nasdaq
Fax: 317-631-3750	Employees: 457	Symbol: EMMS

Broadcasting - radio (one AM & 6 FM stations); magazine publishing

ENCYCLOPÆDIA BRITANNICA, INC.

310 S. Michigan Ave.
Chicago, IL 60604
Phone: 312-347-7000
Fax: 312-347-7135

CEO: Joseph J. Esposito
CFO: James E. Goulka
HR: Karl Steinberg
Employees: 2,300

1995 Sales: $405.0 million
1-Yr. Sales Change: (10.6%)
Ownership: Privately Held

Publishing - reference books (*Encyclopædia Britannica, Merriam-Webster*); educational services

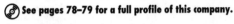 **See pages 78–79 for a full profile of this company.**

ENLIGHTEN SOFTWARE SOLUTIONS, INC.

999 Baker Way, Ste. 390
San Mateo, CA 94404
Phone: 415-578-0700
Fax: 415-578-0118

CEO: Peter J. McDonald
CFO: Michael A. Morgan
HR: Mena Baloun
Employees: 54

1995 Sales: $6.6 million
1-Yr. Sales Change: (13.2%)
Exchange: Nasdaq
Symbol: SFTW

Computers - software designed to automate the management of computer systems for banking, finance, telecommunications, information technology & other major industries

ENTERACTIVE, INC.

110 W. 40th St., Ste. 2100
New York, NY 10018
Phone: 212-221-6559
Fax: 212-730-6045

CEO: Andrew Gyenes
CFO: Kenneth Gruber
HR: —
Employees: 48

1995 Sales: $0.4 million
1-Yr. Sales Change: (83.3%)
Exchange: Nasdaq (SC)
Symbol: ENTR

Computers - interactive multimedia products for the home & school markets

ESSENCE COMMUNICATIONS INC.

1500 Broadway
New York, NY 10036
Phone: 212-642-0600
Fax: 212-921-5173

CEO: Edward Lewis
CFO: Harry Dedyo
HR: Elaine P. Williams
Employees: 102

1995 Sales: $80.1 million
1-Yr. Sales Change: 3.4%
Ownership: Privately Held

Publishing - magazines (*Essence*); TV production; direct-mail catalogs

ETELA-SAIMAAN KUSTANNUS OY

Lauritsalantie 1, PL 3
FIN-53501 Lappeenranta, Finland
Phone: +358-953-5521
Fax: +358-953-559-209

CEO: Esa Lavander
CFO: —
HR: —
Employees: 348

1995 Sales: $17.8 million
1-Yr. Sales Change: (3.7%)
Exchange: Helsinki

Publishing - local newspapers in southeastern Finland, magazines & periodicals

E*TRADE GROUP, INC.

4 Emarcadero Place, 2400 Geng Rd.	CEO: Christos M. Cotsakos	1995 Sales: $23.3 million
Palo Alto, CA 94303	CFO: Stephen C. Richards	1-Yr. Sales Change: 113.8%
Phone: 415-842-2500	HR: Robin N. Rosenberg	Ownership: Privately Held
Fax: 415-842-2575	Employees: 245	

Computers - electronic brokerage services, including automated order placement, portfolio tracking & related market information news & other 24-hour information services online & via telephone & interactive TV

EUROMONEY PUBLICATIONS PLC

Nestor House, Playhouse Yard	CEO: P. R. Ensor	1995 Sales: $183.9 million
London EC4V 5EX, UK	CFO: —	1-Yr. Sales Change: 29.3%
Phone: +44-171-779-8888	HR: —	Exchange: London
Fax: +44-171-779-8656	Employees: 718	

Publishing - books, newsletters for investors & magazines (*Euromoney Magazine*)

EUROPE 1 COMMUNICATION SA

57, rue Grimaldi	CEO: Jacques Lehn	1995 Sales: $541.5 million
98000 Monaco, France	CFO: —	1-Yr. Sales Change: 6.2%
Phone: +33-93-30-74-98	HR: —	Exchange: Paris
Fax: +33-93-15-93-04	Employees: 1,715	

TV production & programming; radio production; billboard advertisements

EUROPE ONLINE S.A.

45, rue des Scillas	CEO: Juergen Becker	1995 Sales: $0.0 million
Howald L-2529, Luxembourg	CFO: —	1-Yr. Sales Change: —
Phone: +352-40-101-1	HR: —	Ownership: Privately Held
Fax: +352-40-101-201	Employees: 160	

Computers - World Wide Web-based consumer online service

EVERGREEN MEDIA CORPORATION

433 E. Las Colinas Blvd., Ste. 1130	CEO: Scott K. Ginsburg	1995 Sales: $162.9 million
Irving, TX 75039	CFO: Matthew E. Devine	1-Yr. Sales Change: 29.8%
Phone: 214-869-9020	HR: M. Kopel	Exchange: Nasdaq
Fax: 214-869-3671	Employees: 585	Symbol: EVGM

Broadcasting - radio (34 stations)

THE E.W. SCRIPPS COMPANY

312 Walnut St., Ste. 2800	CEO: William R. Burleigh	1995 Sales: $1,030.1 million
Cincinnati, OH 45202	CFO: Daniel J. Castellini	1-Yr. Sales Change: (15.6%)
Phone: 513-977-3000	HR: Daniel J. Castellini	Exchange: NYSE
Fax: 513-977-3721	Employees: 6,700	Symbol: SSP

Publishing - newspapers (24); TV stations (9) & cable TV systems

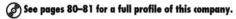 **See pages 80–81 for a full profile of this company.**

EXCALIBUR TECHNOLOGIES CORPORATION

2000 Corporate Ridge	CEO: John M. Kennedy	1996 Sales: $18.7 million
McLean, VA 22102	CFO: James Buchanan	1-Yr. Sales Change: 73.1%
Phone: 619-438-7900	HR: —	Exchange: Nasdaq
Fax: 619-438-7901	Employees: 92	Symbol: EXCA

Computers - document imaging & multimedia information retrieval software (RetrievalWare)

EXCITE INC.

1091 N. Shoreline Blvd.	CEO: George Bell	1995 Sales: $0.4 million
Mountain View, CA 94043	CFO: Richard B. Redding	1-Yr. Sales Change: 300.0%
Phone: 415-934-3611	HR: —	Exchange: Nasdaq
Fax: 415-934-3610	Employees: 38	Symbol: XCIT

Computers - World Wide Web search service (NetSearch), reviews of web sites (NetDirectory), personal information interface (Personal Excite) & regional web search database (City.Net)

EZ COMMUNICATIONS, INC.

10800 Main St.	CEO: Alan Box	1995 Sales: $95.6 million
Fairfax, VA 22030	CFO: Ronald H. Peele Jr.	1-Yr. Sales Change: 44.8%
Phone: 703-591-1000	HR: Linda Osterday	Exchange: Nasdaq
Fax: 703-934-1200	Employees: 532	Symbol: EZCIA

Broadcasting - radio (17 AM & FM radio stations)

FACTSET RESEARCH SYSTEMS INC.

One Greenwich Plaza	CEO: Howard E. Wille	1995 Sales: $36.2 million
Greenwich, CT 06830	CFO: Ernest S. Wong	1-Yr. Sales Change: 24.8%
Phone: 203-863-1500	HR: —	Exchange: NYSE
Fax: 203-863-1501	Employees: 116	Symbol: FDS

Computers - online database services, including company information, for the financial community

FALCON CABLE SYSTEMS COMPANY, A CALIFORNIA LIMITED PARTNERSHIP

10900 Wilshire Blvd., 15th Fl.	CEO: Marc B. Nathanson	1995 Sales: $52.9 million
Los Angeles, CA 90024	CFO: Michael K. Menerey	1-Yr. Sales Change: —
Phone: 310-824-9990	HR: Joan Scully	Exchange: AMEX
Fax: 310-208-3655	Employees: 166	Symbol: FAL

Cable TV

FALLON MCELLIGOTT, INC.

901 Marquette Ave., Ste. 3200	CEO: Pat Fallon	1995 Sales: $35.9 million
Minneapolis, MN 55402	CFO: Irving Fish	1-Yr. Sales Change: 21.3%
Phone: 612-321-2345	HR: John Forney	Ownership: Subsidiary
Fax: 612-321-2346	Employees: 300	

Advertising (subsidiary of Scali, McCabe, Sloves)

FCL GRAPHICS, INC.

4600 N. Olcott Ave.	CEO: Frank C. Calabrese	1995 Sales: $54.0 million
Harwood Heights, IL 60656	CFO: Phil Bauman	1-Yr. Sales Change: 12.5%
Phone: 708-867-5500	HR: Russ Reeves	Ownership: Privately Held
Fax: 708-867-7768	Employees: 260	

Printing - commercial

FILIPACCHI MÉDIAS SA

63, avenue des Champs-Elysees	CEO: Daniel Filipacchi	1995 Sales: $308.5 million
75008 Paris, France	CFO: P. Bellanger	1-Yr. Sales Change: (1.5%)
Phone: +33-1-40-74-73-07	HR: —	Exchange: Paris
Fax: +33-1-41-34-77-77	Employees: 757	

Publishing - magazines (*Femme, Jeune et Jolie, Paris Match, Interview, Lui, Newlook, Salut*) & newspapers; advertising; radio programming

FILM ROMAN, INC.

12020 Chandler Blvd., Ste. 200	CEO: Phil Roman	1995 Sales: $34.3 million
North Hollywood, CA 91607	CFO: Gregory Arsenault	1-Yr. Sales Change: (5.2%)
Phone: 818-761-2544	HR: Genny Sanchez	Ownership: Privately Held
Fax: 818-985-2973	Employees: 236	

TV production & programming - independent animation studio (#1 in the US: *The Simpsons, Garfield & Friends, Bobby's World, Felix the Cat, Mighty Max, The Critic, The Mask*)

FINANCIAL WORLD PARTNERS

1328 Broadway	CEO: Barry Rupp	1995 Est. Sales: $35.0 mil.
New York, NY 1001-2116	CFO: Robert Hughes	1-Yr. Sales Change: —
Phone: 212-594-5030	HR: Eileen Lurie	Ownership: Privately Held
Fax: 212-629-0021	Employees: 70	

Publishing - periodicals (*Financial World*)

FIND/SVP, INC.

625 Avenue of the Americas, 2nd Fl.	CEO: Andrew P. Gavin	1995 Sales: $28.6 million
New York, NY 10011	CFO: Peter J. Fiorillo	1-Yr. Sales Change: 17.2%
Phone: 212-645-4500	HR: —	Exchange: Nasdaq (SC)
Fax: 212-645-7681	Employees: 220	Symbol: FSVP

Consulting & information services

FIRST AMERICAN HEALTH CONCEPTS, INC.

7776 South Pointe Pkwy. West, Ste. 150	CEO: John A. Raycraft	1995 Sales: $4.7 million
Phoenix, AZ 85044-5424	CFO: Charles P. Stanford Jr.	1-Yr. Sales Change: 11.9%
Phone: 602-414-0300	HR: —	Exchange: Nasdaq (SC)
Fax: 602-414-1383	Employees: 37	Symbol: FAHC

Business services - organization of networks of health care product & service providers who offer same to company's members at preferential prices

FIRST ENTERTAINMENT, INC.

1380 Lawrence St., Ste. 1400	CEO: A. B. Goldberg	1995 Sales: $1.8 million
Denver, CO 80204	CFO: —	1-Yr. Sales Change: (37.9%)
Phone: 303-592-1235	HR: —	Exchange: Nasdaq (SC)
Fax: 303-592-1306	Employees: 19	Symbol: VCRI

Motion pictures & services - low-budget motion pictures (First Films Inc.); prerecorded videotapes; radio station & comedy clubs (Comedy Works)

FIRST NATIONAL ENTERTAINMENT CORP.

2443 Warrenville Rd., Ste. 600	CEO: Eugene E. Denari Jr.	1995 Sales: $0.8 million
Lisle, IL 60606	CFO: Eugene E. Denari Jr.	1-Yr. Sales Change: (85.2%)
Phone: 708-245-5155	HR: —	Exchange: Nasdaq (SC)
Fax: 708-245-5156	Employees: 14	Symbol: FNAT

Retail - video stores in California (Video Plus, Video Tyme, Speedy Video), Las Vegas (Video Tyme) & Des Moines, IA (Five Star Video)

FLEMING PACKAGING CORPORATION

1028 SW Adams St.
Peoria, IL 61602
Phone: 309-676-2121
Fax: 309-676-8930

Printing - specialty

CEO: William J. Mannlein
CFO: Allyn Schmid
HR: Marc Harman
Employees: 450

1995 Est. Sales: $110.0 mil.
1-Yr. Sales Change: 0.9%
Ownership: Privately Held

FLEXTECH PLC

Twyman House, 16 Bonny St.
London NW1 9PG, UK
Phone: +44-171-813-5000
Fax: +44-171-911-0145

CEO: R. D. E. Luard
CFO: Mark Luiz
HR: —
Employees: 271

1995 Sales: $52.6 million
1-Yr. Sales Change: 46.6%
Exchange: London

Satellite, cable transmission & related communications & media activities

FLIPSIDE COMMUNICATIONS, INC.

1550 Bryant St., Ste. 950
San Francisco, CA 94103
Phone: 415-865-2277
Fax: 415-865-2280

CEO: Anthony Perkins
CFO: John Hardy
HR: —
Employees: 38

1995 Est. Sales: $3.0 million
1-Yr. Sales Change: —
Ownership: Privately Held

Publishing - investment & finance magazine (*The Red Herring*) & online service (herring.com)

FMR CORPORATION

82 Devonshire St.
Boston, MA 02109
Phone: 617-570-7000
Fax: 617-476-6345

CEO: Edward "Ned" C. Johnson III
CFO: Denis M. McCarthy
HR: Gerald M Lieberman
Employees: 14,600

1995 Sales: $4,270.0 million
1-Yr. Sales Change: 21.0%
Ownership: Privately Held

Financial - mutual fund management & discount brokerage (Fidelity Investments); magazine publishing (*Worth*); community newspapers; limo service

FOLLETT CORPORATION

2233 West St.
River Grove, IL 60171-1895
Phone: 708-583-2000
Fax: 708-452-9347

CEO: P. Richard Litzsinger
CFO: Kenneth J. Hull
HR: Richard Waichler
Employees: 7,500

1996 Sales: $811.0 million
1-Yr. Sales Change: 13.8%
Ownership: Privately Held

Diversified operations - college bookstores; software; publishing

(ⓖ) **See page 248 for a full profile of this company.**

FOOD COURT ENTERTAINMENT NETWORK, INC.

34-12 36th St.	CEO: Stephen G. Bowen	1995 Sales: —
Astoria, NY 11106	CFO: Darren M. Sardoff	1-Yr. Sales Change: —
Phone: 718-937-5757	HR: —	Exchange: Nasdaq (SC)
Fax: 718-706-5388	Employees: 12	Symbol: FCENA

TV production & programming - direct advertising via satellite into mall food courts (Cafe USA)

FORBES, INC.

60 Fifth Ave.	CEO: Malcolm S. "Steve" Forbes Jr.	1995 Est. Sales: $287.5 mil.
New York, NY 10011	CFO: Joel B. Redler	1-Yr. Sales Change: 7.9%
Phone: 212-620-2200	HR: Rose Ateniese	Ownership: Privately Held
Fax: 212-206-5534	Employees: 502	

Publishing - magazines (*Forbes, Forbes FYI, Forbes ASAP, Audacity, American Heritage*), books (*Social Register, MediaGuide 500*) & weekly newspapers (Forbes Newspapers)

 See page 249 for a full profile of this company.

FOUR MEDIA COMPANY

2813 W. Alameda Ave.	CEO: Robert Walston	1995 Sales: $60.1 million
Burbank, CA 91505	CFO: John Sabin	1-Yr. Sales Change: 42.1%
Phone: 818-840-7000	HR: Kristi Kleckner	Ownership: Privately Held
Fax: 818-840-7195	Employees: 486	

Motion pictures & services - digital visual effects & postproduction services

FRANKLIN ELECTRONIC PUBLISHERS, INCORPORATED

One Franklin Plaza	CEO: Morton E. David	1995 Sales: $83.3 million
Burlington, NJ 08016	CFO: Kenneth H. Lind	1-Yr. Sales Change: 26.0%
Phone: 609-261-4800	HR: —	Exchange: NYSE
Fax: 609-261-2984	Employees: 271	Symbol: FEP

Publishing - electronic books (#1 worldwide: Spelling Ace, Med-Spell MED-55, Holy Bible - New International Version)

 See page 250 for a full profile of this company.

FRANKLIN QUEST CO.

2200 W. Parkway Blvd.	CEO: Hyrum W. Smith	1995 Sales: $277.1 million
Salt Lake City, UT 84119-2331	CFO: Jon H. Rowberry	1-Yr. Sales Change: 28.3%
Phone: 801-975-1776	HR: Daken Tanner	Exchange: NYSE
Fax: 801-977-1431	Employees: 2,771	Symbol: FNQ

Business services - productivity seminars, business calendars & planners

FREEDOM COMMUNICATIONS, INC.

17666 Fitch Ave.	CEO: James N. Rosse	1995 Sales: $530.0 million
Irvine, CA 92714	CFO: David Kuykendall	1-Yr. Sales Change: (0.2%)
Phone: 714-553-9292	HR: Mark Ernst	Ownership: Privately Held
Fax: 714-474-4943	Employees: 5,500	

Publishing - daily (25, including the *Orange County Register*) & weekly newspapers (34); TV stations (5) & a cable network (Orange County NewsChannel); magazines (*Latin Trade, World Trade, P.O.V.*)

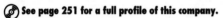 **See page 251 for a full profile of this company.**

FRONTEER DIRECTORY COMPANY, INC.

216 N. 23rd St.	CEO: Dennis W. Olsen	1995 Sales: $17.2 million
Bismarck, ND 58501	CFO: Lance Olsen	1-Yr. Sales Change: 91.1%
Phone: 701-258-4970	HR: Ione Good	Exchange: Nasdaq (SC)
Fax: 701-258-4258	Employees: 287	Symbol: FDIR

Publishing - telephone directories in North & South Dakota, Montana, Idaho, Utah, Wyoming & Minnesota

FUNCO, INC.

10120 W. 76th St.	CEO: David R. Pomije	1996 Sales: $81.4 million
Minneapolis, MN 55344	CFO: Robert M. Hiben	1-Yr. Sales Change: 1.2%
Phone: 612-946-8883	HR: Jeffery R. Gatesmith	Exchange: Nasdaq
Fax: 612-946-7251	Employees: 951	Symbol: FNCO

Retail - used video games (FuncoLand)

FUTUREMEDIA PUBLIC LIMITED COMPANY

Media House, Arundel Rd., Walberton	CEO: Norman Burton	1995 Sales: $9.1 million
Arundel, West Sussex BN18 0QP, UK	CFO: Philip Lingard	1-Yr. Sales Change: 30.2%
Phone: +44-1243-555-000	HR: Hilary Channing	Exchange: Nasdaq
Fax: +44-1243-555-020	Employees: 60	Symbol: FMDAY (ADR)

Computers - interactive multimedia training programs & merchandising systems

GAKKEN

4-40-5, Kami-Ikedai, Ohta-ku	CEO: Kazuhiko Sawada	1995 Sales: $1,356.0 million
Tokyo 145, Japan	CFO: —	1-Yr. Sales Change: (5.4%)
Phone: +81-3-3726-8111	HR: —	Exchange: Tokyo
Fax: +81-3-3727-3424	Employees: 1,935	

Publishing - educational magazines & books

GAMETEK INC.

2999 NE 191st St.	CEO: James Harris	1995 Sales: $33.9 million
North Miami Beach, FL 33180	CFO: Lynn Anderson	1-Yr. Sales Change: (27.7%)
Phone: 305-935-3995	HR: —	Exchange: Nasdaq
Fax: 305-932-8651	Employees: 79	Symbol: GAME

Computers - interactive entertainment (Saturday Night Live 20th Anniversary CD-ROM) & educational & productivity software

GANNETT CO., INC.

1100 Wilson Blvd.	CEO: John J. Curley	1995 Sales: $4,006.7 million
Arlington, VA 22234	CFO: Douglas H. McCorkindale	1-Yr. Sales Change: 4.8%
Phone: 703-284-6000	HR: Richard L. Clapp	Exchange: NYSE
Fax: 703-558-3506	Employees: 39,100	Symbol: GCI

Publishing - newspapers (83, including *USA TODAY*); broadcasting (7 radio & 15 TV stations); TV programming (Multimedia Entertainment: *Donahue, Sally Jesse Raphael*); outdoor advertising

 See pages 82–83 for a full profile of this company.

GARDEN STATE CABLE TV

1250 Haddonfield Berlin Rd.	CEO: J. Bruce Llewellyn	1995 Est. Sales: $100.0 mil.
Cherry Hill, NJ 08034	CFO: John Barrett	1-Yr. Sales Change: —
Phone: 609-354-1880	HR: Curlene Autrey	Ownership: Privately Held
Fax: 609-428-2591	Employees: 320	

Cable TV

GATEWAY EDUCATIONAL PRODUCTS, LTD.

1050 W. Katella Ave.	CEO: John M. Shanahan	1995 Est. Sales: $175.0 mil.
Orange, CA 92667	CFO: Tom Arendt	1-Yr. Sales Change: —
Phone: 714-633-2223	HR: Mary K. Dana	Ownership: Privately Held
Fax: 714-633-3374	Employees: 500	

Audio & video home products - training tapes (Hooked on Phonics)

GAUMONT SA

30, avenue Charles de Gaulle	CEO: Nicolas Seydoux	1995 Sales: $252.5 million
92522 Neuilly Cedex, France	CFO: L. Reyes	1-Yr. Sales Change: 9.0%
Phone: +33-1-46-43-20-00	HR: —	Exchange: Paris
Fax: +33-1-46-43-21-68	Employees: 892	

Movie theaters; magazine publishing; production of films & serials for TV & video

GAYLORD COMPANIES, INC.

4006 Venture Ct.	CEO: John Gaylord	1995 Sales: $13.7 million
Columbus, OH 43228	CFO: John Gaylord	1-Yr. Sales Change: 8.7%
Phone: 614-771-2777	HR: Georgia Pappas	Exchange: Nasdaq
Fax: 614-771-8826	Employees: 144	Symbol: GJCO

Retail - bookstores (Little Professor) & cookware & serving equipment stores (Cookstores)

GAYLORD ENTERTAINMENT COMPANY

One Gaylord Dr.	CEO: Earl W. Wendell	1995 Sales: $707.5 million
Nashville, TN 37214	CFO: Terry E. London	1-Yr. Sales Change: 2.8%
Phone: 615-316-6000	HR: Elwyn Taylor	Exchange: NYSE
Fax: 615-316-6320	Employees: 10,000	Symbol: GET

Leisure & recreational products - musical show park, convention/resort complex; TV & radio stations & cable networks

 See page 252 for a full profile of this company.

GC COMPANIES INC.

27 Boylston St.	CEO: Richard A. Smith	1995 Sales: $451.3 million
Chestnut Hill, MA 02167	CFO: G. Gail Edwards	1-Yr. Sales Change: (0.3%)
Phone: 617-277-4320	HR: Daniel Stravinski	Exchange: NYSE
Fax: 617-278-5397	Employees: 7,400	Symbol: GCX

Motion pictures & services - theaters (General Cinema)

 See page 253 for a full profile of this company.

GENERAL MEDIA INTERNATIONAL, INC.

277 Park Ave.	CEO: Bob Guccione	1995 Sales: $120.4 million
New York, NY 10172	CFO: Patrick Gavin	1-Yr. Sales Change: (2.3%)
Phone: 212-702-6000	HR: Iris Frank	Ownership: Privately Held
Fax: 212-702-6262	Employees: 224	

Publishing - magazines (*Penthouse*, *Stock Car Racing*, *Women's Forum*); pay-per-view TV channel

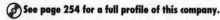 **See page 254 for a full profile of this company.**

GOLDEN BOOKS FAMILY ENTERTAINMENT INC.

444 Madison Ave.	CEO: Richard E. Snyder	1996 Sales: $374.3 million
New York, NY 10022	CFO: Steven M. Grossman	1-Yr. Sales Change: (6.0%)
Phone: 212-688-4500	HR: Ira A. Gomberg	Exchange: Nasdaq
Fax: 212-888-5025	Employees: 3,800	Symbol: GBFE

Publishing - children's books (Golden Books)

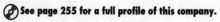 **See page 255 for a full profile of this company.**

GOLDHIRSH GROUP, INC.

38 Commercial Wharf	CEO: Bernard A. Goldhirsh	1995 Sales: $65.0 million
Boston, MA 02110	CFO: John Reardon	1-Yr. Sales Change: —
Phone: 617-248-8000	HR: Deborah W. Reed	Ownership: Nonprofit
Fax: 617-248-8090	Employees: 170	

Publishing - monthly business magazine (Inc.)

GOODTIMES ENTERTAINMENT WORLDWIDE

16 E. 40th St.	CEO: Joe Cayre	1995 Sales: $1,200.0 million
New York, NY 10016	CFO: Maria Haggerty	1-Yr. Sales Change: 20.0%
Phone: 212-951-3000	HR: Lily Rettis	Ownership: Privately Held
Fax: 212-213-9319	Employees: 1,000	

Leisure & recreational products - diversified multimedia entertainmment, including videos (Cindy Crawford Workouts, Animated Classics), children's & family TV programming, children's books (Berenstain Bears), infomercials (Richard Simmons) & feature film production

GRAFF PAY-PER-VIEW INC.

536 Broadway	CEO: J. Roger Faherty	1995 Sales: $51.1 million
New York, NY 10012	CFO: Philip Callaghan	1-Yr. Sales Change: 26.5%
Phone: 212-941-1434	HR: Joan Simari	Exchange: Nasdaq
Fax: 212-941-4746	Employees: 154	Symbol: GPPV

Cable TV - adult entertainment channels (Spice, Spice 2); pay-per-view movie channels (Cable Video Store, Theatre VisioN)

 **See page 256 for a full profile of this company.**

GRANADA GROUP PLC

36 Golden Square	CEO: Charles Allen	1995 Sales: $3,769.2 million
London W1R 4AH, UK	CFO: Henry Staunton	1-Yr. Sales Change: 13.5%
Phone: +44-171-734-8080	HR: Stephanie Monk	Exchange: London
Fax: +44-171-494-2893	Employees: 39,085	

Broadcasting - TV (Channel 3); TV rental; VCRs; satellite equipment; computer services; hotels, restaurants & in-flight catering (70% ownership of Forte PLC)

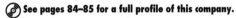 **See pages 84–85 for a full profile of this company.**

GRANITE BROADCASTING CORPORATION

767 Third Ave.	CEO: W. Don Cornwell	1995 Sales: $99.9 million
New York, NY 10017	CFO: Lawrence I. Wills	1-Yr. Sales Change: 58.8%
Phone: 212-826-2530	HR: —	Exchange: Nasdaq
Fax: 212-826-2858	Employees: 590	Symbol: GBTVK

Broadcasting - TV (9 network-affiliated stations)

GRAPHIC INDUSTRIES, INC.

2155 Monroe Dr. NE	CEO: Mark C. Pope III	1996 Sales: $417.3 million
Atlanta, GA 30324	CFO: David S. Fraser	1-Yr. Sales Change: 19.9%
Phone: 404-874-3327	HR: —	Exchange: Nasdaq
Fax: 404-874-7589	Employees: 2,961	Symbol: GRPH

Printing - financial & corporate printing, reprographic services, commercial printing, direct mail printing & other graphic communications

GRAY COMMUNICATIONS SYSTEMS, INC.

126 N. Washington St.	CEO: Ralph W. Gabbard	1995 Sales: $58.6 million
Albany, GA 31702-0048	CFO: William A. Fielder III	1-Yr. Sales Change: 60.5%
Phone: 912-888-9390	HR: Melvyn Carter	Exchange: NYSE
Fax: 912-888-9374	Employees: 740	Symbol: GCS

Broadcasting - TV (3 NBC & 2 CBS affiliates); newspaper publishing (*The Albany* [Georgia] *Herald*)

GREENSTONE ROBERTS ADVERTISING, INC.

One Huntington Quadrangle, Ste. 1C14	CEO: Ronald M. Greenstone	1995 Sales: $9.7 million
Melville, NY 11747	CFO: Gregory A. Rice	1-Yr. Sales Change: (7.6%)
Phone: 516-249-2121	HR: Jean Mostaccio	Exchange: Nasdaq (SC)
Fax: 516-249-6641	Employees: 116	Symbol: GRRI

Advertising - marketing, consulting, market & product research & direct mail advertising

GREY ADVERTISING INC.

777 Third Ave.	CEO: Edward H. Meyer	1995 Sales: $688.2 million
New York, NY 10017	CFO: William P. Garvey	1-Yr. Sales Change: 16.0%
Phone: 212-546-2000	HR: Kevin Bergin	Exchange: Nasdaq
Fax: 212-546-1495	Employees: 1,418	Symbol: GREY

Advertising - marketing consultation, product publicity, public relations & sales promotion services for clients in such industries as apparel, automobile, beverages, chemicals & computers

GROLIER INCORPORATED

Sherman Tnpk.	CEO: Arnaud Lagardere	1995 Sales: $400.0 million
Danbury, CT 06816	CFO: Lester Rackoff	1-Yr. Sales Change: —
Phone: 203-797-3500	HR: Anne Graves	Ownership: Subsidiary
Fax: 203-797-3197	Employees: 3,600	

Publishing - encyclopedias (*Encyclopedia Americana*), children's books, reference sets & electronic products (subsidiary of Lagardere Group)

GT INTERACTIVE SOFTWARE CORPORATION

16 E. 40th St.
New York, NY 10016
Phone: 212-726-6500
Fax: 212-726-6590

CEO: Ronald W. Chaimowitz
CFO: Andrew Gregor
HR: —
Employees: 597

1995 Sales: $204.1 million
1-Yr. Sales Change: 139.6%
Exchange: Nasdaq
Symbol: GTIS

Publishing - interactive entertainment (Doom II, Hexen, Mortal Kombat), edutainment & reference software publishing & distribution

HAL RINEY & PARTNERS

735 Battery St.
San Francisco, CA 94111
Phone: 415-981-0950
Fax: 415-955-4267

CEO: Hal Riney
CFO: Lyn Muegge
HR: Mary Kelly
Employees: 365

1995 Sales: $68.8 million
1-Yr. Sales Change: 15.6%
Ownership: Privately Held

Advertising

HANDLEMAN COMPANY

500 Kirts Blvd.
Troy, MI 48084-4142
Phone: 810-362-4400
Fax: 810-362-3615

CEO: Stephen Strome
CFO: Richard J. Morris
HR: Rodger Apple
Employees: 4,147

1996 Sales: $1,132.6 million
1-Yr. Sales Change: (7.6%)
Exchange: NYSE
Symbol: HDL

Wholesale distribution - music audiocassettes & compact discs, videos, books & personal computer software

HARCOURT GENERAL, INC.

27 Boylston St.
Chestnut Hill, MA 02167
Phone: 617-232-8200
Fax: 617-278-5397

CEO: Robert J. Tarr Jr.
CFO: John R. Cook
HR: Gerald T. Hughes
Employees: 15,219

1995 Sales: $3,034.7 million
1-Yr. Sales Change: (3.8%)
Exchange: NYSE
Symbol: H

Diversified operations - publishing (Harcourt Brace; Holt, Rinehart & Winston; Academic Press); specialty retailing (Neiman Marcus, Bergdorf Goodman)

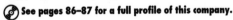 **See pages 86–87 for a full profile of this company.**

HARMONY HOLDINGS, INC.

6806 Lexington Ave.
Hollywood, CA 90038
Phone: 213-960-1400
Fax: 213-960-1415

CEO: Gary Horowitz
CFO: Brian Rackohn
HR: Maggie Adams
Employees: 108

1995 Sales: $61.2 million
1-Yr. Sales Change: 46.8%
Exchange: Nasdaq (SC)
Symbol: HAHO

TV programming & production - TV commercials

HARPO ENTERTAINMENT GROUP

110 N. Carpenter St.	CEO: Oprah Winfrey	1995 Sales: $130.0 million
Chicago, IL 60607	CFO: Doug Pattison	1-Yr. Sales Change: 8.3%
Phone: 312-633-1000	HR: —	Ownership: Privately Held
Fax: 312-633-1111	Employees: 166	

Film & TV production (*The Oprah Winfrey Show*); studio rental

 **See page 257 for a full profile of this company.**

HARRY W. SCHWARTZ BOOKSHOPS

209 E. Wisconsin Ave.	CEO: A. David Schwartz	1995 Sales: $11.0 million
Milwaukee, WI 53202	CFO: Avin Domnitz	1-Yr. Sales Change: —
Phone: 414-274-6400	HR: Shawn Quinn	Ownership: Privately Held
Fax: 414-274-6408	Employees: 140	

Retail - bookstores in the Midwest (Harry W. Schwartz, Dickens Discount Books); mail-order business-related books

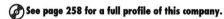 **See page 258 for a full profile of this company.**

HART GRAPHICS, INC.

8000 Shoal Creek Blvd.	CEO: David E. Hart	1995 Sales: $112.0 million
Austin, TX 78757	CFO: Britt Kauffman	1-Yr. Sales Change: —
Phone: 512-454-4761	HR: Brian Oetzel	Ownership: Privately Held
Fax: 512-467-4583	Employees: 800	

Printing - books

HARTE-HANKS COMMUNICATIONS, INC.

200 Concord Plaza Dr., Ste. 800	CEO: Larry Franklin	1995 Sales: $532.9 million
San Antonio, TX 78216	CFO: Richard L. Ritchie	1-Yr. Sales Change: 3.8%
Phone: 210-829-9000	HR: Carolyn Oatman	Exchange: NYSE
Fax: 210-829-9403	Employees: 4,957	Symbol: HHS

Diversified operations - newspaper publishing; television broadcasting; direct mail; TV & radio broadcasting

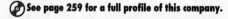 **See page 259 for a full profile of this company.**

THE HARVEY ENTERTAINMENT COMPANY

100 Wilshire Blvd., Ste. 1400	CEO: Jeffrey A. Montgomery	1995 Sales: $9.1 million
Santa Monica, CA 90401-1115	CFO: Gregory M. Yulish	1-Yr. Sales Change: 62.5%
Phone: 310-451-3377	HR: —	Exchange: Nasdaq (SC)
Fax: 310-458-6995	Employees: 10	Symbol: HRVY

Business services - owner & licensor of a cartoon library (*Casper the Friendly Ghost*, *Richie Rich*)

HASTINGS BOOKS, MUSIC & VIDEO, INC.

3601 Plains Blvd., Ste. One	CEO: John H. Marmaduke	1995 Est. Sales: $260.0 mil.
Amarillo, TX 79120-5350	CFO: Bill Millikin	1-Yr. Sales Change: 19.8%
Phone: 806-376-2300	HR: Dan Crunk	Ownership: Privately Held
Fax: 806-374-0093	Employees: 3,500	

Retail - music & bookstores; video rental

HAVAS ADVERTISING SA

84, rue de Villiers	CEO: Alain de Pouzilhac	1995 Sales: $791.2 million
92683 Levallois-Perret Cedex, France	CFO: Jacques Herail	1-Yr. Sales Change: (2.7%)
Phone: +33-1-41-34-34-34	HR: —	Exchange: Paris
Fax: +33-1-47-47-12-23	Employees: 7,000	

Advertising - direct marketing, sales promotion, design & public relations services

HAVAS S.A.

136, avenue Charles de Gaulle	CEO: Pierre Dauzier	1995 Sales: $9,117.6 million
92522 Neuilly-sur-Seine Cedex, France	CFO: Guy Saigne	1-Yr. Sales Change: 18.2%
Phone: +33-1-47-47-30-00	HR: Anne Brucy	Exchange: Pink Sheets
Fax: +33-1-47-47-32-32	Employees: 18,324	Symbol: HAVSY (ADR)

Advertising - communications group (#1 in France) that provides advertising for local & international media, directories (France Telecom), tourism & publishing industries & audiovisual equipment

 **See pages 88–89 for a full profile of this company.**

THE HEARST CORPORATION

959 Eighth Ave.	CEO: Frank A. Bennack Jr.	1995 Sales: $2,331.0 million
New York, NY 10019	CFO: Victor F. Ganzi	1-Yr. Sales Change: 1.4%
Phone: 212-649-2000	HR: Kenneth A. Feldman	Ownership: Privately Held
Fax: 212-765-3528	Employees: 13,500	

Publishing - magazines, newspapers, books & multimedia; broadcasting & cable TV; comic strip & feature syndication

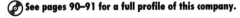 **See pages 90–91 for a full profile of this company.**

HEARTLAND WIRELESS COMMUNICATIONS, INC.

903 N. Bowser, Ste. 140	CEO: David E. Webb	1995 Sales: $15.3 million
Richardson, TX 75081-2858	CFO: John R. Bailey	1-Yr. Sales Change: 595.5%
Phone: 214-479-9244	HR: Bonnie Calamari	Exchange: Nasdaq
Fax: 214-479-1023	Employees: 1,040	Symbol: HART

Cable TV - wireless cable TV systems in 35 small to midsize markets, primarily in the southwestern US

HEFTEL BROADCASTING CORPORATION

6767 W. Tropicana Ave.	CEO: Cecil Heftel	1995 Sales: $77.1 million
Las Vegas, NV 89103	CFO: H. Carl Parmer	1-Yr. Sales Change: 143.2%
Phone: 702-367-3322	HR: John T. Kendrick	Exchange: Nasdaq
Fax: 213-461-7935	Employees: 379	Symbol: HBCCA

Broadcasting - Spanish-language radio (16 stations); Spanish-language radio network (75 stations)

HERITAGE MEDIA CORPORATION

13355 Noel Rd., Ste. 1500	CEO: David N. Walthall	1995 Sales: $435.8 million
Dallas, TX 75240	CFO: Douglas N. Woodrum	1-Yr. Sales Change: 37.2%
Phone: 214-702-7380	HR: Candi Farley	Exchange: AMEX
Fax: 214-702-7382	Employees: 26,200	Symbol: HTG

Business services - marketing (Actmedia, Actradio); broadcasting (5 TV network affiliates & 15 radio stations)

 See page 260 for a full profile of this company.

HERSANT GROUP

12, rue de Presbourg	CEO: Yves de Chaisemartin	1995 Est. Sales: $1,170 mil.
75116 Paris, Cedex 16, France	CFO: —	1-Yr. Sales Change: —
Phone: +33-144-30-30-00	HR: —	Ownership: Privately Held
	Employees: —	

Publishing - newspapers (#1 in France: *Le Figaro, France-Soir, Le Courrier de l'Ouest*) & magazines

HMG WORLDWIDE CORPORATION

475 10th Ave.	CEO: Michael Wahl	1995 Sales: $47.6 million
New York, NY 10018	CFO: Robert V. Cuddihy Jr.	1-Yr. Sales Change: (14.4%)
Phone: 212-736-2300	HR: Debra Eccles	Exchange: Nasdaq (SC)
Fax: 212-629-8587	Employees: 251	Symbol: HMGC

Advertising - in-store marketing (point-of-sale)

HOLDINGMAATSCHAPPIJ DE TELEGRAAF NV

Basiweg 30, NL-1043 AP	CEO: L. G. Van Aken	1995 Sales: $717.4 million
Amsterdam, The Netherlands	CFO: —	1-Yr. Sales Change: 5.2%
Phone: +31-20-585-9111	HR: —	Exchange: Amsterdam
Fax: +31-20-585-2216	Employees: 4,551	

Publishing - newspapers, advertisements, magazines, free weekly papers, books & audiovisual materials

HOLLINGER INC.

1827 W. Fifth Ave.	CEO: Conrad M. Black	1995 Sales: $1,109.0 million
V6J 1P5 Vancouver, BC, Canada	CFO: J. A. Boultbee	1-Yr. Sales Change: 19.0%
Phone: 416-363-8721	HR: —	Exchange: Nasdaq
Fax: 416-364-0832	Employees: 8,700	Symbol: HLGRF

Publishing - newspapers & magazines in the US, Australia, Canada, Israel & the UK (Hollinger International, UniMedia Inc., Sterling Newspapers)

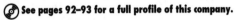 **See pages 92–93 for a full profile of this company.**

HOLLINGER INTERNATIONAL, INC.

401 N. Wabash Ave., Ste. 740	CEO: Jerry Strader	1995 Sales: $965.0 million
Chicago, IL 60611	CFO: J. David Dodd	1-Yr. Sales Change: 128.3%
Phone: 312-321-2492	HR: Roland McBride	Exchange: NYSE
Fax: 312-321-0629	Employees: 7,220	Symbol: HLR

Publishing - daily & nondaily newspapers in Australia, Canada, the US & the UK (137, including the *Chicago Sun-Times*, *The Jerusalem Post*, *The Daily Telegraph*: publicly traded subsidiary of Hollinger Inc.)

HOLLYWOOD ENTERTAINMENT CORPORATION

10300 SW Allen Blvd.	CEO: Mark J. Wattles	1995 Sales: $149.4 million
Beaverton, OR 97005	CFO: Jim Gleason	1-Yr. Sales Change: 103.8%
Phone: 503-677-1600	HR: Mary Geertsen	Exchange: Nasdaq
Fax: 503-677-1680	Employees: 6,723	Symbol: HLYW

Retail - video rental superstores (Hollywood Video, Video Central, Eastman Video, Video Park) in Oregon, Washington, California, Texas, Utah, Virginia, Nevada & New Mexico

HOME SHOPPING NETWORK, INC.

2501 118th Ave. North	CEO: James G. Held	1995 Sales: $1,018.6 million
St. Petersburg, FL 33716-1900	CFO: Kevin J. McKeon	1-Yr. Sales Change: (9.6%)
Phone: 813-572-8585	HR: Ellen Pollin	Exchange: NYSE
Fax: 813-539-6505	Employees: 4,295	Symbol: HSN

Retail - cable TV shopping channel

 **See pages 94–95 for a full profile of this company.**

HOOVER'S, INC.

1033 La Posada, Ste. 250	CEO: Patrick J. Spain	1996 Sales: $2.6 million
Austin, TX 78752	CFO: Lynn Atchison	1-Yr. Sales Change: 62.5%
Phone: 512-374-4500	HR: Lynn Atchison	Ownership: Privately Held
Fax: 512-454-9401	Employees: 48	

Publishing - business reference books (*Hoover's Handbooks*), online services (Hoover's Online & Hoover's Business Resources); CD-ROMs & software

 **See page 261 for a full profile of this company.**

HOUGHTON MIFFLIN COMPANY

222 Berkeley St.
Boston, MA 02116-3764
Phone: 617-351-5000
Fax: 617-351-1105

CEO: Nader F. Darehshori
CFO: Gail Deegan
HR: Margaret M. Doherty
Employees: 2,350

1995 Sales: $529.0 million
1-Yr. Sales Change: 9.5%
Exchange: NYSE
Symbol: HTN

Publishing - textbooks, educational & testing materials, reference works & fiction & nonfiction books

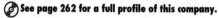 **See page 262 for a full profile of this company.**

HTV GROUP PLC

Culverhouse Cross
Cardiff CF5 6XJ, UK
Phone: +44-1222-590-590
Fax: +44-1222-597-183

CEO: C. J. Rowlands
CFO: —
HR: —
Employees: 633

1995 Sales: $208.9 million
1-Yr. Sales Change: 9.8%
Exchange: London

TV broadcasting, including news programming (ITV network)

HUDSON COUNTY NEWS COMPANY

1305 Paterson Plank Rd.
North Bergen, NJ 07047
Phone: 201-867-3600
Fax: 201-867-0067

CEO: Robert B. Cohen
CFO: Howard Joroff
HR: Lynn Stanton
Employees: 1,100

1995 Est. Sales: $350.0 mil.
1-Yr. Sales Change: (2.8%)
Ownership: Privately Held

Wholesale distribution - newspapers & magazines (#1 on the East Coast)

HUMAN CODE, INC.

1411 West Ave., Ste. 100
Austin, TX 78701
Phone: 512-477-5455
Fax: 512-477-5456

CEO: Chipp Walters
CFO: Chipp Walters
HR: Christine Ross
Employees: 35

1995 Sales: $2.5 million
1-Yr. Sales Change: —
Ownership: Privately Held

Computers - interactive multimedia products

HUNGARIAN BROADCASTING CORP.

90 West St.
New York, NY 10006
Phone: 212-571-7400
Fax: 212-571-2051

CEO: Peter E. Klenner
CFO: Peter E. Klenner
HR: —
Employees: 13

1995 Sales: $0.1 million
1-Yr. Sales Change: —
Exchange: Nasdaq
Symbol: HBCO

Broadcasting - Hungarian broadcasting companies (DNTV & VI-DOK, broadcast over Budapest Channel AM-micro A3)

HYPERMEDIA COMMUNICATIONS, INC.

901 Mariner's Island Blvd. Ste. 365	CEO: Richard Landry	1995 Sales: $9.8 million
San Mateo, CA 94404	CFO: Richard Landry	1-Yr. Sales Change: 5.4%
Phone: 415-573-5170	HR: —	Exchange: Nasdaq (SC)
Fax: 415-573-5131	Employees: 42	Symbol: HYPR

Publishing - multimedia-related periodicals (*NewMedia Magazine*), books & newsletters

IBC GROUP PLC

57-61 Mortimer St.	CEO: Peter S. Rigby	1995 Sales: $150.1 million
London W1N 8JX, UK	CFO: Anthony G. Cropper	1-Yr. Sales Change: 25.0%
Phone: +44-171-637-4383	HR: —	Exchange: London
Fax: +44-171-631-3214	Employees: 770	

Publishing - professional newsletters, magazines, books & directories; conferences, seminars & electronic data services

IMAGE ENTERTAINMENT, INC.

9333 Oso Ave.	CEO: Martin W. Greenwald	1996 Sales: $95.1 million
Chatsworth, CA 91311	CFO: Jeff M. Framer	1-Yr. Sales Change: 11.1%
Phone: 818-407-9100	HR: —	Exchange: Nasdaq
Fax: 818-407-9151	Employees: 94	Symbol: DISK

Leisure & recreational products - video programming for laser discs & CD-ROMs (#1 in North America)

IMAX CORPORATION

38 Isabella St.	CEO: Bradley J. Wechsler	1995 Sales: $88.5 million
Toronto, ON M4Y 1N1, Canada	CFO: John M. Davison	1-Yr. Sales Change: (13.9%)
Phone: 416-960-8509	HR: —	Exchange: Nasdaq
Fax: 416-960-8596	Employees: —	Symbol: IMAXF

Motion pictures & services - giant-screen movie theaters

INDENET, INC.

1640 N. Gower St., 2nd Fl.	CEO: Robert W. Lautz Jr.	1995 Sales: $3.0 million
Los Angeles, CA 90028	CFO: Lewis K. Eisaguirre	1-Yr. Sales Change: —
Phone: 213-466-6388	HR: —	Exchange: Nasdaq
Fax: 213-466-6379	Employees: 159	Symbol: INDE

Duplication & distribution (via satellite, ground or air freight) of audio & video broadcast advertising & syndicated television programming

INDEPENDENT NEWSPAPERS PLC

1-2 Upper Hatch St.	CEO: L. P. Healy	1995 Sales: $559.6 million
2 Dublin, Ireland	CFO: J. J. Parkinson	1-Yr. Sales Change: 29.1%
Phone: +353-1-475-8432	HR: —	Exchange: London
Fax: +353-1-671-7863	Employees: 5,495	

Publishing - newspapers (#1 in Ireland & South Africa) & magazines; electronic media; outdoor advertising; radio stations (#1 in Australia)

INDIVIDUAL, INC.

8 New England Executive Park	CEO: Yosi Amram	1995 Sales: $20.0 million
Cambridge, MA 01803	CFO: Bruce Glabe	1-Yr. Sales Change: 100.0%
Phone: 617-273-6000	HR: Bruce Glabe	Ownership: Privately Held
Fax: 617-273-6060	Employees: 100	

Computers - enterprisewide news service (First! for Notes), agent-based news service (First! for Mosaic)

INDIVIDUAL INVESTOR GROUP, INC.

333 Seventh Ave., 5th Fl.	CEO: Jonathan L. Steinberg	1995 Sales: $12.0 million
New York, NY 10001	CFO: Scot A. Rosenblum	1-Yr. Sales Change: 81.8%
Phone: 212-843-2777	HR: Deirdre Cavanaugh	Exchange: Nasdaq (SC)
Fax: 212-843-2789	Employees: 28	Symbol: INDI

Publishing - market & financial information for individual investors (*Individual Investor*)

INFINITY BROADCASTING CORPORATION

600 Madison Ave.	CEO: Mel Karmazin	1995 Sales: $325.7 million
New York, NY 10022	CFO: Farid Suleman	1-Yr. Sales Change: 18.8%
Phone: 212-750-6400	HR: Tom Gesimondo	Exchange: NYSE
Fax: 212-371-0835	Employees: 1,055	Symbol: INF

Broadcasting - radio (27 AM & FM stations); to be acquired by Westinghouse Electric Corp.

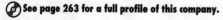 **See page 263 for a full profile of this company.**

See page 263 for a full profile of this company.

INFONAUTICS, INC.

900 W. Valley Rd., Ste. 1000	CEO: Marvin I. Weinberger	1995 Sales: $0.4 million
Wayne, PA 19087-1830	CFO: Ronald A. Berg	1-Yr. Sales Change: —
Phone: 610-971-8840	HR: Robert Palmer	Exchange: Nasdaq
Fax: 610-971-8859	Employees: 52	Symbol: INFO

Computers - online reference services, including an Internet search engine (The Electric Library), online general reference library for kids (Homework Helper) & custom online information services (Electronic Printing Press)

INFORMATION HANDLING SERVICES GROUP INC.

15 Iverness Way East
Englewood, CO 80150
Phone: 303-790-0600
Fax: 303-397-2410

CEO: Mike Timbers
CFO: Chris Meyer
HR: Susan Auxer
Employees: 1,800

1995 Sales: $257.0 million
1-Yr. Sales Change: 15.2%
Ownership: Privately Held

Publishing - technical, regulatory, chemical & consumer reference databases

INFORMATION RESOURCES, INC.

150 N. Clinton St.
Chicago, IL 60661
Phone: 312-726-1221
Fax: 312-726-0360

CEO: Gian M. Fulgoni
CFO: Gary M. Hill
HR: Gary Newman
Employees: 6,360

1995 Sales: $399.9 million
1-Yr. Sales Change: 6.2%
Exchange: Nasdaq
Symbol: IRIC

Business services - information services for the consumer packaged goods industry

INFOSEEK CORPORATION

2620 Augustine Dr., Ste. 250
Santa Clara, CA 95054
Phone: 408-567-2700
Fax: 408-986-1889

CEO: Robert E. L. Johnson III
CFO: Leonard J. LeBlanc
HR: Victoria J. Blakeslee
Employees: 71

1995 Sales: $1.0 million
1-Yr. Sales Change: —
Exchange: Nasdaq
Symbol: SEEK

Computers - World Wide Web search service (Infoseek Guide), access to databases of professional information (Infoseek Professional) & individual information interface (Personal Newswire)

INGRAM INDUSTRIES INC.

One Belle Meade Place, 4400 Harding Rd.
Nashville, TN 37205-2244
Phone: 615-298-8200
Fax: 615-298-8242

CEO: Martha Ingram
CFO: Thomas H. Lunn
HR: W. Michael Head
Employees: 13,000

1995 Est. Sales: $11,000 mil.
1-Yr. Sales Change: 37.3%
Ownership: Privately Held

Diversified - books & microcomputer software wholesaler; drilling equipment; barge service; insurance

 **See pages 96–97 for a full profile of this company.**

INSIDE COMMUNICATIONS INC.

1830 N. 55th St.
Boulder, CO 80301
Phone: 303-440-0601
Fax: 303-444-6788

CEO: Felix Magowan
CFO: Tom Haberthier
HR: —
Employees: 45

1995 Sales: $7.7 million
1-Yr. Sales Change: 28.3%
Ownership: Privately Held

Publishing - cycling books (VeloPress) & magazines (*Inside Triathlon, Velo Catalog, VeloNews, VeloNews Presents*)

INSO CORPORATION

31 St. James Ave.	CEO: Steven R. Vana-Paxhia	1995 Sales: $43.4 million
Boston, MA 02116	CFO: Betty J. Savage	1-Yr. Sales Change: 84.7%
Phone: 617-753-6500	HR: Judith Tavano-Finkle	Exchange: Nasdaq
Fax: 617-753-6666	Employees: 176	Symbol: INSO

Computers - proofing, reference & information management software (IntelliScope)

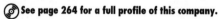 **See page 264 for a full profile of this company.**

INSTANT WEB, INC.

7951 Powers Blvd.	CEO: E. Jerome Carlson	1995 Est. Sales: $100.0 mil.
Chanhassen, MN 55317	CFO: H. Bill Carlson	1-Yr. Sales Change: 9.9%
Phone: 612-474-0961	HR: Nancy Kunkel	Ownership: Privately Held
Fax: 612-474-6467	Employees: 1,200	

Printing - commercial

INTEGRATED COMMUNICATION NETWORK, INC.

444 Brickell Ave., Ste. 900	CEO: David F. Greenberg	1995 Sales: $16.0 million
Miami, FL 33131	CFO: Donald F. Mann	1-Yr. Sales Change: —
Phone: 305-530-0200	HR: —	Exchange: Nasdaq
Fax: 305-577-9755	Employees: 20	Symbol: ICNI

TV production & programming - infomercials & commercials

INTEGRITY MUSIC, INC.

1000 Cody Rd.	CEO: P. Michael Coleman	1995 Sales: $36.3 million
Mobile, AL 36695	CFO: Alison S. Richardson	1-Yr. Sales Change: 4.3%
Phone: 334-633-9000	HR: Judy Hopper	Exchange: Nasdaq
Fax: 334-633-5202	Employees: 157	Symbol: ITGR

Music production & publishing - Christian music audiocassettes, CDs, videos & songbooks

INTELLIQUEST INFORMATION GROUP, INC.

1250 Capital of Texas Highway South	CEO: Peter A. Zandan	1995 Sales: $17.0 million
Bldg. Two, Plaza One, Austin, TX 78746	CFO: James A. Schellhase	1-Yr. Sales Change: 29.8%
Phone: 512-329-0808	HR: —	Exchange: Nasdaq
Fax: 512-314-1823	Employees: 113	Symbol: IQST

Business services - survey-based market research information for technology companies

INTERACTIVE FLIGHT TECHNOLOGIES, INC.

3070 W. Post Rd.	CEO: Michail Itkis	1995 Sales: —
Las Vegas, NV 89118	CFO: Robert J. Aten	1-Yr. Sales Change: —
Phone: 702-896-8900	HR: Robert J. Aten	Exchange: Nasdaq
Fax: 702-896-4234	Employees: 42	Symbol: FLYT

Computers - in-flight entertainment network, including movies, casino & video arcade games & shopping channels

INTEREP RADIO STORE

100 Park Ave.	CEO: Ralph Gild	1995 Est. Sales: $330.0 mil.
New York, NY 10017	CFO: Michael Tsavaris	1-Yr. Sales Change: —
Phone: 212-916-0700	HR: —	Ownership: Privately Held
Fax: 212-916-0772	Employees: 500	

Advertising - radio advertising representation, including exclusive handling of advertising sales to Clear Channel Communications (Clear Channel Radio Sales)

INTERLEAF, INC.

Prospect Place, 9 Hillside Ave.	CEO: Ed Koepfler	1996 Sales: $88.6 million
Waltham, MA 02154	CFO: G. Gordon M. Large	1-Yr. Sales Change: 0.8%
Phone: 617-290-0710	HR: Kate Horseman	Exchange: Nasdaq
Fax: 617-290-4943	Employees: 674	Symbol: LEAF

Computers - UNIX software used in the creation, management & distribution of documents

INTERMEDIA PARTNERS

235 Montgomery St., Ste. 420	CEO: Leo Hindery	1995 Est. Sales: $216.0 mil.
San Francisco, CA 94104	CFO: Edon Hartley	1-Yr. Sales Change: (3.4%)
Phone: 415-616-4600	HR: Grace de Latour	Ownership: Privately Held
Fax: 415-397-4706	Employees: —	

Cable TV

INTERNATIONAL CREATIVE MANAGEMENT, INC.

40 W. 57th St.	CEO: Jeff Berg	1995 Est. Sales: $110.0 mil.
New York, NY 10019	CFO: Michael Cooperman	1-Yr. Sales Change: —
Phone: 212-556-5600	HR: Andrew Suss	Ownership: Privately Held
Fax: 212-556-5603	Employees: 500	

Talent agency

INTERNATIONAL DATA GROUP

One Exeter Plaza, 15th Fl.	CEO: Patrick J. McGovern	1995 Sales: $1,400 million
Boston, MA 02116	CFO: William P. Murphy	1-Yr. Sales Change: 14.1%
Phone: 617-534-1200	HR: Martha Stephens	Ownership: Privately Held
Fax: 617-262-2300	Employees: 8,500	

Publishing - computer magazines (*PC World*, *Publish*, *ComputerWorld*); market research & trade shows

 See pages 98–99 for a full profile of this company.

INTERNATIONAL FAMILY ENTERTAINMENT, INC.

2877 Guardian Ln.	CEO: Timothy B. Robertson	1995 Sales: $294.9 million
Virginia Beach, VA 23452	CFO: Larry W. Dantzler	1-Yr. Sales Change: 21.8%
Phone: 804-459-6000	HR: Carol Kleiber	Exchange: NYSE
Fax: 804-459-6486	Employees: 840	Symbol: FAM

Broadcasting - cable TV network (The Family Channel); TV production (MTM Entertainment, *Xuxa*, *Christy*), TV syndication (*Bob Newhart*, *Lou Grant*, *Mary Tyler Moore*)

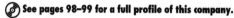 **See page 265 for a full profile of this company.**

INTERNATIONAL MANAGEMENT GROUP

One Erie View Plaza, Ste. 1300	CEO: Mark H. McCormack	1995 Est. Sales: $640.0 mil.
Cleveland, OH 44114	CFO: —	1-Yr. Sales Change: 53.8%
Phone: 216-522-1200	HR: Dan Lewis	Ownership: Privately Held
Fax: 216-522-1145	Employees: 2,000	

Business services - sports, business & entertainment management & marketing

INTERNATIONAL POST LIMITED

545 Fifth Ave.	CEO: Martin Irwin	1995 Sales: $38.3 million
New York, NY 10017	CFO: Jeffrey J. J. Kaplan	1-Yr. Sales Change: 37.8%
Phone: 212-986-6300	HR: Carla Moxham	Exchange: Nasdaq
Fax: 212-986-1364	Employees: 322	Symbol: POST

TV services - film-to-tape transfer, electronic video editing & computer-generated graphics primarily for the TV advertising & program distribution industries

 See page 266 for a full profile of this company.

INTERNATIONAL TOURIST ENTERTAINMENT CORPORATION

7030 Park Centre Dr.	CEO: Kelvyn H. Cullimore	1995 Sales: $2.8 million
Salt Lake City, UT 84121	CFO: Keith E. Turner	1-Yr. Sales Change: 115.4%
Phone: 801-566-9000	HR: —	Exchange: OTC
Fax: 801-568-7711	Employees: 82	Symbol: ITEC

Leisure & recreation services - giant-screen theaters, retail stores & restaurants in selected tourist locations throughout the US & worldwide

THE INTERPUBLIC GROUP OF COMPANIES, INC.

1271 Avenue of the Americas	CEO: Philip H. Geier Jr.	1995 Sales: $2,179.7 million
New York, NY 10020	CFO: Eugene P. Beard	1-Yr. Sales Change: 9.8%
Phone: 212-399-8000	HR: C. Kent Kroeber	Exchange: NYSE
Fax: 212-399-8130	Employees: 19,700	Symbol: IPG

Advertising - market research, sales promotion, product development, direct marketing, telemarketing & other related services

 See pages 100–101 for a full profile of this company.

INTERSCOPE RECORDS

10900 Wilshire Blvd.	CEO: Jimmy Iovine	1995 Est. Sales: $125.0 mil.
Los Angeles, CA 90024	CFO: David Cohen	1-Yr. Sales Change: —
Phone: 310-208-6547	HR: —	Ownership: Privately Held
Fax: 310-208-7374	Employees: 150	

Music production & publishing - music recordings (Bush, Deep Blue Something, Primus, The Toadies), including gangsta rap music (Death Row label: Dr. Dre, Snoop Doggy Dogg, Tupac Shakur)

INTERVISUAL BOOKS, INC.

2850 Ocean Park Blvd., Ste. 225	CEO: Charles E. Gates	1995 Sales: $19.5 million
Santa Monica, CA 90405	CFO: Gail Thornhill	1-Yr. Sales Change: 4.3%
Phone: 310-396-8708	HR: —	Exchange: Nasdaq
Fax: 310-399-0419	Employees: 43	Symbol: IVBK

Publishing - pop-up & novelty books for children

IRVIN FELD & KENNETH FELD PRODUCTIONS, INC.

8607 Westwood Center Dr.	CEO: Kenneth Feld	1995 Est. Sales: $600.0 mil.
Vienna, VA 22182-7506	CFO: Charles E. Smith	1-Yr. Sales Change: 5.3%
Phone: 703-448-4000	HR: Jule Bailey	Ownership: Privately Held
Fax: 703-448-4100	Employees: 2,500	

Leisure & recreational services - Ringling Brothers & Barnum & Bailey Circus, Siegfried & Roy, Walt Disney's World on Ice

IVI PUBLISHING INC.

7500 Flying Cloud Dr.	CEO: Ronald G. Buck	1995 Sales: $12.0 million
Minneapolis, MN 55344-3739	CFO: Thomas P. Skiba	1-Yr. Sales Change: 71.4%
Phone: 612-996-6000	HR: S. Calton	Exchange: Nasdaq
Fax: 612-966-6001	Employees: 143	Symbol: IVIP

Publishing - health & medical multimedia CD-ROMs (Mayo Clinic Family Health Book)

IWERKS ENTERTAINMENT, INC.

4540 W. Valerio St.	CEO: Roy A. Wright	1995 Sales: $45.0 million
Burbank, CA 91505-1046	CFO: Francis T. Phalen	1-Yr. Sales Change: 19.7%
Phone: 818-841-7766	HR: Catherine Giffen	Exchange: Nasdaq
Fax: 818-841-7847	Employees: 175	Symbol: IWRK

Motion pictures & services - specialty theaters with high-end visual & audio systems

See page 267 for a full profile of this company.

J2 COMMUNICATIONS

10850 Wilshire Blvd., Ste. 1000	CEO: James P. Jimirro	1995 Sales: $1.3 million
Los Angeles, CA 90024-4322	CFO: Gary G. Cowan	1-Yr. Sales Change: (27.8%)
Phone: 310-474-5252	HR: —	Exchange: Nasdaq (SC)
Fax: 310-474-1219	Employees: 8	Symbol: JTWO

Motion pictures & services - movie production; humor magazine (*National Lampoon*); licensing of the National Lampoon name for feature films & TV comedy programming

JACOR COMMUNICATIONS, INC.

1300 PNC Center, 201 E. Fifth St.	CEO: Randy Michaels	1995 Sales: $118.9 million
Cincinnati, OH 45202	CFO: R. Christopher Weber	1-Yr. Sales Change: 11.1%
Phone: 513-621-1300	HR: Jon M. Berry	Exchange: Nasdaq
Fax: 513-621-0090	Employees: 1,147	Symbol: JCOR

Broadcasting - radio (7 AM & 8 FM stations)

See page 268 for a full profile of this company.

J.D. POWER AND ASSOCIATES

30401 Agoura Rd.	CEO: J. David Power III	1995 Sales: $30.3 million
Agoura Hills, CA 91301	CFO: Marge Samuelson	1-Yr. Sales Change: —
Phone: 818-889-6330	HR: Margie Long	Ownership: Privately Held
Fax: 818-889-3719	Employees: 320	

Business services - marketing & consulting, including automotive & PC studies

JIM HENSON PRODUCTIONS, INC.

5358 Melrose, West Office, 3rd Fl.	CEO: Brian Henson	1995 Est. Sales: $35.0 mil.
Hollywood, CA 90038	CFO: Linda Govreau	1-Yr. Sales Change: —
Phone: 213-960-4096	HR: Dee Dee Degelia	Ownership: Privately Held
Fax: 213-960-4935	Employees: 180	

Motion pictures & services - film production (*Muppet Treasure Island, The Muppet Christmas Carol*)

THE JIM PATTISON GROUP

1055 W. Hastings St., Ste. 1600	CEO: Jim Pattison	1995 Sales: $3,300.0 million
Vancouver, BC V6E 2H2, Canada	CFO: Bruce Parker	1-Yr. Sales Change: 6.1%
Phone: 604-688-6764	HR: —	Ownership: Privately Held
	Employees: 16,000	

Diversified operations - museums (Ripley's Believe It or Not, Guinness World of Records); food; broadcasting; packaging; transportation; financial services

J.J. KELLER & ASSOCIATES

3003 W. Breezewood Ln.	CEO: R. L. Keller	1995 Est. Sales: $100.0 mil.
Neenah, WI 54957-0368	CFO: R. M. Phillips	1-Yr. Sales Change: 8.7%
Phone: 414-722-2848	HR: Anthony M. LaMalfo	Ownership: Privately Held
Fax: 414-727-7522	Employees: 700	

Printing - publications

JOHN FAIRFAX HOLDINGS LTD.

235-243 Jones St., 14th Fl.	CEO: S. Mulholland	1995 Sales: $670.3 million
Broadway N.S.W. 2007, Australia	CFO: John Greaves	1-Yr. Sales Change: 12.2%
Phone: +61-2-282-2833	HR: —	Exchange: Sydney
Fax: +61-2-282-3133	Employees: 4,752	

Publishing - newspapers (#1 in Australia) & magazines

JOHN WILEY & SONS, INC.

605 Third Ave.	CEO: Charles R. Ellis	1996 Sales: $362.7 million
New York, NY 10158-0012	CFO: Robert D. Wilder	1-Yr. Sales Change: 9.5%
Phone: 212-850-6000	HR: William J. Arlington	Exchange: NYSE
Fax: 212-850-6088	Employees: 1,770	Symbol: JWA

Publishing - textbooks, professional & reference works, journals & other subscription-based products; electronic publishing

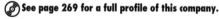 **See page 269 for a full profile of this company.**

JOHNSON PUBLISHING COMPANY, INC.

820 S. Michigan Ave.	CEO: John H. Johnson	1995 Sales: $316.2 million
Chicago, IL 60605	CFO: Eunice W. Johnson	1-Yr. Sales Change: 3.0%
Phone: 312-322-9200	HR: La Doris Foster	Ownership: Privately Held
Fax: 312-322-0918	Employees: 2,680	

Diversified - periodical publishing (*Ebony*, *Jet*), radio broadcasting, cosmetics & hair care

See pages 102–103 for a full profile of this company.

JOHNSTON PRESS PLC

53 Manor Place
Edinburgh EH3 7EG, UK
Phone: +44-131-225-3361
Fax: +44-131-225-4580

CEO: Tim J. Bowdler
CFO: Marco L. A. Chiappelli
HR: —
Employees: 2,238

1995 Sales: $158.6 million
1-Yr. Sales Change: 7.6%
Exchange: London

Publishing - weekly newspapers; commercial printing; bookbinding & conservation; library bookselling & wholesale stationery

JONES COMMUNICATIONS, INC.

9697 E. Mineral Ave., PO Box 3309
Englewood, CO 80155-3309
Phone: 303-792-3111
Fax: 303-790-0533

CEO: Glenn R. Jones
CFO: Kevin P. Coyle
HR: Raymond L. Vigil
Employees: 3,480

1995 Sales: $150.9 million
1-Yr. Sales Change: 14.0%
Exchange: Nasdaq
Symbol: JOIN

Cable TV - acquisition, development & operation of cable TV systems; programming & data encryption service

 **See page 270 for a full profile of this company.**

JONES INTERCABLE INVESTORS, L.P.

9697 E. Mineral Dr.
Englewood, CO 80112
Phone: 303-792-3111
Fax: 303-784-8509

CEO: Glenn R. Jones
CFO: Kevin P. Coyle
HR: Raymond L. Vigil
Employees: —

1995 Sales: $29.9 million
1-Yr. Sales Change: 8.7%
Exchange: AMEX
Symbol: JTV

Cable TV - cable television systems in Independence & Kansas City, MO

JORDAN, MCGRATH, CASE & TAYLOR

445 Park Ave.
New York, NY 10022
Phone: 212-326-9100
Fax: 212-326-9357

CEO: Patrick McGrath
CFO: Thomas Finneran
HR: Chris Martin
Employees: 350

1995 Sales: $48.0 million
1-Yr. Sales Change: 2.1%
Ownership: Privately Held

Advertising

JOSTENS, INC.

5501 Norman Center Dr.
Minneapolis, MN 55437-1088
Phone: 612-830-3300
Fax: 612-830-3293

CEO: Robert C. Buhrmaster
CFO: Trudy A. Rautio
HR: John L. Jones
Employees: 5,600

1995 Sales: $665.1 million
1-Yr. Sales Change: (19.6%)
Exchange: NYSE
Symbol: JOS

Diversified operations - class rings, yearbooks, student photos & graduation announcements, business promotional products

JOURNAL COMMUNICATION INC.

PO Box 661	CEO: Robert Kahlor	1995 Sales: $591.8 million
Milwaukee, WI 53201	CFO: Paul Bonaiuto	1-Yr. Sales Change: 14.2%
Phone: 414-224-2000	HR: Daniel Harmsen	Ownership: Privately Held
Fax: 414-224-2599	Employees: 6,500	

Publishing - newspapers (*Milwaukee Sentinel*); broadcasting; printing; telecommunications

JOURNAL REGISTER COMPANY

51 W. State St.	CEO: Robert Jelenic	1995 Est. Sales: $350.0 mil.
Trenton, NJ 08608	CFO: Jean Clifton	1-Yr. Sales Change: 2.6%
Phone: 608-396-2200	HR: Linne Tomicki	Ownership: Privately Held
Fax: 609-396-2292	Employees: —	

Publishing - weekly (Imprint Newspapers) & daily (*The New Haven Register*) newspapers

JUNIPER FEATURES LTD.

111 Great Neck Rd., Ste. 604	CEO: Paul V. Hreijanovic	1995 Sales: $3.6 million
Great Neck, NY 11021-5402	CFO: Murray Wiener	1-Yr. Sales Change: 38.5%
Phone: 516-829-4670	HR: —	Exchange: Nasdaq (SC)
Fax: 516-829-4691	Employees: 14	Symbol: JUNI

Motion pictures & services - feature film distribution; music & jingles for advertising; medical revenue enhancement services

JUSTIN INDUSTRIES, INC.

2821 W. Seventh St.	CEO: John Justin	1995 Sales: $461.4 million
Fort Worth, TX 76107	CFO: Richard J. Savitz	1-Yr. Sales Change: (4.5%)
Phone: 817-336-5125	HR: John Bennett	Exchange: Nasdaq
Fax: 817-390-2477	Employees: 5,007	Symbol: JSTN

Diversified operations - boots (Tony Lama); building materials (Acme Brick); subsidiary Northland publishes books on western and southwestern American, art, and Native American culture

K-III COMMUNICATIONS CORPORATION

745 Fifth Ave.	CEO: William F. Reilly	1995 Sales: $1,046.3 million
New York, NY 10151	CFO: Curtis A. Thompson	1-Yr. Sales Change: 8.5%
Phone: 212-745-0100	HR: Michaelanne C. Discepolo	Exchange: NYSE
Fax: 212-745-0169	Employees: 6,300	Symbol: KCC

Publishing - periodicals (*American Baby, Chicago, Modern Bride, New Woman, New York, Sail, Seventeen, Soap Opera Digest*) & books (*World Almanac*); educational TV programming (*Channel One*)

(🌀) **See pages 104–105 for a full profile of this company.**

KANE/MILLER CORPORATION

555 White Plains Rd.
Tarrytown, NY 10591
Phone: 914-630-6900
Fax: 914-631-6901

CEO: Stanley B. Kane
CFO: Michael Raffia
HR: —
Employees: 750

1995 Est. Sales: $185.0 mil.
1-Yr. Sales Change: —
Ownership: Privately Held

Publishing - children's book publishing; meat processing

KATZ DIGITAL TECHNOLOGIES, INC.

21 Penn Plaza
New York, NY 10001
Phone: 212-594-4800
Fax: 212-594-4488

CEO: Gary Katz
CFO: Mitchell Cohen
HR: Jeffrey Barsky
Employees: 116

1995 Sales: $10.6 million
1-Yr. Sales Change: 30.9%
Exchange: Nasdaq
Symbol: KATC

Printing - digital prepress & digital short-run printing services

KATZ MEDIA GROUP, INC.

125 W. 55th St.
New York, NY 10019
Phone: 212-424-6000
Fax: 212-424-6110

CEO: Thomas F. Olson
CFO: Richard E. Vendig
HR: Anne Strafaci
Employees: 1,600

1995 Sales: $184.7 million
1-Yr. Sales Change: (0.1%)
Exchange: AMEX
Symbol: KTZ

Business services - national, local & network advertising time sales to radio, TV & cable stations

 **See page 271 for a full profile of this company.**

KING WORLD PRODUCTIONS, INC.

1700 Broadway, 33rd Fl.
New York, NY 10019
Phone: 212-315-4000
Fax: 212-582-9255

CEO: Michael King
CFO: Steven A. LoCascio
HR: Patsy Bundy
Employees: 430

1995 Sales: $574.2 million
1-Yr. Sales Change: 19.5%
Exchange: NYSE
Symbol: KWP

TV production & programming - first-run syndicated programming (*Wheel of Fortune, Jeopardy!, The Oprah Winfrey Show*)

 **See pages 106–107 for a full profile of this company.**

KINGS ROAD ENTERTAINMENT, INC.

1901 Avenue of the Stars, Ste. 605
Los Angeles, CA 90067
Phone: 310-552-0057
Fax: 310-277-4468

CEO: Stephen J. Friedman
CFO: Christopher M. Trunkey
HR: Kenneth Aguado
Employees: 8

1995 Sales: $4.3 million
1-Yr. Sales Change: (46.9%)
Exchange: Nasdaq (SC)
Symbol: KREN

Motion pictures & services - film production

KIRCHGRUPPE

Robert Burkle Strasse 2	CEO: Leo Kirch	1995 Est. Sales: $4,000 mil.
D-85737 Ismaning, Germany	CFO: —	1-Yr. Sales Change: —
Phone: +49-89-95-08-80	HR: —	Ownership: Privately Held
Fax: +49-89-95-08-81-23	Employees: —	

TV production & programming (#1 in Europe); theatrical & video distribution; cable & pay TV; music publishing

KNIGHT-RIDDER, INC.

One Herald Plaza	CEO: P. Anthony Ridder	1995 Sales: $2,751.8 million
Miami, FL 33132-1693	CFO: Ross Jones	1-Yr. Sales Change: 3.9%
Phone: 305-376-3800	HR: Mary Jean Connors	Exchange: NYSE
Fax: 305-376-3828	Employees: 22,800	Symbol: KRI

Publishing - newspapers (28, including the *Philadelphia Inquirer*); electronic news-retrieval & information services & financial information services

 See pages 108–109 for a full profile of this company.

KNOWLEDGE ADVENTURE, INC.

1311 Grand Central Ave.	CEO: Larry Gross	1995 Sales: $39.0 million
Glendale, CA 91201	CFO: Frank Greico	1-Yr. Sales Change: 11.4%
Phone: 818-246-4400	HR: —	Ownership: Privately Held
Fax: 818-246-5604	Employees: 115	

Computers - entertainment & education multimedia software (My First Encyclopedia, 3-D Dinosaur Adventure, Kid's Zoo)

KOCH INTERNATIONAL L.P.

2 Tri-Harbor Ct.	CEO: Michael Koch	1995 Sales: $60.0 million
Port Washington, NY 11050	CFO: Liz Jones	1-Yr. Sales Change: 15.4%
Phone: 516-484-1000	HR: Nancy Young	Ownership: Privately Held
Fax: 516-484-4746	Employees: 143	

Prerecorded music

K-TEL INTERNATIONAL, INC.

2605 Fernbrook Ln. North	CEO: Philip Kives	1995 Sales: $65.9 million
Minneapolis, MN 55447-4736	CFO: Mark Dixon	1-Yr. Sales Change: 21.4%
Phone: 612-559-6888	HR: —	Exchange: Nasdaq
Fax: 612-559-6848	Employees: 186	Symbol: KTEL

Music publishing - packaged music & video entertainment & consumer convenience products

 See page 272 for a full profile of this company.

KUKLA PRESS, INC.

855 Morse Ave.
Elk Grove Village, IL 60007
Phone: 847-593-1090
Fax: 847-593-0406

CEO: Stanley J. Kukla
CFO: Steve Funk
HR: Darlene McPhearson
Employees: 200

1995 Sales: $42.0 million
1-Yr. Sales Change: —
Ownership: Privately Held

Printing - commercial web offset printing

THE KUSHNER-LOCKE COMPANY

11601 Wilshire Blvd., 21st Fl.
Los Angeles, CA 90025
Phone: 310-445-1111
Fax: 310-445-1191

CEO: Donald Kushner
CFO: Lenore Nelson
HR: —
Employees: 100

1995 Sales: $20.4 million
1-Yr. Sales Change: (59.8%)
Exchange: Nasdaq
Symbol: KLOC

TV production & programming - network & cable TV programming; theatrical feature films for domestic theater release & cable; direct-to-video films

LAGARDERE GROUPE

4, rue de Presbourg
75116 Paris, France
Phone: +33-1-40-69-16-00
Fax: +33-1-47-23-01-92

CEO: Raymond H. Levy
CFO: Philippe Camus
HR: Thierry Funck-Brentano
Employees: 43,622

1995 Sales: $10,742.7 mil.
1-Yr. Sales Change: (0.8%)
Exchange: OTC
Symbol: LGDDY (ADR)

Publishing - magazines, newspapers & books; broadcasting; defense; automobiles; transit systems; telecommunications

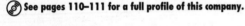 **See pages 110–111 for a full profile of this company.**

LAMAR ADVERTISING COMPANY

5551 Corporate Blvd.
Baton Rouge, LA 70808
Phone: 504-926-1000
Fax: 504-923-0658

CEO: Kevin P. Reilly Jr.
CFO: Keith A. Istre
HR: Sarah Hill
Employees: 825

1995 Sales: $102.4 million
1-Yr. Sales Change: 21.2%
Ownership: Privately Held

Advertising - outdoor advertising in 33 US markets (23,000 displays); logo sign operations

LANCIT MEDIA PRODUCTIONS, LTD.

601 W. 50th St.
New York, NY 10019
Phone: 212-977-9100
Fax: 212-477-9164

CEO: Cecily Truett
CFO: Gary Appelbaum
HR: JoAnn Pezzella
Employees: 43

1995 Sales: $17.9 million
1-Yr. Sales Change: 96.7%
Exchange: Nasdaq
Symbol: LNCT

TV production & programming - children's TV programming (*The Puzzle Place*, *Backyard Safari*); film production

LANDMARK COMMUNICATIONS, INC.

150 W. Brambleton Ave.	CEO: John O. Wynne	1995 Est. Sales: $500.6 mil.
Norfolk, VA 23510	CFO: Alfred Ritter	1-Yr. Sales Change: 7.2%
Phone: 804-446-2000	HR: Charlie Hill	Ownership: Privately Held
Fax: 804-664-2163	Employees: 4,500	

Publishing - newspapers & magazines; cable (Weather Channel) & broadcast TV

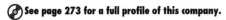 **See page 273 for a full profile of this company.**

LANE INDUSTRIES, INC.

1200 Shermer Rd.	CEO: William N. Lane III	1995 Sales: $625.0 million
Northbrook, IL 60062	CFO: Forrest M. Schneider	1-Yr. Sales Change: 13.0%
Phone: 847-498-6789	HR: Linda Datz	Ownership: Privately Held
Fax: 847-498-2104	Employees: 8,300	

Diversified operations - business machines & supplies; ranching; lodging; broadcasting

LASER-PACIFIC MEDIA CORPORATION

809 N. Cahuenga Blvd.	CEO: James R. Parks	1995 Sales: $28.7 million
Hollywood, CA 90038	CFO: Robert McClain	1-Yr. Sales Change: (5.3%)
Phone: 213-462-6266	HR: Louise McCann	Exchange: Nasdaq (SC)
Fax: 213-960-2192	Employees: 310	Symbol: LPAC

Motion pictures & services - film processing, film-to-video transfer, special effects, color correction & sound editing

LAURIAT'S, INC.

10 Pequot Way	CEO: Daniel Gurr	1995 Est. Sales: $140.0 mil.
Canton, MA 02021	CFO: Steve Kuptsis	1-Yr. Sales Change: 174.5%
Phone: 617-821-0071	HR: Richard Markiewicz	Ownership: Subsidiary
Fax: 617-821-0167	Employees: 1,600	

Retail - bookstores in the Northeast (Encore Books, Lauriat's Booksellers, Royal Discount Bookstores, Book Corner)(subsidiary of CMI Holding)

LCS INDUSTRIES, INC.

120 Brighton Rd.	CEO: Arnold J. Scheine	1995 Sales: $78.9 million
Clifton, NJ 07012	CFO: Pat R. Frustaci	1-Yr. Sales Change: 25.8%
Phone: 201-778-5588	HR: Monica A. Mahon	Exchange: Nasdaq
Fax: 201-778-6001	Employees: 1,637	Symbol: LCSI

Business services - direct-response, fulfillment & list-marketing services

LEE ENTERPRISES, INCORPORATED

400 Putnam Bldg., 215 N. Main St.	CEO: Richard D. Gottlieb	1995 Sales: $443.2 million
Davenport, IA 52801-1924	CFO: Larry L. Bloom	1-Yr. Sales Change: 10.1%
Phone: 319-383-2100	HR: Floyd Whellan	Exchange: NYSE
Fax: 319-323-9609	Employees: 4,700	Symbol: LEE

Publishing - newspapers; network-affiliated TV stations; graphic arts products for the newspaper industry

LEGACY SOFTWARE, INC.

8521 Reseda Blvd.	CEO: Ariella J. Lehrer	1995 Sales: $0.1 million
Northridge, CA 91324	CFO: William E. Sliney	1-Yr. Sales Change: (50.0%)
Phone: 818-885-5773	HR: Ariella J. Lehrer	Exchange: Nasdaq
Fax: 818-885-5779	Employees: 15	Symbol: LGCY

Computers - edutainment software (CAREER SIM series)

LEGAL RESEARCH CENTER, INC.

331 Second Ave. South	CEO: Christopher R. Ljungkull	1995 Sales: $1.4 million
Minneapolis, MN 55401	CFO: —	1-Yr. Sales Change: 16.7%
Phone: 612-332-4950	HR: —	Exchange: Nasdaq (SC)
Fax: 612-332-7454	Employees: —	Symbol: LRCI

Outsourced legal & factual research & writing services for attorneys

LENFEST GROUP

200 Cresson Blvd.	CEO: H. F. Lenfest	1995 Sales: $266.2 million
Oaks, PA 19456	CFO: Harry F. Brooks	1-Yr. Sales Change: 8.7%
Phone: 610-650-3000	HR: Rose McGinley	Ownership: Privately Held
Fax: 610-650-3001	Employees: 1,200	

Cable TV

LEO BURNETT COMPANY, INC.

35 W. Wacker Dr., Ste. 2200	CEO: William T. Lynch	1995 Sales: $780.5 million
Chicago, IL 60601	CFO: Roger A. Haupt	1-Yr. Sales Change: 15.2%
Phone: 312-220-5959	HR: Michael Breslin	Ownership: Privately Held
Fax: 312-220-3299	Employees: 2,049	

Advertising

(☉) **See pages 112–113 for a full profile of this company.**

LEXI INTERNATIONAL, INC.

1645 N. Vine St., Ste. 400
Los Angeles, CA 90028
Phone: 213-467-3334
Fax: 213-848-5500

CEO: Robin Richards
CFO: Don McCrea
HR: Steve Hemmert
Employees: 1,500

1995 Sales: $50.0 million
1-Yr. Sales Change: 66.7%
Ownership: Privately Held

Business - telemarketing & database marketing

LIBERTY MEDIA CORPORATION

5619 DTC Pkwy.
Englewood, CO 80111-3000
Phone: 303-267-5500

CEO: Peter Barton
CFO: —
HR: —
Employees: —

1995 Sales: $1,018.6 million
1-Yr. Sales Change: (9.5%)
Exchange: Nasdaq
Symbol: LBTYA

TV production & programming - entertainment, educational & informational programs for TV & other media

LIFETIME TELEVISION

309 W. 49th St.
New York, NY 10019
Phone: 212-957-4610
Fax: 212-957-4449

CEO: Douglas McCormick
CFO: James Wesley
HR: Deborah Henderson
Employees: 270

1995 Est. Sales: $310.0 mil.
1-Yr. Sales Change: 28.6%
Ownership: Privately Held

Broadcasting - cable network

LIN TELEVISION CORPORATION

4 Richmond Sq., Ste. 200
Providence, RI 02906
Phone: 401-454-2880
Fax: 401-454-5286

CEO: Gary R. Chapman
CFO: Peter E. Maloney
HR: Debby Kaczmarzyk
Employees: 1,006

1995 Sales: $217.2 million
1-Yr. Sales Change: 44.3%
Exchange: Nasdaq
Symbol: LNTV

Broadcasting - TV (7 network-affiliated stations); program development

LINOTYPE-HELL AG

Mergenthaler Allee 55-75
65760 Eschborn, Germany
Phone: +49-6196-98-0
Fax: +49-6196-98-2597

CEO: Erwin Koenigs
CFO: K. H. Midunsky
HR: —
Employees: 3,761

1995 Sales: $601.2 million
1-Yr. Sales Change: (13.2%)
Exchange: Frankfurt

Printing - graphics systems for reproducing fine structures in graphics

LIVE ENTERTAINMENT INC.

15400 Sherman Way, Ste. 500	CEO: Roger A. Burlage	1995 Sales: $140.1 million
Van Nuys, CA 91406	CFO: Ronald B. Cushey	1-Yr. Sales Change: 19.5%
Phone: 818-988-5060	HR: Nancy Coleman	Exchange: Nasdaq (SC)
Fax: 818-908-9539	Employees: 194	Symbol: LIVE

Motion pictures & services - acquisition of motion pictures, children's films, music & video recordings & marketing of films to wholesalers, retailers & consumers

LODGENET ENTERTAINMENT CORPORATION

808 W. Ave. North	CEO: Tim C. Flynn	1995 Sales: $63.2 million
Sioux Falls, SD 57104	CFO: Jeffrey T. Weisner	1-Yr. Sales Change: 56.8%
Phone: 605-330-1330	HR: Don McCoy	Exchange: Nasdaq
Fax: 605-330-1323	Employees: 300	Symbol: LNET

Cable TV - in-room, pay-per-view television entertainment services to the lodging industry, serving 315,000 guest rooms in more than 2,200 hotel properties in the US & Canada

LONELY PLANET PUBLICATIONS, INC.

155 Filbert St., Ste. 251	CEO: Eric Kettunen	1996 Sales: $7.1 million
Oakland, CA 94607-2538	CFO: Erin Reid	1-Yr. Sales Change: 26.8%
Phone: 510-893-8555	HR: —	Ownership: Privately Held
Fax: 510-893-8563	Employees: 90	

Publishing - guidebooks & phrase books for independent travelers (#1 worldwide); online travel center (Lonely Planet Travel Centre)

LOPEX PLC

4-7 Red Lion Ct., Fleet St.	CEO: P. R. Thomas	1995 Sales: $204.7 million
London EC4A 3ES, UK	CFO: B. A. Warman	1-Yr. Sales Change: (8.8%)
Phone: +44-171-353-5653	HR: —	Exchange: London
Fax: +44-171-353-4653	Employees: 1,038	

Advertising - communication, promotions & public relations services

LOTTO WORLD, INC.

2150 Goodlette Rd., Ste. 200	CEO: Dennis B. Schroeder	1995 Sales: $0.8 million
Naples, FL 33940	CFO: Judith Schroeder	1-Yr. Sales Change: 300.0%
Phone: 941-643-1677	HR: —	Exchange: Nasdaq (SC)
Fax: 941-643-6670	Employees: 22	Symbol: LTTO

Publishing - magazines (*LottoWorld*)

LUCASARTS ENTERTAINMENT COMPANY

PO Box 10307
San Rafael, CA 94912
Phone: 415-472-3400
Fax: 415-662-2460

CEO: Jack Sorensen
CFO: Tom McCarthy
HR: Karen Chelini
Employees: 230

1995 Est. Sales: $96.0 mil.
1-Yr. Sales Change: —
Ownership: Privately Held

Computers - film production & interactive games software (The Dig, Rebel Assault II, Full Throttle, Indiana Jones)

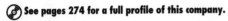 **See pages 274 for a full profile of this company.**

COMPAGNIE LUXEMBOURGEOISE POUR L'AUDIO-VISUEL ET LA FINANCE

1, rue de Namur
Luxembourg, Luxembourg
Phone: +352-44-40-26
Fax: +352-44-36-26

CEO: Nicolas Duhamel
CFO: —
HR: —
Employees: 3,089

1995 Sales: $3,100.4 million
1-Yr. Sales Change: 10.2%
Exchange: Brussels

Broadcasting - radio & TV; pay TV (CLT); periodicals

LYCOS, INC.

293 Boston Post Rd. West
Marlborough, MA 01752
Phone: 508-229-0717
Fax: 508-229-2866

CEO: Robert J. Davis
CFO: Edward M. Philip
HR: Jon Gilthwell
Employees: 28

1995 Sales: $0.0 million
1-Yr. Sales Change: —
Exchange: Nasdaq
Symbol: LCOS

World Wide Web search service (Lycos Catalog), web site reviews (Point Reviews) & directory of popular web sites (a2z Directory)

MACK PRINTING GROUP

1991 Northampton St.
Easton, PA 18042
Phone: 610-258-9111
Fax: 610-250-7285

CEO: Paul F. Mack
CFO: Steven H. Smith
HR: Scott E. M. DeNardo
Employees: 1,100

1995 Sales: $113.0 million
1-Yr. Sales Change: 6.6%
Ownership: Privately Held

Printing - short- to medium-run technical, scientific & business journals, magazines, catalogs & directories

MACROMEDIA INC.

150 River St.
Hackensack, NJ 07601
Phone: 201-646-4000
Fax: 201-646-4782

CEO: Malcolm Borg
CFO: Charles Gibney
HR: Jennifer Borg
Employees: 1,100

1995 Est. Sales: $185.0 mil.
1-Yr. Sales Change: (0.5%)
Ownership: Privately Held

Publishing - newspapers (*The Hackensack Record*); TV stations

MADISON GROUP ASSOCIATES, INC.

One E. Broward Blvd., Ste. 1400	CEO: Richard J. Ferayorni	1995 Sales: $1.2 million
Fort Lauderdale, FL 33301	CFO: Terrence A. Zielinski	1-Yr. Sales Change: —
Phone: 954-463-0777	HR: —	Exchange: OTC
Fax: 954-463-0778	Employees: 20	Symbol: MADI

Broadcasting - media acquisitions & entertainment programming for distribution

M.A.I.D PLC

48 Leicester Sq.	CEO: Daniel M. Wagner	1995 Sales: $20.0 million
London WC2H 7DB, UK	CFO: David G. Mattey	1-Yr. Sales Change: 55.0%
Phone: +44-171-930-6900	HR: —	Exchange: Nasdaq
	Employees: 165	Symbol: MAIDY (ADR)

Computers - online distributor of business information, market research reports, company statistics, stockbroker research analyses, stock market & commodity prices

THE M/A/R/C GROUP

7850 N. Belt Line Rd.	CEO: Sharon M. Munger	1995 Sales: $74.4 million
Irving, TX 75063	CFO: Harold R. Curtis	1-Yr. Sales Change: 8.6%
Phone: 214-506-3400	HR: Jim Farrell	Exchange: Nasdaq
Fax: 214-500-3416	Employees: 1,010	Symbol: MARC

Business services - management consulting, marketing research & database marketing

MARCUS CABLE COMPANY L.P.

2911 Turtle Creek Blvd., Ste. 1300	CEO: Jeffrey A. Marcus	1995 Sales: $198.3 million
Dallas, TX 75219	CFO: Tom McMillin	1-Yr. Sales Change: 206.5%
Phone: 214-521-7898	HR: Cindy Mannes	Ownership: Privately Held
Fax: 214-526-2154	Employees: 2,000	

Cable TV systems

MARITZ INC.

1375 N. Highway Dr.	CEO: William E. Maritz	1995 Sales: $1,078.0 million
Fenton, MO 63099	CFO: David L. Fleisher	1-Yr. Sales Change: (25.2%)
Phone: 314-827-4000	HR: Terry Goring	Ownership: Privately Held
Fax: 314-827-5505	Employees: 6,410	

Business services - market research

MARKET FACTS, INC.

3040 W. Salt Creek Ln.
Arlington Heights, IL 60005
Phone: 847-590-7000
Fax: 847-590-7325

CEO: Thomas H. Payne
CFO: Timothy J. Sullivan
HR: Karen Duncan
Employees: 1,100

1995 Sales: $64.6 million
1-Yr. Sales Change: 16.4%
Exchange: Nasdaq
Symbol: MFAC

Business services - market research

MARKKINOINTI VIHERJUURI OY

Bulevardi 6 A
FIN-00120 Helsinki, Finland
Phone: +358-0-12551
Fax: +358-0-125-52260

CEO: Arto Liinpaa
CFO: —
HR: —
Employees: 146

1995 Sales: $55.7 million
1-Yr. Sales Change: 32.9%
Exchange: Helsinki

Advertising - advertising & public relations

MARLTON TECHNOLOGIES, INC.

2828 Charter Rd., Ste 101
Philadelphia, PA 19154
Phone: 215-676-6900
Fax: 215-664-6900

CEO: Robert B. Ginsburg
CFO: Edmond D. Costantini Jr.
HR: Robert B. Ginsburg
Employees: 180

1995 Sales: $27.7 million
1-Yr. Sales Change: 12.6%
Exchange: AMEX
Symbol: MTY

Business services - trade show exhibits, displays, architectural & museum interiors, graphics & signage, trade show services, portable & panelized portable exhibits; online information services

MARUZEN

2-3-10, Nihonbashi, Chuo-ku
Tokyo 103, Japan
Phone: +81-3-3272-7211
Fax: +81-3-3274-4695

CEO: Kumao Ebihara
CFO: —
HR: —
Employees: 2,187

1995 Sales: $1,506.4 million
1-Yr. Sales Change: 2.3%
Exchange: Tokyo

Retail - books & periodicals; apparel, stationery & OA equipment

MARVEL ENTERTAINMENT GROUP, INC.

387 Park Ave. South
New York, NY 10016
Phone: 212-696-0808
Fax: 212-576-8598

CEO: William C. Bevins Jr.
CFO: Bobby G. Jenkins
HR: D. Erik Pogue
Employees: 1,625

1995 Sales: $829.3 million
1-Yr. Sales Change: 61.1%
Exchange: NYSE
Symbol: MRV

Publishing - comic books (#1 worldwide) & sports trading cards (Fleer Corp., Skybox International Inc.); distribution & marketing of cartoon character-related cards, games & toys (Superhero Enterprises Inc.)

See page 275 for a full profile of this company.

MAXIS, INC.

2121 N. California Blvd., Ste. 600	CEO: Jeffrey B. Braun	1996 Sales: $55.4 million
Walnut Creek, CA 94596-3572	CFO: Fred M. Gerson	1-Yr. Sales Change: 45.4%
Phone: 510-254-9700	HR: Deborah L. Gross	Exchange: Nasdaq
Fax: 510-253-3736	Employees: 210	Symbol: MXIS

Computers - entertainment & educational software (SimCity, SimCity 2000, SimTown)

MCA INC.

100 Universal City Plaza	CEO: —	1995 Sales: $5,772 million
Universal City, CA 91608	CFO: Bruce Hack	1-Yr. Sales Change: 1.3%
Phone: 818-777-1000	HR: Ken Khars	Ownership: Subsidiary
Fax: 818-733-1402	Employees: 13,564	

Motion pictures & services - film & music production & distribution (subsidiary of Seagram Co.)

 See pages 114–115 for a full profile of this company.

MCCLATCHY NEWSPAPERS, INC.

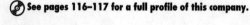

2100 Q St.	CEO: Gary Pruitt	1995 Sales: $540.9 million
Sacramento, CA 95816	CFO: James P. Smith	1-Yr. Sales Change: 14.7%
Phone: 916-321-1846	HR: Peter M. CaJacob	Exchange: NYSE
Fax: 916-321-1996	Employees: 7,464	Symbol: MNI

Publishing - newspapers (*The Sacramento Bee*) & online legal-news service

THE MCGRAW-HILL COMPANIES, INC.

1221 Avenue of the Americas	CEO: Joseph L. Dionne	1995 Sales: $2,935.3 million
New York, NY 10020-1095	CFO: Robert J. Bahash	1-Yr. Sales Change: 6.3%
Phone: 212-512-2000	HR: Barbara B. Maddock	Exchange: NYSE
Fax: 212-512-4871	Employees: 15,004	Symbol: MHP

Publishing - books, periodicals & electronic (*Business Week*, *BYTE*, *Standard & Poor's*); financial services; radio & TV broadcasting

 See pages 116–117 for a full profile of this company.

MCRAE INDUSTRIES, INC.

402 N. Main St.	CEO: Branson J. McRae	1995 Sales: $40.6 million
Mt. Gilead, NC 27306	CFO: D. K. Helms	1-Yr. Sales Change: 2.8%
Phone: 910-439-6147	HR: Bobby Ray Stewart	Exchange: AMEX
Fax: 910-439-9596	Employees: 375	Symbol: MRIA

Diversified operations - combat boots; bar code printing & reading devices; office equipment; commercial printing

MECKLERMEDIA CORPORATION

20 Ketchum St.	CEO: Alan M. Meckler	1995 Sales: $14.5 million
Westport, CT 06880	CFO: Christopher S. Cardell	1-Yr. Sales Change: 74.7%
Phone: 203-226-6967	HR: —	Exchange: Nasdaq (SC)
Fax: 203-454-5840	Employees: 80	Symbol: MECK

Publishing - magazines (*Internet World, Web Developer*), books & newspapers (*Web Week*); trade shows & seminars

(◉) **See page 276 for a full profile of this company.**

MEDIA GENERAL INC.

333 E. Grace St.	CEO: J. Stewart Bryan III	1995 Sales: $707.8 million
Richmond, VA 23219	CFO: Marshall N. Morton	1-Yr. Sales Change: 13.0%
Phone: 804-649-6000	HR: Edward C. Tosh	Exchange: AMEX
Fax: 804-649-6898	Employees: 7,500	Symbol: MEGA

Publishing - newspapers (*Richmond Times-Dispatch, Winston-Salem Journal*) & business information; broadcast & cable TV; newsprint production; commercial printing & publications

(◉) **See page 277 for a full profile of this company.**

MEDIANEWS GROUP, INC.
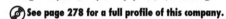

1560 Broadway, Ste. 1450	CEO: W. Dean Singleton	1995 Sales: $375.0 million
Denver, CO 80202	CFO: Joseph J. Lodovic	1-Yr. Sales Change: (24.2%)
Phone: 303-837-0886	HR: Nick Lebra	Ownership: Privately Held
Fax: 303-894-9327	Employees: 4,500	

Publishing - daily & weekly newspapers (76, including the *Denver Post*)

(◉) **See page 278 for a full profile of this company.**

MEEHAN-TOOKER INC.

55 Madison Circle Dr.	CEO: Michael D. Voss	1995 Est. Sales: $100.0 mil.
East Rutherford, NJ 07073	CFO: Thomas Morely	1-Yr. Sales Change: 1.1%
Phone: 201-933-9600	HR: Diane Caivano	Ownership: Privately Held
Fax: 201-933-8322	Employees: 24	

Printing - commercial

MELDRUM & FEWSMITH COMMUNICATIONS, INC.

1350 Euclid Ave.	CEO: Chris N. Perry	1995 Est. Sales: $125.0 mil.
Cleveland, OH 44115	CFO: Robert Huddilston	1-Yr. Sales Change: —
Phone: 216-241-2141	HR: Laura Strickoven	Ownership: Privately Held
Fax: 216-241-3929	Employees: 144	

Business services - marketing, advertising, sales promotion, direct mail & yellow page advertising

MEREDITH CORPORATION

1716 Locust St.	CEO: Jack D. Rehm	1995 Sales: $884.6 million
Des Moines, IA 50309-3023	CFO: Larry D. Hartsook	1-Yr. Sales Change: 10.6%
Phone: 515-284-3000	HR: Denise Rock	Exchange: NYSE
Fax: 515-284-2700	Employees: 2,400	Symbol: MDP

Publishing - magazines (*Better Homes & Gardens, Ladies' Home Journal*) & books; TV stations

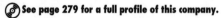 **See page 279 for a full profile of this company.**

MERRILL CORPORATION

One Merrill Circle	CEO: John W. Castro	1996 Sales: $245.3 million
St. Paul, MN 55108-5267	CFO: Kay Barber	1-Yr. Sales Change: 3.5%
Phone: 612-646-4501	HR: Kathleen A. Larkin	Exchange: Nasdaq
Fax: 612-649-1348	Employees: 2,253	Symbol: MRLL

Printing - transactional documents, catalogs, directories & technical manuals

 **See page 280 for a full profile of this company.**

METATEC CORPORATION

7001 Metatec Blvd.	CEO: Jeffrey M. Wilkins	1995 Sales: $39.3 million
Dublin, OH 43017	CFO: William H. Largent	1-Yr. Sales Change: 36.0%
Phone: 614-761-2000	HR: Barry Rellaford	Exchange: Nasdaq
Fax: 614-761-4258	Employees: 340	Symbol: META

Computers - CD-ROM manufacturing & distribution; software development & media preparation services for the creation of custom CD-ROMs

METRO GLOBAL MEDIA, INC.

1060 Park Ave.	CEO: Kenneth Guarino	1995 Sales: $17.8 million
Cranston, RI 02910	CFO: T. Blair	1-Yr. Sales Change: 38.0%
Phone: 401-942-7876	HR: Ann Goldman	Exchange: Nasdaq (SC)
Fax: 401-943-6363	Employees: 101	Symbol: STPN

Motion pictures & services - adult movies, videos & magazines

METRO NETWORKS, INC.

2700 Post Oak Blvd., Ste. 1400	CEO: David I. Saperstein	1995 Sales: $72.4 million
Houston, TX 77056	CFO: Curtis H. Coleman	1-Yr. Sales Change: 20.7%
Phone: 713-621-2800	HR: Danyce Rundell	Ownership: Privately Held
Fax: 713-621-5841	Employees: 1,374	

Broadcasting - traffic reporting (#1 in US) & local news, sports, weather & other information reporting services for the TV & radio broadcast industries

METRO-GOLDWYN-MAYER, INC.

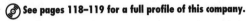

2500 Broadway
Santa Monica, CA 90404
Phone: 310-449-3000
Fax: 310-449-3100

CEO: Frank G. Mancuso
CFO: Daniel Rosett
HR: Steven Shaw
Employees: 700

1995 Sales: $270.0 million
1-Yr. Sales Change: (71.2%)
Ownership: Subsidiary

Motion pictures & services - production (subsidiary of Credit Lyonnais)

See pages 118–119 for a full profile of this company.

METROMEDIA INTERNATIONAL GROUP, INC.

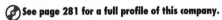

945 E. Paces Ferry Rd., Ste. 2210
Atlanta, GA 30326
Phone: 404-261-6190
Fax: 404-524-4713

CEO: John D. Phillips
CFO: Silvia Kessel
HR: —
Employees: 289

1995 Sales: $138.9 million
1-Yr. Sales Change: (74.8%)
Exchange: AMEX
Symbol: MMG

Diversified operations - lawn & garden products (Snapper); entertainment (Orion Pictures); wireless communications services in Eastern Europe

See page 281 for a full profile of this company.

MICROGRAFX, INC.

1303 Arapaho Rd.
Richardson, TX 75081
Phone: 214-234-1769
Fax: 214-994-6475

CEO: J. Paul Grayson
CFO: Gregory A. Peters
HR: Mary Boyd
Employees: 239

1995 Sales: $60.4 million
1-Yr. Sales Change: (0.2%)
Exchange: Nasdaq
Symbol: MGXI

Computers - high-powered graphics software for business, professional & home markets

MICROLEAGUE MULTIMEDIA, INC.

750 Dawson Dr.
Newark, DE 19713
Phone: 302-368-9990
Fax: 302-368-5164

CEO: Neil B. Swartz
CFO: Peter Flanagan
HR: —
Employees: 54

1995 Sales: $5.0 million
1-Yr. Sales Change: 78.6%
Exchange: Nasdaq (SC)
Symbol: MLMI

Computers - interactive multimedia computer software for entertainment & education

MICROLYTICS, INC.

2 Tobey Village Office Park
Pittsford, NY 14534
Phone: 716-248-3875
Fax: 716-248-5612

CEO: Robert C. Harris Jr.
CFO: —
HR: Carolyn Hotchkiss
Employees: 35

1995 Sales: $2.8 million
1-Yr. Sales Change: (60.2%)
Exchange: OTC

Publishing - electronic telephone directories (MicroPages), electronic directory assistance products & Internet advertising media

MICROSOFT CORPORATION

One Microsoft Way	CEO: William H. Gates III	1995 Sales: $5,937.0 million
Redmond, WA 98052-6399	CFO: Michael W. Brown	1-Yr. Sales Change: 27.7%
Phone: 206-882-8080	HR: Michael R. Murray	Exchange: Nasdaq
Fax: 206-883-8101	Employees: 17,801	Symbol: MSFT

Computers - operating systems manufacture (#1 worldwide: MS-DOS, Windows 95); application & language software, CD-ROMs (Microsoft Encarta, Microsoft Flight Simulator); publishing (Slate); news (MSNBC)

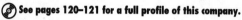 **See pages 120–121 for a full profile of this company.**

MIDISOFT CORPORATION

1605 NW Sammamish Rd., Ste. 205	CEO: Larry Foster	1995 Sales: $5.4 million
Issaquah, WA 98027	CFO: Melinda Bryden	1-Yr. Sales Change: (6.9%)
Phone: 206-391-3610	HR: —	Exchange: Nasdaq (SC)
Fax: 206-391-3422	Employees: 51	Symbol: MIDI

Computers - interactive multimedia audio software

MIDLAND INDEPENDENT NEWSPAPERS

28 Colmore Circus, Queensway	CEO: Chris J. Oakley	1995 Sales: $152.1 million
Birmingham B4 6AX, UK	CFO: John Whitehouse	1-Yr. Sales Change: 9.8%
Phone: +44-121-236-3366	HR: —	Exchange: London
Fax: +44-121-233-3958	Employees: 1,904	

Publishing - regional newspapers (over 30), magazines & direct marketing

MIRROR GROUP PLC

One Canada Sq., Canary Wharf	CEO: D. J. Montgomery	1995 Sales: $731.3 million
London E14 5AP, UK	CFO: C. J. Allwood	1-Yr. Sales Change: (2.7%)
Phone: +44-171-510-3000	HR: —	Exchange: London
Fax: +44-171-293-3360	Employees: 2,907	

Publishing - newspapers in the UK (*Daily Mirror, Daily Record, Sunday Mirror, Sunday Mail, The Sporting Life*)

MODEM MEDIA

228 Saugatuck Ave.	CEO: Gerald M. O'Connell	1995 Sales: $7.5 million
Westport, CT 06880	CFO: Peter Massey	1-Yr. Sales Change: 127.3%
Phone: 203-341-5200	HR: Marilyn Fidler	Ownership: Privately Held
Fax: 203-341-5260	Employees: 70	

Advertising agency specializing in developing corporate web sites (AT&T, Zima)

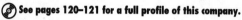 **See page 282 for a full profile of this company.**

MOOVIES, INC.

3172 Wade Hampton Blvd.
Taylors, SC 29687
Phone: 864-213-1700
Fax: 803-292-0364

Retail - video specialty stores

CEO: John L. Taylor
CFO: F. Andrew Mitchell
HR: Kelly McCurley
Employees: 1,043

1995 Sales: $24.7 million
1-Yr. Sales Change: 461.4%
Exchange: Nasdaq
Symbol: MOOV

MORE O'FERRALL

33 Golden Sq.
London W1R 3PA, UK
Phone: +44-171-287-6100
Fax: +44-171-287-9160

Advertising - outdoor

CEO: Lord Lane of Horsell
CFO: Brian P. Turnbull
HR: —
Employees: 637

1995 Sales: $135.1 million
1-Yr. Sales Change: 18.3%
Exchange: London

MORNINGSTAR, INC.

225 W. Wacker Dr.
Chicago, IL 60606-1224
Phone: 312-696-6000
Fax: 312-696-6001

CEO: Joseph Mansueto
CFO: Patrick Geddes
HR: Liz Michaels
Employees: 350

1995 Est. Sales: $33.0 mil.
1-Yr. Sales Change: 3.1%
Ownership: Privately Held

Publishing - information on mutual funds, annuities & stocks, available in print, diskette, CD-ROM & online formats

 See page 283 for a full profile of this company.

MORRIS COMMUNICATIONS CORPORATION

PO Box 1928
Augusta, GA 30903
Phone: 706-724-0851
Fax: 706-722-7125

CEO: William S. Morris III
CFO: William Herman
HR: Bill Beauchamp
Employees: 5,140

1995 Est. Sales: $425.0 mil.
1-Yr. Sales Change: 2.2%
Ownership: Privately Held

Publishing - newspapers (32 dailies) & magazines; radio & TV broadcasting; outdoor advertising; computer services

MOVIE GALLERY, INC.

739 W. Main St.
Dothan, AL 36301
Phone: 334-677-2108
Fax: 334-677-1169

CEO: Joe T. Malugen
CFO: J. Steven Roy
HR: Jim Pongonis
Employees: 2,159

1995 Sales: $123.1 million
1-Yr. Sales Change: 218.9%
Exchange: Nasdaq
Symbol: MOVI

Retail - videocassette & video game sales & rental primarily in small Southeastern towns (#3 in the US)

MOVIEFONE, INC.

4 World Trade Ctr., Ste. 5290	CEO: Andrew R. Jarecki	1995 Sales: $21.4 million
New York, NY 10048	CFO: Adam H. Slutsky	1-Yr. Sales Change: (5.3%)
Phone: 212-504-7442	HR: Sandy Hughes	Exchange: Nasdaq
Fax: 212-504-7567	Employees: 59	Symbol: MOFN

Business services - interactive telephone advertising, Internet movie preview site, information & ticketing services to the motion picture industry

MTS INC.

2500 Del Monte St., Bldg. C	CEO: Russell M. Solomon	1995 Sales: $950.0 million
West Sacramento, CA 95691	CFO: Dee Searson	1-Yr. Sales Change: 14.5%
Phone: 916-373-2500	HR: Shauna Pompei	Ownership: Privately Held
Fax: 916-373-2535	Employees: 7,600	

Retail - records, books & videos (Tower Records)

 **See page 284 for a full profile of this company.**

MULTI-COLOR CORPORATION

4575 Eastern Ave.	CEO: John C. Court	1996 Sales: $55.4 million
Cincinnati, OH 45226	CFO: William R. Cochran	1-Yr. Sales Change: (10.4%)
Phone: 513-321-5381	HR: Pete Turner	Exchange: Nasdaq
Fax: 513-321-7659	Employees: 376	Symbol: LABL

Printing - printed labels

MULTI-MARKET RADIO, INC.

150 E. 58th St., 19th Fl.	CEO: Bruce Morrow	1995 Sales: $18.3 million
New York, NY 10155	CFO: Jerry D. Emlet	1-Yr. Sales Change: 157.7%
Phone: 212-407-9150	HR: —	Exchange: Nasdaq
Fax: 212-753-3188	Employees: 200	Symbol: RDIOA

Broadcasting - radio (3 AM & 13 FM stations)

MULTI-MEDIA TUTORIAL SERVICE

205 Kings Hwy.	CEO: Morris Berger	1996 Sales: $9.2 million
Brooklyn, NY 11223	CFO: Robert Selevan	1-Yr. Sales Change: 100.0%
Phone: 718-234-0404	HR: —	Exchange: Nasdaq (SC)
	Employees: 90	Symbol: MMTS

Computers - tutorial & educational programs in videotape & CD-ROM formats

MUSICLAND STORES CORPORATION

10400 Yellow Circle Dr.	CEO: Jack W. Eugster	1995 Sales: $1,722.6 million
Minnetonka, MN 55343	CFO: Reid Johnson	1-Yr. Sales Change: 16.5%
Phone: 612-931-8000	HR: Jay Landauer	Exchange: NYSE
Fax: 612-931-8300	Employees: 17,000	Symbol: MLG

Retail - prerecorded music & video (Musicland, Sam Goody)

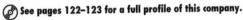 **See pages 122–123 for a full profile of this company.**

MUZAK, INC.

2901 Third Ave., Ste. 400	CEO: John R. Jester	1995 Sales: $86.9 million
Seattle, WA 98121	CFO: Kirk A. Collamer	1-Yr. Sales Change: 4.2%
Phone: 206-633-3000	HR: Matthew McTee	Ownership: Privately Held
Fax: 206-633-6210	Employees: 715	

Business services - music, video, data, advertising & other services to subscribing businesses worldwide, including 16 channels on General Electric's K2 direct broadcast satellite

N2K INC.

435 Devon Park Dr., Ste. 600	CEO: Lawrence Rosen	1995 Est. Sales: $25.0 mil.
Wayne, PA 19087	CFO: Bruce Johnson	1-Yr. Sales Change: 45.3%
Phone: 610-293-4700	HR: —	Ownership: Privately Held
Fax: 610-341-9660	Employees: 86	

Computers - online entertainment & information services

NATIONAL BROADCASTING COMPANY INC.

30 Rockefeller Plaza	CEO: Robert C. Wright	1995 Sales: $3,919.0 million
New York, NY 10112-0002	CFO: Warren C. Jenson	1-Yr. Sales Change: 16.6%
Phone: 212-664-4444	HR: Edward L. Scanlon	Ownership: Subsidiary
Fax: 212-664-6193	Employees: 5,000	

Broadcasting - TV network (NBC) serving more than 200 affiliated stations; TV program production; cable TV stations (CNBC, America's Talking, NBC Super Channel; Canal de Noticias NBC) (subsidiary of GE)

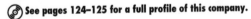 **See pages 124–125 for a full profile of this company.**

NATIONAL GEOGRAPHIC SOCIETY

1145 17th St. NW	CEO: Gilbert M. Grosvenor	1995 Sales: $456.0 million
Washington, DC 20036	CFO: H. Gregory Platts	1-Yr. Sales Change: 8.8%
Phone: 202-857-7000	HR: John Blodger	Ownership: Not-for-profit
Fax: 202-775-6141	Employees: 1,551	

Publishing - nature & cultural magazine; educational organization

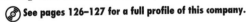 **See pages 126–127 for a full profile of this company.**

NATIONAL MEDIA CORPORATION

1700 Walnut St.	CEO: Mark P. Hershhorn	1996 Sales: $292.6 million
Philadelphia, PA 19103	CFO: Constantinos I. Costalas	1-Yr. Sales Change: 66.1%
Phone: 215-772-5000	HR: Sabrina Childs	Exchange: NYSE
Fax: 215-772-5038	Employees: 178	Symbol: NM

TV production & programming - TV infomercials

NATIONAL RECORD MART, INC.

507 Forest Ave.	CEO: William A. Teitelbaum	1995 Sales: $95.7 million
Carnegie, PA 15106	CFO: Theresa Carlise	1-Yr. Sales Change: 18.7%
Phone: 412-276-6200	HR: —	Exchange: Nasdaq
Fax: 412-276-6201	Employees: 1,337	Symbol: NRMI

Retail - record stores, home entertainment products, compact discs, prerecorded audio- & videocassettes & related accessories

NATIONWIDE ADVERTISING SERVICE, INC.

1228 Euclid Ave.	CEO: John W. Graham	1995 Sales: $37.5 million
Cleveland, OH 44115	CFO: Jim Miller	1-Yr. Sales Change: 30.7%
Phone: 216-579-0300	HR: Richard McAteer	Ownership: Privately Held
Fax: 216-687-6115	Employees: 120	

Full-service recruitment advertising agency

NETCOUNT, LLC

1645 N. Vine St., Level 4	CEO: Paul Grant	1995 Sales: —
Los Angeles, CA 90028	CFO: Jim Spence	1-Yr. Sales Change: —
Phone: 213-848-5480	HR: —	Ownership: Privately Held
Fax: 213-848-5750	Employees: 25	

Computers - web site activity measurement services

NETS INC.

25 First St.	CEO: Jim Manzi	1995 Est. Sales: $25.0 mil.
Cambridge, MA 02141	CFO: Mike Stubler	1-Yr. Sales Change: —
Phone: 617-252-5000	HR: Russ Campanello	Ownership: Privately Held
Fax: 617-252-5551	Employees: 150	

Computers - Internet-based commerce system that links sellers & buyers (Industry.Net); Internet business-information service (AT&T Business Network)

NETSCAPE COMMUNICATIONS CORPORATION

501 E. Middlefield Rd.
Mountain View, CA 94043
Phone: 415-254-1900
Fax: 415-528-4125

CEO: James L. Barksdale
CFO: Peter L. S. Currie
HR: Kandis Malefyt
Employees: 257

1995 Sales: $80.7 million
1-Yr. Sales Change: 11,429%
Exchange: Nasdaq
Symbol: NSCP

Computers - Internet navigation software (Netscape Navigator), netsite server software & transaction security software

NETTER DIGITAL ENTERTAINMENT, INC.

5200 Lankershim Blvd., Ste. 280
North Hollywood, CA 91601
Phone: 818-753-1990
Fax: 818-753-7655

CEO: Douglas Netter
CFO: Margaret M. D'Angelo
HR: —
Employees: 140

1995 Sales: $19.3 million
1-Yr. Sales Change: 8.4%
Exchange: Nasdaq (SC)
Symbol: NETT

Motion pictures & services - science-fiction films that combine live action with computer graphics

NEW IMAGE INDUSTRIES INC.

2283 Cosmos Ct.
Carlsbad, CA 92009
Phone: 619-930-9900
Fax: 619-930-9999

CEO: Dewey F. Edmunds
CFO: Hal Orr
HR: Tracy Chandler
Employees: 86

1995 Sales: $31.6 million
1-Yr. Sales Change: —
Exchange: Nasdaq
Symbol: NIIS

Computers - graphics

NEW WORLD COMMUNICATIONS GROUP INCORPORATED

3200 Windy Hill Rd., Ste. 1100-West
Atlanta, GA 30339
Phone: 770-955-0045
Fax: 770-563-9600

CEO: William C. Bevins
CFO: Joseph P. Page
HR: Jim Gorman
Employees: 2,700

1995 Sales: $605.0 million
1-Yr. Sales Change: 52.4%
Exchange: Nasdaq
Symbol: NWCG

Broadcasting - TV (7 NBC affiliates & one Fox affiliate); TV programming & distribution; film & TV library

See page 285 for a full profile of this company.

THE NEW YORK PUBLIC LIBRARY

Fifth Ave. & 42nd St.
New York, NY 10018
Phone: 212-930-0800
Fax: 212-768-7439

CEO: Paul LeClerc
CFO: Michael Zavelle
HR: Priscilla J. Southon
Employees: 3,608

1996 Est. Sales: $197.5 mil.
1-Yr. Sales Change: 1.7%
Ownership: Privately Held

Public library (#1 worldwide) with 4 research centers & 83 branches in Manhattan, the Bronx & Staten Island

THE NEW YORK TIMES COMPANY

229 W. 43rd St.
New York, NY 10036
Phone: 212-556-1234
Fax: 212-556-4011

CEO: Arthur "Punch" Sulzberger
CFO: Diane P. Baker
HR: Katharine P. Darrow
Employees: 12,300

1995 Sales: $2,409.4 million
1-Yr. Sales Change: 2.2%
Exchange: AMEX
Symbol: NYTA

Publishing - newspapers (*The New York Times*, *The Boston Globe*) & magazines (*Golf Digest*); broadcasting; information services

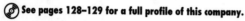 **See pages 128–129 for a full profile of this company.**

NEWS COMMUNICATIONS, INC.

174-15 Horace Harding Expwy.
Fresh Meadows, NY 11365
Phone: 718-357-3380
Fax: 718-357-4833

CEO: Michael Schenkler
CFO: Robert Berkowitz
HR: Evelyn Spiegel
Employees: 307

1995 Sales: $18.1 million
1-Yr. Sales Change: 32.1%
Exchange: Nasdaq (SC)
Symbol: NCOM

Advertising - community newspapers & related target-audience publications

THE NEWS CORPORATION LIMITED

2 Holt St.
2010 Sydney, New South Wales, Australia
Phone: +61-2-288-3000
Fax: +61-2-288-2300

CEO: Keith R. Murdoch
CFO: David F. DeVoe
HR: —
Employees: 26,600

1995 Sales: $8,641.0 million
1-Yr. Sales Change: 4.8%
Exchange: NYSE
Symbol: NWS (ADR)

Publishing - newspapers (*The Sun*, *The Times*), magazines (*TV Guide*) & inserts; film & TV programming (*The X-Files*, *Melrose Place*); book publishing (HarperCollins)

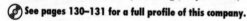 **See pages 130–131 for a full profile of this company.**

NEWS INTERNATIONAL PLC

PO Box 495, Virginia St.
London E1 9XY, UK
Phone: +44-171-782-6000
Fax: +44-171-895-9020

CEO: L. Hinton
CFO: R. Linford
HR: —
Employees: 4,163

1995 Sales: $1,340.9 million
1-Yr. Sales Change: 14.6%
Exchange: London

Publishing - national newspapers in the UK; satellite TV broadcasting facilities; transportation services

NIGHTINGALE-CONANT CORPORATION

7300 N. Lehigh Ave.
Niles, IL 60714
Phone: 847-647-0300
Fax: 847-647-7145

CEO: Vic Conant
CFO: Sid Lemer
HR: Michael Burgess
Employees: 310

1995 Sales: $70.8 million
1-Yr. Sales Change: 10.5%
Ownership: Privately Held

Publishing - motivational audio programs

NIPPON TELEVISION NETWORK CORPORATION

14, Niban-cho, Chiyoda-ku
Tokyo 102-40, Japan
Phone: +81-3-5275-4139
Fax: +81-3-5275-4008

CEO: Seiichiro Ujiie
CFO: —
HR: —
Employees: 1,361

1995 Sales: $2,413.0 million
1-Yr. Sales Change: 6.1%
Exchange: Tokyo

Broadcasting - TV

(🅰) **See pages 132–133 for a full profile of this company.**

NORTHWEST TELEPRODUCTIONS, INC.

4455 W. 77th St.
Minneapolis, MN 55435
Phone: 612-835-4455
Fax: 612-835-0971

CEO: Robert C. Mitchell
CFO: James N. Steffen
HR: —
Employees: 120

1995 Sales: $13.2 million
1-Yr. Sales Change: (4.3%)
Exchange: Nasdaq
Symbol: NWTL

TV production & services - videotape commercials & industrial, educational & government programs;
planning, recording, editing & duplication services

NRJ SA

22, rue Boileau
75016 Paris, France
Phone: +33-1-40-71-40-00
Fax: +33-1-40-71-40-40

CEO: A. Weill
CFO: Luc Marot
HR: —
Employees: 623

1995 Sales: $162.8 million
1-Yr. Sales Change: 27.8%
Exchange: Paris

Radio production & advertising sales

NTN COMMUNICATIONS, INC.

5966 La Place Ct.
Carlsbad, CA 92008
Phone: 619-438-7400
Fax: 619-438-7470

CEO: Patrick J. Downs
CFO: Ronald E. Hogan
HR: —
Employees: 275

1995 Sales: $31.8 million
1-Yr. Sales Change: 29.3%
Exchange: AMEX
Symbol: NTN

TV production & programming - interactive subscription-based TV network (NTN Network)

N W AYER INC.

825 Eighth Ave.
New York, NY 10019
Phone: 212-474-5000
Fax: 212-474-5400

CEO: Beth Gordon
CFO: Anthony O'Gorman
HR: Jane Beale
Employees: 525

1995 Sales: $87.1 million
1-Yr. Sales Change: (11.8%)
Ownership: Privately Held

Advertising - media planning & buying (The Media Edge, Inc.)

NYNEX CABLECOMMS

The Tolworth Tower, Ewell Rd.
KT6 7ED Surbiton, Surrey, UK
Phone: +44-181-873-5450
Fax: +44-181-873-5256

Cable TV & telecommunications

CEO: John F. Killian
CFO: N. P. Mearing-Smith
HR: —
Employees: 2,964

1995 Sales: $84.8 million
1-Yr. Sales Change: 32.1%
Exchange: Nasdaq
Symbol: NYNCY (ADR)

OMNICOM GROUP INC.

437 Madison Ave.
New York, NY 10022
Phone: 212-415-3600
Fax: 212-415-3530

CEO: Bruce Crawford
CFO: Fred J. Meyer
HR: Leslie Chiocco
Employees: 19,400

1995 Sales: $2,257.5 million
1-Yr. Sales Change: 28.5%
Exchange: NYSE
Symbol: OMC

Advertising (BBDO Worldwide, DDB Needham, TBWA)

 See pages 134–135 for a full profile of this company.

ONESOURCE INFORMATION SERVICES INC.

150 Cambridge Park Dr.
Cambridge, MA 02140
Phone: 617-441-7000
Fax: 617-441-7058

Computers - databases on CD-ROM

CEO: Dan Schimmel
CFO: Roy Landon
HR: —
Employees: 200

1995 Sales: $30.0 million
1-Yr. Sales Change: —
Ownership: Privately Held

OPINION RESEARCH CORPORATION

23 Orchard Rd.
Skillman, NJ 08558
Phone: 908-281-5100
Fax: 908-281-5105

CEO: Michael R. Cooper
CFO: John F. Short
HR: Judi Fabian
Employees: 2,902

1995 Sales: $44.1 million
1-Yr. Sales Change: 10.8%
Exchange: Nasdaq
Symbol: ORCI

Business services - market analysis & public opinion polling

ORYX PRESS

4041 N. Central Ave.
Phoenix, AZ 85012
Phone: 602-265-2651
Fax: 602-265-6250

CEO: Phyllis B. Steckler
CFO: Terrence Basom
HR: Wilma Froeschke
Employees: 53

1995 Est. Sales: $5.0 million
1-Yr. Sales Change: —
Ownership: Privately Held

Publishing - books; electronic databases (BioScan)

OSBORN COMMUNICATIONS CORPORATION

130 Mason St.
Greenwich, CT 06830
Phone: 203-629-0905
Fax: 203-629-1749

CEO: Frank D. Osborn
CFO: Thomas S. Douglas
HR: —
Employees: 322

1995 Sales: $39.1 million
1-Yr. Sales Change: 14.7%
Exchange: Nasdaq
Symbol: OSBN

Broadcasting - radio (16 AM & FM stations)

PADDOCK PUBLICATIONS, INC.

155 E. Algonquin Rd.
Arlington Heights, IL 60005
Phone: 847-427-4300

CEO: Stuart Paddock Jr.
CFO: Robert Donahue
HR: Judi Orgell
Employees: 600

1995 Sales: $76.0 million
1-Yr. Sales Change: 7.0%
Ownership: Privately Held

Publishing - newspapers (*Daily Herald*)

PAGES, INC.

801 94th Ave. North
St. Petersburg, FL 33702
Phone: 813-578-3300
Fax: 813-578-3100

CEO: S. Robert Davis
CFO: Charles R. Davis
HR: Steve Canan
Employees: 831

1995 Sales: $72.8 million
1-Yr. Sales Change: (7.8%)
Exchange: Nasdaq
Symbol: PAGZ

Publishing - children's books, audio- & videocassettes & computer software; incentive/recognition awards

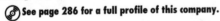 **See page 286 for a full profile of this company.**

PARK COMMUNICATIONS, INC.

Terrace Hill
Ithaca, NY 14850
Phone: 607-272-9020
Fax: 607-272-6057

CEO: Wright M. Thomas
CFO: Randel N. Stair
HR: —
Employees: 2,100

1995 Est. Sales: $200.0 mil.
1-Yr. Sales Change: 8.2%
Ownership: Privately Held

Broadcasting - 9 TV stations, 11 AM & 11 FM radio stations; 30 daily newspapers, 17 Sunday newspapers, 28 nondaily newspapers & 46 nondaily controlled distribution publications

THE PAUL ALLEN GROUP

110 110th Ave. NE, Ste. 530
Bellevue, WA 98004
Phone: 206-453-6101
Fax: 206-453-1985

CEO: Vern Raburn
CFO: Vern Raburn
HR: Pam Faber
Employees: 60

1996 Sales: —
1-Yr. Sales Change: —
Ownership: Privately Held

Financial - investments in high-tech companies, including Asymetrix, C/Net, DreamWorks SKG, Egghead, Starwave, & Ticketmaster

PAXSON COMMUNICATIONS CORPORATION

18401 US Highway 19 North	CEO: Lowell W. Paxson	1995 Sales: $103.1 million
Clearwater, FL 34624	CFO: Arthur D. Tek	1-Yr. Sales Change: 66.0%
Phone: 407-659-4122	HR: R. Paxson	Exchange: AMEX
Fax: 407-659-4252	Employees: 626	Symbol: PXN

Broadcasting - radio (7 AM & 7 FM stations in Florida markets)

PEACHES ENTERTAINMENT CORPORATION

1180 E. Hallandale Beach Blvd.	CEO: Allan Wolk	1995 Est. Sales: $25.0 mil.
Hallandale, FL 33009	CFO: Jason Wolk	1-Yr. Sales Change: (26.5%)
Phone: 954-454-5554	HR: Jason Wolk	Ownership: Privately Held
Fax: 954-454-8828	Employees: —	

Retail - prerecorded music

PEARSON PLC

3 Burlington Gardens	CEO: Frank Barlow	1995 Sales: $2,931.1 million
London W1X 1LE, UK	CFO: John Makinson	1-Yr. Sales Change: 22.2%
Phone: +44-171-411-2000	HR: Melanie Zebler	Exchange: Pink Sheets
Fax: +44-171-411-2390	Employees: 19,422	Symbol: PRSNY (ADR)

Publishing - books (Penguin, Addison-Wesley) & periodicals (*The Financial Times*, Westminster Press, Penguin, 50% of *The Economist*); TV (Thames)

 See pages 136–137 for a full profile of this company.

PEGASUS COMMUNICATIONS CORPORATION

100 Matsonford Rd., Ste. 454	CEO: Marshall W. Pagon	1995 Sales: $32.1 million
Radnor, PA 19087	CFO: Robert N. Verdecchio	1-Yr. Sales Change: 13.8%
Phone: 610-341-1801	HR: Polly Epright	Ownership: Privately Held
Fax: 610-341-1835	Employees: 235	

Broadcasting - TV (5 Fox affiliate stations); DIRECTV access for rural areas of Connecticut, Massachusetts, New Hampshire & New York; cable TV systems in Puerto Rico & New England

PEOPLE'S CHOICE TV CORP.

2 Corporate Dr.	CEO: Matthew Oristano	1995 Sales: $26.0 million
Shelton, CT 06484	CFO: Charles F. Schwartz	1-Yr. Sales Change: 106.3%
Phone: 203-925-7900	HR: Pamela Yager	Exchange: Nasdaq
Fax: 203-929-1454	Employees: 521	Symbol: PCTV

Cable TV

PETERSEN PUBLISHING COMPANY

6420 Wilshire Blvd.
Los Angeles, CA 90048
Phone: 213-782-2000
Fax: 213-782-2467

CEO: Robert E. Petersen
CFO: Richard Willis
HR: Leo La Rew
Employees: 763

1995 Est. Sales: $300.0 mil.
1-Yr. Sales Change: (1.3%)
Ownership: Privately Held

Publishing - magazines (*4-Wheel & Off-Road*, *All About You*, *Guns & Ammo*, *Hot Rod*, *Motor Trend*, *Mountain Bike Magazine*, *Sassy*, *Skin Diver*, *'Teen*); real estate operations; art gallery

PHARMACEUTICAL MARKETING SERVICES INC.

2394 E. Camelback Rd.
Phoenix, AZ 85016
Phone: 602-381-9800
Fax: 602-381-9650

CEO: Dennis M. J. Turner
CFO: Lyle R. Scritsmier
HR: Jerry Strimbu
Employees: 651

1995 Sales: $129.8 million
1-Yr. Sales Change: 13.9%
Exchange: Nasdaq
Symbol: PMRX

Business services - integrated marketing services generated from proprietary databases containing health care, pharmaceutical, managed care & medical prescriber data

PHILLIPS PUBLISHING INTERNATIONAL, INC.

7811 Montrose Rd.
Potomac, MD 20814
Phone: 301-340-2100
Fax: 301-251-3758

CEO: Thomas Phillips
CFO: Stephen Peck
HR: —
Employees: 900

1995 Est. Sales: $170.0 mil.
1-Yr. Sales Change: 17.2%
Ownership: Privately Held

Publishing - newsletters (#1 in the US), magazines & directories for business & consumer markets

PITTWAY CORPORATION

200 S. Wacker Dr., Ste. 700
Chicago, IL 60606-5802
Phone: 312-831-1070
Fax: 312-831-0808

CEO: King Harris
CFO: Paul R. Gauvreau
HR: —
Employees: 5,400

1995 Sales: $945.7 million
1-Yr. Sales Change: 21.6%
Exchange: AMEX
Symbol: PRYA

Diversified operations - trade magazine publishing (Penton); burglar & fire alarms (Ademco Security); real estate

PIXAR

1001 W. Cutting Blvd.
Richmond, CA 94804
Phone: 510-236-4000
Fax: 510-236-0388

CEO: Steven P. Jobs
CFO: Lawrence B. Levy
HR: Lisa Ellis
Employees: 167

1995 Sales: $12.1 million
1-Yr. Sales Change: 116.1%
Exchange: Nasdaq
Symbol: PIXR

Motion pictures & services - digital animated features (*Toy Story*), CD-ROM titles & related products

(◉) **See page 287 for a full profile of this company.**

PLATINUM ENTERTAINMENT, INC.

2001 Butterfield Rd., Ste. 1400	CEO: Steve Devick	1995 Sales: $11.1 million
Downers Grove, IL 60515	CFO: Douglas C. Laux	1-Yr. Sales Change: 6.7%
Phone: 708-769-0033	HR: —	Exchange: Nasdaq
Fax: 708-769-0049	Employees: 75	Symbol: PTET

Music production & publishing - gospel music recordings

PLAYBOY ENTERPRISES, INC.

680 N. Lake Shore Dr.	CEO: Christie Hefner	1995 Sales: $247.2 million
Chicago, IL 60611	CFO: Hugh M. Hefner	1-Yr. Sales Change: 12.9%
Phone: 312-751-8000	HR: Denise M. Bindelglass	Exchange: NYSE
Fax: 312-751-2818	Employees: 593	Symbol: PLA

Publishing - periodicals (*Playboy*); cable TV programming; catalog & product marketing

(☛) **See page 288 for a full profile of this company.**

PLENUM PUBLISHING CORPORATION

233 Spring St.	CEO: Martin E. Tash	1995 Sales: $52.2 million
New York, NY 10013	CFO: Ghanshyam A. Patel	1-Yr. Sales Change: (0.6%)
Phone: 212-620-8000	HR: —	Exchange: Nasdaq
Fax: 212-463-0742	Employees: 300	Symbol: PLEN

Publishing - books, journals & database products in scientific, medical & technical fields; English translations of foreign journals; database of chemical patents

POINTCAST, INCORPORATED

10101 N. De Anza Blvd.	CEO: Christopher R. Hassett	1995 Sales: —
Cupertino, CA 95014	CFO: John P. Jewett	1-Yr. Sales Change: —
Phone: 408-253-0894	HR: —	Ownership: Privately Held
Fax: 408-253-1062	Employees: —	

Computers - personalized news, stock quotes, weather & other information services transmitted via the Internet (The PointCast Network)

POLIGRAFICI EDITORIALE SPA

Via Enrico Mattei, N. 106	CEO: Andrea Riffeser	1995 Sales: $327.4 million
40138 Bologna, Italy	CFO: —	1-Yr. Sales Change: 9.1%
Phone: +39-5153-6111	HR: —	Exchange: Milan
Fax: +39-5153-64-44	Employees: 1,173	

Publishing - newspapers

POLYGRAM N.V.

Gerrit van der Veenlaan 4
3743 DN Baarn, The Netherlands
Phone: +31-2154-19911
Fax: +31-2154-16400

CEO: Alain Levy
CFO: Jan Cook
HR: —
Employees: 12,002

1995 Sales: $5,499.0 million
1-Yr. Sales Change: 15.7%
Exchange: NYSE
Symbol: PLG (ADR)

Music production & publishing - music recordings, including pop & classical; film & TV production

 **See pages 138–139 for a full profile of this company.**

PORTSMOUTH & SUNDERLAND NEWSPAPERS PLC

Buckton House, 37 Abingdon Rd.
London W8 6AH, UK
Phone: +44-171-937-9741
Fax: +44-171-937-1479

CEO: C. D. Brims
CFO: G. H. Toop
HR: —
Employees: 2,140

1995 Sales: $194.5 million
1-Yr. Sales Change: 7.1%
Exchange: London

Publishing - newspapers

POWELL'S BOOKS, INC.

7 NW Ninth Ave.
Portland, OR 97209
Phone: 503-228-4651
Fax: 503-228-0540

CEO: Michael Powell
CFO: Betty Eby
HR: Sylvie Horne
Employees: 387

1996 Sales: $32.0 million
1-Yr. Sales Change: 10.3%
Ownership: Privately Held

Retail - bookstores in the Portland, OR, area

PRACTICE MANAGEMENT INFORMATION CORPORATION

4727 Wilshire Blvd.
Los Angeles, CA 90010
Phone: 213-954-0224
Fax: 213-954-0253

CEO: James B. Davis
CFO: James B. Davis
HR: —
Employees: 45

1995 Sales: $13.0 million
1-Yr. Sales Change: (1.5%)
Ownership: Privately Held

Publishing - medical coding, reimbursement & practice management books

PREMIERE RADIO NETWORKS, INC.

15260 Ventura Blvd., 5th Fl.
Sherman Oaks, CA 91403-5339
Phone: 818-377-5300
Fax: 818-377-5333

CEO: Stephen C. Lehman
CFO: Dan Yukelson
HR: —
Employees: 85

1995 Sales: $20.8 million
1-Yr. Sales Change: 30.0%
Exchange: Nasdaq
Symbol: PRNIA

Radio production & programming - comedy, entertainment & music-related programs & services

PRICE COMMUNICATIONS CORPORATION

45 Rockefeller Plaza	CEO: Robert Price	1995 Sales: $29.2 million
New York, NY 10020	CFO: Kim I. Pressman	1-Yr. Sales Change: 21.7%
Phone: 212-757-5600	HR: Jim Kreps	Exchange: AMEX
Fax: 212-397-3755	Employees: 222	Symbol: PR

Broadcasting - TV (one ABC affiliate & 3 NBC affiliates)

PRIMARK CORPORATION

1000 Winter St., Ste. 4300N	CEO: Joseph E. Kasputys	1995 Sales: $617.3 million
Waltham, MA 02154	CFO: Steven H. Curran	1-Yr. Sales Change: 29.4%
Phone: 617-466-6611	HR: Diane Robesen	Exchange: NYSE
Fax: 617-890-6187	Employees: 5,131	Symbol: PMK

Computers - information services to the US government (The Analytic Sciences Corp.); financial information services (Datastream); weather imaging systems & software (WSI); aircraft maintenance

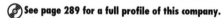 **See page 289 for a full profile of this company.**

PRIMESTAR PARTNERS L.P.

3 Bala Plaza West	CEO: James L. Gray	1995 Est. Sales: $400 mil.
Bala Cynwyd, PA 19004	CFO: Larry Epstein	1-Yr. Sales Change: 400%
Phone: 610-660-6100	HR: Barbara Caprice	Ownership: Partnership
Fax: 610-660-6112	Employees: 75	

Cable TV - digital satellite programming (partnership of Comcast, Continental Cablevision, Cox, Newhouse Broadcasting, TCI, Time Warner & General Electric)

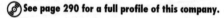 **See page 290 for a full profile of this company.**

PRINTWARE, INC.

1270 Eagan Industrial Rd.	CEO: Daniel A. Baker	1995 Sales: $8.4 million
St. Paul, MN 55121	CFO: Thomas W. Petschauer	1-Yr. Sales Change: 27.3%
Phone: 612-456-1400	HR: Cory Lomen	Ownership: Privately Held
Fax: 612-454-3684	Employees: 48	

Machinery - computer-to-plate systems (Platesetters) for creating offset printing plates directly from computer data

PRO CD, INC.

222 Rosewood Dr.	CEO: James Bryant	1995 Sales: $20.0 million
Danvers, MA 01923	CFO: Greg Andrews	1-Yr. Sales Change: 100.0%
Phone: 508-750-0000	HR: Deirdre Purple	Ownership: Subsidiary
Fax: 508-750-0020	Employees: 100	

Publishing - telephone directories (Select Phone) on CD-ROM (subsidiary of Axciom Corp.)

PRODIGY SERVICES COMPANY

445 Hamilton Ave.
White Plains, NY 10601
Phone: 914-448-8000
Fax: 914-448-8083

CEO: Edward A. Bennett
CFO: J. Mark Hattendorf
HR: Nicolas Lapko
Employees: 485

1995 Sales: $220.0 million
1-Yr. Sales Change: 10.0%
Ownership: Privately Held

Computers - online consumer information services, including reference databases, financial information, travel services & Internet access

 **See page 291 for a full profile of this company.**

THE PRODUCERS ENTERTAINMENT GROUP LTD.

9150 Wilshire Blvd., Ste. 205
Beverly Hills, CA 90212
Phone: 310-285-0400
Fax: 310-281-2585

CEO: Irwin Meyers
CFO: Irwin Meyers
HR: —
Employees: 14

1995 Sales: $5.3 million
1-Yr. Sales Change: (51.4%)
Exchange: Nasdaq (SC)
Symbol: TPEG

TV production & services - TV shows (*Dave's World*), made-for-TV movies (*When A Stranger Calls*, *Against The Wall*) & instructional programming

PROVIDENCE JOURNAL COMPANY

75 Fountain St.
Providence, RI 02902-0050
Phone: 401-277-7000
Fax: 401-277-7346

CEO: Stephen Hamblett
CFO: Thomas Matlack
HR: John A. Bowers
Employees: 2,500

1995 Sales: $312.5 million
1-Yr. Sales Change: (47.9%)
Ownership: Privately Held

Publishing - newspapers (*Providence Journal-Bulletin*); network-affiliated & independent TV stations in 11 cities; video programming

 **See page 292 for a full profile of this company.**

PUBLICIS SA

133, avenue des Champs-Elysees
75008 Paris, France
Phone: +33-1-47-20-78-00
Fax: +33-1-47-20-28-55

CEO: Maurice Levy
CFO: —
HR: —
Employees: 6,000

1995 Sales: $4,178.2 million
1-Yr. Sales Change: 2.2%
Exchange: Paris

Business services - advertising, communication & marketing services, including research, press & public relations & direct marketing; drugstores (Le Drugstore)

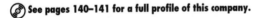 **See pages 140–141 for a full profile of this company.**

PUBLISHERS GROUP WEST INCORPORATED

4065 Hollis St.
Emeryville, CA 94608
Phone: 510-658-3453
Fax: 510-658-1934

CEO: Charlie Winton
CFO: Paul Rooney
HR: John Ross
Employees: 210

1995 Sales: $90.0 million
1-Yr. Sales Change: 13.8%
Ownership: Privately Held

Wholesale distribution - independently published books

PUBLISHING & BROADCASTING LIMITED

24 Artarmon Rd.	CEO: James Packer	1996 Sales: $790.4 million
Willoughby NSW 2068, Australia	CFO: —	1-Yr. Sales Change: 20.1%
Phone: +61-2-9906-9999	HR: —	Exchange: Sydney
Fax: +61-2-9437-4607	Employees: —	

Publishing - magazines (Australian versions of *Cosmopolitan*, *Woman's Day*); TV Network (Channel Nine); investments in John Fairfax Holdings Ltd. (newspapers) & Regency Enterprises (movie production); controlled by Australian media baron Kerry Packer

PUBLISHING COMPANY OF NORTH AMERICA, INC.

577 Deltona Blvd.	CEO: Peter S. Balise	1995 Sales: $1.9 million
Deltona, FL 32725	CFO: James M. Koller	1-Yr. Sales Change: 280.0%
Phone: 407-860-3000	HR: James M. Koller	Exchange: Nasdaq
Fax: 407-574-4422	Employees: 48	Symbol: PCNA

Publishing - print directories & Internet services for bar associations

PULITZER PUBLISHING COMPANY

900 N. Tucker Blvd.	CEO: Michael E. Pulitzer	1995 Sales: $472.3 million
St. Louis, MO 63101	CFO: Ronald H. H. Ridgway	1-Yr. Sales Change: (2.7%)
Phone: 314-340-8000	HR: Preston Vanderford	Exchange: NYSE
Fax: 314-340-3125	Employees: 2,500	Symbol: PTZ

Publishing - newspapers (*St. Louis Post-Dispatch*, *The* [Tucson] *Arizona Daily Star*, *The Tucson Citizen*); TV (9 network-affiliated stations) & radio (one AM & one FM station) broadcasting

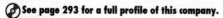 **See page 293 for a full profile of this company.**

QUAD/GRAPHICS, INC.

W224 N3322 DuPlainville Rd.	CEO: Harry V. Quadracci	1995 Sales: $1,002.0 million
Pewaukee, WI 53072	CFO: John C. Fowler	1-Yr. Sales Change: 25.3%
Phone: 414-246-9200	HR: Emily M. Labode	Ownership: Privately Held
Fax: 414-246-4322	Employees: 8,444	

Printing - commercial

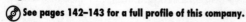 **See pages 142–143 for a full profile of this company.**

QUARK, INC.

1800 Grant St.	CEO: Farhad Fred Ebrahimi	1995 Est. Sales: $200.0 mil.
Denver, CO 80203	CFO: Kenneth J. Collins	1-Yr. Sales Change: 19.0%
Phone: 303-894-8888	HR: D. Witonsky	Ownership: Privately Held
Fax: 303-894-3399	Employees: 600	

Computers - desktop publishing software (Quark XPress) & multilingual electronic publishing software (QuarkXPress Passport)

See page 294 for a full profile of this company.

QUEBECOR INC.

612 Saint-Jacques St.	CEO: Pierre Peladeau	1995 Sales: $4,067 million
Montreal, QC H3C 4M8, Canada	CFO: Francois R. Roy	1-Yr. Sales Change: 40.1%
Phone: 514-877-9777	HR: Yves Dubuc	Exchange: AMEX
Fax: 514-877-9757	Employees: 28,900	Symbol: PQB

Printing - commercial (#2 in North America), including advertising inserts, books, checks, magazines, newsprint, phone books, and passports; newspapers (*Le Journal de Montreal*, *Le Journal de Quebec*)

 **See pages 144–145 for a full profile of this company.**

QUEENS GROUP, INC.

52-35 Barnett Ave.	CEO: Eric Kaltman	1995 Est. Sales: $175.0 mil.
Long Island City, NY 11104	CFO: Erwin Moskowitz	1-Yr. Sales Change: (6.9%)
Phone: 718-457-7700	HR: Patricia Kern	Ownership: Privately Held
Fax: 718-457-9285	Employees: 1,050	

Printing - specialty

QUOTE.COM, INC.

3375 Scott Blvd., Ste. 300	CEO: Chris Cooper	1995 Est. Sales: $5.0 million
Santa Clara, CA 95054	CFO: Jeff Tang	1-Yr. Sales Change: —
Phone: 408-327-0700	HR: —	Ownership: Privately Held
Fax: 408-327-0707	Employees: 5	

Computers - online financial information service, providing current quotes for stocks, options, commodity futures, mutual funds & indexes for US & foreign markets

RAND MCNALLY & COMPANY

8255 N. Central Park Ave.	CEO: Andrew McNally IV	1995 Sales: $468.5 million
Skokie, IL 60076-2970	CFO: James J. Habschmidt	1-Yr. Sales Change: 7.0%
Phone: 847-329-8100	HR: Kurt D. Steele	Ownership: Privately Held
Fax: 847-673-0539	Employees: 4,650	

Publishing - maps, atlases & other geographic information books, including travel guide CD-ROMs (TripMaker); airline & surface transportation tickets & baggage tags; specialty labels, tags & cards

 **See page 295 for a full profile of this company.**

THE RANK ORGANISATION PLC

6 Connaught Place	CEO: Andrew Teare	1995 Sales: $4,139.4 million
London W2 2EZ, UK	CFO: Nigel V. Turnbull	1-Yr. Sales Change: 19.1%
Phone: +44-171-706-1111	HR: —	Exchange: Nasdaq
Fax: +44-171-262-9886	Employees: 40,094	Symbol: RANKY (ADR)

Leisure & recreational services - film (*Jurassic Park*) & TV operations, holiday services & associated undertakings (Universal Studios Florida)

THE READER'S DIGEST ASSOCIATION, INC.

Reader's Digest Rd.	CEO: James P. Schadt	1995 Sales: $3,068.5 million
Pleasantville, NY 10570-7000	CFO: Stephen R. Wilson	1-Yr. Sales Change: 9.3%
Phone: 914-238-1000	HR: Glenda K. Burkhardt	Exchange: NYSE
Fax: 914-238-4559	Employees: 6,200	Symbol: RDA

Publishing - periodicals (#1 magazine worldwide: *Reader's Digest*), condensed best-selling and how-to books, music, videos & CD-ROMS

 **See pages 146–147 for a full profile of this company.**

READING COMPANY

30 S. 15th St., 13th Fl.	CEO: S. Craig Tompkins	1995 Sales: $20.0 million
Philadelphia, PA 19102-4813	CFO: James A. Wunderle	1-Yr. Sales Change: 81.8%
Phone: 215-569-3344	HR: —	Exchange: Nasdaq
Fax: 215-735-1271	Employees: 243	Symbol: RDGCA

Real estate operations - motion picture theaters in Puerto Rico (Cine Vista); real estate in Philadelphia, PA

REED ELSEVIER PLC

Reed House, 6 Chesterfield Gardens	CEO: Ian A. N. Irvine	1995 Sales: $5,646.1 million
London W1A 1EJ, UK	CFO: John Mellon	1-Yr. Sales Change: 20.2%
Phone: +44-171-499-4020	HR: —	Ownership: Consortium
Fax: +44-171-491-8212	Employees: 30,400	

Publishing - consumer, business, scientific, medical & professional publications; LEXIS/NEXIS online information service (jointly owned by Reed International PLC & Elsevier N.V.)

 See pages 148–149 for a full profile of this company.

REGAL CINEMAS, INC.

7132 Commercial Park Dr.	CEO: Michael L. Campbell	1995 Sales: $190.1 million
Knoxville, TN 37918	CFO: Lewis Frazer III	1-Yr. Sales Change: 40.1%
Phone: 423-922-1123	HR: Debbie Robertson	Exchange: Nasdaq
Fax: 423-922-3188	Employees: 3,816	Symbol: REGL

Motion pictures & services - theaters

RENAISSANCE COMMUNICATIONS CORP.

One Fawcett Place, Ste. 120	CEO: Michael Finkelstein	1995 Sales: $179.2 million
Greenwich, CT 06830	CFO: John C. Ferrara	1-Yr. Sales Change: 11.2%
Phone: 203-629-1888	HR: —	Exchange: NYSE
Fax: 203-629-9821	Employees: 513	Symbol: RRR

Broadcasting - 6 TV stations (4 Fox affiliates & 2 WB affiliates)

RENTRAK CORPORATION

7227 NE 55th Ave.	CEO: Ron A. Berger	1996 Sales: $113.3 million
Portland, OR 97218	CFO: Mervyn Benjet	1-Yr. Sales Change: 1.0%
Phone: 503-284-7581	HR: Maureen Haggerty	Exchange: Nasdaq
Fax: 503-288-1563	Employees: 280	Symbol: RENT

Wholesale distribution - prerecorded videotapes to video rental stores; sports apparel

REUTERS HOLDINGS PLC

85 Fleet St.	CEO: Peter J. D. Job	1995 Sales: $4,188.0 million
London EC4P 4AJ, UK	CFO: Robert O. Rowley	1-Yr. Sales Change: 17.1%
Phone: +44-171-250-1122	HR: Patrick A. V. Mannix	Exchange: Nasdaq
Fax: +44-171-510-5896	Employees: 14,348	Symbol: RTRSY (ADR)

Business services - gathering & electronic supply of exchange, over-the-counter, contributed & reference data & general, financial & business news & pictures

 See pages 150–151 for a full profile of this company.

RHINO GROUP PLC

Rhino House, Lavender Park Rd.	CEO: John Steinbrecher	1995 Sales: $92.1 million
West Byfleet, Surrey KT14 6ND, UK	CFO: Martin Long	1-Yr. Sales Change: 21.7%
Phone: +44-1703-702-345	HR: —	Exchange: London
Fax: +44-1703-702-570	Employees: 599	

Retail - computer & video games (Future Zone)

RICH PRODUCTS CORPORATION

1150 Niagara St.	CEO: Robert E. Rich Sr.	1995 Sales: $1,000.0 million
Buffalo, NY 14213	CFO: James Haddad	1-Yr. Sales Change: (44.4%)
Phone: 716-878-8000	HR: Brian Townson	Ownership: Privately Held
Fax: 716-878-8266	Employees: 6,500	

Diversified operations - soybean-based creamer (Coffee Rich); frozen foods; pro sports (Buffalo Bisons [AAA baseball] and Sabres [hockey]); radio broadcasting

RICHARDSON, MYERS & DONOFRIO INC.

120 W. Fayette St.	CEO: Hal Donofrio	1995 Est. Sales: $12.4 mil.
Baltimore, MD 21201	CFO: Michelle Bucey	1-Yr. Sales Change: —
Phone: 410-576-9000	HR: —	Ownership: Privately Held
Fax: 410-528-8809	Employees: 48	

Advertising

RIFKIN ACQUISITION PARTNERS, L.L.L.P.

360 S. Monroe St., Ste. 600	CEO: Monroe M. Rifkin	1995 Sales: $50.2 million
Denver, CO 80209	CFO: Dale D. Wagner	1-Yr. Sales Change: 11.8%
Phone: 303-333-1215	HR: Cheryl Rowls-Stokes	Ownership: Privately Held
Fax: 303-322-3553	Employees: 300	

Cable TV - systems in Georgia, Tennessee, Illinois & Michigan

R. L. POLK & CO.

1155 Brewery Park Blvd.	CEO: Stephen R. Polk	1995 Est. Sales: $320.0 mil.
Detroit, MI 48207-2697	CFO: Bob Tatum	1-Yr. Sales Change: (6.2%)
Phone: 313-393-0880	HR: Joan Miszak	Ownership: Privately Held
Fax: 313-393-2860	Employees: 5,000	

Publishing - city & bank directories; direct marketing; automotive statistics

 See page 296 for a full profile of this company.

RODALE PRESS, INC.

33 E. Minor St.	CEO: Ardath Rodale	1995 Sales: $420.0 million
Emmaus, PA 18098	CFO: Paul Wessel	1-Yr. Sales Change: 1.7%
Phone: 610-967-5171	HR: John Volanski	Ownership: Privately Held
Fax: 610-967-8962	Employees: 1,300	

Publishing - magazines & books relating primarily to gardening, recreational activities, and health & fitness

ROSS ROY COMMUNICATIONS

100 Bloomfield Hills Pkwy.	CEO: Peter Mills	1995 Sales: $65.0 million
Bloomfield Hills, MI 48304	CFO: Chris Lawson	1-Yr. Sales Change: 8.3%
Phone: 810-433-6000	HR: David Jansen	Ownership: Privately Held
Fax: 810-433-6421	Employees: 750	

Advertising

R. R. DONNELLEY & SONS COMPANY

77 W. Wacker Dr.	CEO: John R. Walter	1995 Sales: $6,511.8 million
Chicago, IL 60601-1696	CFO: Cheryl A. Francis	1-Yr. Sales Change: 33.2%
Phone: 312-326-8000	HR: Ann Weiser	Exchange: NYSE
Fax: 312-326-8543	Employees: 41,000	Symbol: DNY

Printing - telephone books, magazines, mail-order catalogs & hard- & softcover books; information services, including database management & electronic media production; mailing list services

 See pages 152-153 for a full profile of this company.

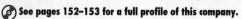

RUBIN POSTAER & ASSOCIATES

1333 Second St.
Santa Monica, CA 90401
Phone: 310-394-4000
Fax: 310-917-2526

Advertising

CEO: Gerald Rubin
CFO: Vince Mancuso
HR: Lark Baskerville
Employees: 320

1995 Sales: $40.7 million
1-Yr. Sales Change: 13.4%
Ownership: Privately Held

SAGA COMMUNICATIONS, INC.

73 Kercheval Ave.
Grosse Pointe Farms, MI 48236-3603
Phone: 313-886-7070
Fax: 313-886-7150

CEO: Edward K. Christian
CFO: Norman L. McKee
HR: Norman L. McKee
Employees: 545

1995 Sales: $49.7 million
1-Yr. Sales Change: 11.9%
Exchange: AMEX
Symbol: SGA

Broadcasting - TV (one CBS affiliate) & radio (15 FM & 9 AM radio stations in 9 markets)

ST. IVES PLC

St. Ives House, Lavington St.
London SE1 0NX, UK
Phone: +44-171-928-8844
Fax: +44-171-928-4838

CEO: Brian Edwards
CFO: —
HR: —
Employees: 3,141

1995 Sales: $421.6 million
1-Yr. Sales Change: 11.5%
Exchange: London

Printing - books & magazines & financial, direct response & commercial documents

THE SAMUEL GOLDWYN COMPANY

10203 Santa Monica Blvd.
Los Angeles, CA 90067-6403
Phone: 310-552-2255
Fax: 310-284-8493

CEO: Samuel Goldwyn Jr.
CFO: Hans W. Turner
HR: Meyer Gottlieb
Employees: 269

1996 Sales: $107.8 million
1-Yr. Sales Change: 18.1%
Exchange: AMEX
Symbol: SG

Motion pictures & services - production & distribution; TV programming

🔘 **See page 297 for a full profile of this company.**

SANCTUARY WOODS MULTIMEDIA CORPORATION

1825 S. Grant St.
San Mateo, CA 94402
Phone: 415-286-6000
Fax: 415-286-6010

CEO: Charlotte Walker
CFO: Allen Barr
HR: Lee Ann Normoyle
Employees: 100

1995 Sales: $11.0 million
1-Yr. Sales Change: 74.6%
Exchange: Nasdaq (SC)
Symbol: SWMFC

Computers - entertainment & education multimedia software for the home & school markets

SAVOY PICTURES ENTERTAINMENT, INC.

Carnegie Hall Tower, 152 W. 57th St.	CEO: Victor A. Kaufman	1995 Sales: $92.6 million
New York, NY 10019	CFO: Howard K. Bass	1-Yr. Sales Change: 7.9%
Phone: 212-247-5810	HR: Courtney Carmack	Exchange: Nasdaq
Fax: 212-247-5811	Employees: 130	Symbol: SPEI

Motion pictures & services - production & distribution

SCHIBSTED A/S

Akersgaten 55	CEO: Kjell Aamot	1995 Sales: $530.1 million
N-0107 Oslo, Norway	CFO: S. Munck	1-Yr. Sales Change: 10.1%
Phone: +47-22-86-41-00	HR: —	Exchange: Oslo
Fax: +47-22-86-38-80	Employees: 2,228	

Publishing - newspapers (*Aftenposten*) & books

SCHOLASTIC CORPORATION

555 Broadway	CEO: Richard Robinson	1995 Sales: $749.9 million
New York, NY 10012-3999	CFO: Kevin J. McEnery	1-Yr. Sales Change: 18.7%
Phone: 212-343-6100	HR: Larry V. Holland	Exchange: Nasdaq
Fax: 212-343-6928	Employees: 5,636	Symbol: SCHL

Publishing - books (*The Baby-Sitters Club*, *The Magic School Bus*) & periodicals; online services for schools (Scholastic Network)

 **See page 298 for a full profile of this company.**

SCITEX CORPORATION LTD.

Herzlia Industrial Park, PO Box 330	CEO: Yoav Z. Chelouche	1995 Sales: $728.9 million
Herzlia B 46103, Israel	CFO: Giora Bitan	1-Yr. Sales Change: 3.5%
Phone: +972-9-597-222	HR: Ilan Gonen	Exchange: Nasdaq
Fax: +972-9-502-922	Employees: 3,500	Symbol: SCIXF

Computers - digital visual information communication systems, including electronic prepress, digital printing, video editing & digital photography products

SCOTTISH TELEVISION PLC

Cowcaddens	CEO: A. Flanagan	1995 Sales: $153.0 million
Glasgow G2 3PR, UK	CFO: Gary Hughes	1-Yr. Sales Change: (16.2%)
Phone: +44-141-300-3000	HR: —	Exchange: London
Fax: +44-141-300-3030	Employees: 615	

Scottish TV broadcasting (ITV Network)

SEATTLE TIMES COMPANY

1120 John St.
Seattle, WA 98108
Phone: 206-339-4137
Fax: 206-464-2582

CEO: H. Mason Sizemore
CFO: Carolyn Kelly
HR: James Schaefer
Employees: 2,400

1995 Est. Sales: $275.0 mil.
1-Yr. Sales Change: 1.9%
Ownership: Privately Held

Publishing - newspapers (*Seattle Post-Intelligencer*)

SFX BROADCASTING, INC.

150 E. 58th St., 19th Fl.
New York, NY 10155-5749
Phone: 212-407-9191
Fax: 212-753-3188

CEO: R. Steven Hicks
CFO: D. Geoffrey Armstrong
HR: —
Employees: 432

1995 Sales: $76.8 million
1-Yr. Sales Change: 38.1%
Exchange: Nasdaq
Symbol: SFXBA

Broadcasting - radio (4 AM & 9 FM stations)

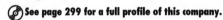 **See page 299 for a full profile of this company.**

SHOCHIKU

1-13-5, Tsukiji, Chuo-ku
Tokyo 104, Japan
Phone: +81-3-3542-5551
Fax: +81-3-5550-1639

CEO: Takeomi Nagayama
CFO: —
HR: —
Employees: 778

1995 Sales: $506.6 million
1-Yr. Sales Change: (8.0%)
Exchange: Tokyo

Motion pictures & services - distribution

SHOP AT HOME, INC.

5210 Schubert Rd.
Knoxville, TN 37912
Phone: 423-688-0300
Fax: 423-848-7724

CEO: Kent E. Lillie
CFO: Joseph Nawy
HR: Kathy Campbell
Employees: 190

1995 Sales: $26.8 million
1-Yr. Sales Change: 23.5%
Exchange: OTC
Symbol: SATH

Retail - consumer goods sold through TV programs

SHOWSCAN ENTERTAINMENT INC.

3939 Landmark St.
Culver City, CA 90232-2315
Phone: 310-558-0150
Fax: 310-559-7984

CEO: William C. Soady
CFO: Dennis Pope
HR: —
Employees: 48

1996 Sales: $17.5 million
1-Yr. Sales Change: 26.8%
Exchange: Nasdaq
Symbol: SHOW

Motion pictures & services - motion-simulation theater systems

SIERRA ON-LINE, INC.

3380 146th Place SE, Ste. 300	CEO: Kenneth A. Williams	1996 Sales: $158.2 million
Bellevue, WA 98007	CFO: Mike A. Brochu	1-Yr. Sales Change: 89.7%
Phone: 206-649-9800	HR: Marianne Sulkowsky	Exchange: Nasdaq
Fax: 206-641-7617	Employees: 629	Symbol: SIER

Computers - edutainment software (Berlitz for Business, The Incredible Machine, King's Quest, Leisure Suit Larry, Front Page Sports)

SILVER KING COMMUNICATIONS, INC.

12425 28th St. North, Ste. 300	CEO: Barry Diller	1995 Sales: $47.9 million
St. Petersburg, FL 33716	CFO: Steven H. Grant	1-Yr. Sales Change: (6.6%)
Phone: 813-573-0339	HR: Barbara O'Grady	Exchange: Nasdaq
Fax: 813-527-1488	Employees: 182	Symbol: SKTV

Broadcasting - TV (12 stations that carry programming produced by the Home Shopping Network)

 **See page 300 for a full profile of this company.**

SINCLAIR BROADCAST GROUP

2000 W. 41st St.	CEO: David D. Smith	1995 Sales: $206.1 million
Baltimore, MD 21211	CFO: David B. Amy	1-Yr. Sales Change: 66.9%
Phone: 410-467-5005	HR: —	Exchange: Nasdaq
Fax: 410-467-5043	Employees: 562	Symbol: SBGI

Broadcasting - TV (5 Fox-affiliated stations, 3 United Paramount Network, one NBC/UPN & one Fox/UPN)

SINGAPORE PRESS HOLDINGS LTD.

News Centre, 82 Genting Ln.	CEO: Lim Kim San	1995 Sales: $586.6 million
1334, Singapore	CFO: —	1-Yr. Sales Change: 8.6%
Phone: +65-743-8800	HR: —	Exchange: Singapore
Fax: +65-748-0747	Employees: —	

Publishing - daily newspapers in Singapore (7 dailies in 3 languages) & magazines (Times Periodicals)

SIRIUS PUBLISHING INCORPORATED

7320 E. Butherus Dr., Ste. 100	CEO: Richard Gnant	1995 Sales: $21.6 million
Scottsdale, AZ 85260	CFO: Robert Tierney	1-Yr. Sales Change: 1.4%
Phone: 602-951-3288	HR: Marilyn McChristy	Ownership: Privately Held
Fax: 602-951-3884	Employees: 55	

Computers - 5-foot & 6-foot bundles of CD-ROMs; music, entertainment & multimedia software publishing

SLEEPECK PRINTING COMPANY

815 25th Ave.
Bellwood, IL 60104
Phone: 708-544-8900
Fax: 708-544-8928

CEO: Michael W. Sleepeck
CFO: Bob Gardner
HR: —
Employees: 400

1995 Sales: $57.0 million
1-Yr. Sales Change: 0.7%
Ownership: Privately Held

Printing - card packs & packaged promotions for the direct-marketing industry

SOFTKEY INTERNATIONAL INC.

One Athenaeum St.
Cambridge, MA 02142
Phone: 617-494-1200
Fax: 617-494-1219

CEO: Michael J. Perik
CFO: R. Scott Murray
HR: Mary De Saint Croix
Employees: 775

1995 Sales: $167.0 million
1-Yr. Sales Change: 37.7%
Exchange: Nasdaq
Symbol: SKEY

Computers - consumer software including word processing, education & entertainment products (The Trail Family, The Mathkeys Family, The GeoGraph Family)

 See page 301 for a full profile of this company.

SOFTWARE PUBLISHERS ASSOCIATION

1730 M St. NW, Ste. 700
Washington, DC 20036-4510
Phone: 202-452-1600
Fax: 202-223-8756

CEO: Ken Wasch
CFO: Thomas Meldrum
HR: Joan Luedtkey
Employees: 65

1995 Sales: $10.4 million
1-Yr. Sales Change: 6.1%
Ownership: Not-for-profit

Computers - not-for-profit trade association of publishers, developers, distributors, retailers & consultants for the computer software industry

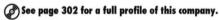 **See page 302 for a full profile of this company.**

SOLAR COMMUNICATIONS INC.

1120 Frontenac Rd.
Naperville, IL 60563
Phone: 708-983-1400
Fax: 708-983-1494

CEO: Frank C. Hudetz
CFO: Kelly Gilroy
HR: Barbara Gunning
Employees: 548

1995 Sales: $62.8 million
1-Yr. Sales Change: (0.6%)
Ownership: Privately Held

Printing - graphic design; offset & flexographic printing; specialty packaging services

SONY CORPORATION

7-35 Kitashinagawa 6-chome
Shinagawa-ku, Tokyo 141, Japan
Phone: +81-35448-2111
Fax: +81-35448-2244

CEO: Norio Ohga
CFO: Tsunao Hashimoto
HR: —
Employees: 138,000

1995 Sales: $44,758 million
1-Yr. Sales Change: 6.0%
Exchange: NYSE
Symbol: SNE (ADR)

Electronics - video & audio equipment, TVs & other products, including semiconductors, telephone & telecommunications equipment & computers; music & motion picture operations

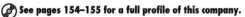 **See pages 154–155 for a full profile of this company.**

SOUTH CHINA MORNING POST HOLDINGS LTD.

Cedar House, 41 Cedar Ave.	CEO: Lindley J. Holloway	1995 Sales: $162.0 million
Hamilton HM12, Bermuda	CFO: —	1-Yr. Sales Change: 2.4%
Phone: 809-295-2244	HR: Milly Liew	Exchange: Hong Kong
Fax: 809-292-8666	Employees: 780	

Publishing - principal English language daily newspaper in Hong Kong

🔘 **See page 303 for a full profile of this company.**

SOUTHAM INC.

1450 Don Mills Rd.	CEO: William E. Ardell	1995 Sales: $749.5 million
Toronto, ON M3B 2X7, Canada	CFO: Christian M. Paupe	1-Yr. Sales Change: 4.7%
Phone: 416-445-6641	HR: John Minardi	Exchange: Montreal
Fax: 416-442-2077	Employees: 7,864	

Publishing - 17 daily newspapers (#1 in Canada: *The Gazette, The Ottawa Citizen, The Spectator*), 33 weekly newspapers & 37 business magazines; trade show & consumer exhibition production & management

SPANISH BROADCASTING SYSTEMS INC.

26 W. 56th St.	CEO: Raul Alarcon Jr.	1995 Sales: $47.3 million
New York, NY 10019	CFO: Jose Antonio Garcia	1-Yr. Sales Change: 18.0%
Phone: 212-541-9200	HR: Albert Riera	Ownership: Privately Held
Fax: 212-541-8535	Employees: 175	

Broadcasting - radio stations

SPECTRAVISION, INC.

1501 N. Plano Rd.	CEO: Gary G. Weik	1995 Sales: $124.0 million
Richardson, TX 75081	CFO: M. Scott Smith	1-Yr. Sales Change: (13.6%)
Phone: 214-234-2721	HR: Scott Campbell	Exchange: AMEX
Fax: 214-301-9607	Employees: 365	Symbol: SVN

Cable TV - pay-per-view movies for hotels & motels

SPELLING ENTERTAINMENT GROUP INC.

5700 Wilshire Blvd.	CEO: Aaron Spelling	1995 Sales: $664.4 million
Los Angeles, CA 90036-3659	CFO: Thomas P. Carson	1-Yr. Sales Change: 10.8%
Phone: 213-965-5700	HR: Cheryl Wingard	Exchange: NYSE
Fax: 213-965-6984	Employees: 900	Symbol: SP

TV production & programming - series (*Beverly Hills 90210, Melrose Place*), miniseries, feature films & movies-for-TV; interactive video games & feature films; music & merchandising rights licensing

🔘 **See page 304 for a full profile of this company.**

SPIR COMMUNICATIONS SA

Route. de Vauvenargues
13100 Aix-en-Provence, France
Phone: +33-42-33-65-00
Fax: +33-42-24-90-36

CEO: Phillipe Leoni
CFO: L. Berthelot
HR: —
Employees: 1,350

1995 Sales: $223.1 million
1-Yr. Sales Change: 5.3%
Exchange: Paris

Publishing - free newspapers; direct marketing & advertising

SPORTS MEDIA, INC.

101 E. 52nd St., 9th Fl.
New York, NY 10022
Phone: 212-308-6666
Fax: 212-826-9033

CEO: James Mason
CFO: Michael Puccini
HR: —
Employees: 21

1995 Sales: $2.3 million
1-Yr. Sales Change: 76.9%
Exchange: Nasdaq (SC)
Symbol: SPTS

Publishing - professional sports team yearbooks

SPORTS SCIENCES, INC.

2075 Case Pkwy. South
Twinsburg, OH 44087
Phone: 216-963-0660
Fax: 216-963-0661

CEO: John D. Lipps
CFO: Nicholas J. Chuma
HR: —
Employees: 7

1995 Sales: $1.4 million
1-Yr. Sales Change: (65.0%)
Exchange: Nasdaq (SC)
Symbol: SSCI

Computers - graphic & video software, develops & assembles interactive electronic game simulators for the consumer electronics industry (Pro Swing, TeeV Golf, Batter Up & PC Golf)

STARPRESS, INC.

425 Market St., 5th Fl.
San Francisco, CA 94105
Phone: 415-778-3100
Fax: 415-495-5407

CEO: Douglas D. Cole
CFO: John C. Lukrich
HR: Jill Lewis
Employees: 100

1995 Sales: $2.2 million
1-Yr. Sales Change: 2,100%
Exchange: OTC
Symbol: GTBR

Computers - CD-ROM & floppy software products, primarily those focusing on health, infotainment, personal productivity & travel, for homes, schools & small businesses

STARSIGHT TELECAST, INC.

39650 Liberty St.
Fremont, CA 94538
Phone: 510-657-9900
Fax: 510-657-5022

CEO: Larry W. Wangberg
CFO: Martin W. Henkel
HR: —
Employees: 104

1995 Sales: $1.9 million
1-Yr. Sales Change: 1,800%
Exchange: Nasdaq
Symbol: SGHT

Video equipment - on-screen interactive TV program guides & VCR control service

STECK-VAUGHN PUBLISHING CORPORATION

8701 N. MoPac Expwy., Ste. 200	CEO: Roy E. Mayers	1995 Sales: $58.2 million
Austin, TX 78759-8365	CFO: Floyd D. Rogers	1-Yr. Sales Change: 8.6%
Phone: 512-343-8227	HR: Gabriele Madison	Exchange: Nasdaq
Fax: 512-795-3397	Employees: 367	Symbol: STEK

Publishing - supplemental educational materials for elementary, secondary & adult levels; library reference books for children & young adults

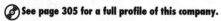 **See page 305 for a full profile of this company.**

STERN PUBLISHING, INC.

36 Cooper Square	CEO: David Schneiderman	1995 Est. Sales: $10 mil.
New York, NY 10003	CFO: Bill Dwyer	1-Yr. Sales Change: —
Phone: 212-475-3333	HR: —	Ownership: Privately Held
Fax: 212-475-8861	Employees: —	

Publishing - weekly news magazines (*L.A. Weekly*, *Orange County Weekly*, *Village Voice*)

SUNSET & VINE PLC

30 Sackville St.	CEO: N. Healy	1995 Sales: $14.2 million
London W1X 1DB, UK	CFO: Stephen Callen	1-Yr. Sales Change: 48.3%
Phone: +44-171-287-5700	HR: —	Exchange: London
Fax: +44-171-287-6524	Employees: 31	

Broadcasting, including sports & entertainment program development

TANDYCRAFTS, INC.

1400 Everman Pkwy.	CEO: Michael J. Walsh	1995 Sales: $256.5 million
Fort Worth, TX 76140	CFO: Michael J. Walsh	1-Yr. Sales Change: 19.4%
Phone: 817-551-9600	HR: —	Exchange: NYSE
Fax: 817-551-9795	Employees: 4,200	Symbol: TAC

Diversified operations - retail leathercrafts (Tandy Leather); inspirational books & gifts (Joshua's Christian Stores); office supplies (Sav-On Discount Office Supplies) & furniture (Cargo Furniture); manufacturing of frames & framed art, belts & accessories, outerwear & leather products

TATTERED COVER, INC.

1628 16th St.	CEO: Joyce Meskis	1995 Est. Sales: $27.5 mil.
Denver, CO 80202	CFO: Margie Keenan	1-Yr. Sales Change: 10.0%
Phone: 303-322-1965	HR: Geoffrey Godwin-Austen	Ownership: Privately Held
Fax: 303-629-1704	Employees: 400	

Retail - #1 US independent new-book bookseller (Tattered Cover Book Store)

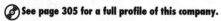 **See page 306 for a full profile of this company.**

TAYLOR CORPORATION

1725 Roecrest Dr.
North Mankato, MN 56003
Phone: 507-625-2828
Fax: 507-625-2988

Printing - commercial

CEO: Glen Taylor
CFO: Al Fallenstein
HR: Marie Eckert
Employees: 8,000

1995 Est. Sales: $485.0 mil.
1-Yr. Sales Change: 2.3%
Ownership: Privately Held

TAYLOR NELSON AGB PLC

AGB House, Westgate
London W5 1UE, UK
Phone: +44-181-967-0007
Fax: +44-181-967-4060

CEO: Anthony Cowling
CFO: Martin S. C. Frame
HR: —
Employees: 835

1995 Sales: $124.1 million
1-Yr. Sales Change: 30.4%
Exchange: London

Business services - marketing for consumer businesses, health care & media; telemarketing; publications

TBWA CHIAT/DAY

180 Maiden Ln.
New York, NY 10038
Phone: 212-804-1000
Fax: 212-804-1200

Advertising

CEO: Ira Matathia
CFO: Colette Chestnut
HR: Donna Nadler
Employees: 656

1995 Sales: $130.7 million
1-Yr. Sales Change: 6.3%
Ownership: Privately Held

TCA CABLE TV, INC.

3015 S.S.E. Loop 323
Tyler, TX 75701
Phone: 903-595-3701
Fax: 903-595-1929

Cable TV

CEO: Robert M. Rogers
CFO: Jimmie F. Taylor
HR: Jerry Yandell
Employees: 1,141

1995 Sales: $189.2 million
1-Yr. Sales Change: 16.6%
Exchange: Nasdaq
Symbol: TCAT

TCI COMMUNICATIONS, INC.

5619 DTC Pkwy.
Englewood, CO 80111-3000
Phone: 303-267-5500
Fax: 303-779-1228

CEO: Brendan R. Clouston
CFO: Bernard W. Schotters
HR: —
Employees: 32,500

1995 Sales: $5,118.0 million
1-Yr. Sales Change: 38.8%
Exchange: Nasdaq
Symbol: TCOMA

Cable TV - #1 system in the US; cable programming services

👁 **See pages 156–157 for a full profile of this company.**

TDX CORPORATION

222 Third St., Ste. 1101	CEO: Donald T. Pascal	1995 Sales: $6.9 million
Cambridge, MA 02142	CFO: Steven F. Smith	1-Yr. Sales Change: (64.1%)
Phone: 617-876-2900	HR: Bill McGrath	Exchange: OTC
Fax: 617-876-7922	Employees: 217	Symbol: TDXC

Broadcasting - distribution of consumer health information programs (Xenejenex) weight control products & services (The Diet Workshop)

TELE-COMMUNICATIONS INTERNATIONAL, INC.

5619 DTC Pkwy.	CEO: F. A. Vierra	1995 Sales: $190.5 million
Englewood, CO 80111-3000	CFO: Graham E. Hollis	1-Yr. Sales Change: 333.0%
Phone: 303-267-5500	HR: —	Exchange: Nasdaq
	Employees: 18	Symbol: TINTA

Cable TV - broadband cable TV & telephony distribution networks in Europe, Latin America & Asia

TELEMUNDO GROUP, INC.

2290 W. Eighth Ave.	CEO: Roland A. Hernandez	1995 Sales: $169.1 million
Hialeah, FL 33010	CFO: Peter J. Housman II	1-Yr. Sales Change: (8.0%)
Phone: 305-884-8200	HR: Raymond R. Gutierrez	Exchange: Nasdaq
Fax: 305-889-7980	Employees: 1,300	Symbol: TLMD

Broadcasting - Spanish-language TV broadcasting

TELESCAN, INC.

10550 Richmond Ave., Ste. 250	CEO: David L. Brown	1995 Sales: $14.0 million
Houston, TX 77042	CFO: Karen R. Fohn	1-Yr. Sales Change: 33.3%
Phone: 713-588-9700	HR: Wendy Boudreaux	Exchange: Nasdaq (SC)
Fax: 713-588-9797	Employees: 153	Symbol: TSCN

Computers - online financial information services, including databases & software for individual, corporate & institutional customers

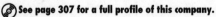 **See page 307 for a full profile of this company.**

TELE-TV

875 3rd Ave., 15th Fl.	CEO: Howard Stringer	1995 Sales: $10.0 million
New York, NY 10022	CFO: Brian Steel	1-Yr. Sales Change: —
Phone: 212-508-4000	HR: Gail Yoshimoto	Ownership: Joint Venture
Fax: 212-508-4070	Employees: 250	

Cable TV - interactive programming delivered over telephone lines (joint venture between Pacific Telesis, Nyex & Bell Atlantic)

GRUPO TELEVISA, S.A.

Av. Chapultepec, 28	CEO: Emilio Azcarraga Milmo	1995 Sales: $1,148.0 million
Mexico, D.F. 06724, Mexico	CFO: Guillermo Canedo White	1-Yr. Sales Change: —
Phone: +52-5-709-3333	HR: A. Gayou Almada	Exchange: NYSE
Fax: +52-5-709-0448	Employees: 20,700	Symbol: TV

Broadcasting - Spanish-language media conglomerate (#1 worldwide), including TV programming, magazine publishing (#1 Spanish-language worldwide: Editorial Televisa) & radio programming

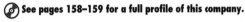 **See pages 158–159 for a full profile of this company.**

TÉLÉVISION FRANÇAISE 1

176/180, rue de l'Universite	CEO: Patrick Le Lay	1995 Sales: $1,863.3 million
75007 Paris, France	CFO: J. P. Morel	1-Yr. Sales Change: 8.3%
Phone: +33-41-41-12-34	HR: —	Exchange: Paris
	Employees: 1,863	

TV production - audiovisual materials & advertising products

TELEWEST COMMUNICATIONS PLC

Genesis Business Park, Albert Dr.	CEO: Alan Michels	1995 Sales: $224.0 million
Woking, Surrey GU21 5RW, UK	CFO: Stephen J. Davidson	1-Yr. Sales Change: 101.1%
Phone: +44-1483-750900	HR: —	Exchange: Nasdaq
Fax: +44-1483-750901	Employees: 2,776	Symbol: TWSTY (ADR)

Cable TV & residential & commercial telephony services

TESCORP, INC.

327 Congress Ave., Ste. 200	CEO: Jack S. Gray Jr.	1995 Sales: $1.1 million
Austin, TX 78701	CFO: John Becker	1-Yr. Sales Change: 450.0%
Phone: 512-476-2995	HR: Lesley Carter	Exchange: Nasdaq (SC)
Fax: 512-474-1610	Employees: 7	Symbol: TESC

Cable TV - Argentinian cable systems

THOMAS NELSON, INC.

Nelson Place at Elm Hill Pike	CEO: Sam Moore	1996 Sales: $308.4 million
Nashville, TN 37214-1000	CFO: Joe Moore	1-Yr. Sales Change: 16.3%
Phone: 615-889-9000	HR: Rusty Faulks	Exchange: NYSE
Fax: 615-883-6353	Employees: 1,130	Symbol: TNM

Publishing - Bibles, religious books, music & gifts

See page 308 for a full profile of this company.

THOMAS PUBLISHING COMPANY

5 Penn Plaza
New York, NY 10001
Phone: 212-695-0500
Fax: 212-290-7311

CEO: Carl T. Holst-Knudsen
CFO: Donald Macpherson
HR: Ivy Molofsky
Employees: 400

1995 Sales: $122.0 million
1-Yr. Sales Change: 10.9%
Ownership: Privately Held

Publishing - industrial directories (*Thomas Register*); online information retrieval systems

THE THOMSON CORPORATION

Toronto Dominion Bank Twr., Ste. 2706
Toronto, ON M5K 1A1, Canada
Phone: 416-360-8700
Fax: 416-360-8812

CEO: W. Michael Brown
CFO: Nigel R. Harrison
HR: Andrew G. Mills
Employees: 48,600

1995 Sales: $7,225.0 million
1-Yr. Sales Change: 13.7%
Exchange: Toronto

Publishing - periodicals & reference books (Gale); travel services; databases (First Call, Information Access Company, MedStat Group, SandPoint); acquiring West Publishing Co.

 See pages 160–161 for a full profile of this company.

THORN EMI PLC

4 Tenterden St., Hanover Square
London W1A 2AY, UK
Phone: +44-171-355-4848
Fax: +44-171-355-1308

CEO: James G. Fifield
CFO: Simon P. Duffy
HR: —
Employees: 33,547

1995 Sales: $7,305.9 million
1-Yr. Sales Change: 5.0%
Exchange: OTC
Symbol: THE (ADR)

Music production & publishing (Capitol, EMI, Virgin); consumer durables rental & rent-to-purchase businesses (Radio Rentals, Rent-a-Center)

 See pages 162–163 for a full profile of this company.

T-HQ, INC.

5016 N. Pkwy. Calabasas, Ste. 100
Calabasas, CA 91302
Phone: 818-591-1310
Fax: 818-591-1615

CEO: Brian J. Farrell
CFO: Stefan Dietrich
HR: Mary Nelson Garrett
Employees: 40

1995 Sales: $33.3 million
1-Yr. Sales Change: 150.4%
Exchange: Nasdaq (SC)
Symbol: TOYH

Computers - interactive entertainment software (Ren & Stimpy, Sports Illustrated)

TIDNINGS AB MARIEBERG

Ralambsvagen 17
S-100 26 Stockholm, Sweden
Phone: +46-8-738-29-00
Fax: +46-8-13-78-60

CEO: Bengt Braun
CFO: Jonas Nyren
HR: —
Employees: 8,254

1995 Sales: $1,468.5 million
1-Yr. Sales Change: 10.0%
Exchange: Stockholm

Publishing - newspapers; food service products; real estate operations; photo agency; market systems & financial management & information

TIME WARNER INC.

75 Rockefeller Plaza	CEO: Gerald M. Levin	1995 Sales: $17,696.0 mil.
New York, NY 10019	CFO: Richard J. Bressler	1-Yr. Sales Change: 11.3%
Phone: 212-484-8000	HR: Carolyn McCandless	Exchange: NYSE
Fax: 212-956-2847	Employees: 65,500	Symbol: TWX

Publishing - periodicals (*Time, People, Sports Illustrated*) & books (Little Brown, Warner); movies (Warner Brothers); cable TV systems (#2 in US); cable programming (HBO, Cinemax); music (Atlantic, Elektra)

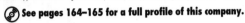 **See pages 164–165 for a full profile of this company.**

THE TIMES MIRROR COMPANY

Times Mirror Square	CEO: Mark H. Willes	1995 Sales: $3,448.3 million
Los Angeles, CA 90053	CFO: Thomas Unterman	1-Yr. Sales Change: 2.7%
Phone: 213-237-3700	HR: James R. Simpson	Exchange: NYSE
Fax: 213-237-3800	Employees: 21,877	Symbol: TMC

Publishing - newspapers (*Los Angeles Times*), magazines & books

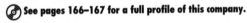 **See pages 166–167 for a full profile of this company.**

TIMES PUBLISHING COMPANY

490 First Ave. South	CEO: Andrew Barnes	1995 Sales: $233.0 million
St. Petersburg, FL 33701	CFO: Catherine Karl	1-Yr. Sales Change: 4.0%
Phone: 813-893-8111	HR: —	Ownership: Privately Held
Fax: 813-893-8675	Employees: 3,762	

Publishing - newspapers (*St. Petersburg Times*) & magazines (*Governing, Florida Trend*) & congressional periodical & online service (*Congressional Quarterly*)

TIMES PUBLISHING LTD.

Times Centre, One New Industrial Rd.	CEO: Kua Hong Pak	1995 Sales: $337.3 million
1953, Singapore	CFO: —	1-Yr. Sales Change: 0.8%
Phone: +65-284-8844	HR: —	Exchange: Singapore
Fax: +65-284-4733	Employees: —	

Printing - commercial; bookstores (The Times Bookshop)

TKR CABLE COMPANY

67 B. Mountain Blvd. Extension	CEO: Paul Freas	1995 Est. Sales: $175.0 mil.
Warren, NJ 07060	CFO: Bill Mitchell	1-Yr. Sales Change: 2.9%
Phone: 908-356-1010	HR: Isabel Arace	Ownership: Privately Held
Fax: 908-271-1446	Employees: 1,700	

Cable TV

TM CENTURY, INC.

2002 Academy
Dallas, TX 75234-9220
Phone: 214-406-6800
Fax: 214-406-6885

CEO: Neil Sargent
CFO: P. K. Skunk
HR: Karyn Fairris
Employees: 72

1995 Sales: $7.6 million
1-Yr. Sales Change: (7.3%)
Exchange: Nasdaq (SC)
Symbol: TMCI

Radio production & programming - music compilations, instrumental music for commericals, sound effects & station ID jingles; radio station commercials for TV broadcast

TMP WORLDWIDE

1633 Broadway
New York, NY 10019
Phone: 212-977-4200
Fax: 212-247-0015

CEO: Andrew McKelvey
CFO: Roxane Previty
HR: Lynn Harris
Employees: 970

1995 Sales: $137.4 million
1-Yr. Sales Change: 16.7%
Ownership: Privately Held

Advertising

THE TODD-AO CORPORATION

1135 N. Mansfield Ave.
Hollywood, CA 90038
Phone: 213-465-2579
Fax: 213-465-1231

CEO: Robert A. Naify
CFO: Silas R. Cross
HR: Kate Reck
Employees: 390

1995 Sales: $50.0 million
1-Yr. Sales Change: 52.0%
Exchange: Nasdaq
Symbol: TODDA

Motion pictures & services - postproduction sound services & special visual effects for the film & TV industries

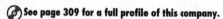 **See page 309 for a full profile of this company.**

TOEI

3-2-17, Ginza, Chuo-ku
Tokyo 104, Japan
Phone: +81-3-3535-4641
Fax: +81-3-3535-7143

CEO: Shigeru Okada
CFO: —
HR: —
Employees: 621

1995 Sales: $1,069.5 million
1-Yr. Sales Change: (1.8%)
Exchange: Tokyo

Motion pictures & services - production & distribution

TOHO

1-2-1, Yuraku-cho, Chiyoda-ku
Tokyo 100, Japan
Phone: +81-3-3591-1221
Fax: +81-3-3591-2414

CEO: Isao Matsuoka
CFO: —
HR: —
Employees: 582

1995 Sales: $790.2 million
1-Yr. Sales Change: (3.7%)
Exchange: Tokyo

Motion pictures & services - production & distribution

TOKYO BROADCASTING SYSTEM

5-3-6, Akasaka, Minato-ku	CEO: Hirozo Isozaki	1995 Sales: $2,386.4 million
Tokyo 107-06, Japan	CFO: —	1-Yr. Sales Change: 8.6%
Phone: +81-3-3746-1111	HR: —	Exchange: Tokyo
Fax: +81-3-5571-2019	Employees: 1,539	

Broadcasting - radio & TV (#1 in Japan), including nationwide network (JNN for TV) & International Cable Network

TOKYO THEATRES

1-16-1, Ginza, Chuo-ku	CEO: Komakichi Sugiyama	1995 Sales: $102.3 million
Tokyo 104, Japan	CFO: —	1-Yr. Sales Change: 2.4%
Phone: +81-3-3561-8531	HR: —	Exchange: Tokyo
Fax: +81-3-3561-8290	Employees: 176	

Motion pictures & services - theaters; real estate leasing

THE TOPPS COMPANY, INC.

One Whitehall St.	CEO: Arthur T. Shorin	1996 Sales: $265.5 million
New York, NY 10004-2109	CFO: Catherine K. Jessup	1-Yr. Sales Change: —
Phone: 212-376-0300	HR: William G. O'Connor	Exchange: Nasdaq
Fax: 212-376-0573	Employees: 1,100	Symbol: TOPP

Leisure & recreational products - picture trading cards (Topps), confections (Bazooka, Ring Pop, Push Pop) & comic books

TOUCHSTONE APPLIED SCIENCE ASSOCIATES, INC.

PO Box 382, Fields Ln.	CEO: Andrew L. Simon	1995 Sales: $2.3 million
Brewster, NY 10509-0382	CFO: Andrew L. Simon	1-Yr. Sales Change: 15.0%
Phone: 914-277-8100	HR: —	Exchange: Nasdaq (SC)
Fax: 914-277-3548	Employees: 23	Symbol: TASA

Publishing - reading comprehension tests, instructional materials & software for elementary & secondary schools, colleges & universities

TRACK DATA CORPORATION

56 Pine St.	CEO: Barry Hertz	1995 Sales: $13.4 million
New York, NY 10005	CFO: Martin Kaye	1-Yr. Sales Change: 50.6%
Phone: 212-422-4300	HR: —	Exchange: Nasdaq
Fax: 212-612-2241	Employees: 84	Symbol: TRAC

Business services - electronically transmitted information for individuals & institutions involved in financial markets

TRANS WORLD ENTERTAINMENT CORPORATION

38 Corporate Circle	CEO: Robert J. Higgins	1996 Sales: $517.0 million
Albany, NY 12203	CFO: John J. Sullivan	1-Yr. Sales Change: (3.7%)
Phone: 518-452-1242	HR: Bert Tobin	Exchange: Nasdaq
Fax: 518-452-3547	Employees: 5,500	Symbol: TWMC

Retail - prerecorded music & videotapes (Coconuts, Saturday Matinee)

TREASURE CHEST ADVERTISING COMPANY, INC.

511 W. Citrus Edge	CEO: Donald Roland	1995 Sales: $897.0 million
Glendora, CA 91740	CFO: Andy Kaplan	1-Yr. Sales Change: 11.2%
Phone: 818-914-3981	HR: Michael Houser	Ownership: Privately Held
Fax: 818-852-3056	Employees: 4,200	

Printing - commercial web offset printing

TRIATHLON BROADCASTING COMPANY, INC.

Symphony Towers, 750 B St., Ste. 1920	CEO: Norman Feuer	1995 Sales: —
San Diego, CA 92101	CFO: Kevin F. Rich	1-Yr. Sales Change: —
Phone: 619-239-4242	HR: Tina-Marie Pinney	Exchange: Nasdaq
Fax: 619-239-4270	Employees: 57	Symbol: TBCOA

Broadcasting - radio (5 stations in the Wichita, KS, market & 2 in the Lincoln, NE, market)

TRIBUNE COMPANY

435 N. Michigan Ave.	CEO: John W. Madigan	1995 Sales: $2,245.0 million
Chicago, IL 60611	CFO: Donald C. Grenesko	1-Yr. Sales Change: 4.2%
Phone: 312-222-9205	HR: John T. Sloan	Exchange: NYSE
Fax: 312-222-0449	Employees: 10,500	Symbol: TRB

Publishing - newspapers (*Chicago Tribune*); radio & TV broadcasting (WGN); newsprint operations; book publishing (Contemporary, NTC); professional baseball team (Chicago Cubs)

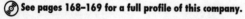 **See pages 168–169 for a full profile of this company.**

TRIMARK HOLDINGS, INC.

2644 30th St.	CEO: Mark Amin	1995 Sales: $85.0 million
Santa Monica, CA 90405-3009	CFO: James E. Keegan	1-Yr. Sales Change: 3.3%
Phone: 310-314-2000	HR: Diana L. Gandy	Exchange: Nasdaq
Fax: 310-399-4238	Employees: 96	Symbol: TMRK

Motion pictures & services - film & video distribution & entertainment software distribution

TRINITY INTERNATIONAL HOLDINGS PLC

6 Heritage Ct., Lower Bridge St.	CEO: C. Philip Graf	1995 Sales: $260.7 million
Chester CH1 1RD, UK	CFO: Michael D. Masters	1-Yr. Sales Change: 2.4%
Phone: +44-1244-350-555	HR: —	Exchange: London
Fax: +44-1244-341-677	Employees: 3,903	

Publishing - regional & local newspapers

TRO LEARNING, INC.

1721 Moon Lake Blvd., Ste. 555	CEO: William R. Roach	1995 Sales: $37.3 million
Hoffman Estates, IL 60194	CFO: Sharon Fierro	1-Yr. Sales Change: 31.3%
Phone: 847-781-7800	HR: Pat Hawver	Exchange: Nasdaq
Fax: 847-781-7835	Employees: 279	Symbol: TUTR

Computers - microcomputer-based interactive learning systems (PLATO) for education & instructional use by schools, colleges, the military, airlines & correctional institutions

TRUE NORTH COMMUNICATIONS INC.

101 E. Erie St.	CEO: Bruce Mason	1995 Sales: $439.1 million
Chicago, IL 60611-2897	CFO: Terry M. Ashwill	1-Yr. Sales Change: 8.8%
Phone: 312-751-7227	HR: Doris Radcliffe	Exchange: NYSE
Fax: 312-751-3501	Employees: 4,369	Symbol: TNO

Advertising - direct marketing, public relations & sales promotions services

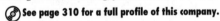 **See page 310 for a full profile of this company.**

T/SF COMMUNICATIONS CORPORATION

2407 E. Skelly Dr.	CEO: Howard G. Barnett Jr.	1995 Sales: $72.1 million
Tulsa, OK 74105	CFO: J. Gary Mourton	1-Yr. Sales Change: 28.1%
Phone: 918-747-2600	HR: Jimmy C. Strong	Exchange: AMEX
Fax: 918-743-1291	Employees: 465	Symbol: TCM

Publishing - trade journals (*Convenience Store News*) & newspapers (*Expo*) for conventions & trade shows; trade show operations, including registration services & exhibitor information & marketing services

TURNER BROADCASTING SYSTEM, INC.

One CNN Ctr., 100 International Blvd.	CEO: Robert "Ted" E. Turner III	1995 Sales: $3,437.4 million
Atlanta, GA 30303	CFO: Wayne H. Pace	1-Yr. Sales Change: 22.4%
Phone: 404-827-1700	HR: William M. Shaw	Exchange: AMEX
Fax: 404-827-2437	Employees: 7,000	Symbol: TBSB

Broadcasting - cable TV networks (CNN, TNT, Headline News, Cartoon Network); pro sports teams (Atlanta Braves, Atlanta Hawks); movie production (Castle Rock, New Line); World Championship Wrestling

See pages 170–171 for a full profile of this company.

UDO HOLDINGS PLC

Blackthorne Rd., Colnbrook
Slough SL3 0TP, UK
Phone: +44-1753-682-196
Fax: +44-1753-682-545

Printing - reprographic services

CEO: Robert A. Flashman
CFO: Graham H. Ede
HR: —
Employees: 995

1995 Sales: $83.6 million
1-Yr. Sales Change: 11.5%
Exchange: London

ULTRAK, INC.

1220 Champion Circle, Ste. 100
Carrollton, TX 75006
Phone: 214-280-9675
Fax: 214-280-9674

Video equipment - closed-circuit TV systems

CEO: George K. Broady
CFO: Tim D. Torno
HR: Patty Cramer
Employees: 148

1995 Sales: $101.2 million
1-Yr. Sales Change: 28.4%
Exchange: Nasdaq
Symbol: ULTK

UNAPIX ENTERTAINMENT, INC.

500 Fifth Ave., 46th Fl.
New York, NY 10110
Phone: 212-575-7070
Fax: 212-575-6869

CEO: David M. Fox
CFO: Steven Low
HR: —
Employees: 38

1995 Sales: $18.3 million
1-Yr. Sales Change: 38.6%
Exchange: AMEX
Symbol: UPX

Motion pictures & services - licensing of movies, TV programs, home video & educational products

UNICO, INC.

8380 Alban Rd.
Springfield, VA 22150
Phone: 703-644-0200
Fax: 703-569-1465

CEO: Gerard R. Bernier
CFO: Bob Palizza
HR: Kimberly Bufton
Employees: 159

1995 Sales: $10.5 million
1-Yr. Sales Change: (28.1%)
Exchange: Nasdaq (SC)
Symbol: UICO

Advertising - cooperative direct-mail advertising (United Coupon Corp.) & distribution point cooperative advertising (Cal-Central Marketing Corp.) distributed through supermarkets, pharmacies & restaurants

UNITED ARTISTS THEATRE CIRCUIT, INC.

9110 E. Nichols Ave., Ste. 200
Englewood, CO 80112
Phone: 303-792-3600
Fax: 303-790-8907

CEO: Stewart Blair
CFO: Kurt Hall
HR: Elizabeth Moravak
Employees: 11,100

1995 Sales: $646.1 million
1-Yr. Sales Change: 3.8%
Ownership: Privately Held

Motion pictures & services - theaters (420 units)

UNITED INTERNATIONAL HOLDINGS, INC.

4643 S. Ulster St., Ste. 1300
Denver, CO 80237
Phone: 303-770-4001
Fax: 303-770-4207

CEO: Gene W. Schneider
CFO: Bernard G. Dvorak
HR: Amy Blair
Employees: 115

1996 Sales: $2.4 million
1-Yr. Sales Change: 50.0%
Exchange: Nasdaq
Symbol: UIHIA

Cable TV - foreign cable TV systems

UNITED NEWS & MEDIA PLC

Ludgate House, 245 Blackfriars Rd.
London SE1 9UY, UK
Phone: +44-171-921-5000
Fax: +44-171-928-2717

CEO: Clive Hollick
CFO: Charles R. Stern
HR: —
Employees: 13,573

1995 Sales: $1,662.0 million
1-Yr. Sales Change: 4.8%
Exchange: Nasdaq
Symbol: UNEWY (ADR)

Publishing - national & regional newspapers & business & special interest magazines; electronic news distribution

(💿) **See pages 172–173 for a full profile of this company.**

UNITED PRESS INTERNATIONAL, INC.

1400 I St. NW
Washington, DC 20005
Phone: 202-898-8000
Fax: 202-898-1234

CEO: John Hayes
CFO: Anthony Jay
HR: Lin Coppedge-Martin
Employees: 1,000

1995 Est. Sales: $85.0 mil.
1-Yr. Sales Change: 13.3%
Ownership: Privately Held

Business services - newswire services

UNITED STATES SATELLITE BROADCASTING COMPANY, INC.

3415 University Ave.
St. Paul, MN 55114
Phone: 612-645-4500
Fax: 612-642-4314

CEO: Stanley E. Hubbard
CFO: Gerald D. Deeney
HR: Frank Vilotta
Employees: 98

1995 Sales: $42.3 million
1-Yr. Sales Change: —
Exchange: Nasdaq
Symbol: USSB

Cable TV - satellite-based broadcast services

(💿) **See page 311 for a full profile of this company.**

UNITED TELEVISION, INC.

132 S. Rodeo Dr., 4th Fl.
Beverly Hills, CA 90212-2425
Phone: 310-281-4844
Fax: 310-281-5870

CEO: Evan C. Thompson
CFO: Garth S. Lindsey
HR: Thomas L. Muir
Employees: 498

1995 Sales: $165.6 million
1-Yr. Sales Change: 9.7%
Exchange: Nasdaq
Symbol: UTVI

Broadcasting - TV (3 United Paramount Network affiliates & 2 other network affiliates)

UNITED VIDEO SATELLITE GROUP, INC.

7140 S. Lewis Ave.	CEO: Lawrence Flinn Jr.	1995 Sales: $262.9 million
Tulsa, OK 74136-5422	CFO: Peter C. Boylan III	1-Yr. Sales Change: 33.7%
Phone: 918-488-4000	HR: Suzanne Shepherd	Exchange: Nasdaq
Fax: 918-488-4979	Employees: 1,100	Symbol: UVSGA

TV production & programming - satellite-delivered video, audio, data & program-promotion services for cable TV systems & residential satellite dish owners; program information for cable TV (Prevue Network)

 **See page 312 for a full profile of this company.**

UNITEL VIDEO, INC.

510 W. 57th St.	CEO: Barry Knepper	1995 Sales: $83.3 million
New York, NY 10019	CFO: Barry Knepper	1-Yr. Sales Change: 3.2%
Phone: 212-265-3600	HR: —	Exchange: AMEX
Fax: 212-986-9791	Employees: 474	Symbol: UNV

TV services - recording, editing & duplication of TV programs & commercials & film-to-video transfer, studio videotape recording & graphic design services

UNIVERSAL OUTDOOR HOLDINGS, INC.

321 Clark St., Ste. 1010	CEO: Daniel L. Simon	1995 Sales: $38.1 million
Chicago, IL 60610	CFO: Brian T. Clingen	1-Yr. Sales Change: 14.8%
Phone: 312-644-8673	HR: Belva Shinn	Ownership: Privately Held
Fax: 312-644-8071	Employees: 337	

Advertising - outdoor advertising in 8 US markets (12,700 displays)

UNIVERSAL PRESS SYNDICATE

4520 Main St., Ste. 700	CEO: John McMeel	1995 Est. Sales: $200.0 mil.
Kansas City, MO 64111	CFO: Elena Fallon	1-Yr. Sales Change: —
Phone: 816-932-6600	HR: Michael Stewart	Ownership: Nonprofit
Fax: 816-932-6684	Employees: 300	

Publishing - newspaper syndicate of comics (Garfield, Doonesbury, Ziggy, Cathy, Calvin & Hobbes) & columns (Dear Abby, William F. Buckley, Mary McGrory, Garry Wills, James Kilpatrick); book publishing (Andrews & McMeel)

UNIVISION COMMUNICATIONS INC.

1999 Avenue of the Stars, Ste. 3050	CEO: A. Jerrold Perenchio	1995 Sales: $173.1 million
Los Angeles, CA 90067	CFO: George W. Blank	1-Yr. Sales Change: 24.5%
Phone: 310-556-7600	HR: Ed Evans	Ownership: Privately Held
Fax: 310-556-3568	Employees: 1,286	

TV production & programming - 24-hour Spanish-language TV stations (779 affiliates: #1 in US)

UPSIDE PUBLISHING CO.

2015 Pioneer Ct.	CEO: Susan E. Scott	1995 Est. Sales: $3.0 million
San Mateo, CA 94403	CFO: Edward A. Ring	1-Yr. Sales Change: 30.4%
Phone: 415-377-0950	HR: —	Ownership: Privately Held
Fax: 415-377-1962	Employees: 27	

Publishing - business magazine for high-tech company executives

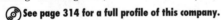 **See page 313 for a full profile of this company.**

U.S. HOSPITALITY CORP.

1004 Old Tree Ct.	CEO: Mark Oldham	1995 Sales: $3.0 million
Nashville, TN 37210	CFO: Danny Oldham	1-Yr. Sales Change: 11.1%
Phone: 615-259-4500	HR: —	Ownership: Privately Held
Fax: 615-259-2095	Employees: 35	

Publishing - hotel guest services directories (#1 in the US)

U.S. NEWS & WORLD REPORT

2400 N St. NW	CEO: Fred Drasner	1996 Est. Sales: $311.0 mil.
Washington, DC 20037-1196	CFO: Joan T. Williams	1-Yr. Sales Change: (2.4%)
Phone: 202-955-2000	HR: —	Ownership: Privately Held
Fax: 202-955-2035	Employees: 500	

Publishing - news magazine (*U.S. News & World Report*)

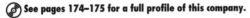 **See page 314 for a full profile of this company.**

U S WEST MEDIA GROUP

7800 E. Orchard Rd., Ste. 290	CEO: Charles M. Lillis	1995 Sales: $2,374.0 million
Englewood, CO 80111	CFO: Douglas D. Holmes	1-Yr. Sales Change: 24.4%
Phone: 303-793-6500	HR: Patty A. Klinge	Exchange: AMEX
Fax: 303-793-6309	Employees: 16,000	Symbol: UMG

Publishing - directories (*Yellow Pages*) & marketing services; domestic & international cable & wireless networks; interactive multimedia services

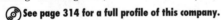 **See pages 174–175 for a full profile of this company.**

UUNET TECHNOLOGIES, INC.

3060 Williams Dr.	CEO: John W. Sidgmore	1995 Sales: $94.5 million
Fairfax, VA 22031-4648	CFO: Jeffrey G. Hilber	1-Yr. Sales Change: 662.1%
Phone: 703-206-5600	HR: Diana E. Lawrence	Exchange: Nasdaq
Fax: 703-206-5601	Employees: 187	Symbol: UUNT

Computers - Internet access services

VALASSIS COMMUNICATIONS, INC.

36111 Schoolcraft Rd.	CEO: David A. Brandon	1995 Sales: $613.8 million
Livonia, MI 48150	CFO: Robert L. Recchia	1-Yr. Sales Change: 13.1%
Phone: 313-591-3000	HR: Angela Morin	Exchange: NYSE
Fax: 313-591-4994	Employees: 1,261	Symbol: VCI

Printing - sales-promotional materials & other consumer purchase incentives

VALUE LINE, INC.

220 E. 42nd St.	CEO: Jean B. Buttner	1995 Sales: $79.1 million
New York, NY 10017-5891	CFO: Paul Ehrenstein	1-Yr. Sales Change: (3.7%)
Phone: 212-907-1500	HR: —	Exchange: Nasdaq
Fax: 212-818-9747	Employees: 375	Symbol: VALU

Publishing - investment analysis newsletters (*Value Line*); investment management (mutual funds)

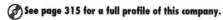 **See page 315 for a full profile of this company.**

VALUEVISION INTERNATIONAL, INC.

6740 Shady Oak Rd.	CEO: Robert L. Johander	1996 Sales: $88.9 million
Minneapolis, MN 55344-3433	CFO: Mark A. Payne	1-Yr. Sales Change: 64.9%
Phone: 612-947-5200	HR: Ray Campbell	Exchange: Nasdaq
Fax: 612-947-0188	Employees: 565	Symbol: VVTV

Retail - TV home shopping network (#3 in the US); TV & radio stations

VANCE PUBLISHING CORPORATION

400 Knightsbridge Pkwy.	CEO: William C. Vance	1996 Sales: $50.0 million
Lincolnshire, IL 60069	CFO: Walter Kay	1-Yr. Sales Change: 22.2%
Phone: 847-634-2600	HR: Ann O'Neil	Ownership: Privately Held
Fax: 847-634-4379	Employees: 350	

Publishing - trade magazines for hair salons (*Modern Salon*), jewelers (*Modern Jewelers*) & agricultural industries (*The Peanut Grower*, *Swine Practitioner*)

NV VERENIGD BEZIT VNU

Ceylonpoort 5-25	CEO: J. L. Brentjens	1995 Sales: $1,902.8 million
NL-2037 AA Haarlem, The Netherlands	CFO: J. J. van der Rest	1-Yr. Sales Change: 9.9%
Phone: +31-23-5-463-463	HR: —	Exchange: OTC
Fax: +31-23-5-463-938	Employees: 10,306	Symbol: VNUNY (ADR)

Publishing - consumer & trade magazines (*Adweek*, *Back Stage*, *Billboard*, *The Hollywood Reporter*), newspapers, business information systems & educational publishing; TV production

See pages 176–177 for a full profile of this company.

VERITAS MUSIC ENTERTAINMENT, INC.

1700 Hayes St.. Ste. 304
Nashville, TN 37203
Phone: 615-329-9902
Fax: 615-321-5074

Music production & publishing

CEO: Roy W. Wunsch
CFO: Wayne Halper
HR: —
Employees: 2

1995 Sales: —
1-Yr. Sales Change: —
Exchange: Nasdaq (SC)
Symbol: VMEI

VERONIS, SUHLER & ASSOCIATES INC.

350 Park Ave.
New York, NY 10022
Phone: 212-935-4990
Fax: 212-935-0877

CEO: John S. Suhler
CFO: Martin I. Visconti
HR: —
Employees: 55

1996 Sales: —
1-Yr. Sales Change: —
Ownership: Privately Held

Financial - investment bankers to the communications, media, broadcasting, publishing, interactive digital
media & information industries

VIACOM INC.

1515 Broadway
New York, NY 10036
Phone: 212-258-6000
Fax: 212-258-6354

CEO: Sumner M. Redstone
CFO: George S. Smith Jr.
HR: William A. Roskin
Employees: 81,700

1995 Sales: $11,688.7 mil.
1-Yr. Sales Change: 58.7%
Exchange: AMEX
Symbol: VIAB

Diversified operations - information & entertainment operations, including broadcasting, film, cable TV,
publishing, video rentals (Blockbuster) & theme parks

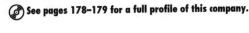 **See pages 178–179 for a full profile of this company.**

VIDEO JUKEBOX NETWORK, INC.

1221 Collins Ave.
Miami Beach, FL 33139
Phone: 305-674-5000
Fax: 305-674-4900

CEO: Alan R. McGlade
CFO: Luann S. Hoffman
HR: —
Employees: 108

1995 Sales: $24.2 million
1-Yr. Sales Change: 26.7%
Exchange: Nasdaq (SC)
Symbol: JUKE

TV production & programming - interactive music-video TV programming (The Box)

VIDEO UPDATE, INC.

287 E. Sixth St.
St. Paul, MN 55101-1926
Phone: 612-222-0006
Fax: 612-297-6086

CEO: Daniel A. Potter
CFO: Christopher J. Gondeck
HR: —
Employees: 685

1995 Sales: $9.1 million
1-Yr. Sales Change: 82.0%
Exchange: Nasdaq
Symbol: VUPDA

Retail - videocassette, video game & audio book rental superstores that carry more than 7,500 items

VIDEOTRON HOLDINGS PLC

Videotron House, 76 Hammersmith Rd.	CEO: Louis D. J. Brunel	1995 Sales: $89.1 million
London W14 8UD, UK	CFO: Joseph Calvalancia	1-Yr. Sales Change: 52.9%
Phone: +44-181-244-1234	HR: —	Exchange: Nasdaq
	Employees: 803	Symbol: VRONY (ADR)

Cable TV - cable system in London & telecommunications services to homes & businesses (#1 in London)

THE VILLAGE GREEN BOOKSTORE, INC.

1357 Monroe Ave.	CEO: Raymond C. Sparks	1995 Sales: $10.0 million
Rochester, NY 14618	CFO: Raymond C. Sparks	1-Yr. Sales Change: —
Phone: 716-442-1151	HR: —	Exchange: Nasdaq (SC)
Fax: 716-442-9237	Employees: 162	Symbol: BOOK

Retail - bookstores in the Northeastern US (8 units: Village Green) that sell books, magazines, stationery, food, gifts, coffee & multimedia products

VIRGIN GROUP PLC

120 Campden Hill Rd.	CEO: Richard Branson	1995 Est. Sales: $2,845 mil.
London W8 7AR, UK	CFO: Anthony J. Bates	1-Yr. Sales Change: —
Phone: +44-171-229-1282	HR: —	Ownership: Privately Held
Fax: +44-171-229-5834	Employees: 9,000	

Diversified operations - airline (#2 in the UK: Virgin Atlantic Airways); retail music, books & video (Virgin Megastores); film production; book publishing

VITT MEDIA INTERNATIONAL, INC.

114 Sixth Ave.	CEO: John Power	1995 Est. Sales: $400.0 mil.
New York , NY 10036	CFO: Ron Shapiro	1-Yr. Sales Change: (11.1%)
Phone: 212-921-0500	HR: Ron Shapiro	Ownership: Privately Held
Fax: 212-455-0519	Employees: 130	

Business services - media planning, buying & syndication; online research & status reports service (Vitt Online)

THE VOYAGER COMPANY

578 Broadway, Ste. 406	CEO: Robert Stein	1995 Sales: $12.0 million
New York, NY 10012	CFO: Jonathan B. Turell	1-Yr. Sales Change: —
Phone: 212-431-5199	HR: —	Ownership: Privately Held
Fax: 212-431-5799	Employees: 100	

Publishing - laserdisc movies (Exotic Japan), CD-ROMs (The Complete Maus, A Hard Day's Night) & interactive books (The Complete Hitchhiker's Guide to the Galaxy, Jurassic Park)

(🔊) **See page 316 for a full profile of this company.**

WACE GROUP PLC

Wace House, Shepherdess Walk	CEO: Trevor C. Grice	1995 Sales: $473.9 million
London N1 7LH, UK	CFO: Stephen R. Puckett	1-Yr. Sales Change: (5.3%)
Phone: +44-171-250-3055	HR: —	Exchange: OTC
Fax: +44-171-608-3337	Employees: 4,328	Symbol: WCGRY (ADR)

Printing - corporate, specialist litho, adhesive label & screen printing for packaging, advertising & publications

THE WALT DISNEY COMPANY

500 S. Buena Vista St.	CEO: Michael D. Eisner	1995 Sales: $12,112.1 mil.
Burbank, CA 91521	CFO: Richard D. Nanula	1-Yr. Sales Change: 20.5%
Phone: 818-560-1000	HR: William J. Wilkinson	Exchange: NYSE
Fax: 818-560-1930	Employees: 71,000	Symbol: DIS

Leisure & recreational services - theme parks & resorts (Walt Disney World), motion pictures (Walt Disney Pictures, Touchstone), radio & TV broadcasting (Capital Cities/ABC), cable TV (the Disney Channel, ESPN)

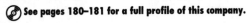 **See pages 180–181 for a full profile of this company.**

THE WASHINGTON POST COMPANY

1150 15th St. NW	CEO: Donald E. Graham	1995 Sales: $1,719.4 million
Washington, DC 20071	CFO: John B. Morse Jr.	1-Yr. Sales Change: 6.5%
Phone: 202-334-6000	HR: Beverly R. Keil	Exchange: NYSE
Fax: 202-334-1031	Employees: 7,010	Symbol: WPO

Publishing - newspapers & magazines (*Newsweek*); TV broadcasting; training centers (Stanley H. Kaplan)

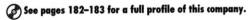 **See pages 182–183 for a full profile of this company.**

WASSER, INC.

2005 Fifth Ave., Ste. 201	CEO: Peg Cheirrett	1995 Sales: $7.0 million
Seattle, WA 98121-2504	CFO: Mark Cheirrett	1-Yr. Sales Change: 11.1%
Phone: 206-441-0707	HR: —	Ownership: Privately Held
Fax: 206-441-6628	Employees: 200	

Business services - staffing & outsourcing services specializing in technical communications, including documentation, training & new media design & production

WATMOUGHS HOLDINGS PLC

Jason House, Hillam Rd., Bradford	CEO: Patrick Walker	1995 Sales: $278.4 million
West Yorkshire BD2 1QN, UK	CFO: —	1-Yr. Sales Change: (0.1%)
Phone: +44-1274-735-663	HR: —	Exchange: London
Fax: +44-1274-734-206	Employees: 2,184	

Printing - newspaper supplements, tabloids, mail-order catalog sections, brochures & magazines

WAVERLY, INC.

351 W. Camden St.
Baltimore, MD 21201-2436
Phone: 410-528-4000
Fax: 410-528-4414

CEO: Edward B. Hutton Jr.
CFO: E. Philip Hanlon
HR: Paul R. Shiah
Employees: 538

1995 Sales: $156.1 million
1-Yr. Sales Change: 18.3%
Exchange: Nasdaq
Symbol: WAVR

Publishing - books, periodicals & electronic media in the fields of medicine, allied health & related disciplines for students, practitioners & companies in the health care industry

W. B. DONER & CO.

25900 Northwestern Hwy.
Southfield, MI 48075
Phone: 810-354-9700
Fax: 810-827-0880

CEO: Alan Kalter
CFO: H. Barry Levine
HR: Carol Cothern
Employees: 600

1995 Sales: $50.4 million
1-Yr. Sales Change: 18.6%
Ownership: Privately Held

Advertising

WEIDER HEALTH & FITNESS

21100 Erwin St.
Woodland Hills, CA 91367
Phone: 818-884-6800
Fax: 818-704-5734

CEO: Joe Weider
CFO: Ron Novak
HR: Janet Petroff
Employees: 150

1995 Est. Sales: $430.0 mil.
1-Yr. Sales Change: —
Ownership: Privately Held

Diversified operations - vitamins (Schiff) & nutritional snacks (Fibar); magazine publishing *(Living Fit, Men's Fitness & Shape, Muscle & Fitness, Prime Health & Fitness, Senior Golfer)*; home-fitness equipment (25% ownership of ICON Health & Fitness)

WENNER MEDIA

1290 Avenue of the Americas
New York, NY 10104
Phone: 212-484-1616
Fax: 212-767-8205

CEO: Jann S. Wenner
CFO: John Lagana
HR: Pamela Fox
Employees: 300

1995 Sales: $200.0 million
1-Yr. Sales Change: 4.8%
Ownership: Privately Held

Publishing - periodicals *(Rolling Stone, US, Men's Journal, Family Life)*

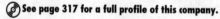 **See page 317 for a full profile of this company.**

WEST COAST ENTERTAINMENT CORPORATION

9990 Global Rd.
Philadelphia, PA 19115
Phone: 215-677-1000
Fax: 215-676-2131

CEO: T. Kyle Standley
CFO: Jerry L. Misterman
HR: —
Employees: 361

1996 Sales: $82.2 million
1-Yr. Sales Change: —
Exchange: Nasdaq
Symbol: WCEC

Retail - video specialty stores (West Coast Video, Videosmith, Palmer Video)

WEST PUBLISHING CO.

610 Opperman Dr.	CEO: Dwight D. Opperman	1995 Sales: $827.0 million
Eagan, MN 55123	CFO: Grant E. Nelson	1-Yr. Sales Change: 39.5%
Phone: 612-687-7000	HR: Timothy J. Blantz	Ownership: Privately Held
Fax: 612-687-5388	Employees: 7,000	

Publishing - law & college textbooks & online services (Westlaw); to be acquired by Thomson Corp.

WESTINGHOUSE/CBS GROUP

51 W. 52nd St.	CEO: Peter A. Lund	1995 Sales: $3,333.0 million
New York, NY 10019-6188	CFO: Fredric G. Reynolds	1-Yr. Sales Change: (10.2%)
Phone: 212-975-4321	HR: Joan Showalter	Ownership: Subsidiary
Fax: 212-975-8714	Employees: 9,000	

Broadcasting - radio & TV (subsidiary of Westinghouse Electric Corporation)

 See pages 184–185 for a full profile of this company.

WESTWOOD ONE, INC.

9540 Washington Blvd.	CEO: Mel A. Karmazin	1995 Sales: $145.7 million
Culver City, CA 90232	CFO: Farid Suleman	1-Yr. Sales Change: 6.9%
Phone: 310-204-5000	HR: Carolyn Jones	Exchange: Nasdaq
Fax: 310-836-1158	Employees: 566	Symbol: WONE

Radio production & programming - news, talk, sports & entertainment programs; special event programming; broadcasting (Mutual Broadcasting System)

 See page 318 for a full profile of this company.

W H SMITH GROUP PLC

Strand House, 7 Holbein Place	CEO: Bill Cockburn	1995 Sales: $4,270.6 million
London SW1W 8NR, UK	CFO: John Napier	1-Yr. Sales Change: 10.1%
Phone: +44-171-730-1200	HR: —	Exchange: London
Fax: +44-171-259-0195	Employees: 33,625	

Retail - prerecorded music, videos & books (W.H. Smith, Waterstone's, Our Price Video)

 See pages 186–187 for a full profile of this company.

WHEREHOUSE ENTERTAINMENT INC.

19701 Hamilton Ave.	CEO: Jerry Goldress	1995 Sales: $500.0 million
Torrance, CA 90502	CFO: Henry Del Castillo	1-Yr. Sales Change: 6.0%
Phone: 310-538-2314	HR: Renee Nesland	Ownership: Privately Held
Fax: 310-538-8698	Employees: 2,700	

Retail - audio & video

WILLIAM H. SADLIER, INC.

9 Pine St.
New York, NY 10005-1002
Phone: 212-227-2120
Fax: 212-267-8696

CEO: William Sadlier Dinger
CFO: Henry E. Christel
HR: —
Employees: 157

1995 Sales: $23.7 million
1-Yr. Sales Change: 6.8%
Exchange: Nasdaq (SC)
Symbol: SADL

Publishing - textbooks & related workbooks, teachers' guides & other supplementary materials

WILLIAM MORRIS AGENCY, INC.

151 El Camino Dr.
Beverly Hills, CA 90212
Phone: 310-274-7451
Fax: 310-786-4462

CEO: Norman Brokaw
CFO: Irving J. Weintraub
HR: Gail Moore
Employees: 600

1995 Sales: $140.0 million
1-Yr. Sales Change: 12.0%
Ownership: Privately Held

Talent agency

 **See page 319 for a full profile of this company.**

WIRED VENTURES, INC.

520 Third St., 4th Fl.
San Francisco, CA 94107-1815
Phone: 415-222-6200
Fax: 415-222-6209

CEO: Louis Rossetto
CFO: Jeffrey Simon
HR: —
Employees: 284

1995 Sales: $25.3 million
1-Yr. Sales Change: 175.0%
Ownership: Privately Held

Publishing - magazine (*Wired*); WWW site (HotWired Internet)

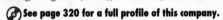 **See page 320 for a full profile of this company.**

WIRELESS CABLE OF ATLANTA, INC.

3100 Medlock Bridge Rd., Ste. 340
Norcross, GA 30071-4139
Phone: 770-409-3570
Fax: 770-409-3579

CEO: Ricky C. Haney
CFO: Allan H. Rudder
HR: —
Employees: 40

1995 Sales: $3.3 million
1-Yr. Sales Change: 13.8%
Exchange: Nasdaq (SC)
Symbol: WCAI

Cable TV - wireless cable TV services

WIRELESS ONE, INC.

5551 Corporate Blvd., Ste. 2G
Baton Rouge, LA 70808-2549
Phone: 504-926-7778
Fax: 504-926-7413

CEO: Sean Reilly
CFO: J. Robert Gary
HR: Bill Hamblin
Employees: 69

1995 Sales: $1.3 million
1-Yr. Sales Change: 225.0%
Exchange: Nasdaq
Symbol: WIRL

Broadcasting - wireless cable television systems

WIZ TECHNOLOGY, INC.

32951 Calle Perfecto	CEO: Mar-Jeanne Tendler	1995 Sales: $3.7 million
San Juan Capistrano, CA 92675	CFO: Billie Jolson	1-Yr. Sales Change: 270.0%
Phone: 714-443-3000	HR: Carmen Walsh	Exchange: AMEX
Fax: 714-443-2333	Employees: 30	Symbol: WIZ

Computers - retail shareware & other software (The $5 Computer Software Store) available through portable displays in grocery chains, airport gift shops, discount & computer stores

WIZARDS OF THE COAST

PO Box 707	CEO: Peter Adkison	1995 Est. Sales: $100.0 mil.
Renton, WA 98057-0707	CFO: David Lewis	1-Yr. Sales Change: 100.0%
Phone: 206-624-0933	HR: Geri Marshall	Ownership: Privately Held
Fax: 206-204-5811	Employees: 220	

Toys - fantasy card games (Magic: The Gathering, NetRunner) & related magazines, books, comics & other merchandise

WMS INDUSTRIES INC.

3401 N. California Ave.	CEO: Neil D. Nicastro	1995 Sales: $385.4 million
Chicago, IL 60618	CFO: Harold H. Bach Jr.	1-Yr. Sales Change: 7.6%
Phone: 312-961-1111	HR: Michael Sirchio	Exchange: NYSE
Fax: 312-961-1090	Employees: 3,381	Symbol: WMS

Leisure & recreational products - pinball & video games (Mortal Kombat); gambling equipment

WOLFF NEW MEDIA LLC

520 Madison Ave., 11th Fl.	CEO: Michael Wolff	1995 Sales: $5.0 million
New York, NY 10022	CFO: Joseph Cohen	1-Yr. Sales Change: 127.3%
Phone: 212-308-8100	HR: Carol Wyatt	Ownership: Privately Held
Fax: 212-308-8837	Employees: 35	

Publishing - Internet guidebooks (Net Chat, Net Games, Net Guide, Net Money, Net Trek); Internet directory (YPN); consulting

 **See page 321 for a full profile of this company.**

WOLTERS KLUWER NV

Stadhouderskade 1, NL-1000 AV	CEO: Cor J. Brakel	1995 Sales: $1,836.7 million
Amsterdam, The Netherlands	CFO: P. W. van Wel	1-Yr. Sales Change: 7.6%
Phone: +31-20-607-0450	HR: C. H. van Kempen	Exchange: OTC
Fax: +31-20-607-0490	Employees: 8,993	Symbol: WTKWY (ADR)

Publishing - business, legal, tax information, educational & medical periodicals; newsletters; looseleaf publications; databanks; electronic libraries

See pages 188–189 for a full profile of this company.

WORLD COLOR PRESS, INC.

101 Park Ave., 19th Fl.	CEO: Robert G. Burton	1995 Sales: $1,296 million
New York, NY 10178	CFO: Marc L. Reisch	1-Yr. Sales Change: 33.3%
Phone: 212-986-2440	HR: Jennifer L. Adams	Exchange: NYSE
Fax: 212-455-9266	Employees: 8,200	Symbol: WRC

Printing - consumer magazines & catalogs

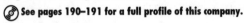 **See pages 190–191 for a full profile of this company.**

WORLDS INC.

605 Market St., 14th Fl.	CEO: Dave Gobel	1995 Est. Sales: $5.0 million
San Francisco, CA 94105	CFO: Mark Brown	1-Yr. Sales Change: 900.0%
Phone: 415-281-1300	HR: —	Ownership: Privately Held
Fax: 415-284-9483	Employees: 90	

Computers - on-screen entertainment & networking software for seriously ill children (Starbright World); Internet messaging software (Worlds Chat)

WPP GROUP PLC

27 Farm St.	CEO: Martin S. Sorrell	1995 Sales: $2,405.9 million
London W1X 6RD, UK	CFO: Robert E. Lerwill	1-Yr. Sales Change: 9.0%
Phone: +44-171-408-2204	HR: Brian J. Brooks	Exchange: Nasdaq
Fax: +44-171-493-6819	Employees: 19,138	Symbol: WPPGY (ADR)

Advertising - worldwide marketing services, including media advertising (J. Walter Thompson, Ogilvy & Mather), market research, public relations & nonmedia advertising & business-to-business marketing

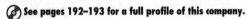 **See pages 192–193 for a full profile of this company.**

W.W. NORTON & COMPANY, INC.

500 Fifth Ave.	CEO: W. Drake McFeely	1995 Est. Sales: $46.0 mil.
New York, NY 10110	CFO: Victor Schmalzer	1-Yr. Sales Change: 17.9%
Phone: 212-354-5500	HR: Lisa Gaeth	Ownership: Privately Held
Fax: 212-869-0856	Employees: 320	

Publishing - trade, college, professional & medical books

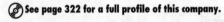 **See page 322 for a full profile of this company.**

XPEDITE SYSTEMS, INC.

446 State Hwy. 35	CEO: Roy B. Andersen Jr.	1995 Sales: $55.7 million
Eatontown, NJ 07724	CFO: Stuart S. Levy	1-Yr. Sales Change: 34.5%
Phone: 908-389-3900	HR: Jayne Droge	Exchange: Nasdaq
Fax: 908-389-8823	Employees: 247	Symbol: XPED

Business services - fax distribution service (Fax Broadcast); Windows software to access service

YAHOO! INC.

635 Vaqueros Ave.	CEO: Timothy Koogle	1995 Sales: $1.4 million
Sunnyvale, CA 94086	CFO: Gary Valenzuela	1-Yr. Sales Change: —
Phone: 408-328-3300	HR: —	Exchange: Nasdaq
Fax: 408-328-3301	Employees: 39	Symbol: YHOO

Internet - World Wide Web search service (Yahoo!), web guide for children (Yahooligans!), country-specific web guides (Yahoo! Canada, Yahoo! Japan) & online & print magazine with Ziff-Davis (Yahoo! Internet Life)

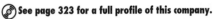 **See page 323 for a full profile of this company.**

YAR COMMUNICATIONS, INC.

220 Fifth Ave.	CEO: Yuri Radzievsky	1995 Est. Sales: $125.0 mil.
New York, NY 10001	CFO: Frank Burke	1-Yr. Sales Change: 4.2%
Phone: 212-447-4000	HR: —	Ownership: Privately Held
Fax: 212-447-4020	Employees: 150	

Multicultural advertising & marketing

YES! ENTERTAINMENT CORPORATION

3875 Hopyard Rd.	CEO: Donald D. Kingsborough	1995 Sales: $55.7 million
Pleasanton, CA 94588	CFO: Sol Kershner	1-Yr. Sales Change: 53.0%
Phone: 510-847-9444	HR: —	Exchange: Nasdaq
Fax: 510-734-0997	Employees: 88	Symbol: YESS

Toys - interactive books (Comes to Life Books, Yes! Interactive Books) & interactive videos (T.V. Teddy) & microrecording devices (Yak Bak)

YORKSHIRE-TYNE TEES TELEVISION HOLDINGS PLC

The Television Centre	CEO: G. E. W. Thomas	1995 Sales: $405.1 million
Leeds LS3 1JS, UK	CFO: Nick Castro	1-Yr. Sales Change: (12.1%)
Phone: +44-113-243-8283	HR: —	Exchange: London
Fax: +44-113-244-5107	Employees: 1,122	

TV broadcasting

YOUNG & RUBICAM INC.

285 Madison Ave.	CEO: Peter A. Georgescu	1995 Sales: $1,122.0 million
New York, NY 10017-6486	CFO: Dave Greene	1-Yr. Sales Change: 5.8%
Phone: 212-210-3000	HR: Robert Wells	Ownership: Privately Held
Fax: 212-370-3796	Employees: 10,404	

Advertising & communications

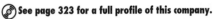 **See pages 194–195 for a full profile of this company.**

YOUNG BROADCASTING INC.

599 Lexington Ave.
New York, NY 10022
Phone: 212-754-7070
Fax: 212-758-1229

CEO: Ronald J. Kwasnick
CFO: James A. Morgan
HR: Alfred A. Porzio
Employees: 820

1995 Sales: $122.5 million
1-Yr. Sales Change: 55.5%
Exchange: Nasdaq
Symbol: YBTVA

Broadcasting - TV (5 ABC affilliates, 3 CBS affiliates & one NBC affiliate)

ZIFF-DAVIS PUBLISHING COMPANY

One Park Ave.
New York, NY 10016-5801
Phone: 212-503-3500
Fax: 212-503-4599

CEO: Eric Hippeau
CFO: Timothy O'Brien
HR: Rajna Brown
Employees: 2,700

1995 Est. Sales: $950.0 mil.
1-Yr. Sales Change: 11.5%
Ownership: Subsidiary

Publishing - computer magazine publisher (#1 in the US: *PC Magazine*, *PC Week*, *Computer Shopper*); TV programming; online services (ZiffNet) & CD-ROMs (subsidiary of Softbank Corp.)

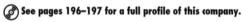 **See pages 196–197 for a full profile of this company.**

ZIFFREN, BRITTENHAM, BRANCA & FISCHER

2121 Avenue of the Stars, 32nd Fl.
Los Angeles, CA 90067
Phone: 310-552-3388
Fax: 310-553-7068

CEO: Ken Ziffren
CFO: Ken Ziffren
HR: Tara Flynn
Employees: 67

1995 Est. Sales: $30.0 mil.
1-Yr. Sales Change: —
Ownership: Privately Held

Law firm - Hollywood's premier dealmakers, negotiating such deals as Turner Broadcasting's purchase of the MGM movie library

ZOMAX OPTICAL MEDIA, INC.

5353 Nathan Ln.
Plymouth, MN 55442
Phone: 612-553-9300
Fax: 612-553-0826

CEO: James T. Anderson
CFO: Stephan P. Jones
HR: Gary Mittelbuscher
Employees: 120

1995 Sales: $13.2 million
1-Yr. Sales Change: 34.7%
Exchange: Nasdaq
Symbol: ZOMX

Business services - CDs, audiocassettes, diskettes & related services such as packaging & graphics design, printing & warehousing for publishers, computer manufacturers, marketing groups & other customers

The Indexes

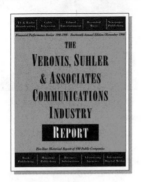